Low-Voltage-Activated T-type Calcium Channels

Low-Voltage-Activated T-type Calcium Channels

Proceedings from the International Electrophysiology Meeting, Montpellier

21–22 October 1996

Guest Editors
Richard W. Tsien
Jean-Paul Clozel
Joël Nargeot

Supported by an educational grant from
F. Hoffmann-La Roche Ltd,
Basel, Switzerland

Adis International Limited
Chowley Oak Lane
Tattenhall
Chester
CH3 9GA
England

ISBN 1 898970 82 3

ROC6-373

Contents

List of corresponding authors

The following list provides contact details for the corresponding authors of each paper presented in this proceedings. Each corresponding author is listed alphabetically by the surname of the first author of each paper.

AKAIKE — Norio Akaike, Department of Physiology, Faculty of Medicine, Kyushu University, 3-1-1 Maidashi, Higashi-ku, Fukuoka 812-82, Japan
Tel: +81 92 642 6086; Fax: +81 92 633 6748;
e-mail: akaike@physiol2.med.kyushu-u.ac.jp

ARMSTRONG — Clay M. Armstrong, Department of Physiology, University of Pennsylvania Medical Center, B701 Richards Bldg, 3700 Hamilton Walk, Philadelphia, PA 19104-6085, USA
Tel: +1 215 898 7816; Fax: +1 215 573 5851;
e-mail: armstrong@a1.mscf.upenn.edu

BARRETT — Paula Q. Barrett, Department of Pharmacology, University of Virginia School of Medicine, Box 448, Charlottesville, VA 22908, USA
Tel: +1 804 924 5454; Fax: +1 804 982 3878; e-mail: pqb4b@virginia.edu

BEAM — Kurt Beam, Department of Anatomy and Neurobiology, Colorado State University, Fort Collins, CO 80523-1670, USA
Tel: +1 970 491 5277; Fax: +1 970 491 7907;
e-mail: KBeam@Lamar.Colostate.edu

BENARDEAU — Eric A. Ertel, F. Hoffmann-La Roche Ltd, Pharma Division, Bldg 70/426, 4070 Basel, Switzerland

BEST — Philip M. Best, University of Illinois, Department of Molecular and Integrative Physiology and the College of Medicine, 524 Burrill Hall, MC-114, 407 S. Goodwin Ave, Urbana, IL 61801, USA
Tel: +1 217 333 1735; Fax: +1 217 333 1133; e-mail: p-best@uiuc.edu

BIRNBAUMER — Lutz Birnbaumer, Department of Anesthesiology, BH-612 CHS, Mail Code 177820, UCLA School of Medicine, 10833 Le Conte Avenue, Los Angeles, CA 90095-1778, USA
Tel: +1 310 794 6696; Fax: +1 310 825 6711;
e-mail: lutz@cvmail.anes.ucla.edu

BOSSU — Jean-Louis Bossu, Laboratoire de Neurobiologie Cellulaire, CNRS, Centre de Neurochimie, 5 rue Blaise Pascal, 67084 Strasbourg Cedex, France
Tel: +33 3 88 60 16 93; Fax: +33 3 88 60 16 64

BOURINET — Emmanuel Bourinet, Institut de Genetique Humaine, CNRS-UPR 1142, Rue de la Cardonille, 34293 Montpellier Cedex 5, France
Tel: +33 467 61 33 54; Fax: +33 467 52 15 59

CARBONE	Emilio Carbone, Dipartimento di Neuroscienze, Corso Raffaello 30, 10125 Torino, Italy Tel: +39 11 6707786; Fax: +39 11 6707708; e-mail: emiliocarbone@unito.it
CATTERALL	William A. Catterall, Department of Pharmacology, Box 357280, University of Washington, Seattle, WA 98195-7280, USA Tel: +1 206 543 1925; Fax: +1 206 685 3822; e-mail: wcatt@u.washington.edu
CLEEMAN	Martin Morad, Department of Pharmacology and Institute of Cardiovascular Sciences, Georgetown University Medical Center, 3900 Reservoir Road NW, Washington, DC 20007-2195, USA Tel: +1 202 687 8453; Fax: +1 202 687 8458
DOLPHIN	Annette C. Dolphin, Department of Pharmacology, Medawar Building, University College London, Gower Street, London WC1E 6BT, UK Tel: +44 171 419 3054; Fax: +44 171 813 2808; e-mail: adolphin@ucl.ac.uk
DZHURA	Platon Kostyuk, Department of General Physiology of the Nervous System, Bogomoletz Institute of Physiology, National Academy of Sciences of Ukraine, Bogomoletz Str. 4, Kiev 252024, Ukraine Fax: +380 44 293 6458; e-mail: pkostyuk@serv.biph.kiev.ua
FRISCHKNECHT	Andy Randall, Neurobiology Division, MRC Laboratory of Molecular Biology, Hills Rd, Cambridge, CB2 2QH, UK Tel: +44 1223 402176; Fax: +44 1223 402310; e-mail: AR1@mrc-lmb.cam.ac.uk
HAN	Xinqiang Han, Department of Medicine, Cardiovascular Division, Brigham and Women's Hospital, 75 Francis Street, Boston, MA 02115-6195, USA Tel: +1 617 732 7056; Fax: +617 732 5132
HARPOLD	Michael M. Harpold, SIBIA Neurosciences Inc., 505 Coast Blvd S., La Jolla, CA 92037-4641, USA Tel: +1 619 452 5892; Fax: +1 619 452 9279
HERMSMEYER	Kent Hermsmeyer, Oregon Regional Primate Research Center, 505 NW 185th Avenue, Beaverton, OR 97006-3499, USA Tel: +1 503 690 5580; Fax: +1 503 690 5563
HUGUENARD	John R. Huguenard, Department of Neurology & Neurological Sciences, Stanford University School of Medicine, Room M016 Medical Center, Stanford, CA 94305-5300, USA Tel: +1 415 723 5522; Fax: +1 415 723 1080; e-mail: john.huguenard@stanford.edu
JOHNSTON	Daniel Johnston, Division of Neuroscience, Baylor College of Medicine, 1 Baylor Plaza, Houston, TX 77030, USA Tel: +1 713 798 5984; Fax: +1 713 799 8544; e-mail: dan@mossy.bcm.tmc.edu

KLUGBAUER Franz Hofmann, Institut für Pharmakologie und Toxikologie der Technischen Universität München, Biedersteiner Str. 29, 80802 Munich, Germany
Tel: +49 89 4140 3260; Fax: +49 89 4140 3261;
e-mail: pharma@ipt.med.tu-muenchen.de

LEI Denis Noble, University Laboratory of Physiology, University of Oxford, Parks Road, Oxford, OX1 3PT, UK
Tel: +44 1865 272533; Fax: +44 1865 272554

LIU Kevin P. Campbell, Howard Hughes Medical Institute, University of Iowa College of Medicine, 400 EMRB, Iowa City, IA 52242-1101, USA
Tel: +1 319 335 7867; Fax: +1 319 335 6957;
e-mail: kevin-campbell@uiowa.edu;
WWW: http://www-camlab.physlog.uiowa.edu/home.htm

MITTERDORFER Hartmut Glossmann, Institut für Biochemische Pharmakologie, Universität Innsbruck, Peter Mayr Str. 1, A-6020 Innsbruck, Austria
Tel: +43 512 507/3163; Fax: +43 512 507/2858

NILIUS Bernd Nilius, Laboratorium voor Fysiologie, Campus Gasthuisberg, K.U. Leuven, Herestraat 49, B-3000 Leuven, Belgium
Tel: +32 16 345 937; Fax: +32 16 345 991;
e-mail: bernd.nilius@med.kuleuven.ac.be

NOCETI Enrico Stefani, UCLA, Department of Anesthesiology, BH-612 CHS, Box 951778, Los Angeles, CA 90095-1778, USA
Tel: +1 310 794 7804; Fax: +1 310 825 6649;
e-mail: estefani@anes.ucla.edu

PEREZ Edward Perez-Reyes, Department of Physiology, Loyola University Medical Center, 2160 South First Avenue, Maywood, IL 60153, USA
Tel: +1 708 216 6305; Fax: +1 708 216 6308
e-mail: EPEREZ@wpo.it.luc.edu

RANDALL Richard W. Tsien, Department of Molecular and Cellular Physiology, Beckman Center B105A, Stanford University Medical Center, Stanford, CA 94305-5426, USA
Tel: +1 415 725 7557; Fax: +1 415 725 2504;
e-mail: rwtsien@leland.stanford.edu

RICHARD Sylvain Richard, Institut de Genetique Humaine, CNRS-UPR 1142, Rue de la Cardonille, 34293 Montpellier Cedex 5, France
Tel: +33 467 61 33 54; Fax: +33 467 52 15 59

ROCK David Rock, Neuroscience Therapeutics, Parke-Davis Research, 2800 Plymouth Rd, Ann Arbor, MI 48105, USA
Tel: +1 313 996 7192; Fax: +1 313 996 7178;
e-mail: ROCKD@AA.WL.COM

ROSSIER Michel F. Rossier, University Hospital, Division of Endocrinology, 24 rue Micheli-du-Crest, 1211 Geneva 14, Switzerland
Tel: +41 22 3729320; Fax: +41 22 3729329; e-mail: rossier@cmu.unige.ch

SHEKTER Richard J. Miller, Department of Pharmacological and Physiological Sciences, University of Chicago, 947 E. 58th Street (MC 0926), Chicago, IL 60637, USA
Tel: +1 773 702 9336; Fax: +1 773 702 5903;
e-mail: rjmx@midway.uchicago.edu

TOTTENE Daniela Pietrobon, Department of Biomedical Sciences and CNR Centre of Biomembranes, University of Padova, Viale G Colombo 3, 35131 Padova, Italy
Tel: +39 49 827 6052; Fax: +39 49 827 6049

VASSORT Guy Vassort, INSERM U-390, CHU Arnaud de Villeneuve, 371 Avenue du Doyen Gaston Giraud, 34295 Montpellier Cedex, France
Tel: +33 4 67 41 52 40; Fax: +33 4 67 41 52 42;
e-mail: vassort@u390.montp.inserm.fr

ZAMPONI Terry P. Snutch, University of British Columbia, Biotechnology Laboratory, 6174 University Blvd, Vancouver, BC V6T 1Z3, Canada
Tel: +604 822 6476; Fax: +604 822 6470; e-mail: snutch@zoology.ubc.ca

ZÜHLKE Harald Reuter, Pharmakologisches Institut, Friedbühlstrasse 49, 3010 Bern, Switzerland
Tel: +41 31 632 32 81; Fax: +41 31 632 49 92
e-mail: Reuter@pki.unibe.ch

Guest Editors

CLOZEL Jean-Paul Clozel, Actelion Ltd, Gewerbestrasse 16, 4123 Allschwil, Switzerland
Tel: +33 3 89 69 19 87; Fax: +33 3 89 67 20 70;
e-mail: clozel@nucleus.fr

NARGEOT Joël Nargeot, Institut de Genetique Humaine, CNRS-UPR 1142, Rue de la Cardonille, 34293 Montpellier Cedex 5, France
Tel: +33 467 61 33 54; Fax: +33 467 52 15 59

TSIEN Richard W. Tsien, Department of Molecular and Cellular Physiology, Beckman Center B105A, Stanford University Medical Center, Stanford, CA 94305-5426, USA
Tel: +1 415 725 7557; Fax: +1 415 725 2504;
e-mail: rwtsien@leland.stanford.edu

Foreword

Across a broad spectrum of cell types, calcium signalling is used to trigger a wide variety of cellular responses, including muscular contraction, hormone or neurotransmitter secretion, gene activation and probably cell growth and proliferation. Ca^{2+} influx may also generate electrical currents critical for the support of pacemaker activity or even the action potential itself. Ca^{2+} entry into cells occurs mainly through the opening of various subtypes of voltage-gated calcium channels, including the mysterious category of 'T-type channels', which are widely expressed and probably involved in several cellular functions. Although they were first identified quite some time ago and are well characterised in terms of biophysical properties, knowledge of their structure and pharmacology is only now entering its most rapid phase. The development of a new ligand (mibefradil; Posicor®) by investigators at Roche has encouraged a reintensification of research on T-type channels, as indicated by a very productive meeting in Montpellier, France, that was devoted to these channels. This book reports on the many interesting perspectives that were shared in the warmth of that Mediterranean climate and hospitality, and also includes a contribution from Perez-Reyes and colleagues that describes their recent accomplishment of the cloning and expression of a T-type channel.

The earliest evidence for the importance of regulated Ca^{2+} entry into cells came from a variety of tissues, including crustacean skeletal muscle and mammalian and amphibian cardiac muscle, and almost certainly involved calcium channels quite distinct from T-type channels. For example, the earliest recordings of transmembrane calcium current in multicellular cardiac preparations, dating back 20 years, demonstrated a 'slow inward current', distinct from the more rapidly inactivating sodium current. This pathway for Ca^{2+} influx was found responsible for excitation–contraction coupling in cardiac and smooth muscle, for the responsiveness of these tissues to 'calcium channel blockers' used extensively in the treatment of cardiovascular disorders, and for the increase in myocardial contraction induced by β–adrenergic stimulation. Later patch-clamp experiments in the 1980s not only provided detailed characterisation of so-called 'L-type calcium channels' supporting the slow inward current, but also indicated the existence of a distinct category of 'low-voltage-activated (LVA) calcium current', generated by channels designated as 'T type'. Indeed, the distinction between T-type channels and high-voltage-activated (HVA) channels gave great impetus to growing awareness of the diversity of calcium channels that was also emerging from parallel studies of invertebrate systems. There was considerable interest in the possible role of LVA T-type channels in pacemaker activity and in generation of forms of electrical activity contingent upon prior hyperpolarisation. However, investigations of T-type calcium channels soon reverted back to a secondary position, overshadowed by the major advances in understanding other kinds of calcium channels through physiology, biochemistry and molecular biology. At roughly the same time that several subtypes of HVA calcium channels were uncovered through single-channel recordings and pharmacological studies using specific toxins (N, P and Q type), the purification and cloning of the dihydropyridine receptor from skeletal muscle led to the identification of several genes coding for diverse pore-forming α_1 subunits. Most of the HVA calcium channel types that were defined by biophysical and pharmacological properties in native tissues have now been convincingly identified with a cloned α_1 subunit (e.g. α_{1B} as N type and α_{1A} as P or Q type). The development of new ligands has provided added motivation to try to understand the functional and molecular properties of T-type calcium channels. Thus, the recent cloning of α_{1G} and the demonstration that it can support T-type channel activity provides a very important benchmark to an era of rapid progress.

Richard W. Tsien

Jean-Paul Clozel

Joël Nargeot

List of abbreviations

aCSF	artificial cerebrospinal fluid
ATP	adenosine triphosphate
BAPTA	1,2-*bis*(*o*-aminophenoxy)ethane-*N*,*N*,*N'*,*N'*-tetraacetic acid
CNS	central nervous system
CSF	cerebrospinal fluid
EGTA	ethyleneglycoltetraacetic acid
GDP	guanosine diphosphate
GTP	guanosine triphosphate
HEPES	*N*-2-hydroxyethylpiperazine-*N'*-3-propanesulphonic acid
ω-Aga-IIIA	ω-agatoxin IIIA
ω-Aga-IVA	ω-agatoxin IVA
ω-CTx-GVIA	ω-conotoxin VIA from *Conus geographus*
ω-CTx-MVIIC	ω-conotoxin VIIC from *Conus magus*
s	second(s)
S	siemens (unit of conductance, g)
TEA	tetraethylammonium
TEAC	TEACl; tetraethylammonium chloride
TRIS	tris(hydroxymethyl)-aminomethane

Section 1

Biophysical properties and classification

Introduction

This first section includes papers that address basic questions about the distinctions between T-type calcium channels and other calcium channels, important as a foundation for the rest of the book. What are the key biophysical and pharmacological properties that delineate T-type calcium channels in native tissues? How much diversity exists within the category of low-voltage-activated (LVA) currents loosely known as T-type and what are their most salient distinguishing characteristics?

The first three chapters review key features of what might be called the 'classical' T-type calcium channel, a set of characteristics that have been found in several different kinds of cells, including endocrine cells, cardiac, smooth and skeletal muscle cells, and sensory neurons. In reviewing his original work in clonal pituitary cells, **Armstrong** focuses on one of the major distinguishing features of T-type calcium channels, the speed of their closure following a sudden membrane repolarisation (deactivation), which is almost an order of magnitude slower than that found with other voltage-gated calcium channels. The slow deactivation greatly influences the timing and magnitude of Ca^{2+} entry that T-type channels support, and also provides a means for kinetically dissecting T-type activity from that of other kinds of calcium channels. **Nilius** reviews other characteristics of classical T-type channels, revealed by his unitary recordings in heart cells. Their small single-channel conductance (6–9 pS) and the equivalence of their conductance to Ca^{2+} and Ba^{2+} set them apart from most if not all other channel subtypes. In addition, T-type channels display a striking kinetic signature at the single-channel level, marked by a brief burst of openings following a relatively long initial silent period, reflecting kinetic details of their transitions between closed and open states. **Randall and Tsien** describe biophysical and pharmacological properties of T-type calcium channels that distinguish them from R-type channels, their closest counterpart among the high-voltage-activated (HVA) channel types. Another kinetic fingerprint of T-type channels, evident even in recordings from large numbers of channels, is a crossing-over of current records obtained with increasingly strong depolarising pulses. A major pharmacological difference is that R-type channel current undergoes inhibition with the spider toxin ω-Aga-IIIA while T-type current does not.

The next chapters examine calcium channel activity in other central neurons and provide evidence for additional subcategories of T-type calcium channels that may be distinguished from the 'classical' T-type channel. **Dzhura et al.** describe two kinds of LVA current in slice recordings from neurons in the dorsolateral thalamic nucleus of young rats. One type ('fast') inactivates rapidly and appears at an early postnatal age, the other ('slow') inactivates more slowly and emerges later in development. The first type is blocked preferentially by nifedipine and La^{3+}, the second by Ni^{2+}. Neither of these corresponds well to the 'classical' T-type channel mentioned above. **Akaike** surveys neuronal cell bodies derived from several different brain regions, including cortex, hippocampus, cerebellum, nucleus of Meynert, nucleus tractus solitarius and substantia nigra. He found considerable variation in the ratio of LVA and HVA calcium current amplitudes. When the HVA current is split up into pharmacologically defined components, the central neurons generally exhibit significant contributions of L-, N-, P/Q- and R-type currents. The exception is the cerebellar Purkinje cell, which carries the well-known preponderance of P-type current. **Bossu et al.** examine calcium channel activity in dendrites of Purkinje cells in slices kept in organotypic culture and find evidence for a substantial contribution of LVA calcium current, supported by 9 pS channels, similar but probably not identical to 'classical' T-type channels. These are easily distinguished from HVA current by their resistance to pharmacological inhibitors and to run down. In another type of cerebellar neuron, the granule cell, **Tottene et al.** provide an intriguing perspective on the diversity of calcium channels based on single-channel recordings. Two types of channels, designated G2 and G3, were found to be resistant to known inhibitors of L-, N- and P/Q-type channels and were thus classified as 'R type' on pharmacological grounds. The G2 and G3 channels activated at more negative potentials than G1 channels (P or P/Q type) and displayed a time-course of inactivation consistent with that seen in whole-cell recordings (but slower than for R-type current as it was first described).

Two chapters provide perspective on the use of divalents to distinguish between various types of calcium channels. **Carbone et al.** focus on the blocking effects of Mg^{2+} ions, which act as a 'one-way' calcium channel blocker. In contrast to well-known blockers such as Cd^{2+}, Mg^{2+} cannot readily be pushed clear through the channel by strong electrical gradients. LVA and HVA channels respond in very similar ways to Mg^{2+} block. For either category of calcium channel, currents carried by Na^{+} are far more susceptible than calcium currents to Mg^{2+} block, consistent with the idea that the binding of Ca^{2+} causes structural rearrangements of acidic side chains. **Zamponi et al.** describe the effects of Ni^{2+}, another widely used blocking ion, and separate out inhibitory actions resulting from interference with ion permeation and those arising from displacement of the voltage-dependence of gating. The relative importance of these two forms of inhibition differs widely between various α_1 subunits to the next and over a range of test voltages, suggesting that great caution must be exercised in trying to use Ni^{2+} or other divalent cations as probes for discriminating among various types of calcium channels.

Calcium channel properties in endocrine cells of pituitary origin

Clay M. Armstrong

Department of Physiology, University of Pennsylvania, Philadelphia, Pennsylvania, USA

When calcium channels were first discovered by Fatt and Katz[1] and Fatt and Ginsborg,[2] they were regarded perhaps more as a curiosity than as objects requiring serious study. Their importance was forcefully underlined when Katz and Miledi found clear evidence for the role of calcium channels in transmitter release in the giant synapse of the squid.[3] Other landmarks were the discovery of calcium currents in heart muscle,[4] smooth muscle, skeletal muscle,[5] neurons and endocrine cells.[6]

In some cases the function of the calcium channels is well understood, as in nerve terminals or secretory cells. In skeletal muscle, early research indicated that calcium channels might somehow be involved in excitation–contraction coupling, but it was far from clear how the very slow calcium current seen experimentally[5] was related to calcium release from the internal stores in the sarcoplasmic reticulum. It is now known that skeletal muscle calcium channels serve as the voltage sensors for excitation–contraction coupling. They undergo a voltage-driven conformational change which is transmitted to the release channels in the membrane of the sarcoplasmic reticulum (the ryanodine receptors) by a direct mechanical action involving a known segment of the calcium channel protein.[7,8] The function of calcium channels in neuronal cell bodies and dendrites is less well understood. Perhaps they serve to notify enzymes within the cytoplasm that activity has occurred.

The first intimation of multiple calcium channel types came from Hagiwara's laboratory.[9] Before the age of cloning the suggestion of a new channel type was usually received with some reservation, but a clear biophysical distinction of two channel types was achieved almost simultaneously in endocrine (GH3) cells,[10–12] neuronal (chick dorsal root ganglion) cells[13,14] and heart muscle.[15]

This paper contains a brief account of research with GH3 cells that led to the separation of two types of calcium channel, and a description of their properties. It is still not known why an endocrine cell needs two types of calcium channel, but speculation based on the properties of the channel types is presented.

Results

Our experiments were performed on GH3 cells, a transformed line of anterior pituitary cell. These cells have a variety of currents and vary in the degree of expression of each type. Figure 1 (A) shows three of the major components that we recorded upon stepping membrane voltage from –70 to +20 mV, using a patch-clamp and whole-cell configuration. There is a fast transient of inward current carried by

Na^+ ions (sodium current), followed by a slower outward current carried by K^+ ions (potassium current). These currents are very similar to sodium and potassium currents recorded from nerve fibres and are probably the major contributors to the action potentials generated by GH3 cells. When membrane voltage is returned to –70 mV, there is a large, slowly decaying tail of inward current that, as described below, is carried by Ca^{2+} ions.

Potassium current can be eliminated by filling the patch pipette with Cs^+ 130 mM instead of K^+. Figure 1 (B) shows the traces from a cell with a relatively small sodium

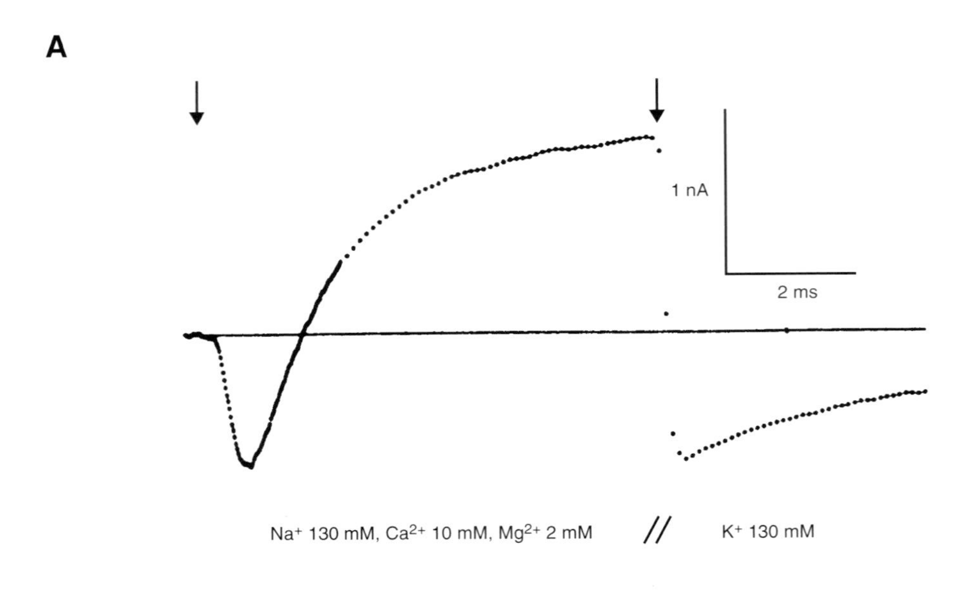

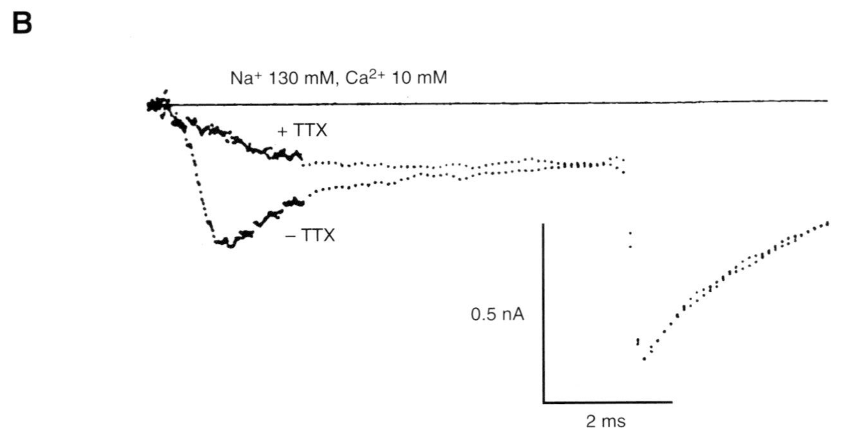

Fig. 1. Major current components in GH3 cells. A) Membrane voltage was stepped to +20 mV between the arrows, from a holding potential of –70 mV. During the step there is a rapidly activating inward current, followed by a sustained outward current. After repolarisation there is a large and slowly decaying tail of inward current. Solutions: Na^+ 130 mM, Ca^{2+} 10 mM (external); K^+ 130 mM, Cs^+ 10 mM (internal). B) Tetrodotoxin (TTX) blocks the fast transient of inward sodium current, without affecting either the sustained current during the pulse or the tail current, both of which are calcium current flowing through slowly deactivating calcium channels.

current which could be blocked by tetrodotoxin (TTX). Addition of TTX reveals a rather slowly developing inward current that is sustained until the end of the pulse. On repolarisation to –70 mV there is a slow tail of inward current that is unaffected by TTX. The slow tail can be eliminated by removing external Ca^{2+}. This, combined with its insensitivity to TTX, identifies it as calcium current.

Na^+ and Ca^{2+} contributions to the inward current can also be analysed by interrupting a depolarisation to +20 mV at various times (with return to –70 mV) and analysing the tail currents (fig. 2 (A)). The continuous trace shows the current for a sustained step to +20 mV; the tails were recorded at –70 mV after 0.5–8 ms activating pulses to +20 mV. For steps of 0.5 and 1 ms, all or nearly all of the current decays with the rapid time-course of sodium channels. This rapid component becomes smaller as sodium channels inactivate with time, and is quite small after a pulse lasting a few milliseconds. As the activating pulse duration increases in duration, a slow component of the tail develops, carried by Ca^{2+} ions.

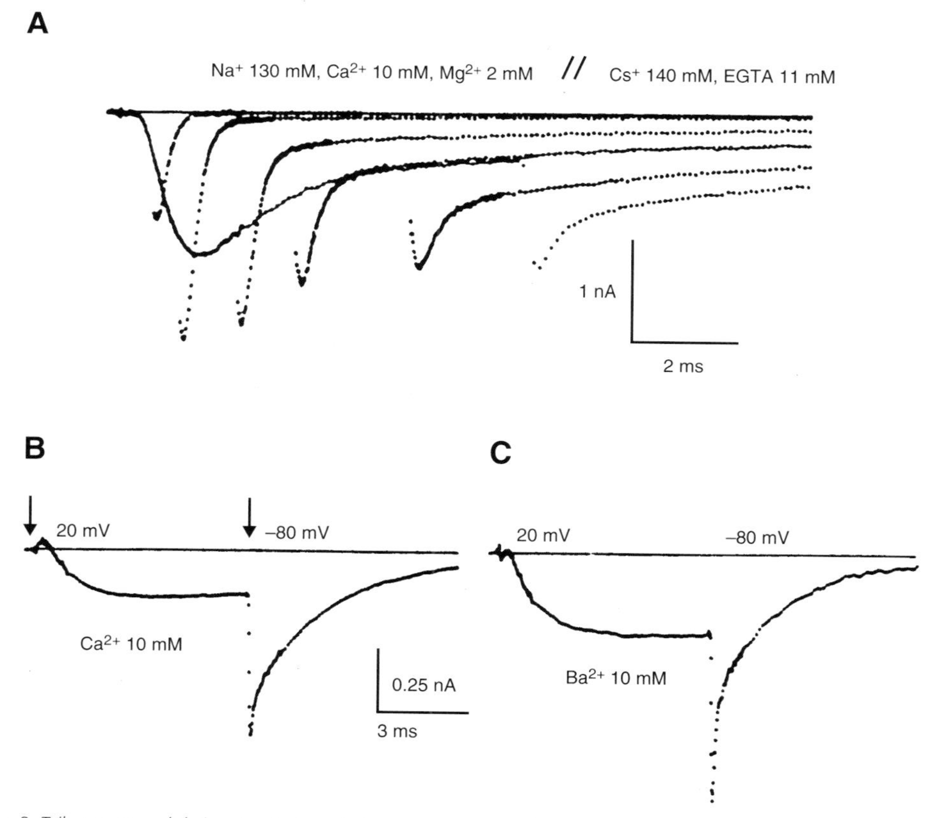

Fig. 2. Tail currents and their components. A) The continuous trace shows the current during an activating pulse to +20 mV. After 0.5–8 ms, membrane voltage was returned to –70 mV, producing the decaying tails of inward current (the tails from 6 trials are superimposed). For activating steps >1 ms, there are two components in the tail: a fast component of sodium current, and a slow calcium current component. B & C) Changing from Ca^{2+} 10 mM (B) to Ba^{2+} 10 mM (C) approximately doubles the current flow at +20 mV and enhances the fast component in the tail at –80 mV. This is the result of increased current through fast-deactivating channels, which carry Ba^{2+} in preference to Ca^{2+}. The slow component of the tail current is unaffected, because the slowly deactivating channels conduct Ca^{2+} and Ba^{2+} equally well.

At this point we thought we were dealing with a slowly deactivating calcium channel combined with a rapid component related to sodium channels. We were therefore puzzled to find that in the presence of TTX, switching from Ca^{2+} 10 mM to Ba^{2+} 10 mM in the external solution led to the development of a prominent fast component in the tail current, which obviously could not be sodium current (Fig. 2 (B & C)). As can be seen in the figure, the slowly deactivating component of the tail is almost unaffected by the change from Ca^{2+} to Ba^{2+}. This was the first, and initially quite puzzling, indication of the existence of a second type of 'fast deactivating' calcium channel, which appeared to have a preference for Ba^{2+} as a charge carrier.

It became apparent that there were two keys to differentiating the components: the difference in deactivation rate, and the relatively fast and complete inactivation of the slowly deactivating component, as shown in figure 3. Panel A of figure 3 shows the current tails recorded after activating pulses of 7–200 ms. Each tail is composed of an initial fast-decaying component, followed by a slowly decaying component. The

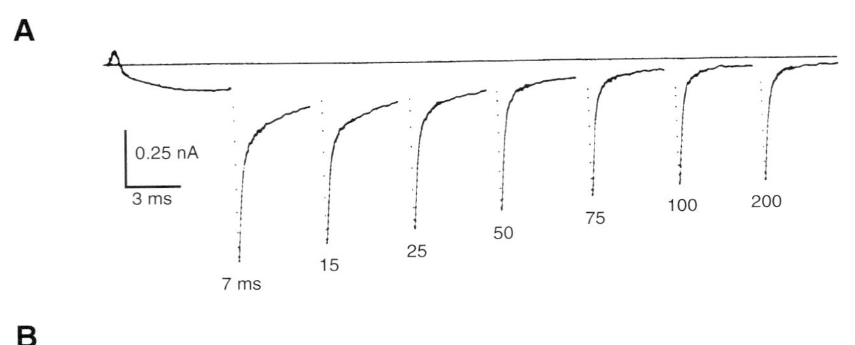

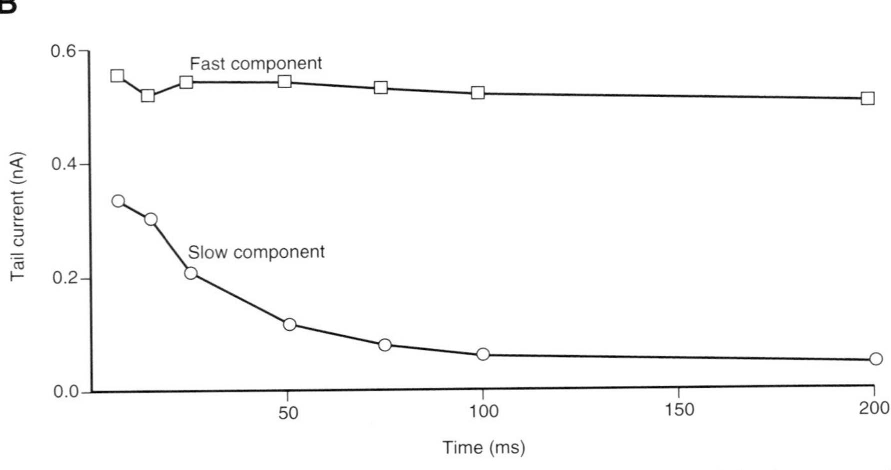

Fig. 3. Inactivation of the slow component of the tail current through calcium channels, recorded in the presence of tetrodotoxin. A) An activating pulse to +20 mV was terminated after 7–200 ms in 7 trials, and the results are superimposed. The slow component decreases in size with pulse duration, while the fast component remains unchanged. B) The tails in panel A were fitted with two exponentials, and the amplitudes are plotted to show the inactivation of the slow (slowly deactivating) component and the near constancy of the fast-decaying fast-deactivating component. Charge carrier: Ba^{2+} 10 mM.

fast component (extracted by a biexponential fit) has almost the same amplitude throughout the series (fig. 3 (B)). On the other hand, the slow component inactivates, with a time constant of about 25 ms, and is quite small after a 200 ms activating pulse.

Using inactivation of the slow component as a dissecting tool, the two components can be separated explicitly by subtraction, as illustrated in figure 4, panel A of which shows the amplitudes of the fast and slow components after activating pulses of 6, 21 and 101 ms duration. At 101 ms the slow component has inactivated almost completely. Using the 101 ms tail as a sample (almost pure) of the fast component, it can be subtracted from the 6 and 21 ms tails to yield the slow components shown in panel B of the figure. These slow tails decay with a time constant of 3.3 ms (18 °C; –80 mV).

Analysis of the tails also gives the time- and voltage-dependence of the activation of the two components. Panel A of figure 5 shows the amplitudes of the fast and slow components upon repolarisation after activating pulses to +20 mV (22 °C). At this voltage the fast-deactivating channels activate approximately twice as quickly as the slowly deactivating channels, as shown in panel B. The voltage-dependence of activation, obtained by tail analysis, is shown in panel C. The activation curve for slowly deactivating channels is about 20 mV to the left of the fast-deactivating activation curve. At –20 mV, almost half of the slowly deactivating channels are activated, judging from tail amplitude, while only about 10% of the fast-deactivating channels are activated. Also shown is the activation curve for sodium channels, as deduced from tail amplitudes after very short pulses. Activation of sodium channels and fast-deactivating channels becomes detectable at about the same voltage, but the sodium channel activation curve rises somewhat more steeply than the gradually rising fast-deactivating curve.

Figure 6 shows a curious behaviour of the fast-deactivating channels in external solutions containing both Ba^{2+} and Ca^{2+}. Ca^{2+} is known to interfere with Ba^{2+}

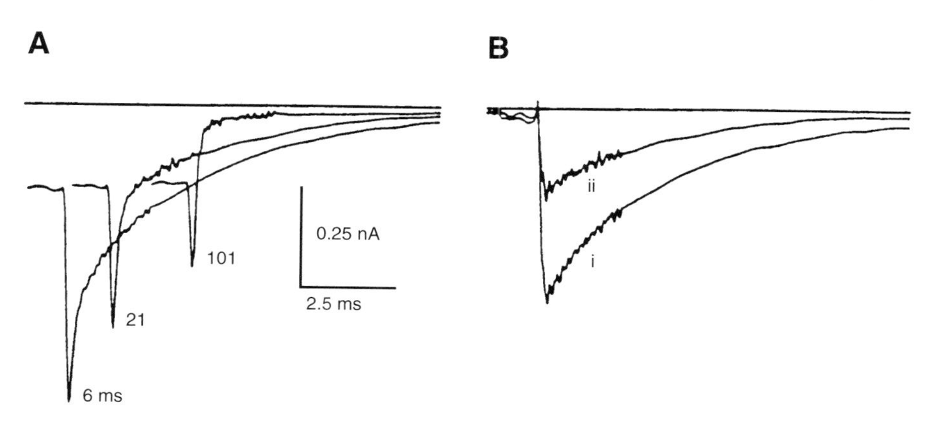

Fig. 4. A) Closing of calcium channels after activating pulses of 6, 21 and 101 ms, for a cell in Ba^{2+} 10 mM. The slow component is very small after the 101 ms pulse. B) Current through the slowly deactivating channels, obtained by subtracting the 101 ms tail (almost pure fast-deactivating current) from the tails at (i) 6 and (ii) 21 ms.

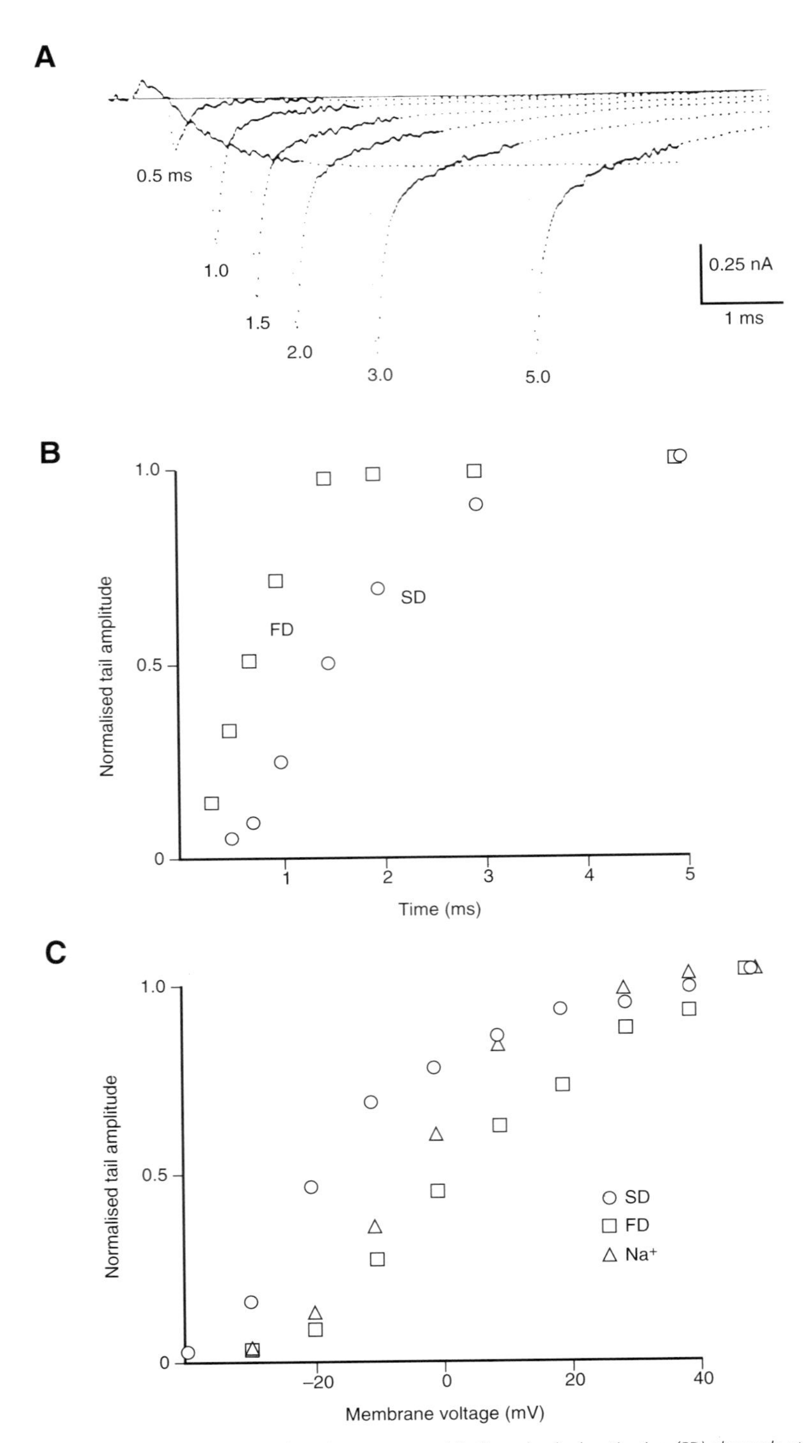

Fig. 5. A & B) Fast-deactivating (FD) channels activate more rapidly than slowly deactivating (SD) channels at +20 mV. Upper traces show the development of the FD and SD components of the tails. The FD component develops more rapidly (B: plot of the amplitudes of FD and SD components). C) Activation curves for SD, FD and sodium channels, obtained by tail analysis.

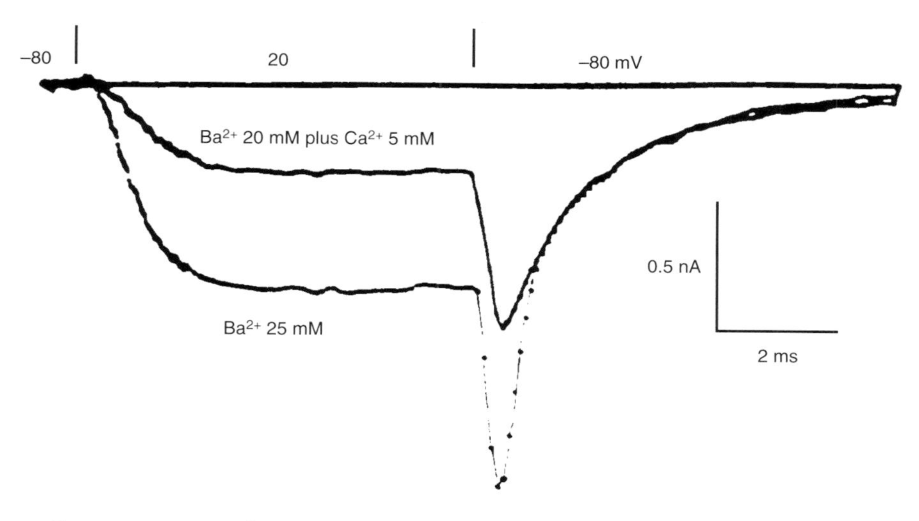

Fig. 6. Ca^{2+} blocks the flow of Ba^{2+} through fast-deactivating but not slowly deactivating channels.

permeation through the calcium channels,[16,17] an effect sometimes called the 'anomalous mole fraction effect'. Changing the external solution from Ba^{2+} 25 mM to Ba^{2+} 20 mM plus Ca^{2+} 5 mM reduces the current during the pulse to about half, and essentially eliminates the fast-deactivating component in the tail. This dramatically illustrates the inhibition of Ba^{2+} permeation by Ca^{2+}. Interestingly, the slowly deactivating component is unaffected by the solution change. Experiments that are not illustrated here show that Ba^{2+} (in the absence of Ca^{2+}) permeates through fast-deactivating channels about twice as well as Ca^{2+} (both ions at saturating concentrations for permeation), while the permeation ratio for slowly deactivating channels is about 1:1. Thus Ca^{2+} and Ba^{2+} are handled with equal efficiency by slowly deactivating channels, and Ca^{2+} shows no detectable tendency to interfere with Ba^{2+} permeation.

A summary of the properties of fast- versus slowly deactivating channels in GH3 cells is shown in table I. Judging from the literature, the equivalent of slowly deactivating channels in other cells has a conductance of ~8 pS in Ba^{2+} 110 mM, while that of fast-deactivating channels is ~25 pS.

Table I. Properties of slowly deactivating (SD) and fast-deactivating (FD) channels from GH3 cells, at 19–22 °C

Property	SD channels	FD channels
Voltage for detectable activation	–40 mV	–20 mV
Half-time of activation	1.5 ms (20 mV)	0.7 ms (20 mV)
Deactivation time constant	3 ms (–80 mV)	0.15 ms (–80 mV)
Inactivation time constant	23 ms (20 mV)	No detectable inactivation in 100 ms
$I_{Ba}:I_{Ca}$ ratio	1.0	2.2

Abbreviations: I_{Ba} = barium current; I_{Ca} = calcium current.

Discussion

Channel classification

There are two main types of calcium channels, which are referred to above as fast- and slowly deactivating channels, respectively. The former channels are also called 'high-voltage-activated' (HVA) channels (or L-, N-, P-type channels, etc.), while the latter are also referred to as 'low-voltage-activated' (LVA) channels (or T-type channels). The two *functional* types have the characteristics listed in table I. The alphabetical classification (L, N, etc.) is based on pharmacological characteristics, and (to this author) makes no better sense than characterising potassium channels by their sensitivity to external TEA^+, which, in the case of *Shaker B*, depends on a single residue. Considered functionally, L-type channels span such a wide range of entities that this terminology is of no practical use. These include channels in endocrine cells that inactivate very slowly, cardiac channels that show rapid Ca^{2+}-dependent inactivation, and skeletal muscle channels whose main function is not to conduct (they activate *very* slowly) but to serve as voltage sensors in excitation–contraction coupling.[7,8] Eventually the need may arise for a more reasonable classification.

Function of slowly deactivating (LVA or T-type) channels

This section is both speculative and dogmatic.

The only completely clarified function for calcium channels is their role in exocytosis. In skeletal muscle the dihydropyridine receptors participate in excitation–contraction coupling, but their essential function is not ion conduction. It seems reasonable to speculate that calcium channels in, for example, neuronal cell bodies are involved in the transmission of signals to the metabolic machinery that the cell has been active. It has also been hypothesised that calcium channels in dendrites are in some way associated with learning. These interesting ideas have not yet been worked out in detail.

Why should there be a second type of calcium channel (slowly deactivating, LVA or T-type channel)? I will speculate here only on the possible usefulness of this type of channel in endocrine cells, specifically cells of pituitary origin, with much emphasis on the excellent results of Gabriel Cota and colleagues. Two calcium channel types have been found not only in GH3 cells but also in cells of the pars intermedia,[18] lactotropes[19] and somatotropes.[20] Many anterior and intermediate pituitary cells can generate action potentials (see Cota for references[18]). Cota and colleagues have shown that lactotropes fall into two groups with regard to their secretion rate, which differs between groups by a factor of about 4. The fast secretors have a higher density of both sodium channels (× 6) and fast-deactivating calcium channels (× 3). Slowly deactivating channel density is about the same in both populations. The role of sodium channels in secretion was tested by Cota and colleagues by applying TTX.[21] The results strongly suggest that fast secretors are blocked by TTX but that slow secretors are unaffected. (Strictly speaking, the fraction of fast secretors in the total population is greatly reduced, while the fraction of slow secretors is unaffected.) Thus sodium channels, fast-deactivating channels and high secretion rate are linked. TTX seems to stop secretion from the fast secretors entirely. The slow secretors have a low density of sodium and fast-deactivating channels, and they are unaffected by TTX. Both fast and slow secretors have approximately equal numbers of slowly deactivating channels.

It seems reasonable to suppose that the fast secretors generate sodium action potentials, which make membrane voltage sufficiently positive to open fast-deactivating channels. The fast-deactivating channels then admit a burst of Ca^{2+}, which reaches a high concentration in a region near the exocytosis machinery. Activation of the machinery for rapid exocytosis in melanotrophs[22] and chromaffin cells[23] requires a local Ca^{2+} concentration in the range of 50–100 μM, one that is likely to be achieved only near the mouth of a calcium channel. In chromaffin cells, however, there is evidence for a slower mode of exocytosis that requires a lower concentration of Ca^{2+}. Clearly it will be impossible to do more than speculate about the role of calcium channels until the Ca^{2+} requirement of the exocytosis machinery is settled. There may be several variants of this machinery expressed in different cells. Cota's studies, for example, suggest that the fast secretors lack the machinery for slow secretion and simply do not secrete when their sodium channels are blocked.[18,19]

The slow secretors, lacking sodium and fast-deactivating channels, probably cannot generate action potentials. In cells that do not generate action potentials there may be two patterns of secretion. Hille and colleagues noted fluctuations of membrane voltage in somatotropes[20] and an average depolarisation of 9 mV in response to growth hormone-releasing hormone. Secretion in these cells depends on the presence of external Ca^{2+} and can be blocked by nitrendipine. This suggests that fast-deactivating channels are involved. The second pattern seen by Hille and colleagues was in gonadotropes.[24] These cells show oscillations in internal Ca^{2+} concentration in response to gonadotrophin-releasing hormone, as a result of release from internal stores, through IP_3-activated channels. Exocytosis is detectable when the Ca^{2+} concentration rises above 300 nM, from a resting level of 100 nM. In view of the estimates above, it should be noted that 300 nM seems to be quite a low concentration for the activation of exocytosis. Perhaps the IP_3 channels that release Ca^{2+} from the endoplasmic reticulum are closely associated with the release sites, or perhaps there may be more than one type of Ca^{2+}-stimulated exocytosis machinery. The calcium waves also elicited potassium current through Ca^{2+}-activated potassium channels, which in the unclamped state would presumably have led to oscillations in membrane voltage. Hille et al. suggest that hyperpolarisation related to potassium current removes inactivation of sodium and Ca^{2+} channels, enhancing excitability.[23] Action potentials have been seen to follow the hyperpolarisations.

It must be admitted that the studies cited do not clearly define the role of slowly deactivating channels in secretion. The suggestion that follows thus cannot be said to be supported by evidence, although it is not ruled out. Thus in pituitary-type cells, slowly deactivating channels may be involved in a form of slow secretion that occurs in cells that are not firing action potentials. The available evidence shows that fast secretion requires action potentials and fast-deactivating channels. Slowly deactivating channels instead might serve as Ca^{2+} injectors in cells that have an oscillating membrane potential in the vicinity of –40 mV (too negative to activate sodium channels and fast-deactivating channels). At this voltage, slowly deactivating channels might conduct Ca^{2+} inward sufficiently well, despite their low conductance, to activate the exocytosis machinery. Their adequacy as Ca^{2+} injectors would be further enhanced, in the presence of an oscillating membrane potential, by their slow deactivation: they would conduct Ca^{2+} for some time as membrane potential became negative. Furthermore, thanks to the increased driving force and the downward curve of their open-channel current–voltage relationship, current per channel would increase with negativity. Inactivation of the channels would terminate the depolarised phase of the oscillation and prevent it from becoming too large.

An intriguing possibility is that a single cell might have the machinery for both modes of secretion. For example, cells that synthesise the common precursor molecule pro-opiomelanocortin, which can be split into several products, might use the high-voltage mode (action potentials and fast-deactivating channel activation) for secreting one product, and the low-voltage mode (oscillations close to –40 mV) for a different product. There would be relatively little overlap in release, because sodium and fast-deactivating channels would not be activated in the low-voltage mode, and in spiking mode the slowly deactivating channels would be inactivated.

Obviously, before these ideas can be evaluated, more needs to be known about the exocytosis machinery and how many forms it takes, and about the activity patterns in single secretory cells.

References

1. Fatt P, Katz B. The electrical properties of crustacean muscle fibres. J Physiol (Lond) 1953; 121: 374–89
2. Fatt P, Ginsborg BL. The ionic requirements for the production of action potentials in crustacean muscle fibres. J Physiol (Lond) 1958; 142: 516–43
3. Katz B, Miledi R. Tetrodotoxin-resistant electric activity in presynaptic terminals. J Physiol (Lond) 1969; 203: 459–87
4. Reuter H. Divalent cations as charge carriers in excitable membranes. Prog Biophys Mol Biol 1973; 26: 1–43
5. Beaty GN, Stefani E. Calcium dependent electrical activity in twitch muscle fibres of the frog. Proc R Soc Lond B Biol Sci 1976; 194: 141–50
6. Tareskevich PS, Douglas WW. Action potentials occur in cells of the normal anterior pituitary gland and are stimulated by the hypophysiotropic peptide thyrotropin-releasing hormone. Proc Natl Acad Sci U S A 1977; 74: 4064–7
7. Rios E, Brum G. Involvement of dihydropyridine receptor in excitation-contraction-coupling in skeletal muscle. Nature 1987; 325: 717–20
8. Tanabe T, Beam KG, Powell JA, et al. Restoration of excitation-contraction coupling and slow calcium current in dysgenic muscle by dihydropyridine receptor complementary DNA. Nature 1988; 336: 134–9
9. Hagiwara S, Byerley L. Calcium channel. Ann Rev Neurosci 1981; 4: 69–125
10. Matteson DR, Armstrong CM. Evidence for two types of Ca channels in GH3 cells. Biophys J 1984; 45: 36a
11. Armstrong CM, Matteson DR. Two distinct populations of calcium channels in a clonal line of pituitary cells. Science 1985; 227: 65–7
12. Matteson DR, Armstrong CM. Properties of two types of calcium channels in clonal pituitary cells. J Gen Physiol 1986; 67: 161–82
13. Carbone E, Lux HD. A low voltage-activated, fully inactivating Ca channel in vertebrate sensory neurones. Nature 1984; 310: 501–2

14. Fox AP, Nowycky MC, Tsien RW. Kinetic and pharmacological properties distinguishing three types of calcium currents in chick sensory neurones. J Physiol 1987; 394: 149–72
15. Nilius B, Hess P, Lansman JB, et al. A novel type of cardiac channel in ventricular cells. Nature 1985; 316: 443–6
16. Hess P, Tsien RW. Mechanism of ion permeation through calcium channels. Nature 1984; 309: 453–6
17. Almers W, McCleskey EW. Non-selective conductance in calcium channels in frog muscle: calcium selectivity in a single-file pore. J Physiol (Lond) 1984; 353: 585–608
18. Cota G. Calcium channel current in pars-intermedia cells of the rat pituitary gland. J Gen Physiol 1986; 88: 83–105
19. Cota G, Hiriart M, Horta J, et al. Calcium channels and basal prolactin secretion in single male rat lactotropes. Am J Physiol 1990; 259: C949–59
20. Naumov AP, Herrington J, Hille B. Actions of growth-hormone-releasing hormone on rat pituitary cells: intracellular calcium and ionic currents. Pflugers Arch 1994; 427: 414–21
21. Horta JM, Hiriart M, Cota G. Differential expression of Na channels in functional subpopulations of rat lactotropes. Am J Physiol 1991; 261: C865–71
22. Thomas P, Wong JG, Almers W. Millisecond studies of secretion in single rat pituitary cells stimulated by flash-photolysis of caged Ca^{2+}. EMBO J 1993; 12: 303–6
23. Neher E, Zucker RS. Multiple calcium-dependent processes related to secretion in bovine chromaffin cells. Neuron 1993; 10: 21–30
24. Hille B, Tse A, Tse FW, et al. Calcium oscillation and exocytosis in pituitary gonadotropes. Ann N Y Acad Sci 1994; 710: 261–70

T-type calcium channels in myocardial cells

Bernd Nilius

Laboratorium voor Fysiologie, Katholieke Universiteit Leuven, Louvain, Belgium

Summary

Cardiac T-type calcium channels have not yet been characterised at the molecular level. However, single-channel and whole-cell measurements clearly demonstrate that T-type calcium currents pass through a distinct channel entity. It has been shown that L-type and T-type channels coexist in the same patches and differ with respect to kinetics, permeability and pharmacology. Furthermore, T-type currents cannot be explained by the passage of Ca^{2+} through sodium channels, and data from single-channel measurements demonstrate a unique kinetic fingerprint for these channels.

T-type channels open mainly in one burst per depolarisation before reaching their absorbent state. Waiting time to the first opening after onset of depolarisation (first latency) is voltage-dependent. There are close correlations between first latency and the macroscopic time constant of inactivation and between the time- and voltage-dependencies of the probability of the channel being open and the convolution of the first latency distribution with burst duration distribution. These correlations support the view that the voltage-dependence of the kinetic pattern of T-type channels is determined predominantly by transition between at least two closed states.

Introduction

It is clear that cardiac cells express different types of calcium channel, all of which may coexist in individual cells.[1–7] One of these, the so-called 'L-type' calcium channel, is well characterised at the functional and molecular levels. The second type of myocardial calcium channel is known as the 'T' type because of its very small conductance and transient time-course, and has not yet been cloned. A reliable candidate is therefore not yet available. This is likely to be related mainly to the lack of specific blockers (which makes the identification of cloned and expressed channels difficult).

At the single-channel level, there are few data relevant to T-type currents. The cardiac T-type calcium channel is biophysically characterised by activation at membrane potentials negative to –50 mV, fast inactivation and slow deactivation, a single-channel conductance of 6–8 pS and a similar level of permeability to Ca^{2+} and Ba^{2+}.

In addition to the difficulties in molecular identification, the rather variable expression of these channels in the different types of myocardial tissue is a complicating factor. In several myocardial tissues, no T-type calcium channels could be detected (e.g. frog ventricle, ferret ventricle, rat ventricle), although they are present in the same species in atrial heart tissue (frog atrium, rat atrium, rabbit atrium, guinea-pig atrium and ventricle, human atrium, chick ventricle, dog atrium). This differential expression is particularly puzzling, given the functional significance of this channel.

In cardiac cells, T-type calcium channels may be the major carriers of calcium current during development.[8,9] This finding seems to be of special interest because, in most cell types, T-type calcium channels are predominantly expressed at the early embryonic or neonatal stage, in a manner dependent on the cell cycle.[10] In mature myocardium, expression of T-type calcium channels is much higher in the less differentiated cells (such as the sinoatrial node and pacemaking tissue) than in cells from the highly differentiated ventricular working myocardium.

The kinetic properties of T-type calcium channels may be responsible for some of their cellular functions. Although the current activated by depolarisation is much smaller for T- than for L-type currents, repolarisation might induce extensive Ca^{2+} entry through T-type calcium channels, because of their slow deactivation.[11] Furthermore, a functionally important feature of these channels is their activation at rather negative potentials, which might be involved in the triggering of spontaneous electrical activity.[12–14] This paper will focus on the kinetic properties of single myocardial T-type calcium channels.

Methods

Most of the cell preparations were made up according to a well-established enzymatic cell isolation method.[15] Cells were isolated from guinea-pig ventricles. Electrophysiological measurements were performed mainly on isolated cells incubated in a depolarising bath solution comprising potassium aspartate 140 mM, $MgCl_2$ 2 mM, EGTA 10 mM, ATP 2 mM and HEPES 10 mM. The pipette solution contained $CaCl_2$ 110 mM and HEPES 10 mM. Replacement of the pipette solution containing $BaCl_2$ 110 mM used more typically for the study of calcium channel currents has proved to be extremely successful in the characterisation of T-type calcium channels. This is because these channels are at least as permeable to Ca^{2+} as Ba^{2+}, whereas L-type calcium channels in the same patches are much less permeable to Ca^{2+} than Ba^{2+}. This characteristic was useful in discriminating both channel types in myocardial cells.

All other details of methods used have been described previously.[2,16]

Results

T-type currents do not pass through sodium channels

From an early stage, we doubted that this novel type of cardiac calcium current might be associated with passage of Ca^{2+} ions through modified L-type calcium channels or through sodium channels. Figure 1 shows a typical example of a cell-

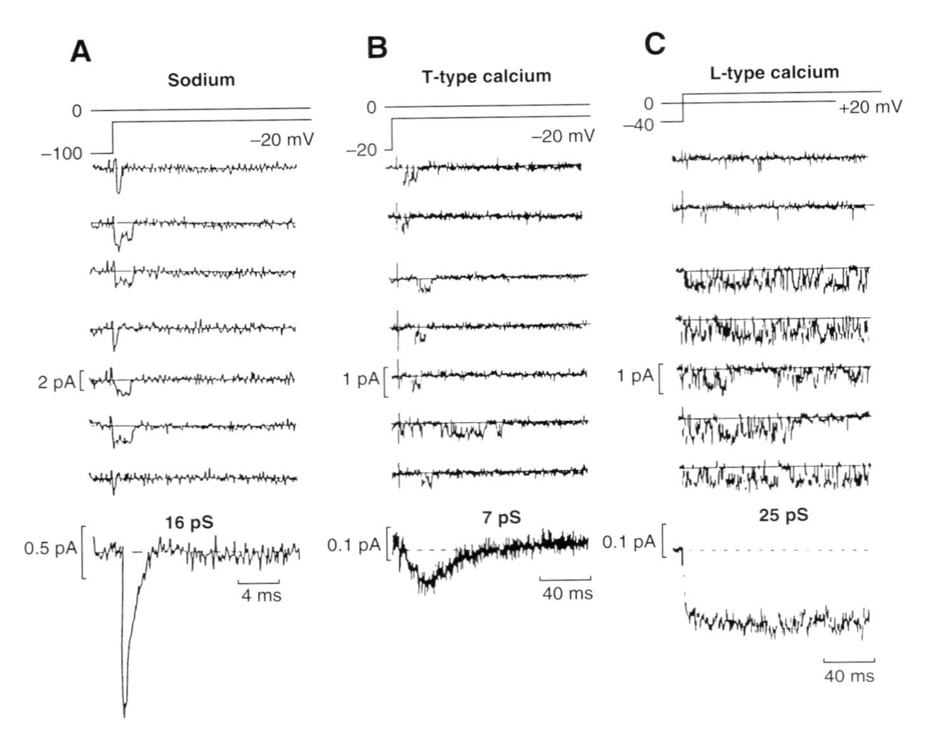

Fig. 1. Ionic currents through sodium channels and various types of calcium channel in guinea-pig ventricle cells. A) Depolarising step from a holding potential of –100 mV to –20 mV. Activation of a 16 pS sodium channel (pipette solution: NaCl 140 mM, KCl 4 mM, $CaCl_2$ 2 mM, $MgCl_2$ 1 mM, HEPES 10 mM); current averaged from 85 sweeps. B) Activation of a T-type calcium channel (pipette solution: $CaCl_2$ 110 mM); current averaged from 155 sweeps. C) L-type calcium channel activated from a holding potential of –40 mV by a depolarising pulse to +20 mV (pipette solution: $BaCl_2$ 110 mM). T-type calcium channels were present in this patch but were inactivated by this method. All data are filtered at 2 kHz and sampled at 150 ms. Current averaged from 100 sweeps.

attached measurement of unitary current from isolated guinea-pig ventricle cells. Sodium currents were measured with Na^+, T-type calcium currents with Ca^{2+} and L-type calcium currents with Ba^{2+} as charge carriers (the main cations present in the pipette solution). Evidently, T-type calcium currents and sodium currents share some qualitative similarities in their kinetic patterns: fast activation, slower inactivation and clustering of openings at the very beginning of the depolarisation step. It became apparent that the tiny inactivating currents that can be activated at very negative membrane potentials (through low-threshold calcium channels[17]) have properties that distinguish them from the high-threshold, classical calcium channel currents (later described as L-type currents). These include clear-cut single-channel currents in cell-attached patches with Ca^{2+} 110 mM in the patch pipette, a different voltage-range of activation, different channel conductances (in the same patch), and distinctive kinetics, pharmacology and pH-dependence, and differences after patch excision.[2,18,19] Furthermore, for whole-cell currents, T-type currents clearly differed from currents through L-type calcium channels. However, the question still remains as to whether a combination of L-type calcium channel subunits or transcripts from the α_1 gene for the L-type calcium channel are responsible for this type of current.[20]

The other problem to solve was whether T-type currents might be caused by Ca^{2+} passing through sodium channels in the absence of extracellular Na^{+}. Together with Peter Hess, we approached this problem as early as 1985 by using some of the most efficient modulators of sodium channel activity available to modify T-type calcium channel activity. Tetrodotoxin (TTX) did not block these currents. Nor did another experimental tool, DPI 201-106, which dramatically changes the kinetics of sodium channels by preventing their inactivation,[21] have any effect on these channels. Furthermore, aconitine, which has been shown to activate cardiac sodium channels,[22,23] had no effect.

In a series of elegant whole-cell experiments, Jan Tytgat in 1990 succeeded in proving that T-type calcium channels are not related to sodium channels.[24] He separated sodium channels and T-type calcium channels by comparing currents at a test potential of –30 mV activated from holding potentials of –90 and –50 mV, respectively. The so-called 'low-threshold' currents can be obtained from the difference currents at both holding potentials, because sodium and T-type calcium currents are inactivated at –50 mV. This method is by far the most sensitive for the measurement of the pharmacological effects of different channel modulators on T-type calcium currents. To compare the properties of T-type calcium currents and sodium currents within the same cells, the difference currents in Na^{+}-free solutions (only T-type calcium currents) and those containing Na^{+} 2 mM (sodium currents) were measured. Both the kinetic properties and the pharmacological profiles of both currents clearly showed T-type calcium currents and sodium currents to be different.[24] Table I summarises data showing the different pharmacological features of T- and L-type calcium channels and cardiac sodium channels. This table has been substantially extended with data by Vassort and Alvarez.[7] Thus, it is most likely that T-type calcium currents pass through a molecular entity quite distinct from the L-type calcium or sodium channel.

Kinetic fingerprint of T-type calcium channels

Figure 2 shows traces of T-type calcium currents measured with Ca^{2+} as the charge carrier. From a holding potential of –100 mV, voltage steps to –40 and –20 mV activated a channel which opened predominantly in short bursts. Mean averaged currents indicate typical fast activation and delayed inactivation, with bursts clustered at the beginning of the depolarising steps. The time to first opening (first latency) was shorter at more positive test potentials. This pattern was highly reproducible for T-type calcium channels. Most of the parameters obtained from single-channel analysis were not very voltage-dependent. Distribution of the open times could be fitted by a single exponential with a voltage-independent time constant (mean open time, t_o). Closed times were described by two exponentials. The fast time constant was voltage-independent, and the slow closed time increased with depolarising voltages. Burst duration was voltage-independent (for details see Droogmans and Nilius[16]). Macroscopic inactivation of T-type calcium currents could be quantitatively reproduced as single-channel measurements from averaged currents that showed the

Table I. Differential modulation of T-type calcium channels compared with L-type calcium channels or sodium channels

Modulator	T-type channel	L-type channel	Sodium channel
Aconitine	None	None	↑↑↑
Tetrodotoxin	None	None	↓↓↓
Lidocaine	None	None	↑↑↑
DPI 201-106	None	None	↑↑↑
Amiloride	↓↓	None	None
Isoproterenol, PKA	None	↑↑↑	(↑)
Adenosine	None	↓	None
Angiotensin II, PKC?	↑↑	?	↑↑
Ethosuximide	↓↓	None	None
Dihydropyridine antagonists	None	↓↓↓	None
D600	↓↓	↓↓↓	(↓)
BayK8644	None	↑↑↑	None
R56865	↓↓	None	None
Flunarizine	↓↓↓	↓	None
Verapamil	↓	↓↓↓	None
Intracellular Ca^{2+}	None	↓↓↓	(↓)
Ni^{2+}	↓↓↓	↓	(↓)
Cd^{2+}	↓	↓↓↓	(↓)
Co^{2+}	↓↓	↓↓	(↓)
Octanol	↓↓↓	(↓)	(↓)

Abbreviations: PKA = protein kinase A; PKC = protein kinase C.

same time-course, voltage-dependence and time constants as whole-cell T-type currents.

Figure 3 summarises some of the inactivation properties of T-type calcium currents. The inactivation curve can be fitted by a single exponential (see fig. 3 (A)). The macroscopic time constant of channel inactivation, τ_h, decreased at more positive potentials (see fig. 3 (B)). From all single-channel events tested, first latency was the most voltage-sensitive parameter. The voltage-dependence (τ_L) is shown in panel C of figure 3. This dependence is very similar to the macroscopic time constant of inactivation, and a very close correlation between τ_L and τ_h was noted (see fig. 3 (D)). Late openings resulting from long waiting times to channel opening may explain the time-course of the macroscopic inactivation, which would then appear as a property of microscopic activation. The inactivation step is not intrinsically voltage-dependent. The kinetic pattern is further characterised by channel openings appearing mainly as one burst per depolarisation; each channel produces one burst per opening before reaching an inactivated absorbing state. The probability of observing a second burst is very low.

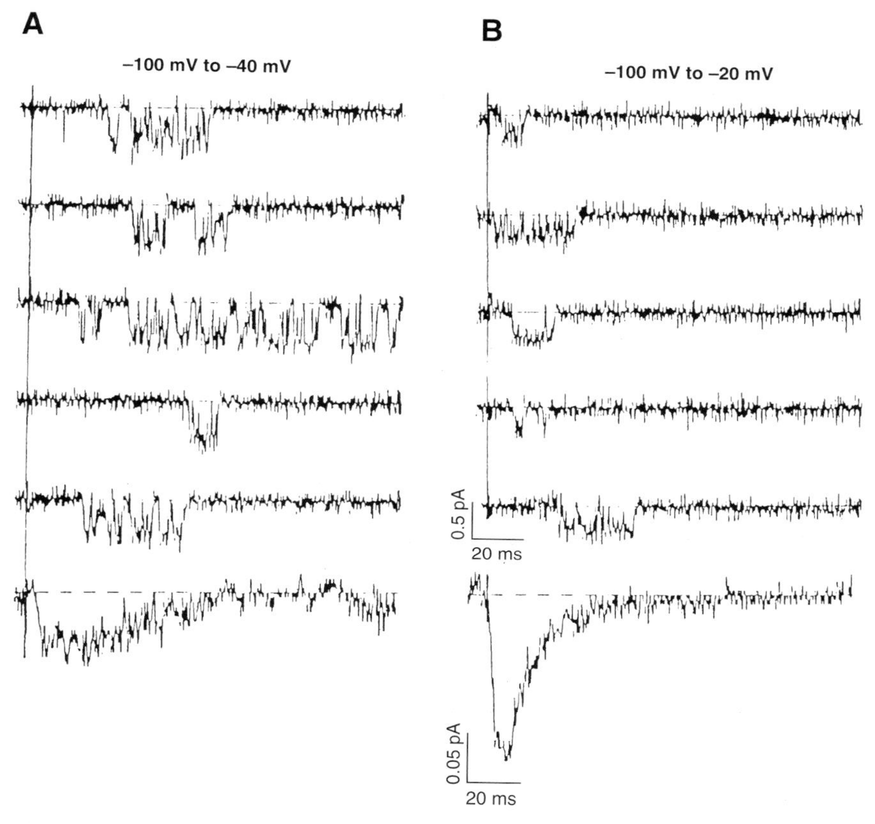

Fig. 2. Kinetic pattern of T-type calcium channel activation by depolarising voltage steps. A) Depolarising step applied from a holding potential of −100 mV to −40 mV; current averaged from 196 sweeps. B) Same patch: test potential −20 mV; current averaged from 198 sweeps. Note the appearance of channel openings as bursts, and the obvious voltage-dependent changes in first latency. The solid lines mark the onset of depolarisation.

Kinetic models

The unique properties of T-type calcium channels that distinguish them clearly from sodium channels and L-type calcium channels have been described by a variety of models which all focus on the strong voltage-dependence of the waiting time of the channel to opening, which may reflect the transition between closed states.[16,25] It has become clear from kinetic analysis that a model must involve only one open state, with a minimum of two closed states as closed-time distributions are obviously biexponential. The distribution of first latencies invariably shows a clear peak (unimodal distribution (fig. 4 (A)). The first latency distribution peaks earlier than the averaged current, which means that channels open when the macroscopic activation is well under way. The probability density function of the waiting time to the first channel opening could be described by a biexponential function, M(t). The probability of the channel being open, P(t), after onset of the depolarising voltage step is given by the convolution, C(t), of the distribution of the first latency with the conditional probability of the channel being open, $f_1(t)$.[26] Although we could not describe P(t) for T-type calcium channels with this approach, we could obtain an

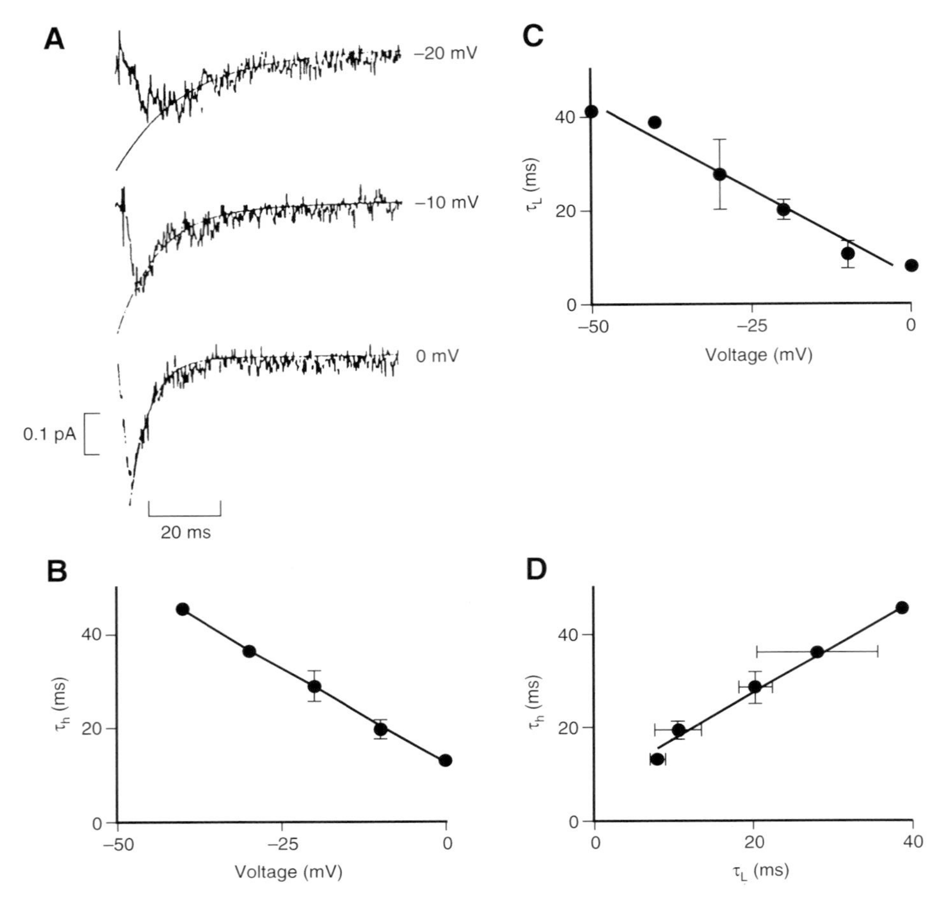

Fig. 3. Properties of macroscopic T-type calcium channel inactivation. A) Voltage-dependence of the inactivation of T-type calcium channels from averaged currents (holding potential −100 mV, test potentials −20, −10 and 0 mV). Decay fitted with a single exponential. B) Voltage-dependence of the inactivation time constants (τ_h). C) Voltage-dependence of the mean first latencies (τ_L). D) Correlation of the first latencies and the macroscopic time constants of inactivation (slope of the regression line is 1.04, r = 0.89) (reproduced with permission of J Physiol (Lond) [16]*).*

almost ideal approximation by using the distribution of the burst durations ($f_2(t)$). This convolution is shown in figure 4 (B). The convolution with the open-time distribution is much too small because it fails to account for reopening of the channel. This quantitative analysis again described the kinetic fingerprint of the T-type calcium channel: openings appear as one burst per depolarisation, with timing dependent on the strongly voltage-dependent first latency.

To evaluate the various possible kinetic models, we found it useful to consider not only such conventional single-channel data as mean open time, closed time, first latency, etc., but also kinetic parameters such as the conditional probability of the reopening of the channel after having already opened once before, or the probability that as a result of activation of the channel, the open state is bypassed and the channel directly enters an absorbing state. By analysing the number of openings per depolarisation (per sweep), these parameters can be easily obtained by

Distribution of first latencies: M(t)

$$M(t) = a \bullet (\exp(-t/\tau_1) - \exp(-t/\tau_2))$$

Distribution of open times: $f_1(t)$

$$f_1(t) = a \bullet \exp(-t/\tau_o)$$

Distribution of burst durations: $f_2(t)$

$$f_2(t) = a \bullet \exp(-t/\tau_{burst})$$

Convolution

'First latency distribution' with
'open time distribution' or 'burst duration distribution

$$C(t) = \int_0^{\infty} M(\tau) \bullet f_i(t - \tau)d\tau \quad \text{where } i = 1,2$$

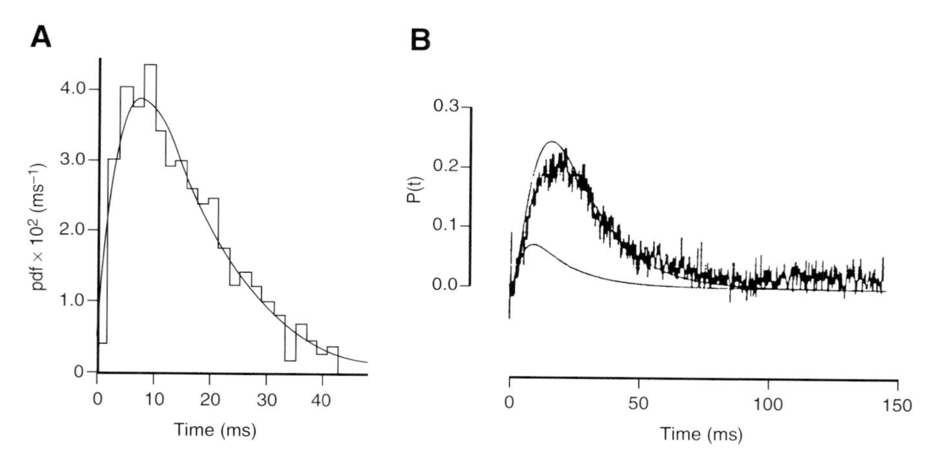

Fig. 4. Kinetic analysis of T-type calcium channels. Top: equations for the distribution of first latency, open times, burst duration and the convolution of the first latency distribution with the two respective distributions of dwell times.
A) Distribution of first latency with clear peak (time constants: t_1 = 5.3 ms; t_2 = 11.7 ms). Data are from step –100 mV to –30 mV. B) Probability of channels being open is best described by the convolution of the first latency distribution with the distribution of the burst duration (t_{burst} = 7.9 ms) (convolution with open-time distribution (t_{open} = 1.7 ms) gives P(t) approximations that are too small and too rapid (reproduced with permission of J Physiol (Lond)[16]).

fitting the distribution of openings per sweep with the model-independent probability, prob(j), of finding j openings per sweep. This depends on both the probability that the channel reopens, p, and the probability that after activation the open state of the channel is bypassed, f.[27] Prob(j) is given by:

$$\text{prob}(j) = (1 - f) \bullet p^{j-1} \bullet (1 - p)$$

The voltage-dependence of all these parameters is given in figure 5. Panel D of figure 5 shows a distribution of the openings per sweep and a least-square fit with prob(j). The values thus obtained for p showed a high probability that the channel reopens (not strikingly voltage-dependent). The number of blanks or the probability that the open state is bypassed during a depolarisation is increased at more positive

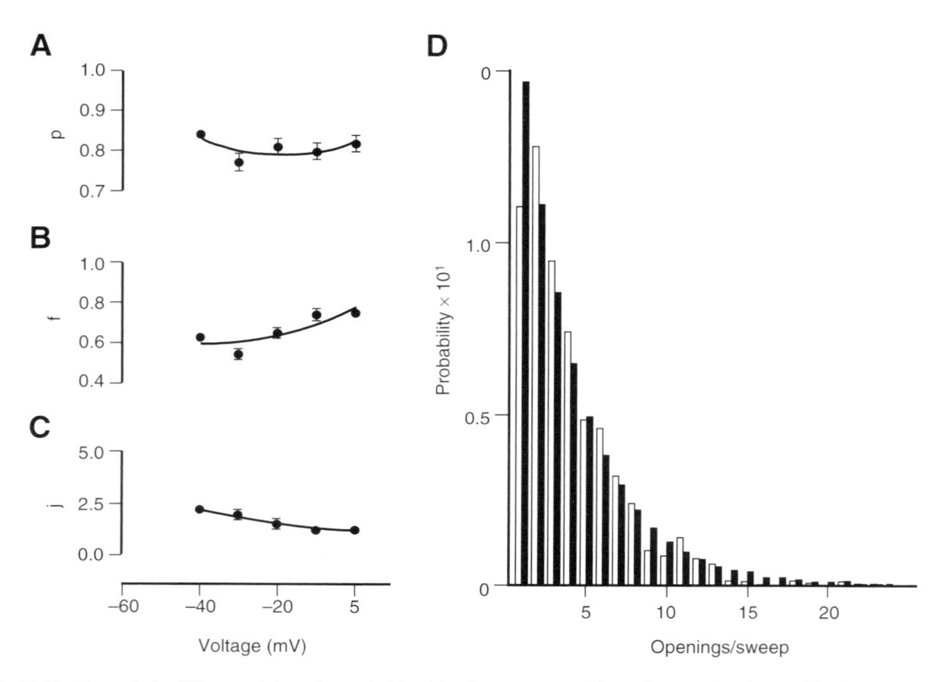

Fig. 5. Kinetic analysis of T-type calcium channels. Top: kinetic parameters. These data can be obtained by fitting of the distribution of openings per sweep according to the given equation (for other means of measuring p and f, see Droogmans and Nilius[16]). A) Voltage-dependence of p. B) Voltage-dependence of f. C) Voltage-dependence of j. D) Fit of the distribution of openings per sweep (open bars represent experimental data, closed bars a theoretical fit with equation prob(j)) (reproduced with permission of J Physiol (Lond)[16]).

potentials (parameter f). The number of openings per sweep decreases slightly at positive potentials (see fig. 5 (A–C)).

For modelling, the time-courses of the probability of the channel being open were fitted by the numerical solution of the differential equations for the particular kinetic model, which was combined with a least-square fitting routine. From this approximation a set of rate coefficients was obtained that was then used to simulate single-channel activity. This reconstructed single-channel activity was then analysed to obtain the relevant kinetic parameters. Reconstructed data were compared with the experimental findings (including p, f and the mean number of openings per sweep). Of all models tested so far,[16] three were found to be reliable. In all three models, the T-type calcium channel is described by transitions between two closed states (R and C) and one open state (O). The inactivated (absorbing) state, I, can be reached

Table II. Kinetic parameters of T-type calcium channels: experimental and modelled values

Parameter	Experimental value	Model 1 R⇄C⇄O, R→I	Model 2 R⇄C⇄O, R→I←O	Model 3 R⇄C⇄O, R→I, C→I, O→I
p (reopening)	0.82	0.79	0.84	0.83
f (bypass)	0.74	0.77	0.79	0.76
j (openings/sweep)	1.44	1.10	1.34	1.39
t_o (ms)	1.41	2.10	1.68	1.57
$t_{closed,\ fast}$ (ms)	0.40	0.47	0.38	0.29
$t_{closed,\ slow}$ (ms)	6.10	8.20	8.30	10.20

from R (model 1), or from R and O (model 2), or is completely uncoupled from the activation pathway (access to I from all other states) (model 3).

By comparing the values for p and f from the reconstructed (simulated) data, we could reject models in which I can be reached from both C and O or only from C. Table II illustrates the analysis and reconstruction of single-channel data from the three chosen models.

The only strikingly voltage-dependent parameters in this scheme are the rate coefficients controlling the transitions between the closed states, R and C. Transitions between C and O, which describe the bursting behaviour of these channels, are not voltage-dependent. Figure 6 illustrates this analysis and the pooled data.

Discussion

Two concepts relevant to T-type calcium channels have been reviewed in this article. First, T-type calcium currents cannot be explained by Ca^{2+} entry through sodium or L-type calcium channels. Thus, although not yet cloned, T-type calcium channels are likely to be a distinct molecular entity in myocardial cells. As shown here, they can be clearly distinguished from other types of cardiac channel, including L-type calcium channels or sodium channels. Second, the kinetic characteristics of T-type calcium channel opening are characterised by a unique feature: the regulation of voltage-dependence occurs predominantly at an early transition between at least two closed states. This kinetic fingerprint may aid in the understanding of the molecular mechanisms of channel gating, and may be important in the discrimination of various channel clones and identification of a specific cardiac T-type calcium channel.

Notwithstanding the above observations, the exact function of cardiac T-type calcium channels remains unclear. One of the most attractive hypotheses to date concerns a putative contribution to automaticity.[12] Another topic of growing interest is the effect of the developmental state of cells on the expression of T-type calcium channels (increased expression in proliferating cells and decreased expression during maturation). Interestingly, completely differentiated myocardial cells re-express T-type calcium channels under conditions of mechanical stress, hypertrophy and stimulation

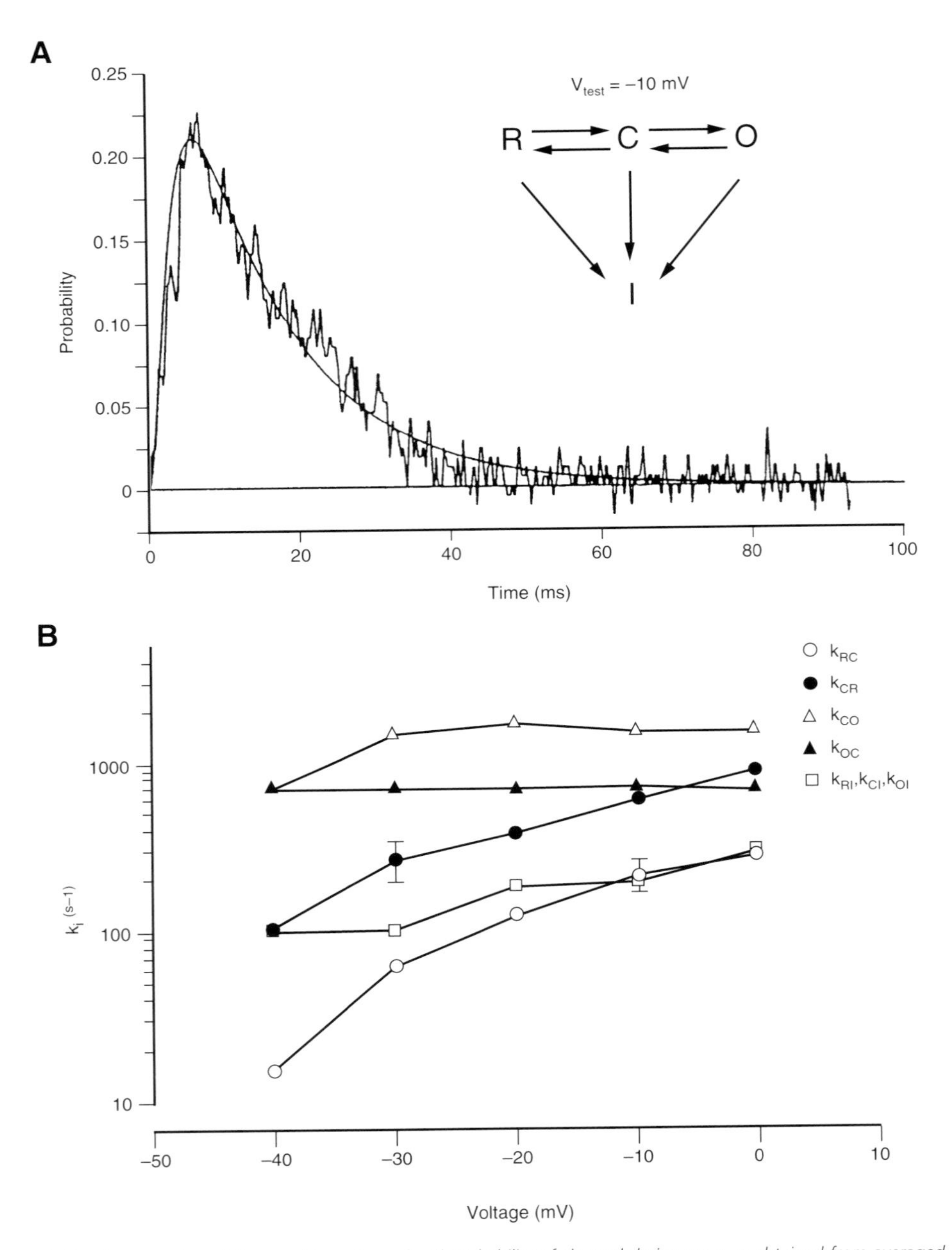

Fig. 6. Kinetic properties of T-type calcium channels. A) Probability of channels being open as obtained from averaged mean currents described by model M6 (in which the absorbing state is reached from all other states) (inset). Time-course at −10 mV was fitted by the following parameters: RC transition $k_{RC} = 26\ s^{-1}$, CR transition $k_{CR} = 201\ s^{-1}$; CO transition $k_{CO} = 3202\ s^{-1}$, OC transition $k_{OC} = 564\ s^{-1}$. Transitions to the inactivated, absorbing state $k_{RI} = k_{CI} = k_{OI} = 74\ s^{-1}$. B) Voltage-dependence of estimated kinetic parameters. Note that k_{RC} and k_{CR} are the most voltage-sensitive rate coefficients.

with growth hormones.[28,29] These properties are related to the cell cycle and might be of interest in the understanding of the function of calcium channels during pressure overload and myopathy. It appears possible that cardiac T-type calcium channels have functional significance in growing myocardium, rather than a specific function in mature myocardium.

Acknowledgements

I am indebted to R.W. Tsien for the opportunity to work in his laboratory and for his scientific support, which has been a significant influence on me. I am also grateful to G. Droogmans for a long and effective collaboration that had its origins in work carried out in common on T-type calcium channels. Furthermore, I wish to thank J. Tytgat for his cooperation, and for permission to use some of his data. None of this early work on T-type calcium channels in cardiac cells would have been possible without the presence of the stimulating personality of Peter Hess, to whom I still owe thanks and admiration.

References

1. Bean BP. Two different kinds of calcium channels in canine atrial cells. Differences in kinetics, selectivity, and pharmacology. J Gen Physiol 1985; 86: 1–30
2. Nilius B, Hess P, Lansman JB, et al. A novel type of cardiac calcium channel in ventricular cells. Nature 1985; 316: 443–6
3. Tsien RW, Hess P, Nilius B. Cardiac calcium currents at the level of single channels. Experientia 1987; 43: 1169–75
4. Bean BP. Classes of calcium channels in vertebrate cells. Ann Rev Physiol 1989; 51: 367–84
5. Hess P. Calcium channels in vertebrate cells. Annu Rev Neurosci 1990; 13: 337–56
6. Nilius B. T-type calcium channels in cardiac muscle: news in kinetics and modulation. NATO ASI Series 1992; H60: 181–9
7. Vassort G, Alvarez J. Cardiac T-type calcium current: pharmacology and role in cardiac tissue. J Cardiovasc Electrophysiol 1994; 5: 376–93
8. Kawano S, DeHaan RL. Low-threshold current is the major calcium current in chick ventricle cells. Am J Physiol 1989; 256: H1505–8
9. Kawano S, DeHaan RL. Developmental changes in the calcium currents in embryonic chick ventricular myocytes. J Membr Biol 1991; 120: 17–28
10. Kuga T, Kobayashi S, Hirakawa Y, et al. Cell cycle-dependent expression of L- and T-type Ca^{2+} currents in rat aortic smooth muscle cells in primary culture. Circ Res 1996; 79: 14–19
11. McCobb DP, Beam KG. Action potential waveform voltage-clamp commands reveal striking differences in calcium entry via low and high voltage-activated calcium channels. Neuron 1991; 7: 119–27
12. Nilius B. Possible functional significance of a novel type of cardiac calcium channel. Biomed Biochim Acta 1986; 45: K37–45
13. Coulter DA, Huguenard JR, Prince DA. Calcium currents in rat thalamocortical relay neurons: kinetic properties of the transient, low threshold current. J Physiol (Lond) 1989; 414: 587–604
14. Destexhe A, Babloyantz A, Sejnowski TL. Ionic mechanisms for intrinsic slow oscillations in thalamic relay neurons. Biophys J 1993; 65: 1538–52
15. Mitra R, Morad M. A uniform enzymatic method for dissociation of myocytes from hearts and stomachs of vertebrates. Am J Physiol 1986; 249: H1056–60
16. Droogmans G, Nilius B. Kinetic properties of the cardiac T-type calcium channel in guinea-pig. J Physiol (Lond) 1989; 419: 627–50
17. Carbone E, Lux HD. A low voltage activated, fully inactivating Ca^{2+} channel in vertebrate sensory neurons. Science 1984; 236: 570–3
18. Tytgat J, Nilius B, Vereecke J, et al. The T-type calcium channel in guinea-pig ventricular myocardium is insensitive to isoproterenol. Pflugers Arch 1988; 411: 704–6
19. Tytgat J, Nilius B, Vereecke J, et al. Modulation of the T-type cardiac calcium channel by changes in proton concentration. J Gen Physiol 1990; 96: 973–90
20. Liévano A, Santi CM, Serrano CJ, et al. T-type Ca^{2+} channels and α_{1E} expression in spermatogenic cells, and their possible relevance to sperm acrosome reaction. FEBS Lett 1996; 388: 150–4
21. Nilius B, Vereecke J, Carmeliet E. Properties of the bursting Na^+ channel in the presence of DPI 201-106 in guinea-pig ventricular myocytes. Pflugers Arch 1989; 413: 234–41
22. Nilius B, Boldt W, Benndorf K. Properties of aconitine-modified Na^+ channels in single cells of ventricular mouse myocardium. Gen Physiol Biophys 1986; 5: 473–82

23. Nilius B, Benndorf K, Markwardt F. Modified gating behaviour of aconitine-treated single sodium channels from adult cardiac myocytes. Pflugers Arch 1986; 407: 640–3
24. Tytgat J, Vereecke J, Carmeliet E. A combined study of sodium current and T-type calcium current in isolated cardiac cells. Pflugers Arch 1990; 417: 142–8
25. Chen C, Hess P. Mechanism of gating of T-type calcium channels. J Gen Physiol 1990; 96: 603–60
26. Aldrich RW, Corey DP, Stevens CF. A reinterpretation of mammalian sodium channel gating based on single channel recordings. Nature 1983; 306: 436–41
27. Kunze DL, Lacerda AE, Wilson DL, et al. Cardiac Na^+ currents and inactivating, reopening, and waiting properties of single cardiac Na^+ channels. J Gen Physiol 1985; 86: 671–719
28. Nuss BH, Houser SR. T-type Ca^{2+} current is expressed in hypertrophic adult feline left ventricular myocytes. Circ Res 1993; 73: 777–82
29. Xu X, Best PM. Increase in T-type calcium current in atrial myocytes from adult rats with growth hormone-secreting tumors. Proc Natl Acad Sci U S A 1990; 87: 4655–9

Distinctive biophysical and pharmacological features of T-type calcium channels

Andrew Randall,[1] Richard W. Tsien [2]

[1] Neurobiology Division, Medical Research Council Laboratory of Molecular Biology, Cambridge, UK; [2] Department of Molecular and Cellular Physiology, Stanford University Medical Center, Stanford, California, USA

Introduction

Despite great interest in the multiple types of calcium channel in excitable cells, important questions remain about how these channels might arise from various isoforms of calcium channel α_1 subunit, including the six or seven distinct classes of α_1 subunits isolated so far as cDNA clones.[1–4] One major remaining controversy concerns T-type calcium channels (fig. 1 (A)) and their possible relationship to the class E calcium channel α_1 subunit (α_{1E}) (see fig. 1 (B)). When expressed in either *Xenopus* oocytes or HEK293 cells, α_{1E} generates currents that inactivate rapidly and are relatively susceptible to block by Ni^{2+} ions.[5–9] It was originally proposed that α_{1E} supports a low-voltage-activated (LVA) calcium channel[5] (see also Bourinet et al.[10]), akin to the T-type calcium channel.[11–14] However, a very different view has been put forward by other groups,[6,7,9] who concluded that currents generated by α_{1E} are very similar to the R-type calcium current found in cerebellar granule neurons (see fig. 1 (C)).[15–17] Uncertainty about the relationship between T- and R-type calcium channels and α_{1E} subunits might have been anticipated given that all three entities support barium currents that are superficially quite similar (see fig. 1).

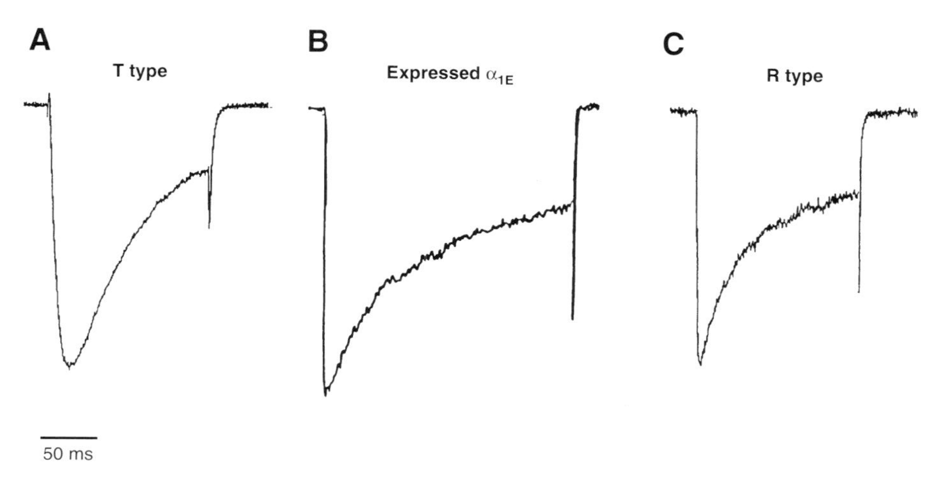

Fig. 1. Comparison between time-courses of T-type current, current supported by expressed α_{1E} subunits and R-type current. Currents evoked by step depolarisation from a strongly negative holding potential (–80 or –90 mV) to a test potential giving maximal inward current. A) T-type current in NG108-15 neuroblastoma cell, Ba^{2+} 10 mM. B) Currents generated by α_{1E} expressed in HEK293 cells, Ba^{2+} 15 mM.[6] C) R-type current in a cerebellar granule neuron, Ba^{2+} 10 mM. NB: apart from the slower activation and deactivation kinetics of the T-type current, all three records appear similar.

Incomplete information about the channels in neuronal cells has hampered comparisons between native calcium channels and those arising from expression of the cloned α_{1E} subunit (see discussion in Williams et al.[6]). We have recently carried out a systematic investigation of the key properties of R- and T-type calcium channels under near-identical recording conditions.[18] Here we review the most important differences in the biophysical and pharmacological profiles of T- and R-type calcium channels and expressed α_{1E} subunits. Our data indicate that R-type currents closely match the behaviour of α_{1E} in various expression systems studied so far, while T-type currents do not.

Experimental isolation of T- and R-type currents

T-type calcium channels were studied in undifferentiated NG108-15 neuroblastoma cells. LVA T-type calcium channels were found to be the only means of Ca^{2+} conductance in over 50% of these cells (see also Kasai and Neher[19]).[18] The remaining NG108 cells also displayed a significant proportion of slowly inactivating, high-voltage-activated (HVA) current and were not used in the study. Here we summarise experimental data based on pure LVA recordings (n=107 cells). The experimental data on R-type calcium channels were obtained from recordings from rat cerebellar granule neurons in primary cultures (n=89 cells). R-type channels were pharmacologically isolated by preincubating the granule neurons for at least 0.5 hour in ω-CTx-MVIIC (0.5 μM), a blocker of N-, P-, and Q-type channels, before making all recordings in the presence of ω-CTx-MVIIC 0.5 μM, the L-type channel blocker nimodipine (10 μM), and the N-type channel blockers ω-CTx-GVIA (1 μM) or ω-CTx-MVIIA (1 μM).

Differences in activation properties

Figure 2 shows comparisons of families of T- and R-type calcium currents, elicited by a series of increasingly strong depolarising pulses from a holding potential of –80 mV. Inward T-type currents were barely detectable at –60 mV, clearly visible at –50 mV and reached maximum amplitude at around –20 mV (see fig. 2 (A)). In contrast, in the case of R-type currents, inward currents were barely detectable upon depolarisation to –40 mV and reached maximum amplitude with a step to +10 mV or thereabouts (see fig. 2 (B)). Thus, T-type calcium channels were found to activate at considerably more negative potentials than R-type calcium channels (fig. 2 (C)), even when extreme care was taken to record the currents under identical experimental conditions. These results indicate substantial differences in voltage- and time-dependence for these two kinds of calcium channel. Apart from positioning along the voltage axis, the families of current waveforms display qualitatively different patterns. With progressively stronger depolarisations, successive records of T-type calcium channel current cross each other in a manner reminiscent of the classical pattern first described for sodium channels by Hodgkin and Huxley (see Hille[20]). This pattern was not found for R-type currents (compare panels A and B of fig. 2).

Another important distinction between channel types, made without regard for absolute values of membrane potential, is the degree of overlap between the voltage-dependences of activation and inactivation. This can be easily gauged by

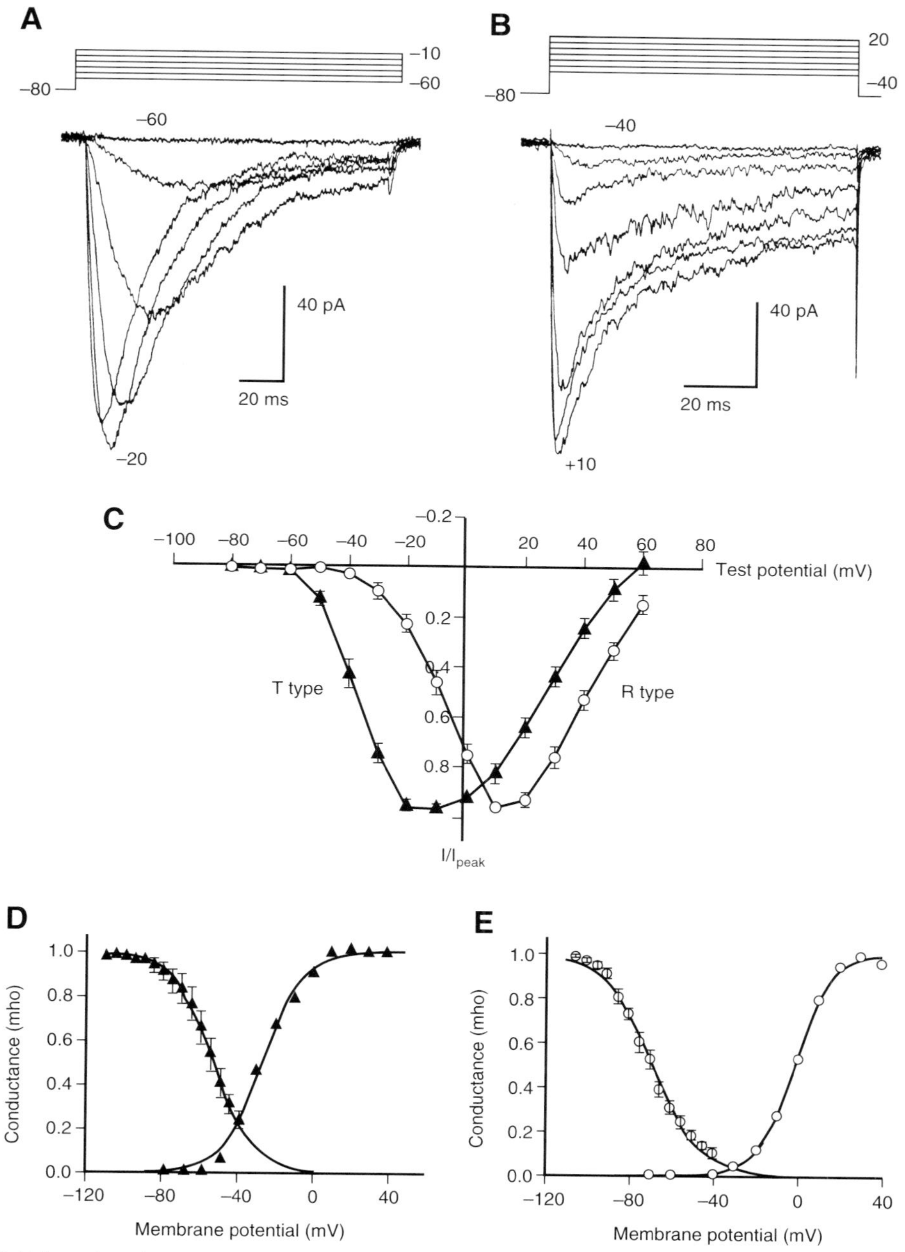

Fig. 2. Voltage-dependent activation of T- and R-type currents. A) Activation of T-type calcium channel currents by increasing strong depolarising pulses from a holding potential of –80 mV. B) Equivalent data for R-type channels. C) Pooled peak current–voltage relationships for T- (n=9) and R-type current (n=13). D) Voltage-dependence gating of T-type current. Availability of T-type current (left) measured with a test pulse to a potential close to the peak of the current–voltage relationship, following a 20 s conditioning pulse (level indicated on the abscissa). Smooth curve is a standard Boltzmann function ($V_{½}$ = –53.4 mV, k = 11.0 mV). Activation of peak T-type conductance (right) defined as $I_{peak}/(V - E_{rev})$, where E_{rev} = +57 mV. Smooth curve is a Boltzmann fit ($V_{½}$ = –26.9 mV, k = 10.1 mV). E) Voltage-dependent gating of R-type current. Availability data (left) fitted by a Boltzmann function with $V_{½}$ = –68.4 mV, k = 11.1 mV. Activation of peak R-type conductance (right) defined as $I_{peak}/(V - E_{rev})$, where E_{rev} = +64 mV. Smooth curve is a Boltzmann fit ($V_{½}$ = –1.7 mV, k = 8.6 mV). NB: spacing between $V_{½}$ values is ~66 mV for R-type current and only ~26 mV for T-type current.

considering the separation between the midpoint voltages of the activation and inactivation curves for T- and R-type currents, respectively (see fig. 2 (D & E). Estimates of the voltage-dependence of activation were obtained from peak current–voltage relationships (see fig. 2 (C)), after appropriate allowance was made for variations in driving force. The voltage-dependence of steady-state inactivation (h_{∞}) was studied in a conventional manner by varying the level of a 20 s conditioning pulse just before a step to a fixed test potential near the peak of the current–voltage curve. For T-type calcium channels, points of half-maximal activation ($V_{½}$ = –26.9 mV) and half-maximal inactivation ($V_{½}$ = –53.4 mV), yielded a separation of 26 mV. In contrast, for R-type channels, $V_{½}$ for activation was –1.7 mV whereas $V_{½}$ for inactivation was –68.4 mV, a difference of 66 mV. Thus, the spacing was approximately 40 mV less for T-type than for R-type current. Since activation and inactivation properties were studied in the same cells, the voltage difference parameter eliminates the effect of possible voltage offsets from one cell to another, including differences in the plasma membrane surface potential. This contrast between T- and R-type calcium channels may be related to the intrinsic nature of the channel, rather than those related to the precise value of membrane potential. Because T-type calcium channels show a much larger overlap between inactivation and activation curves, they are better suited to generating sustained Ca^{2+} entry in support of secretion or pacemaker activity (see Barrett et al. and Lei et al.[21,22]). In contrast, R-type channels are not equipped to provide a steady current, but they are very capable of supplying transient surges of Ca^{2+}.

Quantitative differences in gating kinetics

The activation kinetics of R-type current were generally faster than those of T-type current at positive membrane potentials.[18] At +20 mV, for example, the 10–90% activation time of the R-type current was 0.98 ± 0.05 ms (n=13), compared with 2.03 ± 0.19 ms (n=9) for the T-type calcium channel (fig. 3 (A)). The deactivation kinetics of R-type current were also much faster than those of the T-type current, as documented by recordings of barium current tails (see fig. 3 (C & D)). For example, upon repolarisation to –100 mV, the exponential time constant of deactivation was 0.21 ± 0.01 ms (n=5) for the R-type current and 1.61 ± 0.07 ms (n=11) for the T-type current, a difference approaching 8-fold. Deactivation time constants were voltage-dependent in both cases, increasing by a factor of 'e' per 30 mV of depolarisation for T-type currents and per 45 mV of depolarisation for R-type currents. Inactivation rates were also found to differ somewhat in voltage-dependence between the two channel types (see fig. 3 (B)).[18] In both cases, increasing the strength of depolarisation speeds the inactivation rate until the time constant approaches a lower limit. The limiting decay time constant at strong depolarisations was 20 ms for the T-type channel and 24 ms for the R-type channel.

Contrasting responses to nimodipine

Similarities and differences in the pharmacological characteristics of T- and R-type channels were of considerable interest as a basis for comparisons with currents

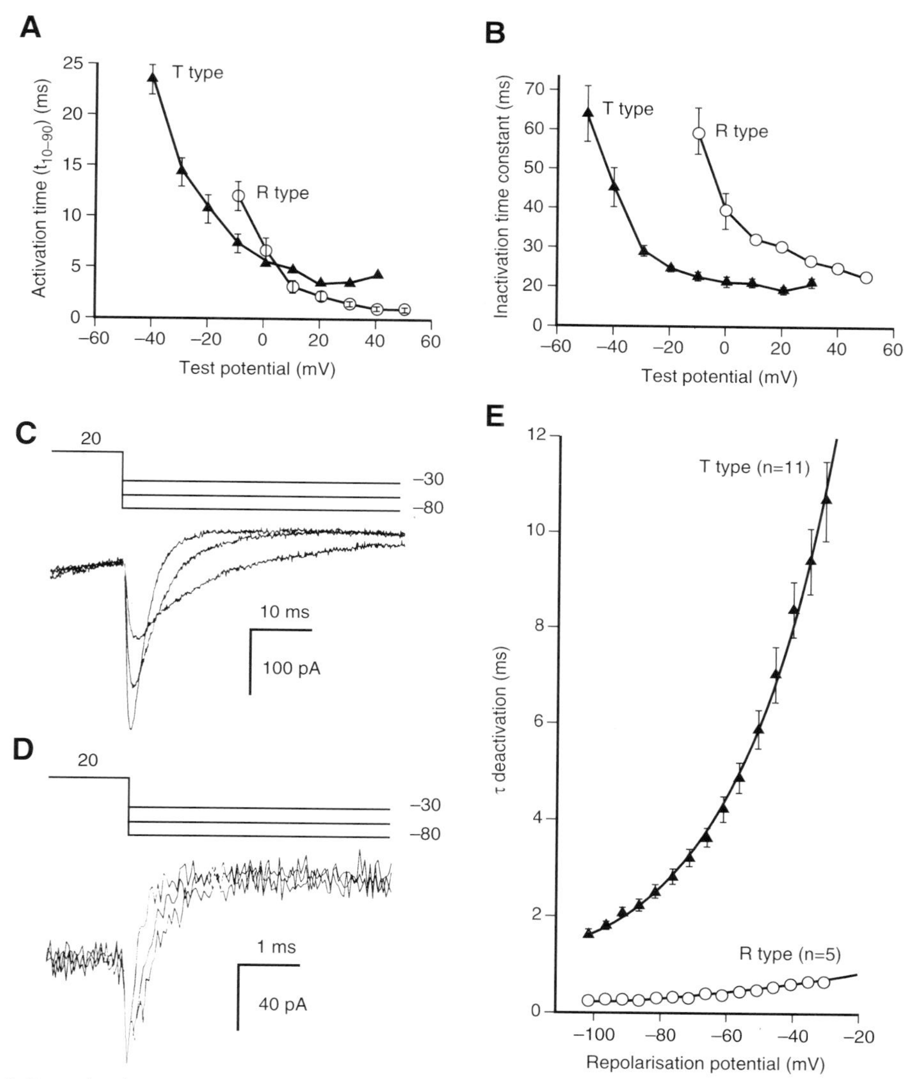

Fig. 3. Comparison between voltage- and time-dependent kinetics of T- and R-type calcium channels. A) Time-dependence of activation, represented by time taken to rise from 10% to 90% of peak current (t_{10-90}). NB: at potentials >0 mV, activation of R type was significantly faster than T type ($p<0.03$). B) Voltage-dependence of the rate of inactivation, represented by the time constant of the best single-exponential fit to current decay. C & D) Typical recordings illustrating deactivation kinetics of T- (C) and R-type currents (D). Activation at +20 mV, followed by repolarisation to −30, −55 or −80 mV. Current signal filtered with corner frequency of 10 kHz, sampling rate 50 kHz. Note progressive increase in speed of tail current decay with more negative repolarisation levels. Note time base expanded 10-fold in (D). E) Voltage-dependence of deactivation time constant. Pooled data for T- and R-type currents. Smooth curves are exponential functions of voltage (e-fold per 29.6 mV for T-type current, e-fold per 45.3 mV for R-type current).

derived from calcium channel subunits, particularly α_{1E}. Accordingly, we examined the effects of a number of calcium channel blockers on T- and R-type currents.[18] As illustrated in figure 4, nimodipine (10 µM) reversibly reduced the T-type current in neuroblastoma cells by 63 ± 3% (n=3), while its vehicle (methanol 0.1%) was without effect (n=3). In contrast, continuous exposure of granule neurons to the same concentration of nimodipine spared a robust R-type current, while the nimodipine-

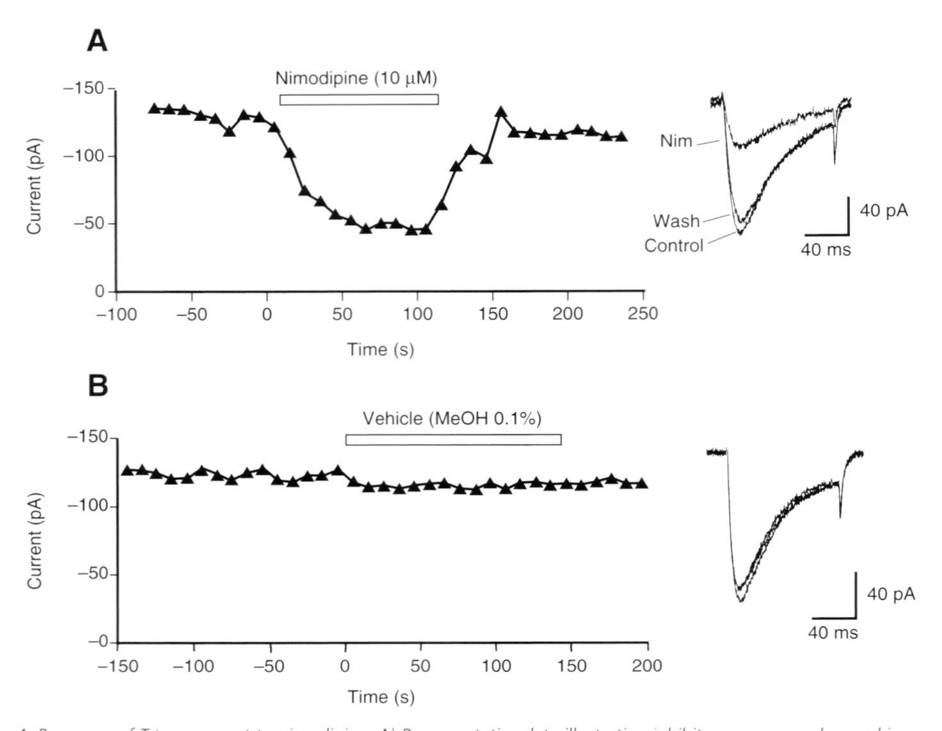

Fig. 4. Response of T-type current to nimodipine. A) Representative data illustrating inhibitory response observed in 5 cells. Corresponding current records shown on the right. B) Control experiment showing that methanol 0.1% (vehicle used to dissolve nimodipine) by itself had no effect (n=3).[18]

sensitive current in these cells lacked any hint of the decaying waveform that characterises R-type current.[16,18] Thus, we inferred that R-type currents are nimodipine-insensitive. This conclusion was in accordance with the well-documented lack of response of α_{1E} to nimodipine and other dihydropyridines.[5–7]

Markedly different responses to ω-Aga-IIIA

The spider toxin ω-Aga-IIIA has been found to block a number of HVA calcium currents.[23,24] This prompted us to compare the effects of this peptide toxin on T- and R-type currents. ω-Aga-IIIA had no detectable effect whatsoever on T-type currents (fig. 5 (A & D)),[18] in agreement with previous reports.[23,24] In contrast, it promptly and reproducibly inhibited R-type currents (see fig. 5 (C & E). The degree of inhibition of R-type current was essentially the same with ω-Aga-IIIA 3 nM (72 ± 4%; n=5) as with ω-Aga-IIIA 10 nM (75 ± 1%; n=6). The extent of the inhibition is in close agreement with that found by Rock et al. for ω-Aga-IIIA block of currents derived from α_{1E} (~70% block at a toxin concentration of 20 nM; see fig. 5 (C)).[9]

Differences in responsiveness to mibefradil

We were also interested in comparing the responses of T- and R-type currents to mibefradil (Ro 40-5967). As discussed elsewhere in this volume, mibefradil is a structurally novel, non-dihydropyridine compound that has been found to decrease

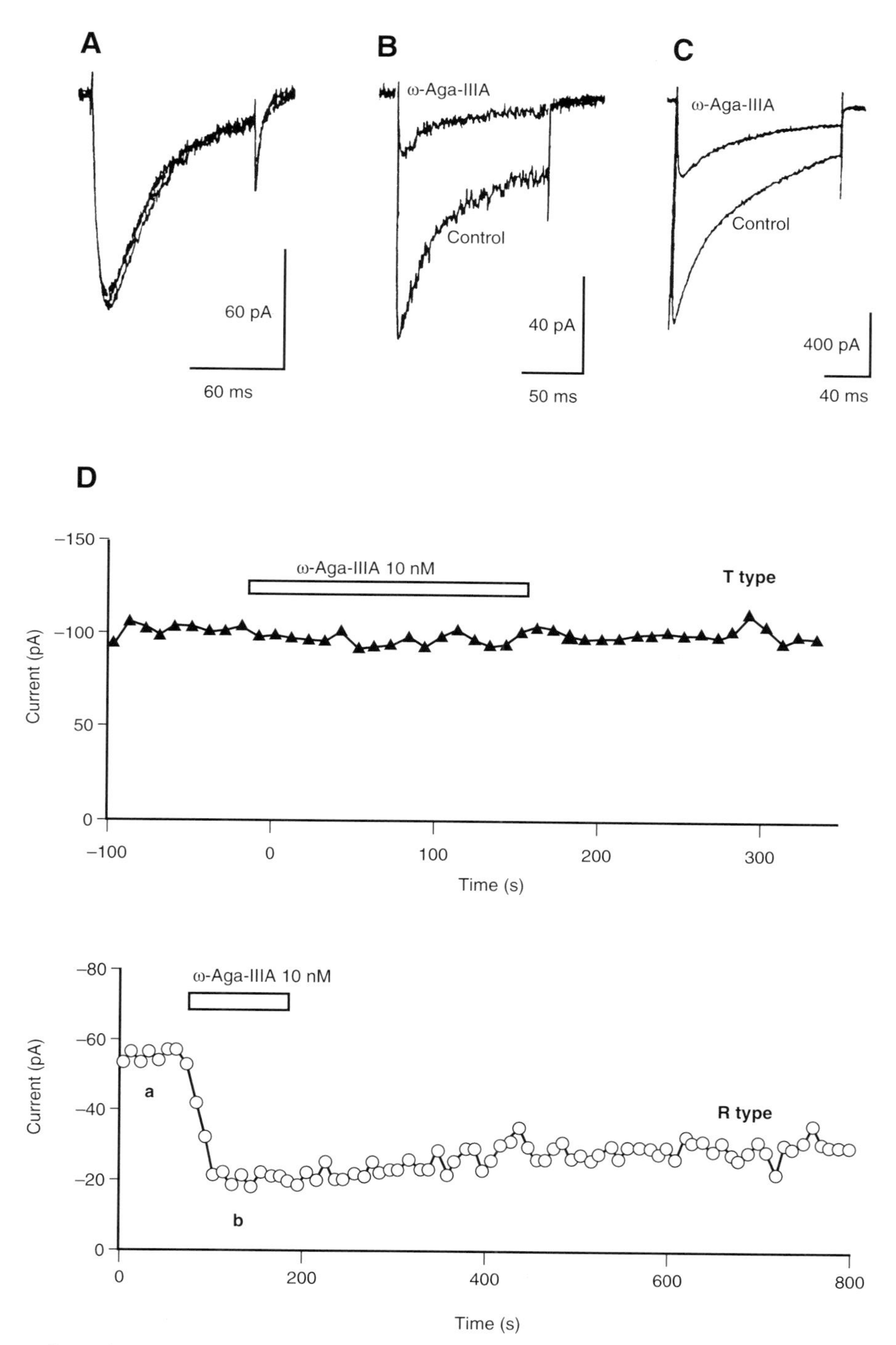

Fig. 5. Effects of the spider toxin ω-Aga-IIIA on T- and R-type current and currents supported by expressed α_{1E} subunits. A) Lack of effect of ω-Aga-IIIA on T-type current. Records taken before and 90 s after beginning of toxin application, and 120 s after toxin washout. Experimental traces representative of results from 5 cells. Holding potential –80 mV, test potential 0 mV. B) Block of R-type current by ω-Aga-IIIA. Records corresponding to data points labelled a and b in panel E.[18] C) ω-Aga-IIIA block of current supported by α_{1E} subunits in HEK293 cells.[9] D) Time-course of effect of ω-Aga-IIIA on T- and R-type currents. (© 1997 Elsevier Science, reproduced with permission.[18])

blood pressure without biologically relevant negative inotropic effects on myocardium, which suggests that the drug may be useful for the treatment of hypertension.[25] Both T- and R-type currents were found to be reversibly blocked by mibefradil in a markedly dose-dependent manner over the range 0.2–5 μM (figs 6–8). At 1 μM, mibefradil reduced T-type current by 54 ± 2% (n=7) (see fig. 6) and R-type current by 63 ± 2% (n=4) (see fig. 7). Raising the concentration of drug increased the speed and degree of inhibition in both cases (see figs 6 (B) and 7 (B)). The concentration-dependence of the blockade of T-type channels in neuroblastoma cells conformed to a one-to-one dose–response relationship with a half-blocking concentration of 1.1 μM (see fig. 6 (C)). This is in reasonable agreement with electrophysiological estimates of mibefradil potency on LVA calcium channel current in other systems (e.g. Mehrke et al.[26]).

The dependence of mibefradil blockade on the gating state of the channel represents a possible point of contrast between T-type calcium channels and expressed α_{1E} subunits. Previous work has demonstrated that mibefradil block of class E α_1 subunits can be strongly affected by inactivation-promoting membrane depolarisation;[8] however, it has been suggested that this may not be the case for

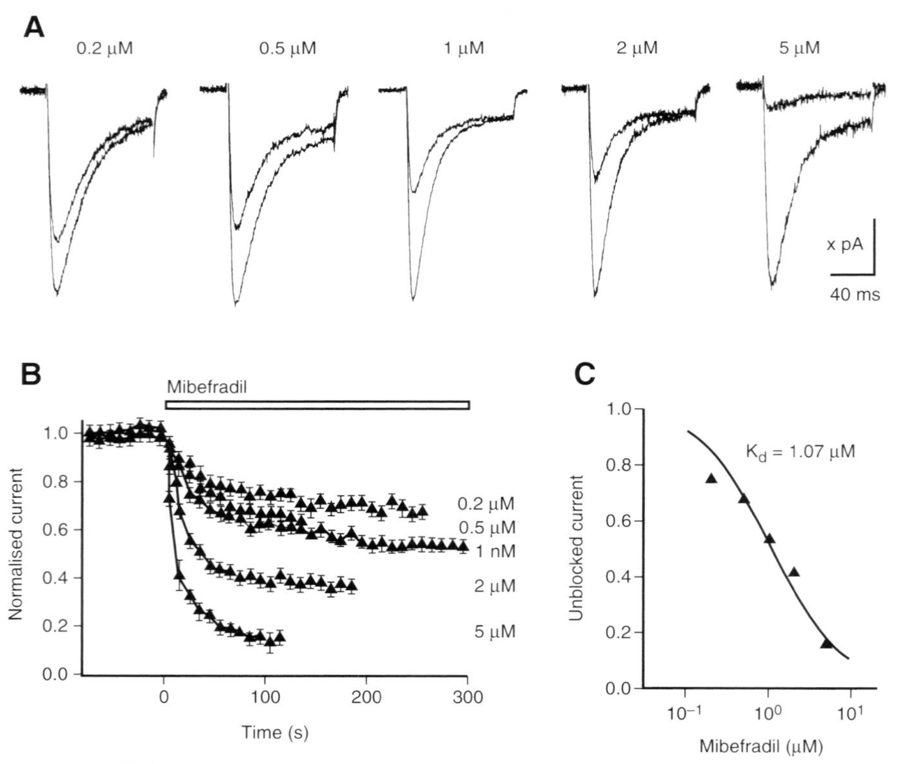

Fig. 6. Mibefradil blockade of T-type current in neuroblastoma cells. A) Representative records illustrating the concentration-dependence of mibefradil action. Holding potential –80 mV, test depolarisations to 0 mV. B) Kinetics of mibefradil inhibition for various drug concentrations. Pooled results for T-type current amplitude (n=9, 8, 7, 6 and 4 for 0.2, 0.5, 1, 2 and 5 μM, respectively). C) Concentration–response relationship. Smooth curve is a one-to-one binding relationship with K_d = 1.07 μM. (© 1997 Elsevier Science, reproduced with permission.[18])

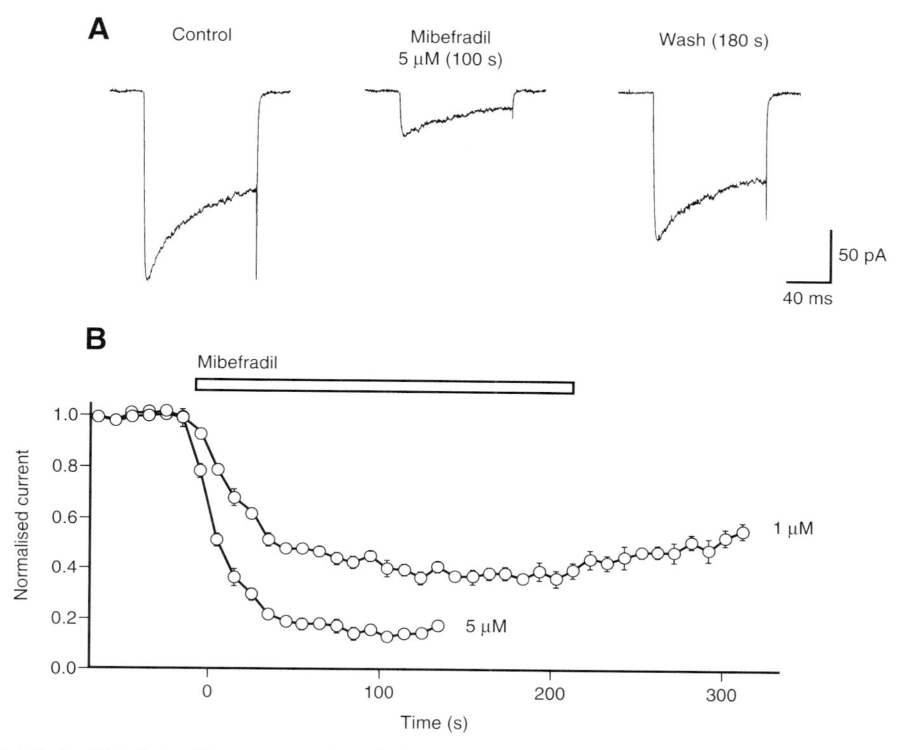

Fig. 7. Mibefradil blockade of R-type current in cerebellar granule neurons. A) Records illustrating the reversible block of R-type current by mibefradil. B) Pooled results showing kinetics of inhibition of mibefradil 1 and 5 μM (n=4 and n=9, respectively). Holding potential –80 mV, test potential +15 mV. (© 1997 Elsevier Science, reproduced with permission.[18])

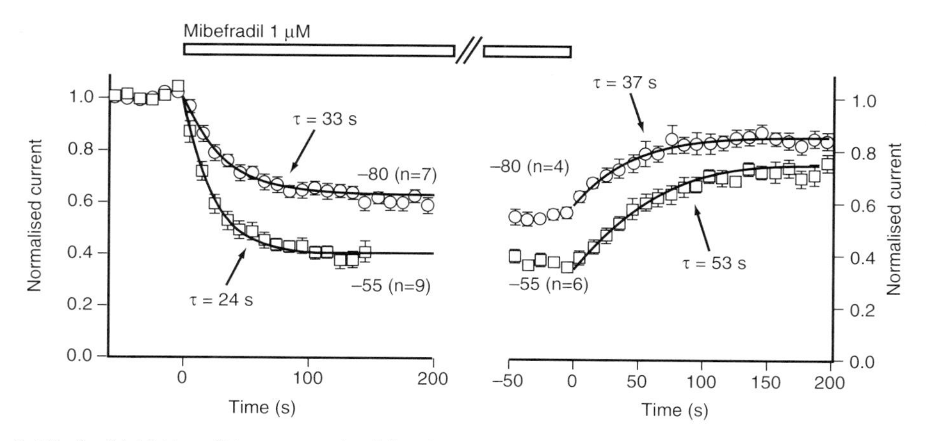

Fig. 8. Mibefradil inhibition of T-type current is mildly voltage-dependent. Pooled data for onset of block and recovery at holding potentials –80 mV (circles) and –55 mV (squares). Number of experiments as shown. Smooth curves show single exponential fits with time constants as indicated. At the depolarised holding potential, block is faster, more extensive and slower to recover following removal of the drug, but the differences are not very large. (© 1997 Elsevier Science, reproduced with permission.[18])

T-type calcium channels.[26] If confirmed, this contrast would represent yet another distinction between current arising from T-type calcium channels and expressed α_{1E}. Accordingly, we looked closely at mibefradil blockade of T-type current at membrane potentials which strongly alter the balance between resting and inactivated states (see fig. 8).[18] We found that the steady-state degree of block was significantly greater at –55 mV than at –80 mV. Furthermore, the onset of mibefradil block was faster at –55 mV (τ = 24 s) than at –80 mV (τ = 33 s), while the recovery after removal of the drug was slower at –55 mV (τ = 53 s) than at –80 mV (τ = 37 s). Thus, depolarisation that promotes channel inactivation favours blockade by a combination of effects on on-rate and off-rate. The voltage-dependence of T-type calcium channel blockade, while significant, was clearly less pronounced than that previously found for other channels, including native L-type channels,[26,27] as well as those derived from α_{1E}, α_{1A}, α_{1B} and α_{1C}.[8] In those cases, inhibition by mibefradil 10 μM was almost completely abolished at membrane potentials negative enough to almost completely remove inactivation. Thus, mibefradil may provide a quantitative, if not a qualitative, distinction between T-type and other calcium channels.

Discussion

Contrasting biophysical characteristics of T- and R-type calcium channels

We have delineated marked differences between T- and R-type calcium channels with respect to their biophysical and pharmacological properties. Neuroblastoma cells and cerebellar granule neurons were good choices for analysis of T- and R-type currents because they allowed reproducible isolation of these components. For both channel types, gating properties of activation, deactivation and inactivation each have characteristic voltage- and time-dependence. On one hand, T-type calcium channels become activated at considerably more negative potentials than R-type channels (see fig. 2 (A–C)), as befits their respective classification as LVA and HVA current components. On the other hand, T-type channels require less negative potentials than R-type channels to be available. Accordingly, T-type channels display a much larger overlap between the curves describing inactivation and activation (see fig. 2 (D & E)). This overlap allows T-type calcium channels to maintain current during relatively mild depolarisation from rest. Sustained Ca^{2+} entry through T-type calcium channels has important functional implications for secretion from adrenal glomerulosa cells[28] and pacemaker potentials in sinoatrial node cells.[29–31] In contrast, R-type calcium channels are poorly suited to the provision of steady current, but they are very capable of supplying transient surges of Ca^{2+} influx, even in response to very brief depolarisations.

The difference in voltage-dependence of T- and R-type calcium channels cannot be attributed to a generalised difference in surface potential in the cell membranes where they were studied. If this were the case, one would expect similar differences in voltage-dependence for both activation and inactivation, contrary to what we observed in the neuroblastoma and cerebellar granule cells. Also, when HVA currents are present in NG108-15 cells, they activate at potentials similar to those found in granule cells (Randall, unpublished data). Further indications of kinetic differences can be appreciated without referring to absolute membrane potential. T- and R-type calcium channels give rise to very different kinetic patterns in families of current records evoked by a series of increasingly strong depolarising pulses (see fig. 2 (A)). In the signature pattern of classical T-type calcium channels, the successive current records cross each other,[12] whereas this is not the case for R-type currents (see fig. 2 (B)). This distinction is immediately clear in the absence of any consideration of absolute membrane potential. The crossing pattern of T-type current recordings is reminiscent of the classical kinetic behaviour of sodium channels, first described by Hodgkin and Huxley (see Hille for references[20]), but is not typical of voltage-gated calcium channels. The crossing arises in part from the dramatic speeding of the rise to peak current with increasing depolarisation, a property that is rooted at the unitary current level in steeply voltage-dependent changes in latency to first opening.[32]

While previous studies have made detailed comparisons of T-type and various HVA channels with regard to their kinetics of deactivation upon sudden repolarisation, this property has not been described for R-type calcium channels. We found that these channels deactivate approximately 8 times more quickly than T-type calcium channels under identical recording conditions. Thus, these components satisfy the classical criteria for fast-deactivating and slowly deactivating currents, respectively.[33] We have described the consequences of these kinetic differences for the generation of Ca^{2+} influx during an action potential (see also McCobb and Beam[34]).[18] R-type calcium channels resemble other HVA channels in the way their contribution varies with the parameters of mock action potentials.[35] In contrast, the divalent cation influx supplied by T-type calcium channels shows a significantly different dependence on depolarisation waveform. Peak influx through T-type calcium channels occurs especially late in the plateau, and its magnitude is particularly sensitive to lengthening of the plateau phase. These differences might have significance in many functional settings, e.g. in the coupling of presynaptic action potentials to neurotransmitter release. Our observations suggest that synaptic transmission mediated by presynaptic T-type calcium channels might be distinguished from that triggered by HVA channels in future studies. We predict that transmitter release triggered by T-type calcium channels would be characterised by:

i) long synaptic delays
ii) high failure rates with brief presynaptic action potentials
iii) strong sensitivity to presynaptic manipulations that broaden the action potential, such as inhibition of potassium channels.

Pharmacological differences between T- and R-type calcium channels

Pharmacological differences between T- and R-type channels are of obvious importance in the determination of the respective contributions of these channels to physiological events. We have focused on various aspects of the pharmacological profiles of these channel types that might set them apart, particularly their responsiveness to nimodipine, ω-Aga-IIIA and mibefradil.

ω-Aga-IIIA

Inhibition of R-type current by ω-Aga-IIIA was a consistent finding (see fig. 5 (C & E)). In contrast, the T-type current failed to respond to ω-Aga-IIIA (see fig. 5 (A & D)), in accordance with previous reports.[24] This represents a clear pharmacological distinction between T- and R-type currents. Thus, it is significant that currents arising from α_{1E} subunits are susceptible to inhibition by ω-Aga-IIIA (see fig. 5 (B)).[9] The degree of inhibition closely matches that found for R-type current. The nature of the R-type channel inhibition by ω-Aga-IIIA, rapid but incomplete block even at seemingly saturating toxin concentrations, was in agreement with previous data for N- and L-type currents[24] and currents derived from α_{1A} subunits expressed in oocytes,[36] which suggests that this characteristic may be common to all HVA calcium currents.

Nimodipine

Our experiments confirmed that T-type calcium channels in a neuronal cell line are susceptible to blockade by nimodipine, in agreement with previous data for 1,4-dihydropyridines and T-type calcium channels in other systems.[37–41] On the other hand, R-type currents are not responsive to nimodipine,[16,42] in line with behaviour of calcium currents derived from α_{1E}.[5–8] By this pharmacological criterion, α_{1E} segregates once again with R-type current, not T-type.

Mibefradil

Our experiments provided new information about the time- and dose-dependence of mibefradil blockade of T-type calcium channels.[18] Mibefradil 1 µM blocked T-type current in the neuronally derived cells by approximately 50% at a holding potential of –80 mV. This was somewhat less than the degree of block (~80%) of T-type current in vascular smooth muscle cells,[43] but more than the approximate 35% block reported for T-type current in human medullary thyroid carcinoma (hMTC) cells.[26] R-type currents in cerebellar granule neurons were also quite responsive to mibefradil 1 µM (63% inhibition), perhaps even more so than currents generated by α_{1E} in oocytes.[8] Pronounced sensitivity of R-type channels to mibefradil might have been expected *a priori* because of the relatively negative position of their inactivation curve.

We found a mild but unmistakable voltage-dependence in the blocking action of mibefradil, seen in the kinetics of channel blocking and unblocking as well as steady-state inhibition (see fig. 8). In this respect, T-type currents in the neuroblastoma cells appear similar to those in heart cells.[44] The observed change in the degree of block with holding potential was in reasonable agreement with the published data of Mehrke et al. for T-type calcium channels in hMTC cells,[26] although these investigators did not interpret the difference as significant. Thus, there is no qualitative discrepancy with regard to the voltage-dependence of mibefradil action between T-type current and HVA currents.[8] Still, it is notable that the voltage-dependence of mibefradil block is much less pronounced for T-type calcium channels than for the other channel types. This might be particularly important in allowing the drug to act preferentially on T-type calcium channels while sparing the HVA channels.

Table I. Comparison of biophysical and pharmacological properties of T- and R-type calcium channels in neurons or neuron-derived cells with those of channels expressed from class E α_1 subunits

Property	Channel[a]		
	T type	Class E	R type
Pattern of family of superimposed currents	Crossing	Non-crossing	Non-crossing
Activation voltage-dependence ($V_{½}$)	–26.9 mV	+3.5 mV	–1.7 mV
Activation time (t_{10-90} or τ)	~4 ms (t_{10-90})	1.3 ms (τ)	~1 ms (t_{10-90})
Deactivation time constant (–60 mV)	4200 μs	294 μs	270 μs
Inactivation voltage-dependence ($V_{½}$)	–53.4 mV	–71 mV	–68.4 mV
Inactivation time at 0 mV (τ)	~22 ms	~50 ms	~40 ms
Response to nimodipine 10 μM	63% block	No effect	No effect
Response to ω-Aga-IIIA	No effect (10 nM)	70% block (20 nM)	72% block (10 nM)
Mibefradil block, voltage-dependence	Mild	Strong	Strong

[a] T- and R-type current characteristics from Randall and Tsien,[18] with Ba^{2+} 10 mM as charge carrier. Properties of expressed α_{1E} from Williams et al.,[6] except for information on ω-Aga-IIIA[9] and mibefradil[8] blockade. See also Soong et al.[5] and Wakamori et al.[7] for biophysical behaviour under different ionic conditions.

When administered *in vivo*, mibefradil would be unlikely to affect R-type calcium channels because these channels are largely localised in the brain, and the compound has limited access to targets beyond the blood–brain barrier. It is no surprise, therefore, that the beneficial cardiovascular actions of mibefradil seem to be unburdened by CNS side effects.

Overview

Table I summarises key features of T- and R-type currents as described in this paper. In all respects tested so far, R-type current behaves similarly to α_{1E} subunits expressed in *Xenopus* oocytes or mammalian cell lines.[5–9] This supports the hypothesis that R-type current is supported by the α_{1E} subunit.[15,18,42] Of course, this does not exclude the possibility that T-type calcium channels are also related in some way to α_{1E}, particularly if one invokes alternative splicing of the α_{1E} subunit or coexpression of different auxiliary subunits.[1] However, our results clearly indicate that classical T-type calcium channels behave very differently from expressed α_{1E} subunits, in any form or auxiliary subunit combination studied thus far.

Acknowledgements

This research was generously supported by research grants from the Medical Research Council (A.R.), the National Institutes of Health (R.W.T.) and a gift from F. Hoffmann-La Roche Ltd (R.W.T.). We thank E.T. Kavalali for comments on the manuscript. We are grateful to Dr Michael Adams (U.C. Riverside) for providing ω-Aga-IIIA, Dr Laszlo Nadasdi (Neurex Corporation) for ω-CTx-MVIIA and ω-CTx-MVIIC, and Dr Jean-Paul Clozel (F. Hoffmann-La Roche Ltd) for mibefradil and for advice and encouragement.

References

1. Birnbaumer L, Campbell KP, Catterall WA, et al. The naming of voltage-gated calcium channels. Neuron 1994; 13: 505–6
2. De Waard M, Gurnett CA, Campbell KP. Structural and functional diversity of voltage-activated calcium channels. In: Narahashi T, editor. Ion channels. New York: Plenum Press, 1996: 41–87
3. Tsien RW, Lipscombe D, Madison D, et al. Reflections on Ca(2+)-channel diversity, 1988–1994. Trends Neurosci 1995; 18: 52–4
4. Tsien RW, Wheeler DB. Voltage-gated calcium channels. In: Carafoli E, Klee CB, editors. Intracellular calcium. New York: Oxford University Press, 1997
5. Soong TW, Stea A, Hodson CD, et al. Structure and functional expression of a member of the low voltage-activated calcium channel family. Science 1993; 260: 1133–6
6. Williams ME, Marubio LM, Deal CR, et al. Structure and functional characterization of neuronal alpha 1E calcium channel subtypes. J Biol Chem 1994; 269: 22347–57
7. Wakamori M, Niidome T, Furutama D, et al. Distinctive functional properties of the neuronal BII (class E) calcium channel. Receptors Channels 1994; 2: 303–14
8. Bezprozvanny I, Tsien RW. Voltage-dependent blockade of diverse types of voltage-gated Ca^{2+} channels expressed in *Xenopus* oocytes by the Ca^{2+} channel antagonist mibefradil (Ro 40-5967). Mol Pharmacol 1995; 48: 540–9
9. Rock DM, Horne WA, Stoehr SJ, et al. Does α_{1E} code for T-type calcium channels? A comparison of recombinant α_{1E} calcium channels with GH3 pituitary T-type and recombinant α_{1B} calcium channels. In: Tsien RW, Clozel J-P, Nargeot J, editors. Low-Voltage-Activated T-Type Calcium Channels. Proceedings from the International Electrophysiology Meeting: 1996 Oct 21–22: Montpellier, France. Chester, UK: Adis International Ltd, 1998: 279–89
10. Bourinet E, Zamponi GW, Stea A, et al. The alpha-1e calcium channel exhibits permeation properties similar to low-voltage-activated calcium channels. J Neurosci 1996; 16: 4983–93
11. Bean BP. Two kinds of calcium channels in canine atrial cells. Differences in kinetics, selectivity, and pharmacology. J Gen Physiol 1985; 86: 1–30
12. Carbone E, Lux HD. A low voltage-activated calcium conductance in embryonic chick sensory neurons. Biophys J 1984; 46: 413–8
13. Nilius B, Hess P, Lansman JB, et al. A novel type of cardiac calcium channel in ventricular cells. Nature 1985; 316: 443–6
14. Nowycky MC, Fox AP, Tsien RW. Three types of neuronal calcium channel with different calcium agonist sensitivity. Nature 1985; 316: 440–3
15. Zhang J-F, Randall AD, Ellinor PT. Distinctive pharmacology and kinetics of cloned neuronal Ca^{2+} channels and their possible counterparts in mammalian CNS neurons. Neuropharmacology 1993; 32: 1075–88
16. Randall A, Tsien RW. Pharmacological dissection of multiple types of Ca^{2+} channel currents in rat cerebellar granule neurons. J Neurosci 1995; 15: 2995–3012
17. Tottene A, Moretti A, Pietrobon D. Functional diversity of P-type and R-type calcium channels in rat cerebellar neurons. J Neurosci 1996; 16: 6353–63
18. Randall A, Tsien RW. Contrasting biophysical and pharmacological properties of T-type and R-type calcium channels. Neuropharmacology. In press
19. Kasai H, Neher E. Dihydropyridine-sensitive and omega-conotoxin-sensitive calcium channels in a mammalian neuroblastoma-glioma cell line. J Physiol 1992; 448: 161–88
20. Hille B. Ionic channels of excitable membranes. 2nd edn. Sunderland, Mass.: Sinauer Associates, 1992
21. Barrett PQ, Liu L-P, Lu H-K, et al. Angiotensin II stimulates aldosterone secretion by two distinct mechanisms that modulate LVA T-type calcium channels. In: Tsien RW, Clozel J-P, Nargeot J, editors. Low-Voltage-Activated T-Type Calcium Channels. Proceedings from the International Electrophysiology Meeting: 1996 Oct 21–22: Montpellier, France. Chester, UK: Adis International Ltd, 1998: 168–75
22. Lei M, Brown H, Noble D. What role do T-type calcium channels play in cardiac pacemaker activity? In: Tsien RW, Clozel J-P, Nargeot J, editors. Low-Voltage-Activated T-Type Calcium Channels. Proceedings from the International Electrophysiology Meeting: 1996 Oct 21–22: Montpellier, France. Chester, UK: Adis International Ltd, 1998: 103–9
23. Mintz IM. Block of Ca channels in rat central neurons by the spider toxin omega-Aga-IIIA. J Neurosci 1994; 14: 2844–53
24. Mintz IM, Venema VJ, Adams ME, et al. Inhibition of N- and L-type Ca^{2+} channels by the spider venom toxin omega-Aga-IIIA. Proc Natl Acad Sci U S A 1991; 88: 6628–31
25. Clozel J-P, Osterrieder W, Kleinbloesem CH, et al. Ro 40-5967: a new nondihydropyridine calcium antagonist. Cardiovasc Drug Rev 1991; 9: 4–17
26. Mehrke G, Zong XG, Flockerzi V, et al. The Ca^{++}-channel blocker Ro 40-5967 blocks differently T-type and L-type Ca^{++} channels. J Pharmacol Exp Ther 1994; 271: 1483–8
27. Liang-min F, Osterrieder W. Potential-dependent inhibition of cardiac Ca^{2+} inward currents by Ro 40-5967 and verapamil: relation to negative inotropy. Eur J Pharmacol 1991; 196: 205–7

28. Cohen CJ, McCarthy RT, Barrett PQ, et al. Ca channels in adrenal glomerulosa cells: K^+ and angiotensin II increase T-type Ca channel current. Proc Natl Acad Sci U S A 1988; 85: 2412–6
29. Nilius B. Possible functional significance of a novel type of cardiac Ca channel. Biomed Biochim Acta 1986; 8: K37–45
30. Hagiwara N, Irisawa H, Kameyama M. Contribution of two types of calcium currents to the pacemaker potentials of rabbit sino-atrial node cells. J Physiol 1988; 395: 233–53
31. Lei M, Brown HF, Noble D. Contribution of T-type current to the pacemaker depolarisation of rabbit isolated SA node cells. J Physiol 1995; 487: 148–9P
32. Droogmans G, Nilius B. Kinetic properties of the cardiac T-type calcium channel in the guinea-pig. J Physiol (Lond) 1989; 419: 627–50
33. Matteson DR, Armstrong CM. Properties of two types of calcium channels in clonal pituitary cells. J Gen Physiol 1986; 87: 161–82
34. McCobb DP, Beam KG. Action potential waveform voltage-clamp commands reveal striking differences in calcium entry via low and high voltage-activated calcium channels. Neuron 1991; 7: 119–27
35. Wheeler DB, Randall A, Tsien RW. Changes in action potential duration alter reliance of excitatory synaptic transmission on multiple types of Ca^{2+} channels in rat hippocampus. J Neurosci 1996; 16: 2226–37
36. Sather WA, Tanabe T, Zhang JF, et al. Distinctive biophysical and pharmacological properties of class A (BI) calcium channel alpha 1 subunits. Neuron 1993; 11: 291–303
37. Cohen CJ, McCarthy RT. Nimodipine block of calcium channels in rat anterior pituitary cells. J Physiol (Lond) 1987; 387: 195–225
38. Akaike N, Kostyuk PG, Osipchuk YV. Dihydropyridine-sensitive low-threshold calcium channels in isolated rathypothalamic neurones. J Physiol 1989; 412: 181–95
39. Takahashi K, Akaike N. Calcium antagonist effects on low-threshold (T-type) calcium current in rat isolated hippocampal CA1 pyramidal neurons. J Pharm Exp Ther 1991; 256: 169–75
40. Richard S, Diochot S, Nargeot J, et al. Inhibition of T-type calcium currents by dihydropyridines in mouse embryonic dorsal root ganglion neurons. Neurosci Lett 1991; 132: 229–34
41. Romanin C, Seydl K, Glossmann H, et al. The dihydropyridine niguldipine inhibits T-type Ca^{2+} currents in atrial myocytes. Pflugers Arch 1992; 420: 410–12
42. Ellinor PT, Zhang JF, Randall AD, et al. Functional expression of a rapidly inactivating neuronal calcium channel. Nature 1993; 363: 455–8
43. Mishra SK, Hermsmeyer K. Selective inhibition of T-type Ca^{2+} channels by Ro 40-5967. Circ Res 1994; 75: 144–8
44. Benardeau A, Ertel EA. Selective block of myocardial T-type calcium channels by mibefradil: a comparison with the 1,4-dihydropyridine amlodipine. In: Tsien RW, Clozel J-P, Nargeot J, editors. Low-Voltage-Activated T-Type Calcium Channels. Proceedings from the International Electrophysiology Meeting: 1996 Oct 21–22: Montpellier, France. Chester, UK: Adis International Ltd, 1998: 386–94

Multiple types of LVA calcium channel in brain neurons

I. Dzhura, A. Eremin, D. Isaev, P. Kostyuk, O. Lyubanova, V. Naidenov, Y. Shuba, A. Tarasenko

Department of General Physiology of the Nervous System, Bogomoletz Institute of Physiology, National Academy of Sciences of Ukraine, Bogomoletz, Ukraine

Summary

Activity of low-voltage-activated (LVA) calcium channels was recorded from neurons in rat laterodorsal thalamic nucleus slices taken 1, 2 and 3 weeks postnatally and compared with activity of channels expressed in Xenopus *oocytes injected with poly-(A⁺)-mRNA from the same brain structures. In neurons of the first age group, LVA calcium channels possessed similar kinetic and pharmacological properties. The corresponding calcium currents demonstrated fast inactivation kinetics that followed a monoexponential time-course, with high sensitivity to nifedipine (K_d = 4.7 μM) and La^{3+} (K_d = 57.5 nM). From the second postnatal week, a more slowly inactivating component was observed in LVA calcium currents of the same neurons. These showed low sensitivity to nifedipine and La^{3+} but high sensitivity to Ni^{2+}. The density of the corresponding calcium channels increased progressively with postnatal development; this increase corresponded to the expansion of cell surface with the development of the dendritic tree. Expression experiments in* Xenopus *oocytes using poly-(A^+)-mRNA from thalamic structures of these animals revealed barium currents with potential dependence and pharmacological sensitivity similar to the fast LVA calcium current recorded* in vivo. *The results indicate the presence of multiple types of LVA calcium channel in brain neurons and the potential future of these neurons for cloning of the corresponding channel subunits.*

Introduction

Although first described some time ago,[1] the low-voltage-activated (LVA or T-type) calcium channels still comprise a somewhat mysterious subgroup of this type of ionic channel. In most excitable cells they can be detected only during a short period of their life cycle; the conditions for their physiological expression remain unclear and no corresponding α_1 subunit has yet been identified. Previous investigations have indicated possible functional heterogeneity of such channels; thus, in rat hypothalamic neurons, LVA channels that reveal completely different pharmacological properties from those of T-type channels in peripheral neurons or muscle fibres were found.[2] This observation prompted us to investigate the functional and structural diversity of LVA calcium channels, using measurements of channel activity in brain neurons *in situ* and activity of channels artificially expressed in *Xenopus* oocytes.

Methods

Electrophysiological measurements *in situ* were made using 1-, 2- and 3-week-old rats. Saggital slices of the thalamic region of 300 μm thickness were prepared in the usual way, and thalamic nuclei were identified according to the rat brain stereotaxic atlas. For isolation of calcium currents the slices were kept in choline Cl 113 mM, TEAC 27 mM, TRIS Cl 20 mM, $CaCl_2$ 2 mM and $MgCl_2$ 0.5 mM, with pH adjusted to 7.4 with TRIS OH. To block sodium channels, tetrodotoxin 1 μM was added. Currents were recorded with a whole-cell patch clamp. The solution in the recording pipette contained CsCl 130 mM, EGTA 10 mM, TRIS Cl 10 mM, $MgCl_2$ 5 mM and $CaCl_2$ 1 mM, with pH adjusted to 7.3 with CsOH. The substances tested were added to the external solution by a fast-application technique through a pressure-ejecting micropipette. Passive electrical properties of the tested neurons from animals in different age groups were measured by analysing the capacitative transients evoked by hyperpolarising voltage steps from a holding potential of –90 mV.

Total mRNA was purified from the same brain region of 2-week-old rats using a single-step guanidinium thiocyanate-phenol-chloroform extraction method. Poly-(A^+)-mRNA was obtained from total mRNA by affinity chromatography on oligo (dT)-cellulose and stored as an ethanol precipitate at –70 °C. This was redissolved in deionised water to give a final concentration of 1 mg/ml and was used for oocyte injections. The volume of injected solution was 50 nl/oocyte. Whole-cell currents were recorded with a two-microelectrode voltage-clamp technique.

For the isolation of calcium channel currents and suppression of the oocyte intrinsic calcium-activated Cl^- conductance, Cl^--free methanesulphonate-substituted extracellular solution containing Ba^{2+} ions as charge carriers was used. This solution comprised $Ba(OH)_2$ 40 mM, TEA OH 50 mM, KOH 2 mM and HEPES 10 mM, with pH adjusted to 7.4 with methanesulphonic acid. The intracellular current-injecting electrode contained CsCl 500 mM, EGTA 50 mM and HEPES 10 mM, with pH adjusted to 7.4 with CsOH. During the experiment an oocyte was placed on a miniature platform that could be immersed in one of the chambers mounted on a revolving stage. The chambers were filled with various test solutions, and by downward movement and subsequent rotation of the stage complete exchange of the solution around the oocyte could be achieved in less than 1 s.

Results

Calcium currents in thalamic neurons in situ

Calcium current recordings were made mainly from neurons in the laterodorsal thalamic nucleus. In all cells tested, such currents could be evoked by membrane depolarisations from a holding potential of –95 mV. They consisted of a transient component in the testing potential range –80 to –45 mV, followed by a sustained component at depolarisations beyond –45 mV. This confirmed the existence of LVA and high-voltage-activated (HVA) calcium channels in these neurons. A more detailed analysis of the LVA currents demonstrated their complex age-dependent structure. In neurons of the first age group (1 week old), the population of LVA calcium channels seemed to be homogeneous: the current–voltage curve had a peak in the region of –55 mV (n=7), and the current decay could be fitted by a single exponential function (fig. 1 (A)). Alternatively, in neurons of other age groups (2 and 3 weeks old), two peaks were observed on the current–voltage curves, at about –65 and –55 mV (n=14). Current decay was complex and included a slow component lasting hundreds of milliseconds. Examples of LVA calcium currents with two components are presented in figure 1 (B). This phenomenon may result from the expression at these postnatal stages of a 'slow' type of LVA calcium channel, in addition to the 'fast' channel expressed earlier.

As substantial morphological changes could occur in these neurons at the chosen postnatal developmental stages, special attention had to be paid to the reliability of voltage control in more mature neurons. Indeed, detailed measurements of the passive electrical properties of laterodorsal neurons indicated a progressive increase in membrane capacitance that corresponded to expansion of the dendritic tree at these stages. It is possible that the newly expressed 'slow' LVA channels result from poor voltage clamping of the dendritic tree. However, no indications of ineffective space clamping were found in neurons of any age group tested. Furthermore, conclusive evidence for the existence of two separate types of LVA calcium channel was obtained in tests of the pharmacological sensitivity of the corresponding calcium current components.

A prominent feature of the 'fast' LVA current in neurons of the first age group was its high sensitivity to dihydropyridines (nifedipine). This was not present in T-type calcium currents in most previously studied excitable cells. Similar high sensitivity has been shown for LVA channels in hypothalamic neurons isolated from rats of the same age.[2] In our experiments, the apparent K_d value for the neurons of the first age group was 4.7 μM (n=8) (fig. 2). The LVA calcium current was completely and

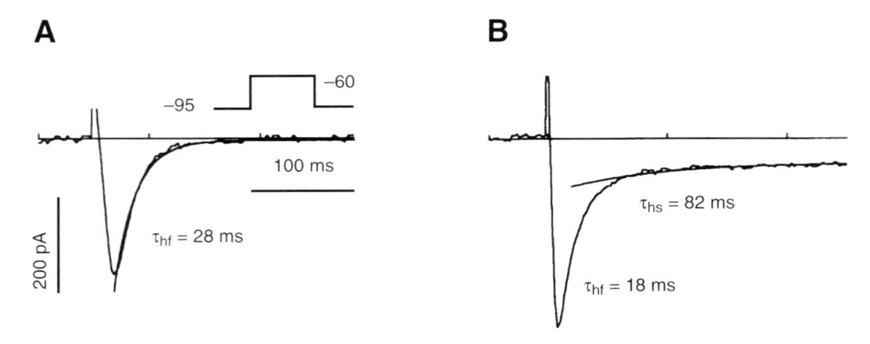

Fig. 1. Analysis of inactivation kinetics of low-voltage-activated (LVA) calcium current in laterodorsal thalamic neurons in three age groups (1, 2 and 3 weeks old). A) Transient LVA calcium current in the first age group evoked by step depolarisation from a holding potential of –95 mV to test potential –60 mV. Inactivation kinetic fitted by a single exponential with time constant τ_{hf} = 28 ms. B) LVA calcium current in neurons of the second age group; inactivation curve fitted by a double-exponential with time constants τ_{hf} = 18 and τ_{hs} = 82 ms. The upper trace indicates stimulus parameters that comprised 35 mV steps of duration 600 ms for both current traces.

reversibly blocked in these cells. However, in neurons of the second and third age groups (fig. 3 (A)), a dihydropyridine-insensitive component was apparent. This accounted for 12 ± 3% (n=7) of the control current in the neurons of the second age group and 25 ± 4% (n=9) in the third age group, even in the presence of 100 μM concentrations of nifedipine. The dihydropyridine-sensitive component could be isolated by subtraction of the nifedipine-insensitive LVA current from the control current (see fig. 3 (B)). This component had a faster inactivation time constant (τ_{hs} = 32 ± 4 ms; n=15) than the dihydropyridine-insensitive component (τ_{hs} = 54.2 ± 4.5 ms (n=26) and 68.6 ± 3.2 ms (n=18) for the second and third age groups, respectively).

The sensitivities of both LVA components to other types of calcium channel blocker have also been compared. La^{3+} ions were found to be potent blockers of the 'fast' dihydropyridine-sensitive component, blockade becoming apparent at a concentration of 10 nM, with an apparent K_d value of 57.5 nM (n=9) (see fig. 2). This is in contrast to T-type channels in many cell types, which show low sensitivity to La^{3+} ions. Thus, La^{3+} ions could be used to separate the 'slow' component from the total current in neurons from the older age groups (see fig. 3 (C & D)). On the other hand, Ni^{2+} ions at 1–25 μM concentrations were more effective in the blockade of the 'slow' dihydropyridine-insensitive component of the complex current (n=13) (see fig. 3 (E & F)), thus isolating the 'fast' dihydropyridine-sensitive component.

A comparison of steady-state inactivation characteristics of both types of LVA calcium current revealed definite quantitative differences between them. The steady-state inactivation curve for the 'fast' component could be best fitted by a Boltzmann

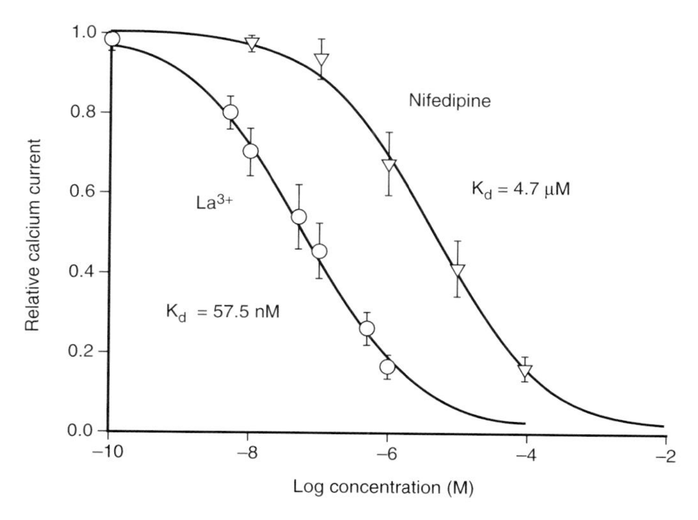

Fig. 2. Blocking of low-voltage-activated (LVA) calcium current by nifedipine and La^{3+} in laterodorsal neurons from the first age group (1 week old). Dose–response relationship of 'fast' LVA calcium current component fitted by Langmuir's isotherm. The currents were obtained by depolarisation from a holding potential of −95 mV with a 40 mV step (current maximum was observed at −55 mV). Curve parameters are K_d = 4.7 μM for nifedipine and K_d = 57.5 nM for La^{3+}. All points show mean data from 7 neurons for nifedipine and from 9 for La^{3+}.

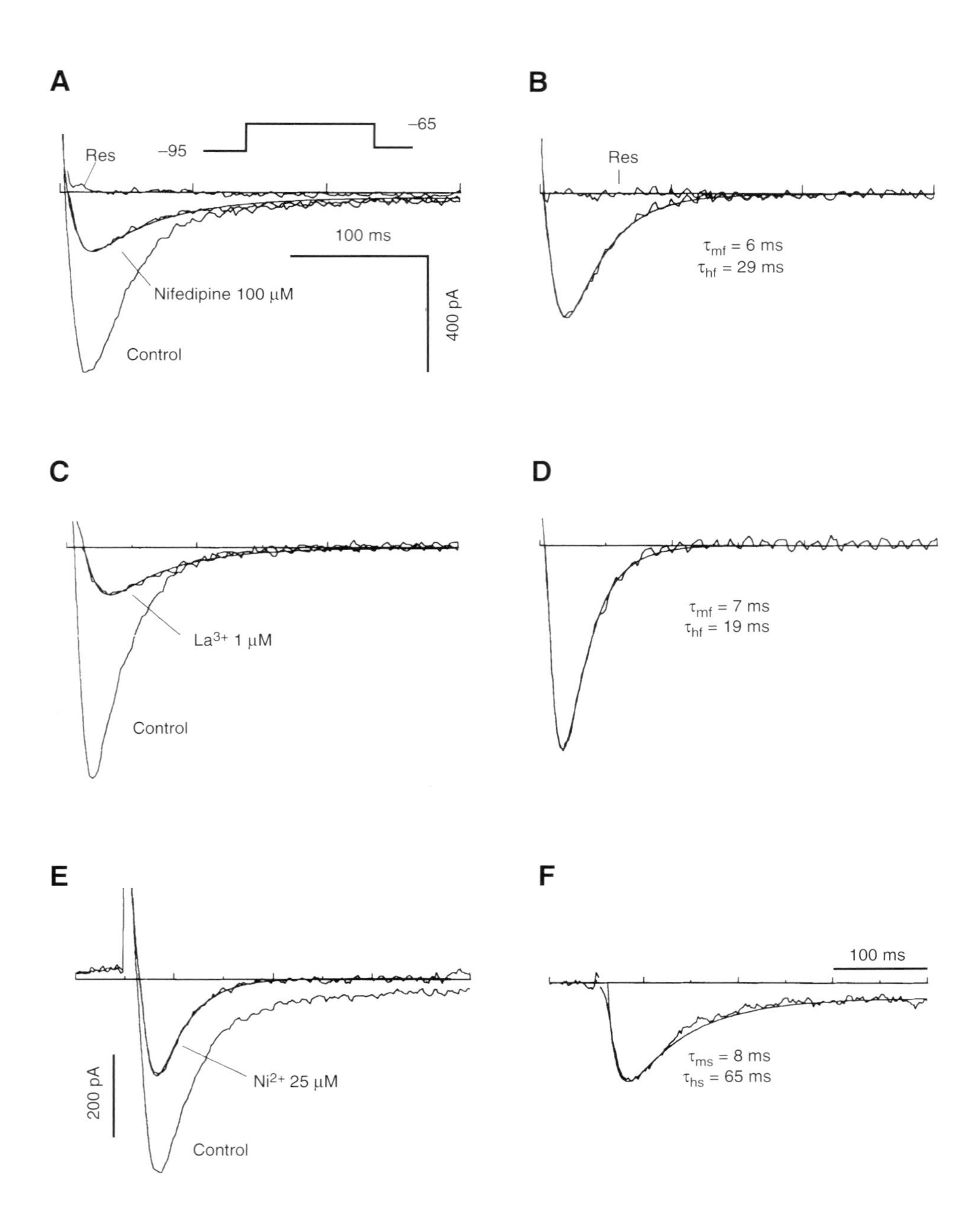

Fig. 3. Pharmacological properties of different components of low-voltage-activated (LVA) calcium currents recorded in situ. A) LVA calcium current before (control) and after blockade by nifedipine 100 μM. The m^2h Hodgkin–Huxley equation used to fit the nifedipine-insensitive current had the following parameters: τ_{ms} = 7 ms and τ_{hs} = 67 ms. Res = difference between recorded 'slow' component and fitted curve. B) Nifedipine-sensitive component obtained by subtraction of 'slow' component from control current (fitted using m^2h model with parameters indicated on the figure). C) LVA calcium current recorded without (control) and in the presence of La^{3+} 1 μM. La^{3+}-resistant LVA calcium current was best fitted by the m^2h equation with τ_{ms} = 8 ms and τ_{hs} = 69 ms. D) La^{3+}-sensitive component obtained by subtraction of LVA calcium current recorded after application of La^{3+}. E) LVA calcium current before and after application of Ni^{2+} 25 μM. F) Ni^{2+}-sensitive component obtained as difference between control current and current after action of Ni^{2+}. Fitted curve is superimposed on the I_{Ts} component, with parameters indicated by the current trace. Pulse protocol indicated at top of figure.

function (fig. 4 (A & B)), with a half-potential of –85.5 mV (n=6). The same curve for the 'slow' component was shifted to more negative potentials with a half-potential of approximately –98 mV (n=7) (see fig. 4 (C & D)).

Calcium currents expressed in oocytes

122 oocytes injected with poly-(A^+)-mRNA were tested. In this case Ba^{2+} ions had to be used as charge carriers to suppress strong endogenous Ca^{2+}-dependent chlorine currents. Of these oocytes, 68 showed substantial barium currents (120–150 nA). Their voltage-dependence appeared similar to that of the LVA calcium currents in thalamic neurons *in situ* described above. They could be activated by depolarisations to about –70 mV from a holding potential of –120 mV, and reached maximal amplitude at about –30 mV (it should be noted that in this case a high concentration of divalent

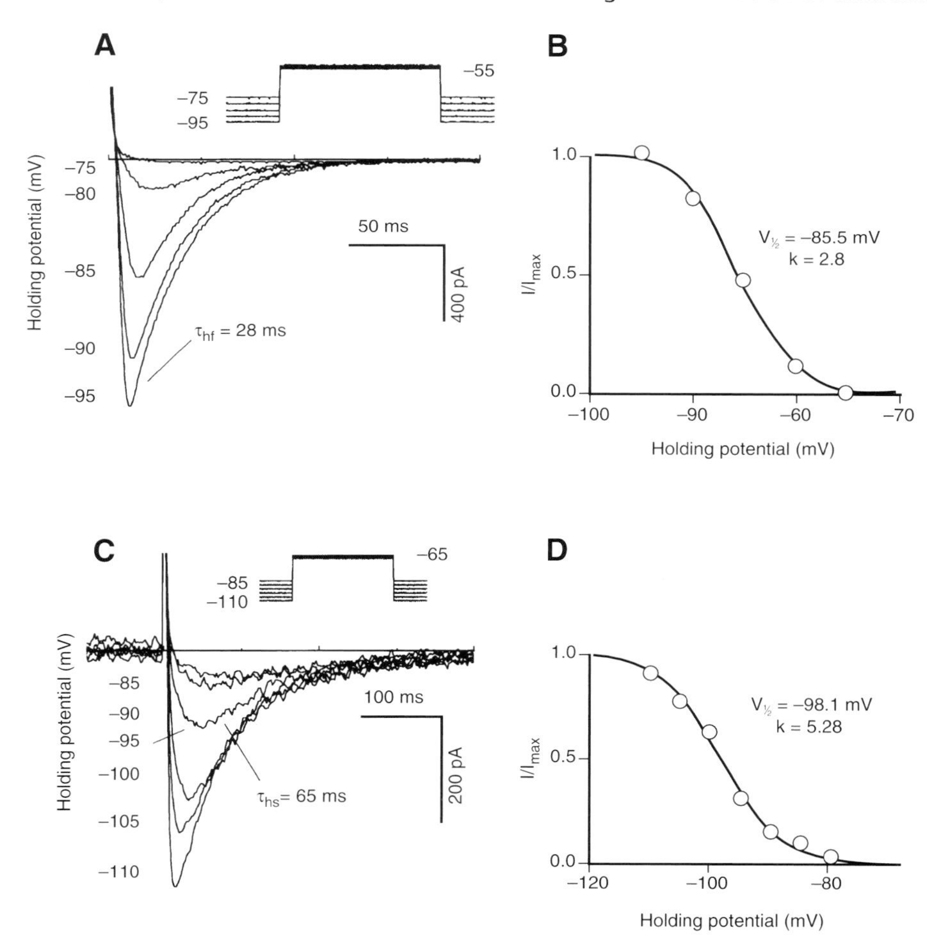

Fig. 4. Steady-state inactivation of 'fast' and 'slow' low-voltage-activated (LVA) calcium current in laterodorsal neurons. A) 'Fast' LVA calcium currents evoked in a neuron of the first age group (1 week old) by step depolarisation to –55 mV from different holding potentials (see traces), changing in the range –95 to –75 mV. B) Steady-state inactivation curve for 'fast' component. C) 'Slow' LVA calcium currents recorded in a neuron of the third age group (3 weeks old). Currents were induced after addition of nifedipine 100 μM by step depolarisation to –65 mV from different holding potentials. D) Steady-state inactivation curve for this component (see figure for curve parameters).

cations in the external solution caused a substantial shift in current–voltage curves). No such currents could be observed in control oocytes, which showed only small HVA barium currents.[3,4]

The dihydropyridines were also effective organic blockers of expressed LVA barium currents. The dose-dependence of the blocking action of nifedipine may be described by Langmuir's isotherms, with an apparent K_d value of 6.2 μM. Testing of the blocking effect of inorganic blockers has shown preferential action of La^{3+} ions, with an apparent K_d of 0.56 μM (Cd^{2+} ions being much less effective). Figure 5 shows the corresponding dose–response curves.

Thus, in terms of pharmacological sensitivity, the expressed LVA channels resemble LVA channels that are responsible for 'fast' LVA calcium currents in neurons *in situ*. Other calcium channel blockers specific for different types of HVA channels were also tested (ω-Aga-IVA, ω-CTx-GVIA). The combined action of both blockers at concentrations of 20 and 10 μM (significantly higher than those known to be effective for P-, Q- and N-type calcium channels) produced, at most, a 10% inhibition of the barium current. This indicates that the expression of these channel types in injected oocytes is very low.

Comparative kinetic analysis of the expressed LVA currents was not possible because of substantial changes in the time-course of the currents compared with those in neurons *in situ*. Their inactivation became slow and incomplete (even during depolarising pulses that were prolonged by several seconds), so that a significant proportion of the current (about 30%) remained. This inactivation time-course of LVA

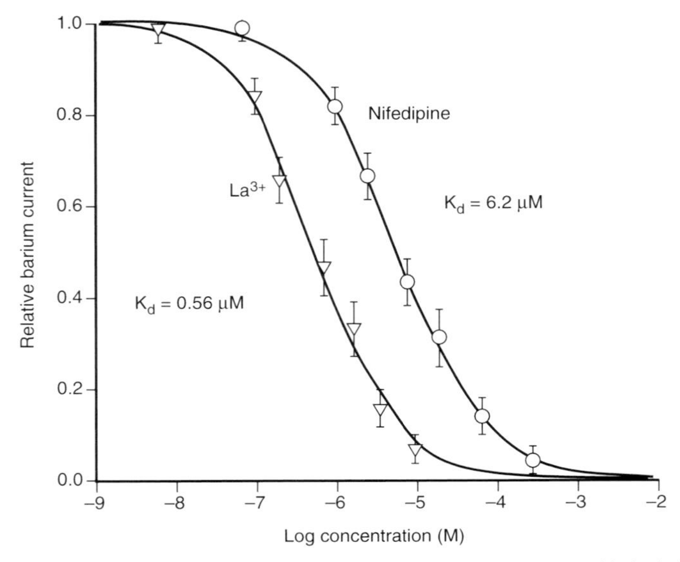

Fig. 5. Pharmacological properties of low-voltage-activated (LVA) barium current in oocytes: blockade by nifedipine and La^{3+}. Dose–response relationship of LVA barium current recorded in oocytes. Currents were evoked by depolarisation steps from the holding potential –120 mV to –20 mV.

channels expressed in oocytes may reflect the specificity of the oocyte translatory and post-translatory mechanisms during expression of foreign calcium channels, possibly leading to changes in the composition of auxiliary channel subunits. It is known that β subunits are quite important in the determination of the electrophysiological properties of expressed calcium channels.[5]

Discussion

The functional and pharmacological diversity of brain LVA calcium channels has been shown previously by several investigators. Huguenard and Prince indicated that LVA calcium currents in thalamic reticular neurons have slow potential-independent inactivation kinetics.[6] Neurons with such unusually slow inactivating currents were also found in dorsal root ganglia.[7] LVA calcium currents highly sensitive to dihydropyridines are typical of hypothalamic neurons.[2] They have also been recorded in some dorsal root ganglion neurons.[8] Importantly, the studies described in this report resulted in the finding of both types of LVA calcium currents in the same thalamic neurons, as well as the demonstration of the different time-courses of their expression at various stages of postnatal development. This facilitated accurate comparisons of their functional and pharmacological properties. The data obtained confirm the suggestion that the 'fast' and 'slow' components of LVA calcium currents in brain neurons are generated by two separate calcium channel sets with activation and inactivation kinetics, pharmacological sensitivities and postnatal expression that differ from those of the known T-type calcium channels in peripheral structures.

It is clear that several subtypes of the α_1 channel subunit responsible for the generation of these currents remain to be described. Our experiments with expression of total mRNA from the thalamic region of *Xenopus* oocytes indicate the presence of α_1 subunits that differ from those already defined. These include the α_{1E} subunit, which has been claimed to generate LVA calcium currents.[9] The expressed channels resemble the 'fast' LVA calcium channels of thalamic and hypothalamic neurons, both in potential-dependence and pharmacology, that predominate in the early stages of postnatal development. This observation has promise for the future possibility of cloning of the corresponding α_1 subunit.

As the expression of the 'slow' LVA calcium channels in thalamic neurons coincides with the development of the dendritic tree, it might be supposed that the corresponding channels are located mostly in the dendritic membrane. In some experiments in brain neurons from adult animals, cutting off the dendrites has been shown to result in the loss of LVA calcium currents.[10,11] The second to third week of postnatal development in mice coincides with the appearance of thalamocortical rhythmic activity; this suggests a possible important role for 'slow' dendritic LVA calcium currents. Special analysis (including computer simulation) has confirmed this suggestion, especially if LVA calcium channels act in conjunction with inhibitory (hyperpolarising) inputs to release them from steady-state inactivation.[12–15]

As 'fast' LVA calcium currents are present in brain neurons at the early postnatal stages (before development of the dendritic tree), as well as in acutely isolated cells, the corresponding channels could be confined to the somatic membrane. Their functional role here may be connected in some way to the triggering of neuronal differentiation, outgrowth of neurites and other processes, as suggested by some authors.[16,17]

Acknowledgements

This work was partially supported by the International Soros Science Education Program (ISSEP) through grant no. 054039 to I.D., no. GSU054275 to A.E. and no. SPU044034 to P.K.

References

1. Veselovsky NS, Fedulova SA. Two types of calcium channels in the somatic membrane of rat dorsal root ganglion neurons. Dokl Akad Nauk SSSR 1983; 268: 747–50
2. Akaike N, Kostyuk PG, Osipchuk YV. Dihydropyridine-sensitive low-threshold calcium channels in isolated rat hypothalamic neurons. J Physiol 1989; 412: 181–95
3. Dzhura I, Kostyuk P, Lyubanova O, et al. Expression of low-voltage activated Ca channels from rat brain neurones in *Xenopus* oocytes. Neuroreport 1994; 5: 1960–2
4. Dzhura IO, Naidenov VG, Lyubanova OP, et al. Characterisation of hypothalamic low voltage-activated Ca channels based on their functional expression in *Xenopus* oocytes. Neuroscience 1996; 70: 729–38
5. Stea A, Dubel SJ, Pragnell M, et al. A β-subunit normalizes the electrophysiological properties of cloned N-type Ca^{2+} channel α_1-subunit. Neuropharmacology 1993; 32: 1103–16
6. Huguenard JR, Prince DA. A novel T-type current underlies prolonged Ca^{2+}-dependent burst firing in GABAergic neurons of rat thalamic reticular nucleus. J Neurosci 1992; 12: 3804–17
7. Kobrinsky EM, Pearsons HA, Dolphin AC. Low- and high-voltage activated calcium channel currents and their modulation in the dorsal root ganglion cell line ND7-23. Neuroscience 1994; 58: 539–52
8. Formenti A, Arrigona E, Mancia M. Low-voltage activated calcium channels are differently affected by nimodipine. Neuroreport 1993; 5: 145–7
9. Soong TW, Stea A, Hodson CD, et al. Structure and functional expression of a member of the low voltage-activated calcium channel family. Science 1993; 260: 1133–6
10. Müller TH, Misgeld U, Swandulla D. Ionic currents in cultured rat hypothalamic neurones. J Physiol 1992; 450: 341–62
11. Karst H, Joels M, Wadman WJ. Low-threshold calcium currents in dendrites of the adult rat hippocampus. J Physiol 1993; 392: 603–16
12. Dossi RC, Nunez A, Steriade M. Electrophysiology of slow (0.5–4 Hz) intrinsic oscillations of cat thalamocortical neurones *in vitro*. J Physiol 1992; 447: 215–34
13. Kang Y, Kitai ST. A whole cell path-clamp study of the pacemaker potential in dopaminergic neurons of rat substantia nigra compacta. Neurosci Res 1993; 18: 209–21
14. Hutcheon B, Miura RM, Yarom Y, et al. Low-threshold calcium current and resonance in thalamic neurons: a model of frequency preference. J Neurophysiol 1994; 71: 583–94
15. Destexhe A, Contreras D, Steriade M, et al. *In vivo, in vitro*, and computational analysis of dendritic calcium currents in thalamic reticular neurons. J Neurosci 1996; 16: 169–85
16. Fedulova SA, Kostyuk PG, Veselovsky NS. Comparative analysis of ionic currents in the somatic membrane of sensory neurons from embryonic and newborn rats. Neuroscience 1994; 58: 341–6
17. Desarmenien MG, Dayanithi G, Tapia-Arancibia L, et al. Developmental autoregulation of calcium currents in mammalian central neurones. Neuroreport 1994; 5: 1953–6

Heterogeneous distribution of LVA and HVA calcium channels in mammalian brain tissue

Norio Akaike

Department of Physiology, Faculty of Medicine, Kyushu University, Fukuoka, Japan

Introduction

Low- and high-voltage-activated (LVA and HVA, respectively) calcium channels play important roles in the regulation of a variety of neuronal functions, including excitability, enzyme activation and exocytosis within the respective neurons, through the properties of the channels mediating Ca^{2+} influx and their distribution. Recent electrophysiological studies have defined five types of pharmacologically distinct HVA calcium channel on the neuronal cell body (soma): L, N, P, Q and R types.[1] Molecular biological approaches have also indicated that several different types of calcium channel are expressed in the brain.[2] There has therefore been great interest in identifying the calcium channels in individual somata acutely dissociated from various CNS regions of immature and mature rats.

Methods

Dissociation of rat CNS neurons has been described previously.[3] Briefly, 0- to 3-day-old, 2-week-old and 6-month-old Wistar rats were decapitated under pentobarbital anaesthesia, and 400 μm brain slices were prepared using a microslicer. The brain slices were then incubated in a well-oxygenated standard external solution with pronase 0.02% for 15 min at 31 °C, then exposed to thermolysin 0.02%. The required brain regions were then micropunched out and the neurons were dissociated mechanically with fire-polished glass pipettes. The dissociated neurons maintained their original morphological features with proximal dendrites. Electrophysiological measurements were carried out after the dissociated neurons had adhered to the bottom of the Petri dish. Electrical recordings were performed in a nystatin-perforated patch-recording mode under voltage-clamp conditions.[4] The macroscopic currents through voltage-activated calcium channels were measured using a patch-clamp amplifier, monitored on a storage oscilloscope and recorded on video tapes after being digitised with a digital audioprocessor for subsequent analysis using the pCLAMP 6.0 system (Axon Instruments, Foster City, California, USA). All currents were corrected for linear leakage and capacitance currents by the use of scaled currents for a 5–20 mV hyperpolarisation from a holding potential. All the experiments were carried out at room temperature (21–24 °C). The ionic composition of the standard external solution was: NaCl 150 mM, KCl 5 mM, $MgCl_2$ 1 mM, $CaCl_2$ 2 mM, HEPES 10 mM and glucose 10 mM. The external solution for recording the calcium or barium current passing through the voltage-gated calcium channels comprised NaCl 145 mM, CsCl 5 mM, $BaCl_2$ 5 mM (or $CaCl_2$ 2.5 mM), $MgCl_2$ 1 mM, HEPES 10 mM and glucose 10 mM. This Ba^{2+} or Ca^{2+} external solution contained tetrodotoxin 5×10^{-7} M, at which concentration the voltage-dependent sodium channels were completely blocked. The patch pipette solution contained CsCl 150 mM and HEPES 10 mM. The pH of the external and internal solutions was adjusted to 7.4 and 7.2, respectively, by the addition of TRIS OH. A stock solution of nystatin 10 mg/ml was prepared and added to the patch pipette solution to give a final concentration of 200 μg/ml.

The following calcium antagonists were used: ω–CTx-GVIA, ω–CTx-MVIIC, ω–Aga-IVA and nicardipine. The drugs were applied using a rapid application technique (the Y-tube method[5]). With this technique, the external solution surrounding a neuron could be changed completely within l0–20 ms.

Results and discussion

Heterogeneous distribution of LVA and HVA calcium channels

The current–voltage relationship for total peak inward currents consisting of both LVA and HVA barium current components in the Meynert neuron acutely dissociated from the 2-week-old rat is shown in figure 1. Depolarising voltage step pulses of 300 ms duration were applied from a holding potential of –90 mV to +30 mV in 10 mV increments. The pronounced hump (*) on the current–voltage relationship is indicative of LVA current.[6] As shown in panel A of figure 1, LVA current could be induced by a step depolarisation to about –60 mV; this increased in amplitude with increasing depolarisation, reaching a peak at about –40 mV. A steady HVA barium current was also seen at potentials more positive than –40 mV. At a holding potential of –60 mV, however, the LVA current component was completely inactivated. Consequently, the

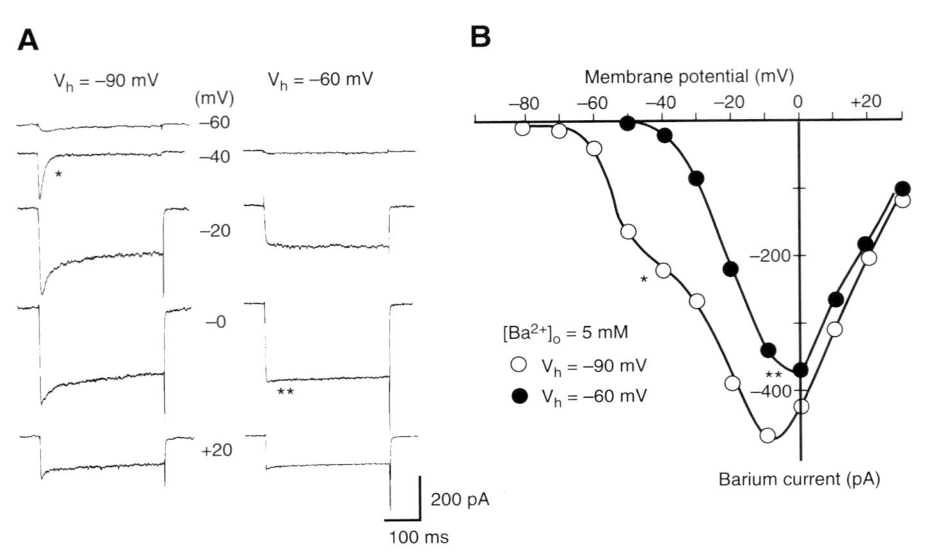

Fig. 1. Properties of low- (LVA) and high-voltage-activated calcium channel currents in Meynert neurons freshly dissected from 2-week-old rats. A) Examples of current recordings at test potentials indicated at two different holding potentials (V_h), –90 and –60 mV. B) Current–voltage relationships from the same neuron plotted according to the maximum current amplitudes induced by individual depolarising test pulses. The difference between the two current–voltage relationships is largely due to LVA calcium channel current.

residual current is composed almost entirely of HVA current (**). Thus, the difference between currents observed from holding potentials of –90 and –60 mV is largely due to LVA current.

In comparing peak amplitudes of LVA and HVA current components in neurons dissociated from various CNS regions, depolarising pulses of –40 and 0 mV from holding potentials of –90 and –60 mV were used for measuring the peak LVA and HVA current components, respectively. The neurons were acutely dissociated from the cortex, hippocampal CA1 region (CA1), basal nucleus of Meynert (Meynert), tuberomamillary nucleus (TMN), ventromedial hypothalamus (VMH), substantia nigra (SN) and nucleus tractus solitarius (NTS) of 2-week-old rats. Figure 2 (A) shows the marked differences in LVA and HVA current densities among the various neurons from different brain regions. Current density followed the order of: NTS > cortex > Meynert > TMN > SN > VMH > CA1 for the HVA current component, and Meynert > NTS > cortex = TMN > CA1 > SN > VMH for the LVA component. The ratio of densities of LVA to HVA in these neurons is shown in panel B of figure 2, with the ratio being greater in both CA1 and Meynert neurons but smaller in cortical, VMH and SN neurons. Typical examples from SN and CA1 neurons are shown in the inset of panel B of figure 2. In Meynert neurons with LVA calcium channels, the generation of rhythmic activity and burst firing of action potentials has been reported.[7] The hippocampal neurons also show a high propensity for burst firing; the voltage and Ca^{2+} requirements of this type of behaviour could be met by LVA calcium channels.[8]

To isolate HVA barium current passing through HVA calcium channels, the CNS neurons dissociated from different brain regions were held at a holding potential of –50 mV. At this potential, LVA calcium channels were completely inactivated. The HVA calcium channel currents in cortical, CA1, Meynert, TMN, VMH and SN neurons were differentiated as L, N, P, Q and R types by the use of calcium antagonists. L-, N- and P-type calcium channels are selectively sensitive to dihydropyridines, ω–CTx-GVIA and ω–Aga-IVA, respectively.[9] ω–CTx-MVIIC has been reported to inhibit dihydropyridine/ω–CTx-GVIA/ω–Aga-IVA-insensitive Q-type calcium channels, although this toxin blocks not only Q-type but also N- and P-type calcium channels.[10] In these experiments, therefore, ω–CTx-MVIIC 3×10^{-6} M was applied after cumulative application of nicardipine 5×10^{-6} M, ω–CTx-GVIA 3×10^{-6} M and ω–Aga-IVA 2×10^{-7} M (saturating concentrations). A small but measurable fraction of residual current component (R type) in the presence of these four calcium channel blockers was sensitive to inorganic calcium channel blockers such as Cd^{2+}, Ni^{2+} and Co^{2+}. Figure 3 shows a typical pharmacological separation of HVA calcium channel currents in the hippocampal CA1 pyramidal neuron and cerebellar Purkinje cell. The HVA barium current was evoked by 50 ms step pulses, from a holding potential of –50 mV to 0 mV at 15 s intervals.

Panel A of figure 4 summarises the proportions of HVA calcium channels in various CNS neurons from 2-week-old rats. The L-type component was greater in CA1, SN and NTS neurons and smaller in TMN and Purkinje (CPJ) neurons. The N-type component was present to a much greater extent in the TMN neurons. Interestingly, a large proportion of HVA barium current in CPJ neurons was carried by P-type calcium channels (89.0 ± 3.1%; n=9). The remainder was carried by L- (2.3 ± 1.3%) and N-type calcium channels (8.7 ± 0.7%). This observation in CPJ neurons was consistent with previous reports.[9,11]

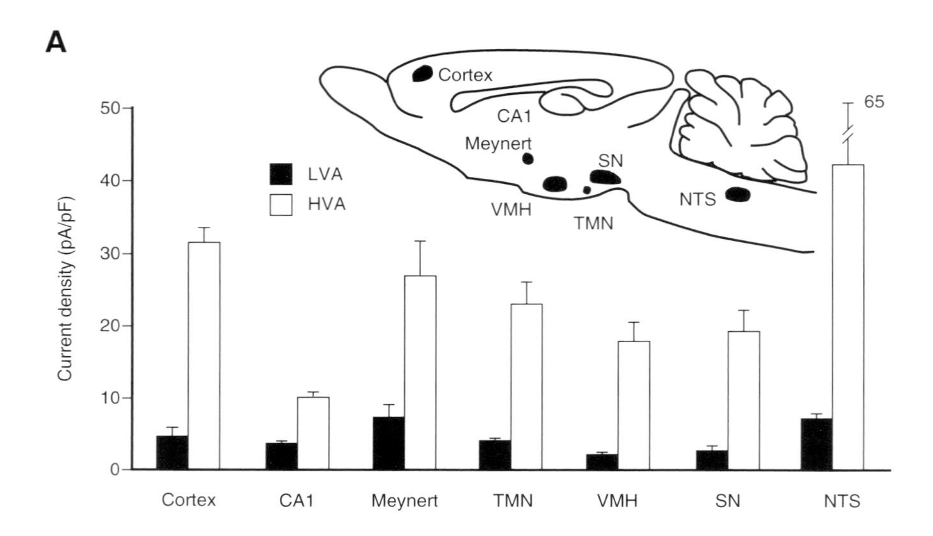

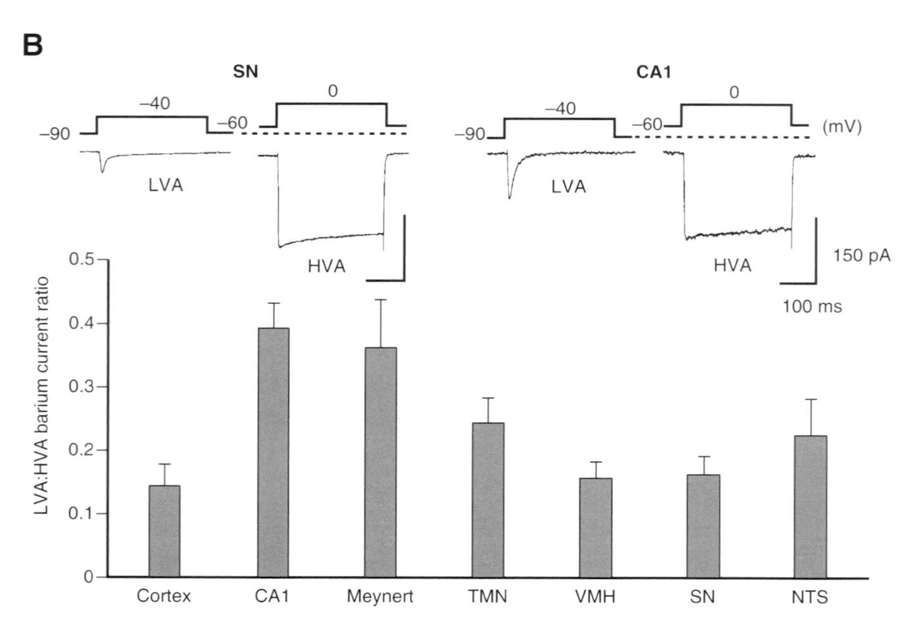

Fig. 2. Heterogeneous distribution of low- (LVA) and high-voltage-activated (HVA) calcium channels in neurons from various CNS regions of 2-week-old rats. A) Current density (± SEM) per unit cell membrane of LVA and HVA calcium current components in various CNS neurons. Inset: schematic illustration of the 7 brain regions used. B) LVA:HVA calcium channel component ratio of current densities. Typical cases are shown for substantia nigra (SN) and hippocampal CA1 (hippocampal CA1 region) pyramidal neurons. Meynert = basal nucleus of Meynert; NTS = nucleus tractus solitarius; TMN = tuberomamillary nucleus; VMH = ventromedial hypothalamus.

It has been reported that HVA calcium channels are oligomeric complexes of four different subunits: α_1, $\alpha_2\delta$, β and γ. To date, at least six different genes encoding α_1 subunits and three distinct genes encoding β subunits have been isolated from various tissues.[12,13] The α_1 subunit alone is sufficient for permeability to Ca^{2+} and has specific receptor sites for calcium channel blockers. Therefore, the variable distribution of HVA calcium channel subtypes in neurons in various CNS regions may result from the expression of region-specific subunits of HVA calcium channels.

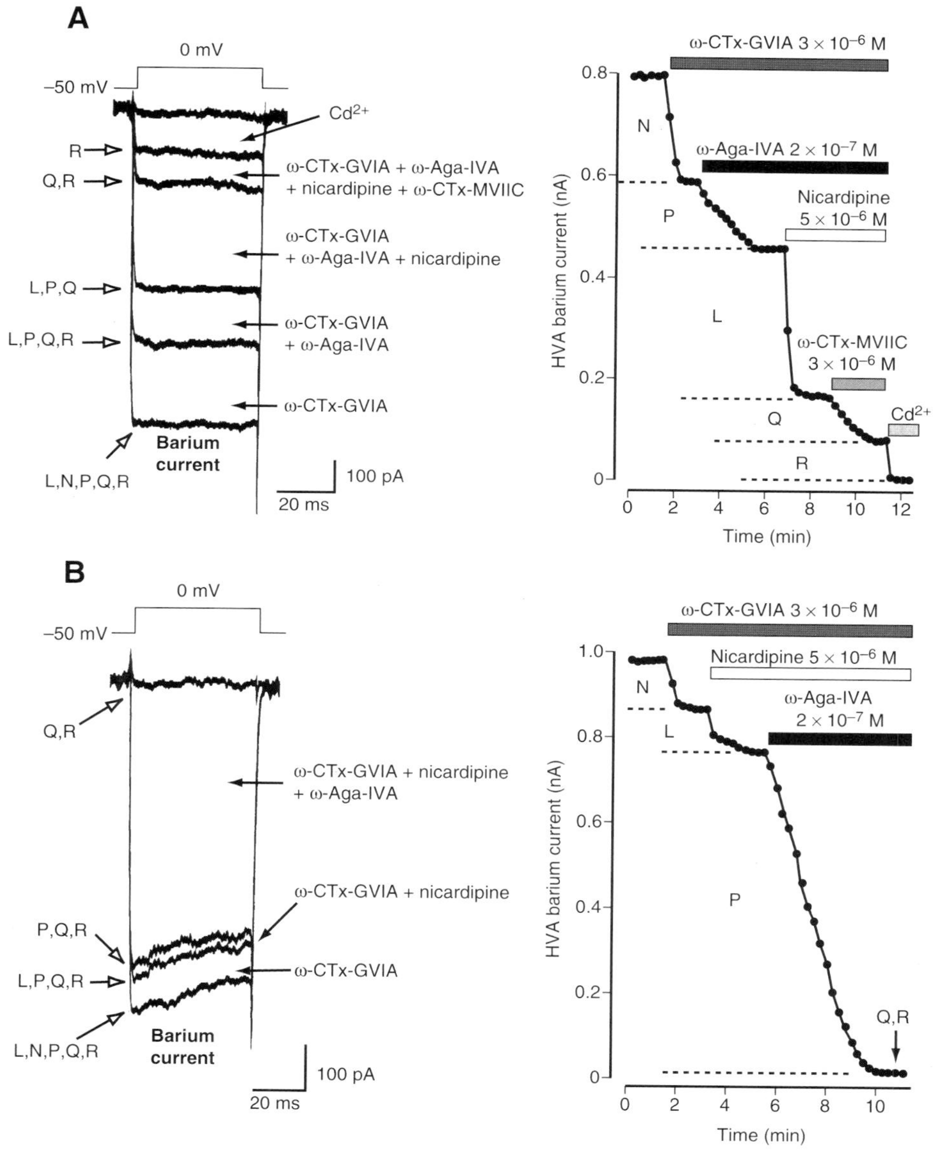

Fig. 3. High-voltage-activated (HVA) calcium channel currents in CNS neurons dissected from 2-week-old rats. A) Pharmacological separation of HVA barium current in hippocampal CA1 pyramidal neurons. Currents were elicited by 50 ms step pulses to 0 mV from a holding potential of –50 mV at l5 s intervals. Calcium antagonists were added cumulatively. B) Pharmacological separation of HVA barium current in cerebellar Purkinje cells.

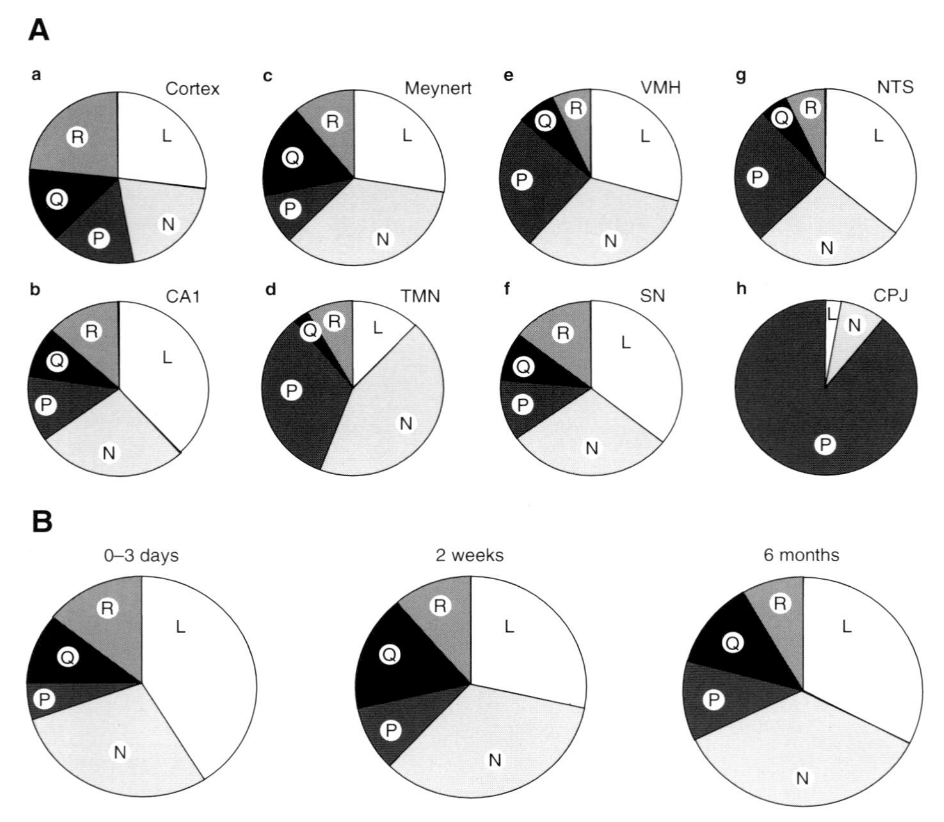

Fig. 4. High-voltage-activated (HVA) calcium channels. A) Heterogeneous distribution of five types of HVA calcium channel in various brain regions of 2-week-old rats. B) Changes in five types of HVA calcium channel in Meynert neurons at three different developmental stages. CA1 = hippocampal CA1 region, CPJ = Purkinje neurons, NTS = nucleus tractus solitarius, SN = substantia nigra, TMN = tuberomamillary nucleus, VMH = ventromedial hypothalamus.

Developmental changes in LVA and HVA calcium channels in Meynert neurons

The nucleus basalis of Meynert is populated by large cholinergic neurons and is a major source of cholinergic input to the cerebral cortex. The GABA-A response in dissociated rat Meynert neurons increased in the order of: newborn > 6 months old > 2 weeks old. Intracellular Cl^- concentrations also decreased throughout the developmental stages (35 and 12 mM in newborn and 6-month-old rat neurons, respectively). With increasing age, *N*-methyl-D-aspartate (NMDA)-induced inward current dramatically decreased while kainate response gradually increased with development.[14] Densities of LVA and HVA calcium current components of Meynert neurons of 2-week-old rats were almost 5 times greater than those of 0- to 3-day-old rats but similar to those of 6-month-old rats. However, the LVA:HVA ratio did not change with advancing age. As shown in panel B of figure 4, N-, P- and Q-type HVA current components increased rapidly over the 2 weeks following birth, whereas both L- and R-type components decreased. However, there were no further changes thereafter. According to Murchison and Griffith, slight increases in LVA current component were noted in basal forebrain neurons of 24-month-old (elderly) rats, but no changes in the HVA component were seen.[15]

Effects of organic calcium antagonists on LVA and HVA calcium channels

The effects of calcium antagonists on LVA calcium channels were examined in acutely dissociated hippocampal CA1 pyramidal neurons immersed in an external solution containing Ca^{2+} 2.5 mM. LVA calcium currents were evoked by a 300 ms step depolarisation to –40 mV from a holding potential of –90 mV every second. All currents were normalised to that induced by a test pulse without calcium antagonists. The half-inhibition doses (IC_{50} values) were 2×10^{-8} M for flunarizine, 1.7×10^{-7} M for nicardipine, 8×10^{-7} M for nicergoline, 9×10^{-6} M for verapamil and 2.3×10^{-5} M for diltiazem (fig. 5 (A)).

Hypoxic-ischaemic neuronal injury is linked to the excessive activation of postsynaptic NMDA receptors, which may be the predominant route of lethal Ca^{2+} entry.[16] This is related to the NMDA-gated channel being highly permeable to both Na^+ and Ca^{2+}.[17] Voltage-gated LVA and HVA calcium channels can also be activated by membrane depolarisation. According to Choi, since the LVA calcium channel has a small conductance and is rapidly inactivated, this channel is unlikely to make a major contribution to net Ca^{2+} influx, whereas the L-type calcium channel, with its high conductance and slow inactivation, may contribute more to net Ca^{2+} influx.[16] However, in rat hypothalamic[6] and hippocampal neurons,[18] flunarizine, nifedipine, nicardipine and nimodipine inhibited both LVA and L-type HVA calcium channels, and the inhibitory effect of flunarizine was stronger in LVA calcium channels than in HVA calcium channels. In *in vivo* studies, these calcium antagonists ameliorated ischaemic neurological damage in various animal models.[19,20] Interestingly, when rabbits were subjected to l5 min periods of stagnant cerebral hypoxia, the intravenous administration of phenytoin (an anticonvulsant) afforded significant protection to neurons on the hippocampus and in the dentate nucleus.[21] Phenytoin firmly blocks LVA calcium channels in cultured rat hippocampal neurons[22] and in freshly dissociated rat hippocampal CA1 pyramidal neurons[18] at a concentration showing little effect on L-type calcium channels. In addition, LVA calcium conductance seems to play an important role by contributing to spontaneous depolarisation waves and rebound excitation in the brain. These observations suggest that the LVA calcium channel is strongly linked to Ca^{2+}-mediated neurotoxicity.

The effect of nilvadipine, a dihydropyridine derivative, on HVA calcium channels was investigated in freshly dissociated rat frontal cortical neurons. HVA barium current in neurons immersed in external solution with Ba^{2+} 5 mM was elicited with a depolarising pulse to 0 mV from a holding potential of –50 mV. The inhibitory action of nilvadipine on HVA barium current reached steady state within 2 min of adding the drug. Nilvadipine caused a slight inhibition of the current at a concentration of 10^{-9} M (see panel B(b) of fig. 5). Further increases in the concentration of nilvadipine reduced the HVA barium current in a concentration-dependent manner without affecting the current–voltage relationship, although the inhibitory effect reached

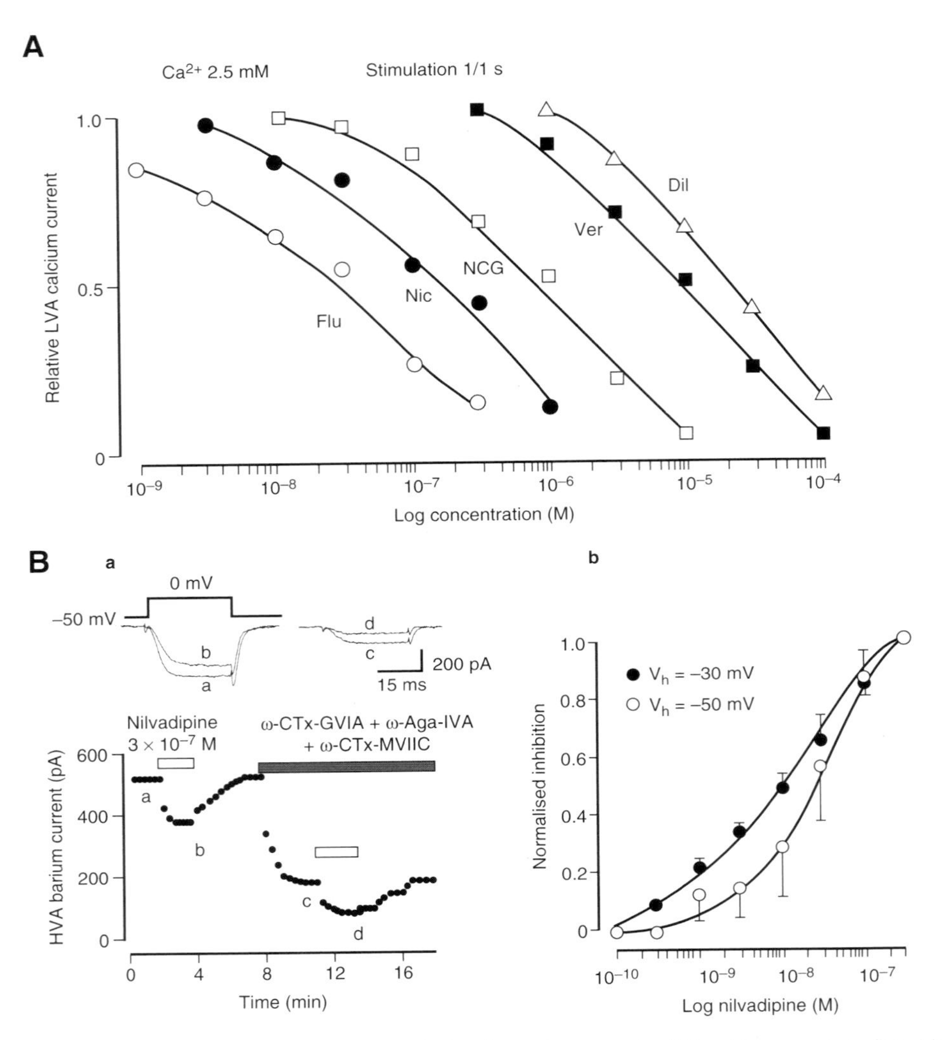

Fig. 5. Effects of organic calcium antagonists. A) Blockade of low-voltage-activated (LVA) calcium currents by flunarizine (Flu), nicardipine (Nic), nicergoline (NCG), verapamil (Ver) and diltiazem (Dil). Hippocampal CA1 pyramidal neurons immersed in external solution with Ca^{2+} 2.5 mM were stimulated by a test pulse of 300 ms duration to –40 mV from a holding potential of –90 mV every second. B) (a) Selective inhibition by nilvadipine of L-type high-voltage-activated (HVA) calcium channels in frontal cortical neurons of 2-week-old rats. HVA barium current was evoked by a depolarising step to 0 mV from a holding potential of –50 mV every 20 s. The effect of nilvadipine was examined with or without ω–CTx-GVIA 3×10^{-6} M, ω–Aga-IVA 2×10^{-8} M and ω–CTx-MVIIC 3×10^{-6} M; (b) voltage-dependent inhibition by nilvadipine of L-type HVA barium current. The responses of L-type calcium channel inhibited by each concentration of nilvadipine were normalised to the responses induced by the maximal effective concentration of nilvadipine.

saturation at concentrations above 3×10^{-7} M. The maximum inhibition was 22.6 ± 4.2% (n=5) of the total HVA barium current. The ability of dihydropyridines to block calcium channels has been reported to be affected strongly by depolarisation of the holding potential.[23] In this experiment, therefore, the effect of holding potential change on the concentration–response relationship for nilvadipine was examined. Panel B of figure 5 shows the relationship between the concentration of nilvadipine and the relative L-type HVA barium current evoked by depolarising pulses to 0 mV from holding potentials of –50 mV and –30 mV. IC_{50} values were 3.4×10^{-8} M at a holding potential of –50 mV and 1.9×10^{-8} M at –30 mV.

In order to assess the proportion of nilvadipine-sensitive calcium current in each calcium channel, the following experiment was carried out. The percentage inhibition of control HVA barium current produced by a maximally effective concentration of nilvadipine was measured before and after pretreatment with the L-type calcium channel blocker nicardipine. Nilvadipine inhibited the HVA barium current by 21.6 ± 4.8% before the application of nicardipine, but by 2.6 ± 1.1% after the addition of nicardipine. Nilvadipine also produced a 16.2 ± 2.0% inhibition in the presence of ω–CTx-GVIA 3×10^{-6} M, ω–Aga-IVA 2×10^{-8} M and ω–CTx-MVIIC 3×10^{-6} M, which comprehensively block N-, P- and Q-type calcium channels. Moreover, BAYK8644 (10^{-7} M), a dihydropyridine agonist, enhanced the HVA barium current by 25.0 ± 7.1% (n=4) and slowed the tail currents under repolarisation. Nilvadipine also inhibited the BAYK8644-enhanced tail currents in all neurons used. These findings suggest a selective inhibitory action of nilvadipine on L-type calcium channels in rat CNS neurons.

The pharmacological characterisation and distribution of five types of HVA calcium channel have important therapeutic and pathophysiological implications. Organic calcium antagonists, already used widely in cardiovascular illness for their vasodilatory and antiarrhythmic actions, have been investigated recently for their therapeutic activity in brain ischaemia.[24] Nimodipine, a dihydropyridine derivative, protected neurons from ischaemic damage not only by improving their blood supply but also by reducing the influx of Ca^{2+} into brain cells through voltage-sensitive calcium channels.[25] Nilvadipine also reduced in a dose-dependent manner infarct volumes following focal cerebral ischaemia in rats when administered immediately after an ischaemic insult,[26] and reduced the infarct size produced by middle cerebral artery occlusion in spontaneously hypertensive rats.[27] Therefore, Ca^{2+} blockade by dihydropyridine derivatives in L-type calcium channels may contribute to an amelioration of ischaemic brain damage, as well as an improvement in cerebral blood flow.

Conclusion

This study demonstrates that LVA calcium channels and at least five pharmacologically distinct HVA calcium channels exist in most rat CNS neurons, with the exception of cerebellar Purkinje cells. These LVA and HVA calcium channels (including their subtypes) are distributed differentially among the various CNS regions. The pharmacological diversity of these channels and their heterogeneous distribution in the CNS appear relevant in the development of new and region-specific pharmacological agents for clinical use.

References

1. Rhee JS, Ishibashi H, Akaike N. Preclinical and clinical strategies for the treatment of neurodegenerative, cerebrovascular and mental disorders. Five different types of Ca^{2+} channels in rat CNS neurons. Int Acad Biomed Drug Res 1996; 11: 116–23

2. Snutch TP, Leonard JP, Gilbert MM, et al. Rat brain expresses a heterogeneous family of calcium channels. Proc Natl Acad Sci U S A 1990; 87: 3391–5
3. Takahashi K, Wakamori M, Akaike N. Hippocampal CA1 pyramidal cells of rats have four voltage-dependent calcium conductances. Neurosci Lett 1989; 104: 229–34
4. Akaike N, Harata N. Nystatin perforated patch recording and its applications to analyses of intracellular mechanisms. Jpn J Physiol 1994; 44: 433–73
5. Nakagawa T, Shirasaki T, Wakamori M, et al. Excitatory amino acid response in isolated nucleus tractus solitarii neurons of the rat. Neurosci Res 1990; 8: 114–23
6. Akaike N, Kostyuk PG, Osipchuk YV. Dihydropyridine-sensitive low-threshold calcium channels in isolated rat hypothalamic neurones. J Physiol (Lond) 1989; 412: 181–95
7. Khateb A, Fort P, Serafin M, et al. Rhythmical bursts induced by NMDA in guinea-pig cholinergic nucleus basalis neurons *in vitro*. J Physiol 1995; 487: 623–38
8. Hablitz JJ, Johnston D. Endogenous nature of spontaneous bursting in hippocampal pyramidal neurons. Cell Mol Neurobiol 1981; 1: 325–34
9. Mintz IM, Adams ME, Bean BP. P–type calcium channels in rat central and peripheral neurons. Neuron 1992; 9: 85–95
10. Hillyard DR, Monje VD, Mintz IM, et al. A new conus peptide ligand for mammalian presynaptic Ca^{2+} channels. Neuron 1992; 9: 69–77
11. Llinas R, Sugimori M, Hillman DE, et al. Distribution and functional significance of the P-type voltage-dependent Ca^{2+} channels in the mammalian central neurons system. Trends Neurosci 1992; 15: 351–5
12. Vardi G, Mori Y, Mikala G, et al. Molecular determinants of Ca^{2+} channels function and drug action. Trends Pharmacol Sci 1995; 16: 43–9
13. Zhang JF, Randall AD, Ellinor PT, et al. Distinctive pharmacology and kinetics of cloned neuronal Ca^{2+} channels and their possible counterparts in mammalian CNS neurons. Neuropharmacology 1993; 32: 1075–88
14. Akaike N, Rhee JS, Jin YH, et al. GABA: receptors, transporters and metabolism. In: Tanaka C, Bowery NG, editors. Ontogenic changes of $GABA_A$ function of the rat Meynert neuron. Basle: Birkhäuser Verlag, 1996: 201–7
15. Murchison D, Griffith WH. Low-voltage-activated calcium channel currents increase in basal forebrain neurons from aged rats. J Neurophysiol 1995; 74: 876–87
16. Choi DW. Calcium-mediated neurotoxicity. Trends Neurosci 1988; 11: 465–9
17. MacDermott AB, Mayer ML, Westbrook GL, et al. NMDA-receptor activation increases cytoplasmic calcium concentration in cultured spinal cord neurones. Nature 1986; 321: 519–22
18. Takahashi K, Akaike NJ. Calcium antagonist effects on low-threshold (T-type) calcium current in rat hippocampal CA1 pyramidal neurons. J Pharmacol Exp Ther 1991; 256: 169–75
19. Alps BJ, Calder C, Wilson AD. Comparative effects of nicardipine, flunarizine, lidoflazine and nimodipine against ischaemic injury in the hippocampus of the Mongolian gerbil. Br J Pharmacol 1988; 93: 877–83
20. Beck T, Nuglish J, Sauer D, et al. Effects of flunarizine on post-ischemic blood flow, energy metabolism and neuronal damage in the rat brain. Eur J Pharmacol 1988; 158: 271–4
21. Cullen JP, Aldrete JA, Jankovsky L, et al. Protective action of phenytoin in cerebral ischaemia. Anesth Analg 1979; 58: 165–9
22. Yaari Y, Hamon B, Lux HD. Development of two types of calcium channels in cultured mammalian hippocampal neurons. Science 1987: 235: 680–2
23. Bean BP. Nitrendipine block of cardiac calcium channels: high-affinity binding to inactivated state. Proc Natl Acad Sci U S A 1984; 8l: 6388–92
24. Endersby CA, Brown EG, Perelman MS. Safety properties of lacidipine: a review of clinical data. J Cardiovasc Pharmacol 1991; 17 Suppl. 4: S45–7
25. Scriabine A, Schuurman T, Traber J. Pharmacological basis for the use of nimodipine in central nervous system disorders. FASEB J 1989; 3: 1799–806
26. Kawamura S, Yasui N, Shirasawa M, et al. Effects of a Ca^{2+} entry blocker (nilvadipine) on acute focal cerebral ischemia. Exp Brain Res 1991; 83: 434–8
27. Shiino A, Matsuda M, Susumu T, et al. Effects of the calcium antagonist nilvadipine on focal cerebral ischaemia in spontaneously hypertensive rats. Surg Neurol 1991; 35: 105–10

Low-threshold fast-inactivating calcium channels in dendrites of cerebellar Purkinje cells

Jean-Louis Bossu,[1] Didier Mouginot,[2] Jean-Luc Dupont,[1] Anne Feltz,[1] Beat H. Gähwiler[3]

[1] Laboratoire de Neurobiologie Cellulaire, Centre National de la Recherche Scientifique, Centre de Neurochimie, Strasbourg, France; [2] Health Science Center, Neuroscience Research Group, Calgary, Alberta, Canada; [3] Brain Research Institute, University of Zurich, Zurich, Switzerland

Introduction

The means by which synaptic information is transmitted from synaptic contacts to the site of spike generation, usually located at the axon hillock, is not completely understood. This holds true particularly for nerve cells exhibiting extensive dendritic arborisations. Recently, Stuart et al. have shown that in neocortical pyramidal cells a regenerative process appears to prevent the expected decremental propagation of synaptic potentials along the dendrites.[1] (For a review, see Stuart et al.[2]) In the complex dendritic trees of Purkinje cells, a regenerative electrical signal is provided by P-type calcium channels.[3] Because this signal has a high threshold, it is probably involved in the generation of dendritic Ca^{2+} spikes.[4] A non-inactivating sodium current, localised at or near the somata,[4,5] is activated at a low threshold and may be important in translating slow dendritic events into axonal action potentials. In addition, we describe the presence of a low-threshold fast-inactivating calcium current, specifically localised with a high density in dendrites of Purkinje cells. This current may also participate in the maintenance of the amplitude and duration of excitatory potentials along dendrites. This calcium current can be recorded in isolation, after run-down of the high-threshold calcium current as a result of whole-cell recordings in the absence of internal ATP[6] or during application of toxins that block P-/Q-type calcium currents, the dominant high-threshold calcium currents observed in this cell type.[7–9] Furthermore, we show that the amplitude of the transient current is small in Purkinje cells maintained in cell culture conditions, whereas it is large in those that form part of an organised synaptic network (as is the case in organotypic slice cultures). Some of these results have been published previously.[10–12]

Materials and methods

Dissociated cell cultures

The procedures for producing primary cerebellar cell cultures and for the morphological identification of Purkinje cells have been described previously.[10] Dendritic calcium currents and channels were recorded at room temperature using the whole-cell recording and cell-attached recording configurations.

For macroscopic calcium current recordings, the bath solution contained choline Cl 130 mM, TEAC 7.5 mM, $CaCl_2$ 10 mM, HEPES-TRIS 5 mM and glucose 10 mM, and pH was 7.4. The pipette (internal) solution contained CsCl 120 mM, TEAC 20 mM, $MgCl_2$ 2 mM, EGTA/CsOH 11 mM, $CaCl_2$ 1 mM (pCa 8) and HEPES/CsOH 10 mM; pH was 7.2.

Single-channel calcium currents were recorded using an isotonic $BaCl_2$ solution in the pipette, with an isotonic KCl solution in the bath to bring the cell membrane potential to zero. The bath solution contained potassium gluconate 140 mM, EGTA/KOH 10 mM, $MgCl_2$ 2 mM and HEPES/KOH 20 mM; pH was 7.4. The pipette solution contained $BaCl_2$ 110 mM and HEPES/TRIS 10 mM, with pH being 7.4.

Membrane currents were amplified using an EPC7 (List Electronic, Darmstadt, Germany), digitised and stored on a video tape before off-line analysis using pCLAMP 6.0 software (Axon Instruments, Foster City, California, USA). Current traces were digitised at 2 and 10 kHz for the analysis of the macroscopic current and for single-channel recordings, respectively, filtered at 25% of the sampling frequency and leak-subtracted.

Organotypic slice cultures

Organotypic slice cultures were prepared from cerebella removed from 0- to 1-day-old rats and cultured as described previously.[13] Patch-clamp recordings were carried out under voltage-clamp conditions at room temperature in both whole-cell recording and cell-attached configurations with an Axopatch 200A amplifier (Axon Instruments, Foster City, California, USA).

For the whole-cell recording configuration, electrodes were filled with a solution containing HEPES 100 mM, TEAC 20 mM, $MgCl_2$ 2 mM, $CaCl_2$ 3 mM and EGTA 30 mM (pCa 8). The pH was adjusted to 7.2 with CsOH. To prevent the run-down of the high-threshold calcium currents, Mg^{2+}-ATP 2 mM and Mg^{2+}-GTP 0.5 mM were added in some experiments. The bath solution contained trichloroacetic acid (TCA) 120 mM, $CaCl_2$ 0.5 or 1 mM, $MgCl_2$ 3 mM, TEAC 20 mM, HEPES/CsOH 10 mM and phenol red 1%. The pH was adjusted to 7.4 with TRIS buffer (2.5 M). Macroscopic calcium currents were digitised at 10 kHz after leak-subtraction using pCLAMP 6.0 software before storage on a personal computer hard disk for off-line analysis.

For the experiments using the cell-attached recording configuration, electrodes were filled with a solution containing TEAC 120 mM, $CaCl_2$ 10 mM, $MgCl_2$ 2 mM, CsCl 1 mM, HEPES 10 mM and 4-aminopyridine 1 mM, with pH adjusted to 7.2 with a TRIS 2.5 M solution. The bath solution contained NaCl 137 mM, KCl 2.7 mM, $CaCl_2$ 2.8 mM, $MgCl_2$ 2 mM, Na_2CO_3 11.6 mM, NaH_2PO_4 0.4 mM, glucose 5.6 mM and tetrodotoxin 5×10^{-7} M. The pH was adjusted to 7.4 by bubbling a mixture of O_2 95% and CO_2 5% through the solution. Current traces were filtered at 10 kHz and digitised at 47.2 kHz before storage on video tape. For off-line analysis using the pCLAMP 6.0 software, data were sampled at 5 kHz, filtered with a cut-off frequency of 1 kHz and leak-subtracted.

Results

Recordings of voltage-dependent calcium currents from dendrites of Purkinje cells in dissociated cell cultures (fig. 1 (A)) and from somata of Purkinje cells in organotypic

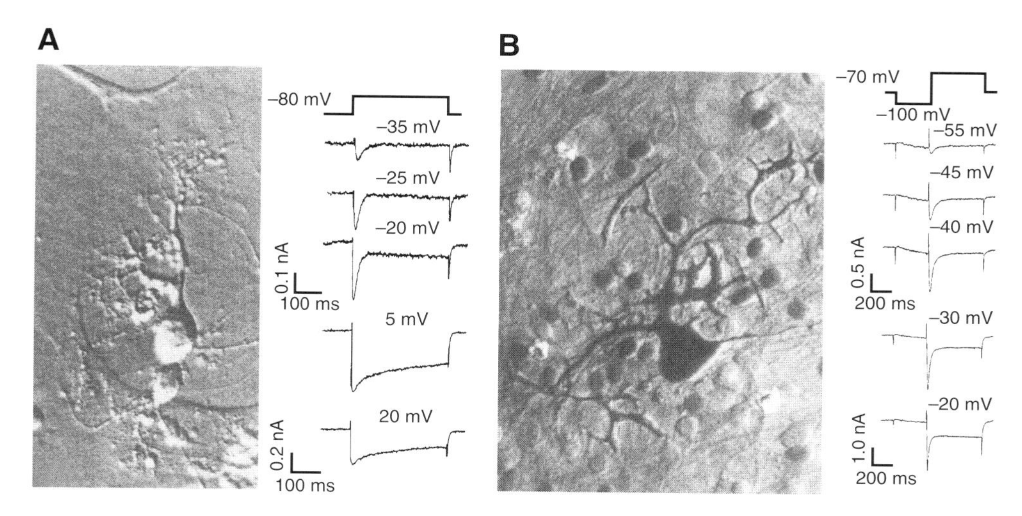

Fig. 1. Calcium currents of Purkinje cells (PCs) in (A) cerebellar cell and (B) organotypic slice cultures. A) (left) Cerebellar neuron in culture, tentatively identified as a PC. Dendritic process visualised with phase contrast microscopy (2 weeks in vitro*); (right) in the presence of $CaCl_2$ 10 mM, calcium currents were elicited by depolarising steps (500 ms) to the values indicated on each trace. Recordings from the dendrite in the whole-cell recording (WCR) configuration. B) (left) PC in an organotypic slice culture (3 weeks* in vitro*) immunocytochemically stained with an antibody raised against the 28 kDa calbindin protein; (right) with Ca^{2+} 0.5 mM in the bathing solution, depolarising steps (500 ms) to the values indicated on each trace elicited calcium currents that were recorded from the somata of PCs in the WCR configuration. NB: the low-threshold calcium currents were larger in PCs from organotypic slice cultures than from PCs dissociated in culture, even in the presence of lower external Ca^{2+} concentrations.*

slice cultures (see fig. 1 (B)) revealed at least two components that could be distinguished on the basis of their activation and inactivation properties. Low-threshold fast-inactivating calcium currents were elicited in cell-cultured Purkinje cells (voltage steps to potentials between –35 and –25 mV; see fig. 1 (A)) as well as in Purkinje cells in slice cultures (voltage steps to potentials between –55 and –40 mV; see fig. 1 (B)). A more sustained component was observed with voltage jumps to more depolarised potentials (see fig. 1 (A & B)).

The low-threshold fast-inactivating current was recorded in isolation at –25 mV in cell-cultured Purkinje cells or after elimination of the high-threshold component (through run-down or after application of the P-/Q-type calcium channel antagonists ω-Aga-IVA 200 nM or ω-CTx-MVIIC 5 μM) in Purkinje cells in slice cultures. This current reached maximum amplitudes of 230 ± 30 pA using extracellular Ca^{2+} 10 mM in cell-cultured Purkinje cells[10] and 690 ± 80 pA using extracellular Ca^{2+} 1 mM in slice-cultured Purkinje cells.[12] Comparison of these data indicates that the number of channels giving rise to the low-threshold fast-inactivating current is 30 times larger in slice-cultured Purkinje cells than in cell-cultured ones, assuming a 10-fold increase in current for a 10-fold increase in Ca^{2+} concentration.[14]

The isolated low-threshold fast-inactivating calcium current was further characterised in Purkinje cells in slice cultures. Its activation properties were determined by using step depolarisations to potentials between –65 and –15 mV after hyperpolarising prepulses to –100 mV to eliminate steady-state inactivation of the current (fig. 2 (A)).

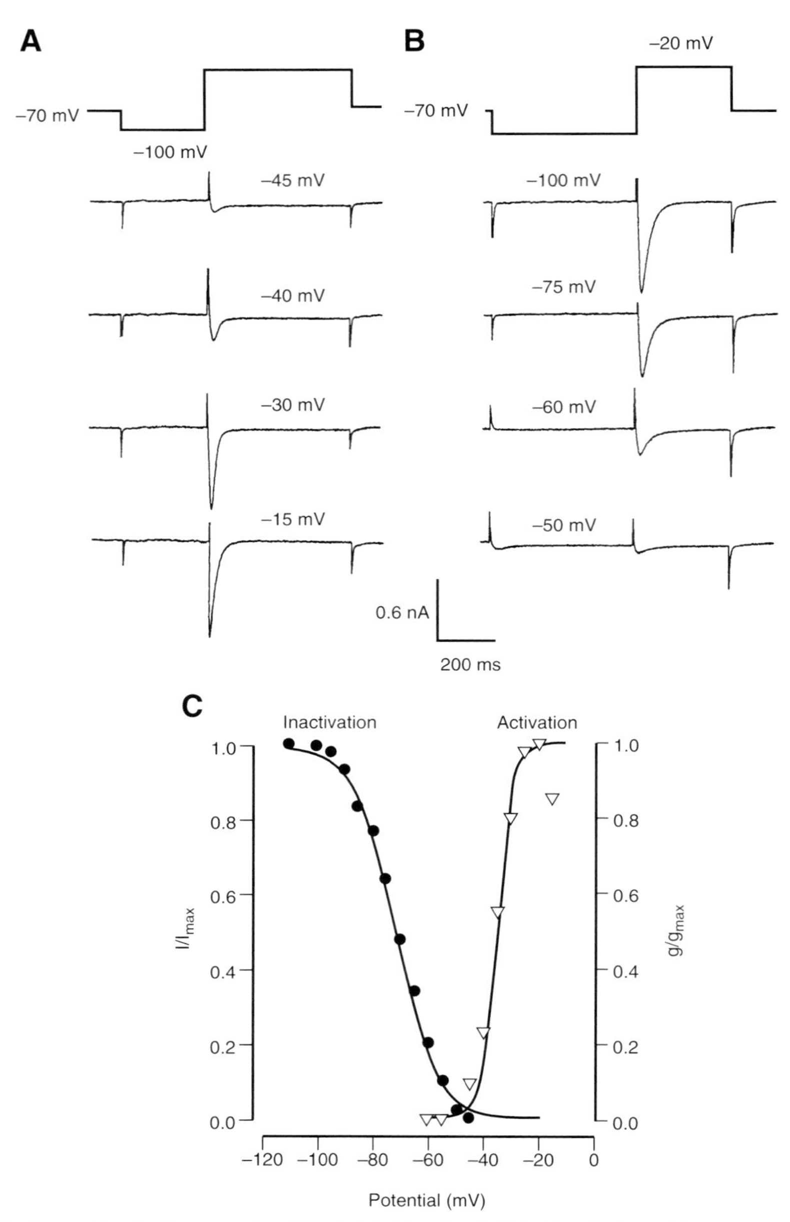

Fig. 2. Activation and inactivation properties of the isolated low-threshold fast-inactivating calcium current recorded from the somata of Purkinje cells in organotypic slice cultures. The fast-inactivating calcium current was recorded in the presence of Ca^{2+} 1 mM in the bath solution and was isolated after run-down of the high-threshold sustained current. A) Representative current traces obtained following an activation sequence where a prepulse to −100 mV (300 ms) was applied before depolarising voltage increments (500 ms) to the values indicated on the traces. B) Representative current traces obtained in the same cell during an inactivation sequence where a test potential (300 ms) giving rise to the maximal current amplitude was preceded by pulses (500 ms) stepping the membrane potential to the values indicated on the traces. C) Activation and inactivation curves for the same cell. Inactivation curve: peak amplitude of the inward current (I) was normalised to its maximal value (I_{max}) and plotted as a function of the holding potential. The continuous line was drawn according to a Boltzmann equation with half-maximal inactivation at −72 mV and a slope of 7.3 mV. Activation curve: normalised conductance (g/g_{max}, where $g = I/(V_{mem} - E_{Ca})$) was plotted as a function of the test potential. The continuous line was drawn according to a Boltzmann equation, with half-maximal activation at −35 mV and a slope of 3 mV.

The relative conductance as a function of the membrane potential was described with a Boltzmann equation (see fig. 2 (C); analysis of data from a single cell) with a potential giving rise to half-maximal activation of –35 mV and a slope factor of 3 (values obtained by averaging data from 20 cells: –51 mV and 4.6, respectively[12]). Steady-state inactivation properties were determined by measuring the peak amplitude of the current elicited from hyperpolarised and depolarised potentials (see fig. 2 (B)). The normalised current amplitude I/I_{max} is illustrated as a function of the holding potential (see fig. 2 (C); analysis of data from a single cell), and the data were best fitted with a Boltzmann equation with a potential giving rise to half-inactivation of –72 mV and a slope of 7.3 (average values obtained from 20 cells: –86 mV and 4.9, respectively[12]).

The low-voltage fast-inactivating calcium current was also characterised pharmacologically. Bath application of Cd^{2+} 10 μM reduced the current amplitude by 90 $\pm$ 2% (not illustrated), whereas Ni^{2+} 100 μM (fig. 3 (A)) and amiloride 250 μM (see fig. 3 (B)) reversibly reduced the current by only 19 $\pm$ 3% (n=5) and 53 $\pm$ 4% (n=5), respectively.[12]

The cell-attached configuration of the patch-clamp technique was used to localise the channels underlying the macroscopic low-threshold fast-inactivating current characterised in Purkinje cells from both types of culture (fig. 4). For recordings from cell-cultured Purkinje cells, Ba^{2+} 110 mM was used as the charge carrier. Channels with a mean conductance of 9.0 $\pm$ 0.7 pS that gave rise to a transient inward current were found at a low density in dendritic membranes (see fig. 4 (A)). For recordings from Purkinje cells in slice cultures, Ca^{2+} 10 mM was used as the charge carrier (see fig. 4 (B)). A channel with a mean conductance of 7 $\pm$ 1 pS (see fig. 4 (A, right-hand side)) was identified as the channel giving rise to the macroscopic fast-inactivating calcium current. A high density of these channels was found in 70% of dendritic recordings (n=10; see fig. 4 (B, middle)), whereas a lower density of channels was present in 25% of somatic recordings (n=20; see fig. 4 (B, left-hand side)). This type of channel activity was still recorded in the presence of the P-/Q-type calcium channel blocker ω-Aga-IVA.[12]

Discussion

In previous studies, the properties of high-threshold P-type calcium channels[3] and the presence of L-type calcium channels have been described in detail.[11] The latter channels were observed only with cell-attached recordings in proximal dendrites of Purkinje cells when the dihydropyridine calcium channel agonist BayK8644 had been added to the pipette solution. In this report, we demonstrate the existence of low-threshold transient calcium channels in Purkinje cells maintained under different culture conditions. The density of these calcium channels was clearly lower in cell-cultured Purkinje cells than in Purkinje cells in organotypic slice culture. Since fast-inactivating calcium channels have been observed in different types of culture, we will first examine whether they represent the same type of channel.

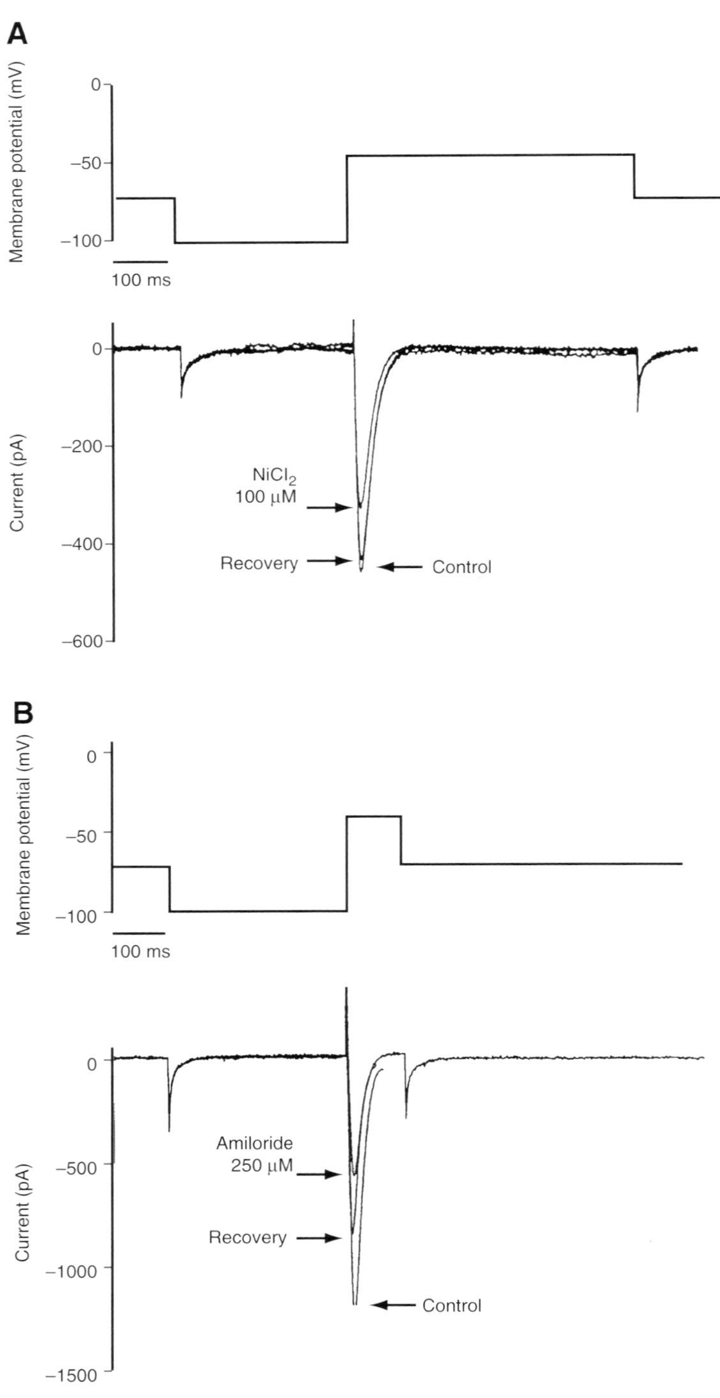

Fig. 3. Pharmacology of the isolated low-threshold fast-inactivating calcium current recorded in Purkinje cells in organotypic slice cultures. A) Bath application of $NiCl_2$ 100 μM reversibly reduced the amplitude of the fast-inactivating calcium current by about 20%. B) Bath application of amiloride 250 μM reversibly reduced the amplitude of the fast-inactivating calcium current by about 50%. In both cases, fast-inactivating calcium currents were isolated after run-down of the high-threshold sustained calcium current.

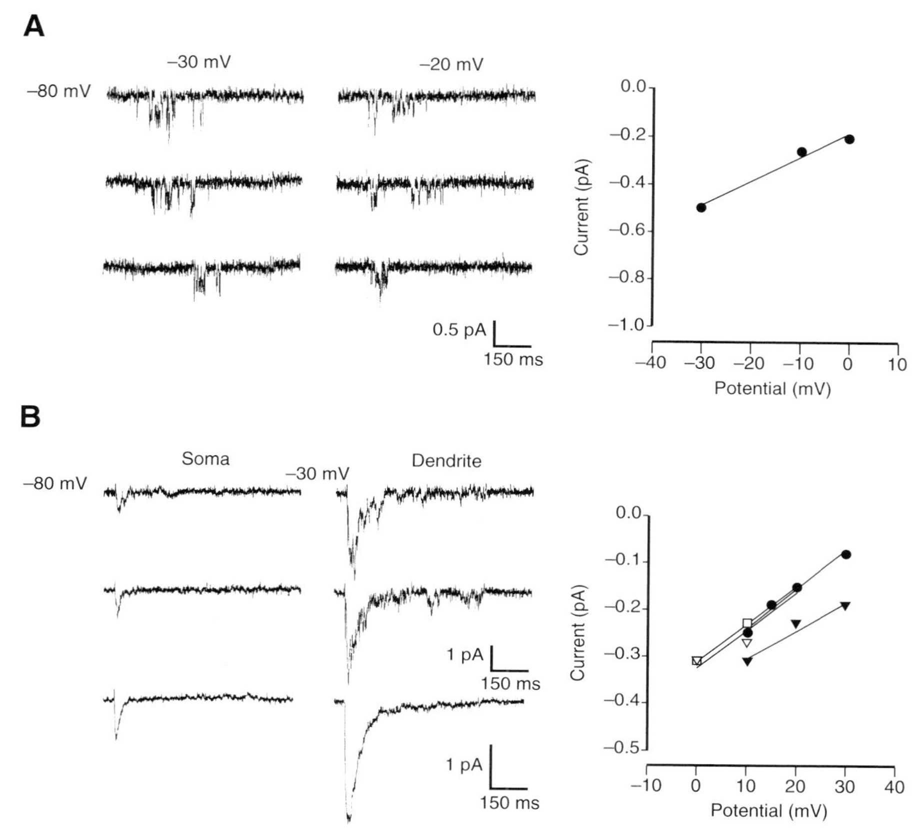

Fig. 4. Single-channel activity underlying the low-threshold fast-inactivating macroscopic calcium current recorded from (A) cell-cultured Purkinje cells (PCs) and (B) those in organotypic slice cultures, using the cell-attached configuration. A) Current traces obtained from the dendrite of a PC in dissociated cell culture during depolarising steps to (left) –30 mV and (centre) –20 mV applied from a holding potential of –80 mV in the presence of $BaCl_2$ 110 mM in the pipette solution. This channel gives rise to a fast-inactivating ensemble current (not illustrated because of its very small amplitude); (right) current–voltage curve showing the mean amplitude of the unitary currents when potential is varied. Linear regression yielded a slope conductance of 9 pS for this channel. B) Calcium channel activity recorded from the (left) somata or (centre) dendrites of PCs in organotypic slice cultures, using Ca^{2+} 10 mM as charge carrier; (right) current–voltage relationship for single channels recorded in four distinct patches. A linear fit yields slope conductances of 8.2 pS (●), 7.5 pS (□), 6.0 pS (▼) and 8 pS (▽).

Direct comparison of the biophysical characteristics of the low-voltage-activated (LVA) calcium currents that are present in Purkinje cells, either in cell or organotypic cultures, is made difficult by the different external divalent cation concentrations used in the two studies (Ca^{2+} 10 mM for dispersed Purkinje cells and Ca^{2+} 1 mM for Purkinje cells in slice culture). In both cases, a fast-inactivating current (time constant around 15 ms at –30 mV) was evoked by step depolarisations above –55 mV from a holding potential of –80 or –100 mV. This peaked for steps to –25/–30 mV and showed no run-down. Similarly, channels underlying this current, with conductances of 9 pS (in $BaCl_2$ 110 mM) and 7 pS (in $CaCl_2$ 10 mM), were recorded in Purkinje cells in dissociated and slice culture, respectively. All the characteristics were similar to those of the T-type calcium current/channel described initially in primary sensory neurons[14–17] and later in other CNS neurons (reviewed by Huguenard[18]). This LVA channel was found to be insensitive to nifedipine and resistant to P-/Q-type calcium channel blockers (ω-Aga-IVA and ω-CTx-MVIIC[12]). In addition, a 50% current reduction was observed after external application of amiloride 250 μM, as described for the T-type calcium current in sensory neurons.[19] However, the extent of blockade induced by Ni^{2+} and Cd^{2+} was more reminiscent of the properties of high-threshold calcium channels. We measured a 22% block caused by Cd^{2+} 50 μM in cell-cultured Purkinje cells[10] and a 90% block caused by Cd^{2+} 10 μM in Purkinje cells in slice cultures,[12] whereas Ni^{2+} 100 μM reduced this LVA calcium current by only 19% in slice cultures (but see also Ozawa et al.[20] and Huguenard and Prince[21]). In summary, our data suggest that the low-threshold fast-inactivating calcium current observed in Purkinje cells closely resembles the low-threshold fast-inactivating calcium current described in sensory neurons.

Antisera specific for the calcium pore-forming subunits bind to specific loci in Purkinje cells. Recent studies point to a particularly high density of α_{1A} and α_{1E} subunits in dendrites of Purkinje cells.[22–25] The α_{1A} subunit is probably responsible at least in part for the high-threshold-activated P-/Q-type calcium current[22] that can be activated in this cell type.[7–9] Since α_{1E} gives rise to a low-threshold calcium current in expression systems, it will be interesting to see whether the latter subunit is also involved in the generation of a low-threshold calcium current in Purkinje cells.

The low-threshold fast-inactivating calcium current is found at high density in dendrites of Purkinje cells. A dendritic localisation of T-type calcium channels has been previously reported in hippocampal neurons,[26] and more recently from experiments using isolated dendritic segments.[27] In solutions containing physiological Ca^{2+} concentrations, this current reached peak values of 500–1000 pA in Purkinje cells in cerebellar slice cultures. In view of its inactivation properties, however, it is probably activated only during the recovery phase that follows a complex discharge and resultant strong hyperpolarisation. This current may play a role in the dendritic propagation of electrical signals and may be involved in the development of Purkinje cells.

References

1. Stuart G, Sakmann B. Amplification of EPSPs by axosomatic sodium channels in neocortical pyramidal neurons. Neuron 1995; 15: 1065–76
2. Stuart G, Spruston N, Sakmann B, et al. Action potential initiation and backpropagation in neurons of the mammalian CNS. Trends Neurosci 1997; 20: 125–31
3. Usowicz MM, Sugimori M, Cherksey B, et al. P-type calcium channels in the somata and dendrites of adult cerebellar Purkinje cells. Neuron 1992; 9: 1185–99
4. Llinás R, Sugimori M. Electrophysiological properties of *in vitro* Purkinje cell dendrites in mammalian cerebellar slices. J Physiol (Lond) 1980; 305: 197–213
5. Gähwiler BH, Llano I. Sodium and potassium conductances in somatic membranes of rat Purkinje cells from organotypic cerebellar cultures. J Physiol (Lond.) 1989; 417: 105–22
6. Levitan IB. Phosphorylation of ion channels. J Membr Biol 1985; 87: 177–90
7. Llinás R, Sugimori M, Lin J-W, et al. Blocking and isolation of a calcium channel from neurons in mammals and cephalopods utilizing a toxin fraction (FTX) from funnel-web spider poison. Proc Natl Acad Sci U S A 1989; 86: 1689–93
8. Mintz IM, Adams ME, Bean BP. P-type calcium channels in rat central and peripheral neurons. Neuron 1992; 9: 85–95

9. Dupere JRB, Moya E, Blagbrough IS, et al. Differential inhibition of Ca^{2+} channels in mature rat cerebellar Purkinje-cells by sFTX-3.3 and FTX-3.3 Neuropharmacology 1996; 35: 1–11
10. Bossu J-L, Dupont J-L, Feltz A. Calcium currents in rat cerebellar Purkinje cells maintained in culture. Neuroscience 1989; 30: 605–17
11. Bossu J-L, Fagni L, Feltz A. Voltage-activated calcium channels in rat Purkinje cells maintained in culture. Pflugers Arch 1989; 414: 92–4
12. Mouginot D, Bossu JL, Gähwiler BH. Low-threshold Ca^{2+} currents in dendritic recordings from Purkinje cells in rat cerebellar slice cultures. J Neurosci 1997; 17: 160–70
13. Gähwiler BH. Organotypic monolayer cultures of nervous tissue. J Neurosci Methods 1981; 4: 329–42
14. Bossu J-L, Feltz A, Thomann JM. Depolarization elicits two distinct calcium currents in vertebrate sensory neurones. Pflugers Arch 1985; 403: 360–8
15. Carbone E, Lux HD. A low voltage-activated, fully inactivating Ca^{2+} channel in vertebrate sensory neurones. Nature 1984; 310: 501–2
16. Fedulova SA, Kostyuk P, Veselovsky NY. Two types of calcium channels in the somatic membrane of newborn rat dorsal root ganglion neurones. J Physiol (Lond) 1985; 359: 431–46
17. Nowycky MC, Fox AP, Tsien RW. Three types of neuronal calcium channels with different calcium agonist sensitivity. Nature 1985; 316: 440–3
18. Huguenard JR. Low threshold calcium currents in central nervous system neurons. Ann Rev Physiol 1996; 58: 329–48
19. Tang CM, Presser F, Morad M. Amiloride selectively blocks the low threshold (T) calcium channel. Science 1988; 240: 213–5
20. Ozawa S, Tsuzuki K, Iono M, et al. Three types of voltage-dependent calcium current in cultured rat hippocampal neurons. Brain Res 1989; 495: 329–36
21. Huguenard JR, Prince DA. A novel T-type current underlies prolonged Ca^{2+}-dependent burst firing in GABAergic neurons of rat thalamic reticular nucleus. J Neurosci 1992; 12: 3804–17
22. Stea A, Tomlinson WJ, Soong TW, et al. Localization and functional properties of a rat brain alpha 1A calcium channel reflect similarities to neuronal Q and P-type Ca^{2+} channels. Proc Natl Acad Sci U S A 1995; 91: 10576–80
23. Yokoyama CT, Westenbroek RE, Hell JW, et al. Biochemical properties and subcellular distribution of the neuronal class E calcium channel α_1 subunit. J Neurosci 1995; 15: 6419–32
24. Westenbroek RE, Sakurai T, Elliot EM, et al. Immunochemical identification and subcellular distribution of the α-1A subunits of the brain calcium channels. J Neurosci 1995; 15: 6403–18
25. Volsen SG, Day NC, McCormack AL, et al. The expression of neuronal voltage-dependent calcium channels in human cerebellum. Brain Res Mol Brain Res 1995; 34: 271–82
26. O'Dell TJ, Alger BE. Single channels in rat and guinea-pig hippocampal neurons. J Physiol (Lond) 1991; 436: 739–67
27. Kavalali T, Zhuo M, Bito H, et al. Dendritic Ca^{2+} channels characterized by recordings from isolated hippocampal dendritic segments. Neuron 1997; 18: 651–63

G2 and G3: two different R-type (toxin-resistant) calcium channels coexpressed in rat cerebellar granule cells

Angelita Tottene, Lia Forti, Alessandra Moretti, Daniela Pietrobon

Department of Biomedical Sciences and Consiglio Nazionale Ricerche Centre of Biomembranes, University of Padova, Padova, Italy

Introduction

A component of neuronal high-voltage-activated (HVA) calcium current resistant to the calcium channel inhibitors nimodipine, ω-CTx-GVIA, ω-Aga-IVA and ω-CTx-MVIIC was first described in rat cerebellar granule cells by Tsien and collaborators, who named it 'R type'.[1,2] The presence of a component of HVA calcium current resistant to the specific calcium channel inhibitors has subsequently been shown to be a property of many types of neuron.[3–7] However, its inactivation kinetics appear to be quite different in different neurons, which suggests the existence of a heterogeneous class of calcium channels resistant to the available inhibitors.

We have characterised at the single-channel level two different calcium channels resistant to dihydropyridines, ω-CTx-GVIA and ω-CTx-MVIIC, coexpressed in rat cerebellar granule cells, that we have termed 'G2' and 'G3'.[8,9] G2 and G3 can be considered as two novel R subtypes, if the term 'R type' is used to identify the class of calcium channel that shows resistance to the specific inhibitors available today. On the basis of their biophysical properties, classification as neither low-voltage-activated (LVA) calcium channels nor HVA calcium channels seems appropriate for the two R subtypes of cerebellar granule cell.

Methods

Cerebellar granule cells from 6- to 7-day-old Wistar rats were grown in primary culture after enzymatic and mechanical dissociation according to the procedure of Levi et al.[9,10] Experiments were performed on granule cells grown for 5–8 days *in vitro*, with the majority of experiments at 6–7 days *in vitro*.

Patch-clamp recordings and data analysis were performed as described by Forti et al.[8] and Tottene et al.[9] All single-channel recordings were obtained in the cell-attached configuration. The pipette solution contained $BaCl_2$ 90 mM, TEAC 10 mM, CsCl 15 mM and HEPES 10 mM, buffered to pH 7.4 with TEA OH. The bath solution was potassium gluconate 140 mM, EGTA 5 mM, L-glucose 35 mM and HEPES 10 mM, buffered to pH 7.4 with KOH. The high-potassium bath solution was used to zero the membrane potential outside the patch. In some experiments the bath solution contained (+)-(S)-202-791 0.5–1 μM. To assess the sensitivity of single channels to ω-CTx-MVIIC, the toxin was usually added to both the pipette solution and the divalent ion-free bath solution. All cells were incubated for at least 10 minutes in the presence of toxin before recording. For whole-cell recordings, cells were placed into a recording chamber with Tyrode solution and, after attainment of the whole-cell configuration, were perfused with an external recording solution containing $BaCl_2$ 5 mM, TEAC 147.5 mM and HEPES 10 mM (adjusted to pH 7.4 with TEA OH). The internal solution contained caesium methanesulphonate 100 mM, $MgCl_2$ 5 mM, HEPES 30 mM, EGTA 10 mM, ATP 4 mM, GTP 0.5 mM and cAMP 1 mM (adjusted to pH 7.4 with CsOH). Cytochrome C (0.1 mg/ml) was included in all recording solutions to block non-specific peptide binding sites.

Results

Table I and figure 1 summarise the single-channel biophysical and pharmacological properties of G2 and G3 and, for comparison, also show the properties of G1, the inactivating P subtype that together with the two R subtypes accounts for most of the dihydropyridine-insensitive calcium current in rat cerebellar granule cells in our

Table I. Single-channel properties of G1, G2 and G3 calcium channels (all values represent averages from at least three cell-attached patches (with Ba^{2+} 90 mM as charge carrier))[8]

Property	G2	G3	G1
Biophysical properties			
Unitary conductance (pS)	15	20	21
Unitary current at 0 mV (pA)	0.5	0.8	1.4
Average open time (ms)	1.2	1.0	0.8
Activation properties			
$V_{½}$ (mV)[a]	–22	–4	11
Threshold (mV)[b]	–40	–25	–10
Inactivation properties			
% (after 720 ms at V_t = 10 mV)[c]	46	n.d.	34
V_h of complete inactivation (mV)[d]	–50	–50	–30
% of nulls (V_h = –90 mV)[e]	66	70	48
Frequency of observations[f]	23	14	32
Pharmacological properties[g]			
Nimodipine (3 μM)	No	No	No
ω-CTx-GVIA (2 μM)	No[h]	No[h]	No[h]
ω-CTx-MVIIC (3 μM)	No[h]	No[h]	Yes
ω-Aga-IVA (50 nM)	No	No	Yes

[a] $V_{½}$ (half-action potential) was obtained by fitting average activation curves (plots of single-channel open probability, P_o, as a function of voltage) with a Boltzmann distribution function.

[b] Lowest voltage at which single-channel openings were observed during 720 ms test depolarisations delivered every 4 s from holding potentials of –90 mV.

[c] Calculated as fraction of inactivating sweeps with single-channel activity or as percentage decay of average single-channel current. V_t = test pulse voltage.

[d] Holding potential (V_h) at which single-channel open probability became zero during a series of test depolarisations delivered every 4 s for at least 2 min.

[e] Percentage of test depolarisations where P_o = 0.

[f] Percentage of cell-attached patches in which a given type of channel was observed. Multichannel patches in which channel type was uncertain were excluded from the statistics.

[g] Saturation concentrations of toxin and nimodipine indicated in parentheses.

[h] Irreversible blockade; these data do not exclude the reversible and partial blockade of some G channels by ω-CTx-GVIA and/or ω-CTx-MVIIC.

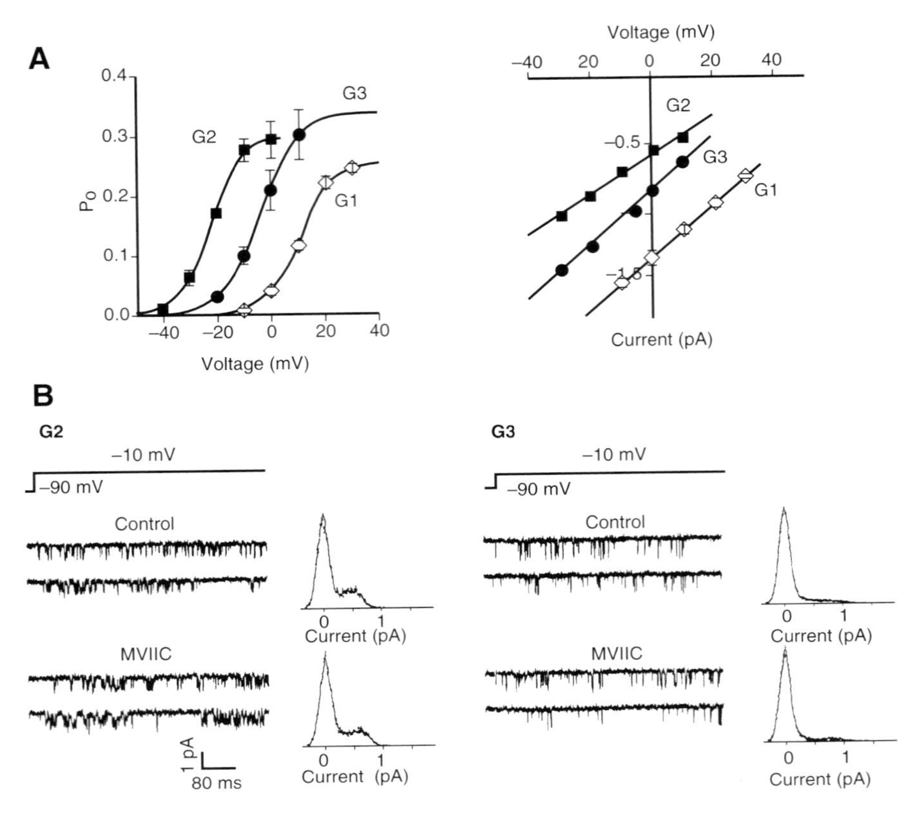

Fig. 1. Single-channel properties of G2, G3 and G1 calcium channels of rat cerebellar granule cells. Cell-attached recordings with Ba^{2+} 90 mM as charge carrier. Depolarisations were 720 ms and were delivered every 4 s from holding potentials of –80 to –100 mV. Records sampled and filtered at 5 and 1 KHz, respectively. A) Voltage-dependence of the open probability, P_o (left) and of the unitary current (right) of G2, G3 and G1 channels from single-channel patches. Open probability and unitary current values are averages. Slope conductances: 15 pS for G2; 20 pS for both G3 and G1. P_o values at a given voltage were obtained by averaging the open probabilities measured in segments with activity in each sweep. B) Representative current traces and normalised current amplitude from all traces with activity of single G2 and G3 channels at –10 mV, in control conditions and with ω-CTx-MVIIC 3 μM after incubation with toxin 10 μM in the potassium gluconate bath solution.

primary cultures.[8,9] According to the frequency of observation in cell-attached patches, G2 is present in larger amounts than G3. G2 has smaller single-channel conductance and unitary current, and it activates at more negative voltages than G3. When the change in surface potential related to the high Ba^{2+} concentration (90 mM) used in the single-channel recordings is taken into account, the activation threshold of G2 channels appears closer to that of LVA rather than HVA channels.[11] Both G2 and G3 activate at more negative voltages and have smaller unitary currents than G1. Steady-state inactivation of both G2 and G3 occurs at quite negative voltages, with complete inactivation at holding potentials of –50 mV and with a high fraction of null sweeps at –90 mV. Both G2 and G3 inactivate relatively slowly.[8] The decay of the average single-channel current after 720 ms depolarisations at +10 mV does not reach 50% for the most rapidly inactivating G2 channels. G1 channels inactivate at less negative voltages than G2 and G3 and more slowly than G2.

Figure 1 (B) shows that neither G2 nor G3 are blocked irreversibly by ω-CTx-MVIIC. Both G2 and G3 were still observed in cell-attached patches with ω-CTx-MVIIC 3 μM in the pipette after incubation of the neurons with 10 μM of toxin in the divalent ion-free bath recording solution, and their activities were similar to those in control patches. A similar protocol was effective in blocking single G1 channels, which were not observed in cell-attached patches after incubation with ω-CTx-MVIIC.[9] Since both G2 and G3 are insensitive to dihydropyridines and are not blocked irreversibly by ω-CTx-GVIA,[8] they can be considered as two novel R subtypes, with biophysical properties (especially of inactivation) different from those of the R-type current originally described by Zhang et al.[1]

Given the different voltage ranges for steady-state activation and inactivation of G1, G2 and G3 channels, the fractional contribution of the three channels to whole-cell current is expected to be quite different at different test depolarisations and different holding potentials. If, as suggested by our single-channel recordings, the large majority of the dihydropyridine-insensitive whole-cell barium current of rat cerebellar granule cells is attributable to influx of Ba^{2+} through G1, G2 and G3, then on the basis of their unitary properties and the frequency of observation of the different channels in cell-attached patches one predicts that most of the dihydropyridine-insensitive current carried by Ba^{2+} 5 mM at –30 mV should be through G2, with some contribution from G3 and a negligible contribution from G1 (cf. the predicted fractional contributions of G1, G2 and G3 shown in figure 2 (A)).[9] Alternatively, most of the dihydropyridine-insensitive current at +10 mV should be through G1, with a small contribution from G2 and G3. Figure 2 (B) shows that, as expected from the more negative voltage range of steady-state inactivation of G2 and G3 relative to G1, the inactivation curve obtained by depolarising at –30 mV was shifted towards more negative voltages than that obtained by depolarising at +10 mV. An intermediate steady-state inactivation was obtained at –10 mV, in which G2 + G3 and G1 channels are expected to contribute similar amounts of whole-cell current. The voltage range for steady-state inactivation of G2 channels, as obtained from whole-cell recordings by depolarising at –30 mV ($V_{½}$ = –90 ± 2 mV; n=3), is similar to that reported for LVA calcium currents in different CNS neurons.[11] An important practical implication of the negative voltage range of inactivation for G2 and G3 is that their contribution to whole-cell current is expected to be quite sensitive to the value of the membrane holding potential. Figure 2 (C) shows that the fractional reduction in dihydropyridine-insensitive whole-cell current, measured when the holding potential was changed from –90 to –60 mV, increased from 45% at –10 mV (where G1 and G2 + G3 channels should contribute comparable amounts of whole-cell current) to 80% at –30 mV (where almost all the current should be through G2 + G3).

Figure 2 (D) shows that in agreement with single-channel pharmacology, a large component of dihydropyridine-insensitive whole-cell current was not inhibited in the presence of nimodipine, ω-CTx-GVIA or ω-CTx-MVIIC (38 ± 1%; n=21) and that this 'resistant' component was similar in size to the component inhibited slowly and

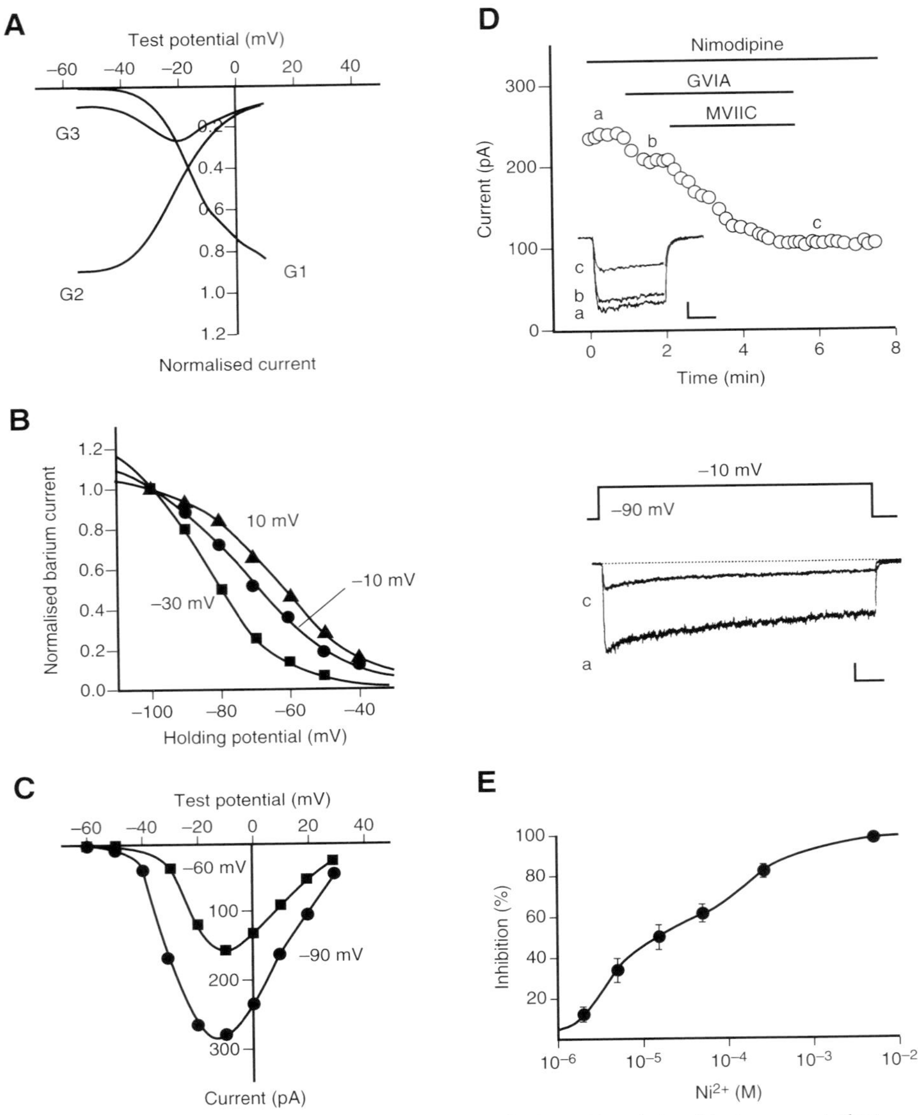

Fig. 2. Biophysical and pharmacological properties of dihydropyridine-insensitive whole-cell barium current of rat cerebellar granule cells. Whole-cell recordings with Ba^{2+} 5 mM as charge carrier in the continuous presence of nimodipine 3–5 μM to inhibit L-type calcium channels. Depolarisations were 56 ms and were delivered every 10 s. A) Fractional contributions to whole-cell current of G1, G2 and G3 at different test voltages, predicted from their single-channel properties on the assumption that the dihydropyridine-insensitive current was entirely attributable to G channels. Surface potential was also assumed to be 20 mV lower (i.e. more negative) at the lower Ba^{2+} concentration with whole-cell versus single-channel recordings [9]. B) Peak normalised barium current as a function of holding potential (V_h) at three test voltages (V_t): –30 mV, –10 mV and 10 mV. Cell U21B. Peak currents were measured after the attainment of the new steady-state after each change of V_h (i.e. after at least 1 min) and were normalised with respect to the current at V_h = –100 mV for each V_t. Fitting the steady-state inactivation curves with Boltzmann functions gave: $V_{½}$ = –85.5 mV, k = 11.5 mV at –30 mV; $V_{½}$ = –73.6, k = 15.3 at –10 mV and $V_{½}$ = –63.7, k = 13.7 at 10 mV. C) Peak barium current as a function of V_t at V_h = –90 mV and V_h = –60 mV. Cell T43E. D) Peak barium current versus time after ω-CTx-GVIA 1 μM and ω-CTx-MVIIC 3 μM were sequentially applied and then washed; inset: examples of traces taken at times indicated by a, b, c (scale bars: 50 pA, 20 ms). V_t = –10 mV, V_h = –90 mV. Cell T84D (top). Representative traces recorded during 720 ms depolarisations (from a different experiment: cell U22H; scale bars: 50 pA, 80 ms) (bottom). E) Dose–response curve for Ni^{2+} inhibition of the resistant current recorded in the presence of nimodipine 5 μM, ω-CTx-GVIA 1 μM and ω-CTx-MVIIC 5 μM. Data pooled from 5 cells.

irreversibly by ω-CTx-MVIIC, added after ω-CTx-GVIA, at −10 mV (43 ± 2%; n=20). The component inhibited irreversibly by ω-CTx-GVIA was on average 10 ± 2% (n=10). In agreement with the inactivation kinetics of single G2 and G3 channels, the resistant whole-cell current inactivated relatively slowly (on average 56 ± 4% at the end of 720 ms depolarisations at −10 mV; n=4) and displayed a biexponential time-course.

Figure 2 (E) shows that the resistant current at −10 mV consisted of at least two components with different sensitivities to Ni^{2+} block: one extremely sensitive and inhibited by Ni^{2+}, with an IC_{50} of 3.8 μM; the other less sensitive and inhibited by Ni^{2+}, with an IC_{50} of 153 μM. The two components contributed approximately equally to the resistant current, suggesting the possibility of a different sensitivity of G2 and G3 channels to Ni^{2+} block (but see Zamponi et al. for an alternative possibility[12]).

Discussion

By showing that both G2 and G3, two of the three novel non-L-, non-N-type calcium channels previously characterised in rat cerebellar granule cells,[8] are not blocked by ω-CTx-MVIIC, we have established the existence of different native (non-LVA) calcium channels that are resistant to the available specific calcium channel inhibitors.[9] Both G2 and G3 have biophysical properties different from those of the R-type current originally described by Tsien and collaborators.[1,2] Following on from the nomenclature of L-type, N-type and P-type calcium channels, which has evolved from the identification of a channel with specific biophysical properties to the subsequent identification of a heterogeneous class of calcium channels sharing sensitivity to dihydropyridine drugs, ω-CTx-GVIA and ω-Aga-IVA, respectively, we propose to use the term 'R type' to identify the heterogeneous class of calcium channels sharing resistance to dihydropyridines, ω-Aga-IVA and ω-CTx-MVIIC.[9] Thus, G2 and G3 can be considered as two novel R subtypes, coexpressed in rat cerebellar granule cells. They differ mainly in single-channel conductance and unitary current and in voltage range for activation (see table I and fig. 1). Given the biphasic dose–response curve for Ni^{2+} block of the whole-cell current resistant to nimodipine, ω-CTx-GVIA and ω-CTx-MVIIC, they might differ also in Ni^{2+} sensitivity, which suggests that a relatively high Ni^{2+} sensitivity may not be a general property of all R subtypes.

With respect to the P subtype G1, both R subtypes G2 and G3 are characterised by a lower threshold for activation and by steady-state inactivation at more negative voltages (see table I). A lower threshold for activation and a more negative voltage range for steady-state inactivation of R-type whole-cell calcium current with respect to N and P types has been observed in other neurons.[3–5,13,14] On the other hand, the biophysical properties of both G2 and G3 appear quite different from those of the R-type channel recently characterised in dendrites of hippocampal CA1 neurons, since the latter activate and inactivate at much more positive voltages and inactivate more rapidly during a test depolarisation.[15] Both G2 and G3 inactivate relatively slowly, in agreement with the rather slow inactivation reported for R-type current in sympathetic and cortical neurons,[5,14] and in contrast with the fast inactivation reported for the R-type current described originally in cerebellar granule cells (in a minority of granule cells we have also observed a small component inactivating rapidly, as reported by Zhang et al.[1]).[1,2] These differences in kinetics of R-type currents in different systems suggest further heterogeneity of R-type calcium channels.

Classification as neither LVA nor HVA calcium channels appears appropriate for the two R subtypes of cerebellar granule cells, especially for G2. The quite negative voltage range for steady-state inactivation of G2 channels is rather similar to that reported for LVA calcium currents in different CNS neurons.[5] The threshold for activation of G2 channels, although less negative than that reported in most neurons for LVA channels, is closer to that of LVA than to that of HVA calcium channels. On the other hand, the time-course of inactivation of G2 is much slower than that of most LVA channels, which completely inactivate in 50–300 ms, and the single-channel conductance of G2 is almost twice that of LVA channels. Unitary currents and conductance and, in particular, the voltage range for activation of G2 and G3 lie between those of LVA and HVA channels, with values closer to those of LVA for G2 and to those of HVA for G3.

Functional diversity of native R-type calcium channels is consistent with the widely varying biophysical properties (especially of inactivation) reported for α_{1E} coexpressed with different β subunits.[16–18] α_{1E} produces calcium channels that are insensitive to blockers of L-, N- and P-/Q-type channels. With respect to other cloned α_1 subunits, recombinant α_{1E} channels are characterised in general by lower thresholds for activation, by higher sensitivity to Ni^{2+} and by smaller single-channel conductance and unitary current.[12,16–20] In contrast with the other cloned calcium channels that show a larger unitary conductance for Ba^{2+} than for Ca^{2+} ions, α_{1E} channels (like most LVA channels) have similar unitary conductance for the two divalent ions.[20] However, they have some properties that distinguish them from the various LVA calcium channels, such as relatively slow inactivation, rapid deactivation and unitary conductance and current.[11] According to our definition, α_{1E} encode R-type calcium channels. However, it remains unclear if all R subtypes are encoded by α_{1E}.
G2 appears to be a good candidate as a native R-type channel encoded by α_{1E}, given that many of its biophysical properties and, in particular, its conductance and unitary currents are quite similar to those reported for recombinant α_{1E} channels.

The threshold for activation of G2 channels is sufficiently low that they are expected to be activated by subthreshold excitatory postsynaptic potentials (EPSPs), as recently shown for LVA channels in dendrites of hippocampal and cortical neurons.[21,22] Moreover, given their steady-state inactivation properties, their contribution to EPSP- or action potential-evoked calcium transients is expected to be strongly dependent on previous hyperpolarisation or prolonged depolarisation of the neuronal membrane. Thus, G2 channels may have a potentially important role in the generation of Ca^{2+} spikes, in synaptic integration and in postsynaptic forms of plasticity known to involve Ca^{2+} influx.

Acknowledgements

The financial support of Telethon-Italy (grant nos. 392 and 720) to D.P. is gratefully acknowledged. This work was partly supported also by grants from the Regione del Veneto (Giunta Regionale-Ricerca Sanitaria Finalizzata-Venezia-Italia) and the Italian Research Council (CNR) Target Project 'Aging' to D.P. We thank Drs J.R. Bell and L. Nadasdi of Neurex Corporation for providing ω-CTx-MVIIC (SNX-230).

References

1. Zhang JF, Randall AD, Ellinor PT, et al. Distinctive pharmacology and kinetics of cloned neuronal Ca^{2+} channels and their possible counterparts in mammalian CNS neurons. Neuropharmacology 1993; 32: 1075–88
2. Randall A, Tsien RW. Pharmacological dissection of multiple types of Ca^{2+} channel currents in rat cerebellar granule neurons. J Neurosci 1995; 15: 2995–3012
3. Bargas J, Howe A, Eberwine J, et al. Cellular and molecular characterization of Ca^{2+} currents in acutely isolated, adult rat neostriatal neurons. J Neurosci 1994; 14: 6667–86
4. Eliot LS, Johnston D. Multiple components of calcium current in acutely dissociated dentate gyrus granule neurons. J Neurophysiol 1994; 72: 762–77
5. Lorenzon NM, Foehring RC. Characterization of pharmacologically identified voltage-gated calcium channel currents in acutely isolated rat neocortical neurons. I. Adult neurons. J Neurophysiol 1995; 73: 1430–42
6. Penington NJ, Fox AP. Toxin-insensitive Ca current in dorsal raphe neurons. J Neurosci 1995; 15: 5719–26
7. McDonough SI, Swartz KJ, Mintz IM, et al. Inhibition of calcium channels in rat central and peripheral neurons by ω-conotoxin MVIIC. J Neurosci 1996; 16: 2612–23
8. Forti L, Tottene A, Moretti A, et al. Three novel types of voltage-dependent calcium channels in rat cerebellar neurons. J Neurosci 1994; 14: 5243–56
9. Tottene A, Moretti A, Pietrobon D. Functional diversity of P-type and R-type calcium channels in rat cerebellar neurons. J Neurosci 1996; 16: 6353–63
10. Levi G, Aloisi M, Ciotti M, et al. Autoradiographic localization and depolarization-induced release of amino acids in differentiating granule cells cultures. Brain Res 1984; 290: 77–86
11. Huguenard JR. Low-threshold calcium currents in central nervous system neurons. Annu Rev Physiol 1996; 58: 329–48
12. Zamponi GW, Bourinet E, Snutch TP. Nickel block of a family of neuronal calcium channels: subtype- and subunit-dependent action at multiple sites. J Membrane Biol 1996; 151: 77–90
13. Boland LM, Morrill JA, Bean BP. ω-Conotoxin block of N-type calcium channels in frog and rat sympathetic neurons. J Neurosci 1994; 14: 5011–27
14. Elmslie KS, Kammermeier PJ, Jones SW. Revaluation of Ca^{2+} channel types and their modulation in bullfrog sympathetic neurons. Neuron 1994; 13: 217–28
15. Magee JC, Johnston D. Characterization of single voltage-gated Na^+ and Ca^{2+} channels in apical dendrites of rat CA1 pyramidal neurons. J Physiol 1995; 487: 67–90
16. Soong TW, Stea A, Hodson CD, et al. Structure and functional expression of a member of the low voltage-activated calcium channel family. Science 1993; 260: 1133–6
17. Olcese R, Qin N, Schneider T, et al. The amino terminus of a calcium channel β subunit sets rates of channel inactivation independently of the subunit's effect on activation. Neuron 1994; 13: 1433–8
18. Wakamori M, Niidome T, Furutama D, et al. Distinctive functional properties of the neuronal BII (class E) calcium channel. Receptors Channels 1994; 2: 303–14
19. Williams ME, Marubio LM, Deal CR, et al. Structure and functional characterization of neuronal α1E calcium channel subtypes. J Biol Chem 1994; 269: 22347–57
20. Bourinet E, Zamponi GW, Stea A, et al. The α_{1E} calcium channel exhibits permeation properties similar to low-voltage-activated calcium channels. J Neurosci 1996; 16: 4983–93
21. Markram H, Sakmann B. Calcium transients in dendrites of neocortical neurons evoked by single subthreshold excitatory postsynaptic potentials via low-voltage-activated calcium channels. Proc Natl Acad Sci U S A 1994; 91: 5207–11
22. Magee JC, Johnston D. Synaptic activation of voltage-gated channels in the dendrites of hippocampal pyramidal neurons. Science 1995; 268: 301–7

Mg^{2+} block of LVA and HVA channels: a probe for studying calcium channel structure

E. Carbone,[1] H. Zucker,[2] H.D. Lux,[†] V. Carabelli,[1] V. Magnelli,[1] P. Baldelli,[1] G. Aicardi[1]*

[1] Dipartimento di Neuroscienze, Università degli Studi di Torino, Torino, Italy;
[2] Max-Planck-Institut für Psychiatrie, Planegg, Germany

** Present address: Dipartimento di Fisiologia, Bologna, Italy*
[†] From the late Hans Dieter Lux

Since monovalent cations are abundant in physiological media (Ca^{2+}:Na^{+} ≈ 1:100), high-threshold (high-voltage-activated; HVA) and low-threshold (low-voltage-activated; LVA) calcium channels must possess an inner pore structure capable of selecting Ca^{2+} against Na^{+}. The two channel families must also have significant structural similarities to account for their common property of permeability to Ca^{2+} when present at millimolar concentrations while allowing high fluxes of Na^{+} when Ca^{2+} is removed from the bath.[1–5] However, since HVA and LVA channels show different Ca^{2+}:Ba^{2+} permeability ratios (1:2 for HVA and 1:1 for LVA channels) and inverse sensitivity to Cd^{2+} and Ni^{2+} block, the pore structure forming the selectivity filter of the two channel families must differ in some critical amino acid region responsible for ion binding and ion transport. Usually, structure modifications responsible for changes in ion selectivity involve well-localised regions of the channel. Substitution of one or more amino acid residues at the channel mouth or in the pore wall may be sufficient to induce pronounced changes to channel permeability. The rat brain sodium channel, for instance, can become a calcium channel through site-directed substitution of a lysine in repeat III and/or an alanine in repeat IV by glutamic acid.[6] In addition, the permeability of the α_{1C} calcium channel subunit appears to be critically controlled by four glutamate residues in equivalent positions in the pore-lining region of repeats I–IV.[7] Thus, single or pairwise replacement of the four glutamates with glutamine or alanine abolishes micromolar Ca^{2+} block of sodium currents. This suggests that the four glutamates form the molecular array of a single rather than a double high-affinity binding site inside the pore.[8] The critical arrangement and charge coordination of the four glutamates may therefore be the locus responsible for Ca^{2+} binding, ion transport and block by heavy metal ions, properties that are characteristic of each calcium channel subtype.

Given that single amino acid replacements inside the pore region produce marked changes to the channel selectivity, the interaction of impermeant cations (Mg^{2+}, Ni^{2+} and Cd^{2+}) with open or closed channels may provide useful information about the charged groups at the regions critical for ion transport. In particular, comparing the action of impermeant cations on sodium and calcium currents may reveal both structural differences induced by the permeating ion and existing differences between distinct calcium channels. In contrast to heavy metal ions (Cd^{2+}, Ni^{2+}, Zn^{2+}), Mg^{2+} has a low affinity for classical Ca^{2+} chelators (EGTA, EDTA) and can be used to block both sodium and calcium currents since it is impermeable through T-type[4,5] and L-type channels.[9,10]

Here we show that Mg^{2+} blocks T-type and HVA (L- and N-type) channels of sensory neurons and that the voltage-dependence and affinity of Mg^{2+} for a site inside the channel changes significantly when the channel carries either Na^+ or Ca^{2+}. Block of sodium currents requires micromolar concentrations of Mg^{2+}, and relatively large positive potentials are needed to release the block. In contrast, calcium currents are only partially depressed by millimolar amounts of Mg^{2+}, and unblocking occurs at much lower positive potentials. Thus, while Mg^{2+} is unable to distinguish LVA from HVA channels, it displays a markedly different blocking capability for currents transported by divalent Ca^{2+} or monovalent Na^+ ions.

A high-affinity site for Ca^{2+} inside the pore region

LVA and HVA calcium channels allow the passage of Ca^{2+} when it is present in millimolar concentrations and, in Ca^{2+}-free media, conduct large sodium currents that are blocked by micromolar amounts of Ca^{2+}.[1–5] Thus, depending on its concentration, Ca^{2+} may act as a permeant or blocking cation for the same channel (fig. 1). In theory, permeant and blocking properties cannot be accounted for by occupancy of a single binding site by Ca^{2+} ions. These properties must reflect: (i) ion–ion repulsion at two sites close enough to allow effective ion interaction;[2,3] (ii) knock-on of bound ions at a single site (ion exchange);[11] or (iii) different arrangements of the negative pore

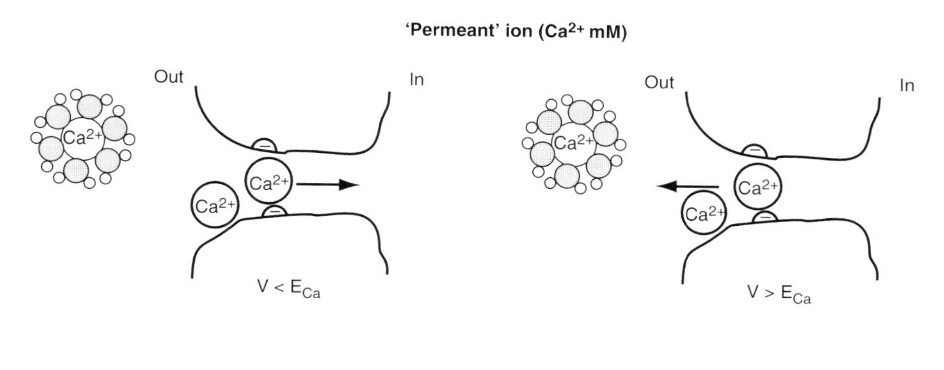

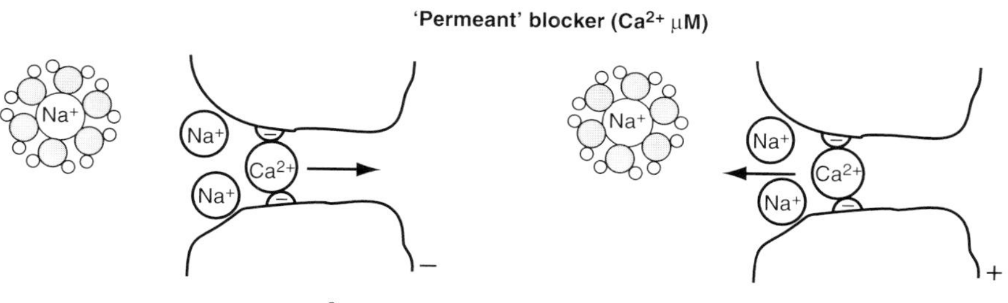

Fig. 1. Representation of dehydrated Ca^{2+} ions moving in or out of their binding site inside the channel in the presence of millimolar concentrations of extracellular Ca^{2+} (top) or with micromolar amounts of Ca^{2+} blocking Na^+ fluxes (bottom).

charges forming the binding site, depending on the permeant ion (ion–channel interaction).[5,12] In the latter case, repeated Ca^{2+} occupancy of the site at millimolar Ca^{2+} concentrations may favour Ca^{2+} permeation, while infrequent Ca^{2+} entry at micromolar Ca^{2+} concentrations may favour the persistence of the Ca^{2+} blocking conformation. If the Ca^{2+} concentration is sufficiently high, the permeable state allows Ca^{2+} ions to pass through the channel quickly enough to produce a measurable current (see fig. 1). In the blocking configuration, Ca^{2+} rests long enough at the binding site to impede the movement of Na^{+} ions through the channel and therefore decreases the sodium current. Location of the binding site inside the pore allows the electrical field to act fully on the blocking ion, resulting in a more rapid clearance of the channel passage with increased driving force. The bound ion is driven in or out of the pore with less block at either more negative or more positive voltages depending on the polarity of the electrical field. In other words, Ca^{2+} acts as a permeant blocker for Na^{+} ions through calcium channels (see fig. 1). Other permeant channel blockers include Cd^{2+},[9,13] Zn^{2+}[14] and the lanthanides,[15] all of which block barium current through L-type channels with high affinity at moderate voltages but have an enhanced exit rate at very negative potentials. Cd^{2+} block can also be attenuated by very positive voltages,[16] making the action of this ion more similar to that of Ca^{2+}. In contrast, the removal of an impermeant blocking ion such as Mg^{2+} is favoured only by strong positive potentials. Negative voltages enhance blockade by specifically limiting the movement of permeant ions towards the interior of the cell.

The ability of Ca^{2+} to act either as a permeant or a blocking ion is exemplified by recordings from the fast-inactivating T-type calcium channel of chick sensory neurons (fig. 2).[5] At concentrations of 4 mM, Ca^{2+} ions carry most of the observed inward current despite the higher extracellular Na^{+} concentration (120 mM). In Ca^{2+}-free media the current is carried by Na^{+} ions and has a 5-fold larger amplitude than the calcium current. This sodium current is markedly depressed by micromolar concentrations of Ca^{2+}. However, sodium current depression by Ca^{2+} appears to be strongly asymmetrical. Inward currents between –50 and 0 mV are more depressed than outward currents above 0 mV because of the voltage-dependent relief of Ca^{2+} block at positive potentials. Block relief may also occur at very negative potentials; independent of step depolarisations, there is a minor reduction of tail currents on return to –110 mV. Investigation of the voltage-dependence of block at various Ca^{2+} concentrations shows that maximal block occurs around 0 mV with Ca^{2+} 1–5 μM and that channels are largely unblocked at potentials positive to +60 mV and negative to –80 mV. At Ca^{2+} concentrations above 25 μM, the influence of voltage is strongly attenuated, and block removal becomes evident only at potentials positive to +100 mV.[5]

Mg^{2+}: a 'one-way' calcium channel blocker

The block of sodium currents through calcium channels by Mg^{2+} is very different from that produced by Ca^{2+}. Although Mg^{2+} ions reach the site responsible for Ca^{2+} block of sodium currents and Ca^{2+} passage, they do so by entering the channel from the external mouth. In contrast to Ca^{2+}, Mg^{2+} is unable to carry inward currents even

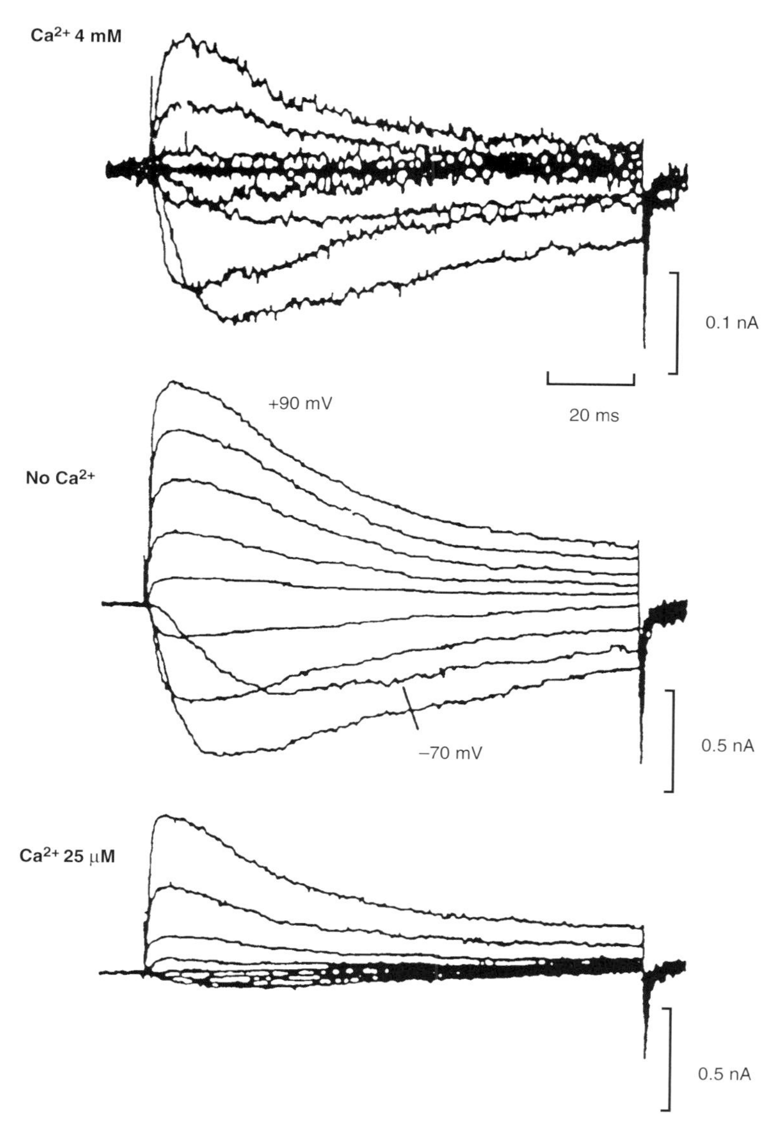

Fig. 2. Calcium and sodium currents through the LVA channel of a chick sensory neuron exposed to different concentrations of Ca^{2+}. Concentration of external and internal Na^+ was 120 mM in all recordings. Step depolarisations were between –70 and +90 mV with 20 mV voltage increments.[5]

when present at millimolar concentrations.[3–5] Block of sodium currents by Mg^{2+} is potent and unidirectional. Negative voltages are unable to remove the block, while positive potentials can drive Mg^{2+} ions out of the binding site, clearing the channel for Na^+ permeation. Unlike Cd^{2+}, Zn^{2+} and La^{3+}, which are able to cross the channel while blocking the passage of permeant ions,[9,13–15] Mg^{2+} is unable to enter the cell interior and therefore behaves as an impermeant blocker of calcium channels. These properties apply equally well to both the LVA and HVA channels of peripheral neurons (figs 3 and 4). Mg^{2+} at concentrations between 25 and 500 μM drastically reduces inward sodium currents through LVA and HVA channels, but at potentials

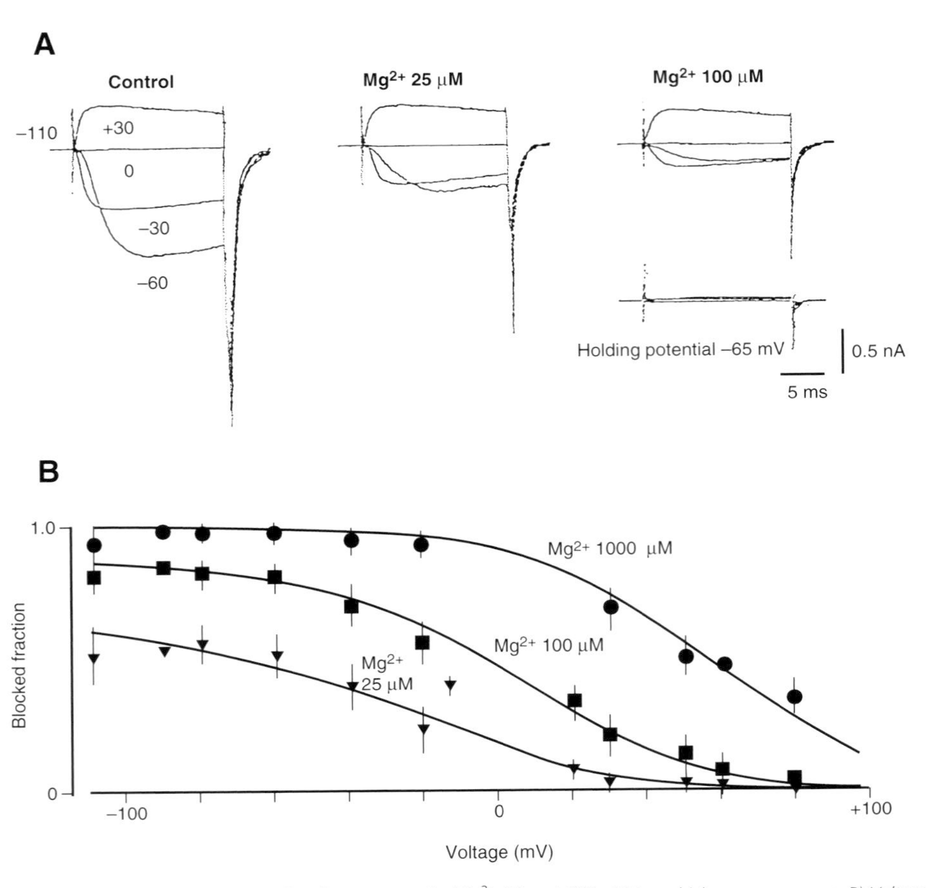

Fig. 3. A) Block of low-voltage-activated sodium currents by Mg^{2+} 25 and 100 μM in a chick sensory neuron. B) Voltage-dependence of sodium current block by Mg^{2+}. Data points represent averages of the blocked fraction of sodium currents collected from 9 cells.[5]

positive to +30 mV it has a weaker effect on the outward currents. Block is more severe on return to the negative holding potential (–110 mV and –60 mV for the LVA and HVA channels, respectively) where tail currents are significantly smaller than the corresponding current at +30 mV (see fig. 3) or at +90 mV (see fig. 4). This is indicative of a rapid reblock of open channels on returning to negative potentials. As Mg^{2+} at micromolar concentrations has little effect on the activation time-course of sodium currents (see fig. 4), most of the inhibitory action of Mg^{2+} derives from blockade of the channel rather than an effect on gating. Voltage shifts related to screening of surface charge or a direct effect of Mg^{2+} on channel gating are negligible at the low concentrations of Mg^{2+} required to block sodium currents.

A full description of the blocked fraction of LVA and HVA channels as a function of membrane potential and Mg^{2+} concentration is shown in figures 3 and 4. Comparison of the two sets of curves reveals a striking similarity in both the voltage-dependence and Mg^{2+} sensitivity (K_d = 30 μM for the LVA channel at –45 mV, and 38 μM for the HVA channel at –10 mV). Mg^{2+} block is maximal at the most negative potentials and

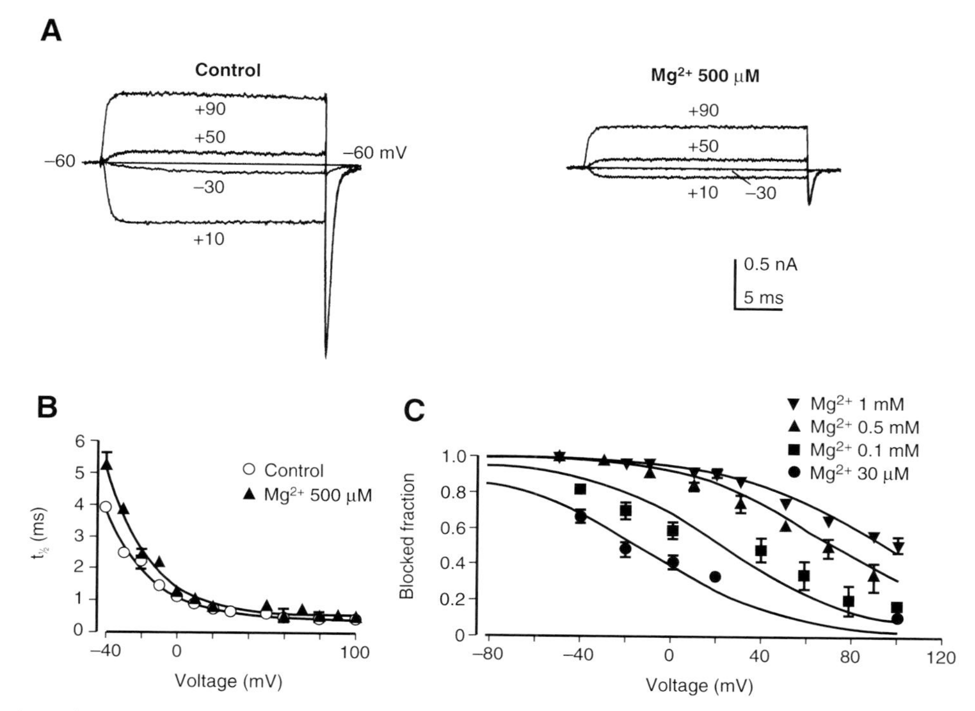

Fig. 4. A) Block of high-voltage-activated (HVA) sodium currents by Mg^{2+} in a chick sensory neuron. B) Effect of Mg^{2+} on the relationship between half-time to peak ($t_{½}$) and voltage. C) Voltage-dependence of HVA sodium current block at various concentrations of Mg^{2+}. Data presented as mean ± SEM for 3–4 data values collected from 10 neurons.

decreases with more positive voltage. The most conserved parameter is the strong voltage-dependence of the block, suggesting that Mg^{2+} binds somewhere inside the channel where the electrical field is fully sensed. Since the pore region of the channel has only one critical position at which the binding site can be located,[6,8] it can be concluded that Mg^{2+} binds to the same site as Ca^{2+} and other ions, although other interaction sites with special affinity for Mg^{2+} within the pore cannot be ruled out.[10] Because binding site and pore charges are the same as with permeant Ca^{2+} ions, structural properties of the channel–ion complex must be responsible for making Mg^{2+} an impermeant blocker. One possibility is that Mg^{2+}, for which the rate of dehydration is 4 orders of magnitude lower than that of both Ca^{2+} and Ba^{2+}, can reach the site without having completely lost its hydration shell (fig. 5). Alternatively,

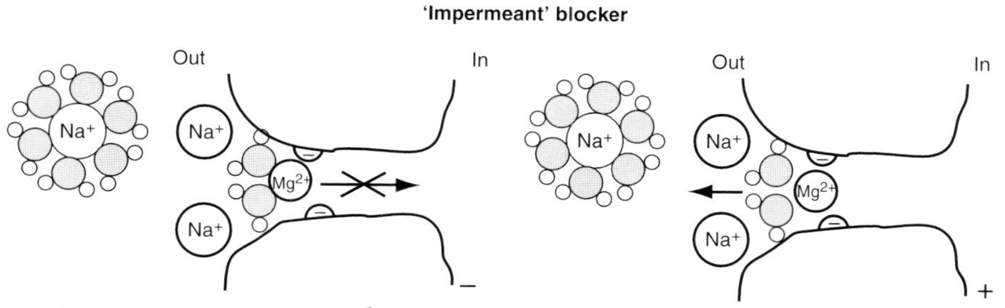

Fig. 5. Schematic representation of how Mg^{2+} ions control Na^+ fluxes.

the inability of Mg^{2+} to cross the channel may derive from a specific interaction of Mg^{2+} with the charges on the four glutamates, whose arrangement may determine the channel permeability of the bound ion.

Block of HVA calcium currents by Mg^{2+}: distinct effects on surface charge and ion permeation

As outlined by early work on mollusc neurons,[17,18] significant block of calcium and barium currents through calcium channels requires Mg^{2+} concentrations in excess of 10 mM. This implies that changes in channel gating as a result of the screening of surface charges and/or direct interaction with gating charges may contribute significantly to the effects of Mg^{2+}. There are several ways to separate the effects of Mg^{2+} on ion permeation and channel gating.[19] We followed one method adopted recently for estimation of the blocking potency of Ca^{2+} and Mg^{2+} ions on sodium currents.[5] This method is based on a three-pulse protocol in which the initial test pulse is followed by depolarisation to +100 mV and return to the initial test potential (fig. 6). The initial step is used to estimate the activation parameter peak half-time ($t_{½}$). The second step allows full activation of all available channels and clearing of Mg^{2+} from blocked channels, while the return to the initial test potential elucidates the kinetics of channel closing and reblocking independently of changes in channel gating. Formation of the instantaneous current–voltage relationships from the third step allows an estimate of ion permeation independent of channel gating effects.

Figure 6 shows HVA calcium currents of a chick sensory neuron in response to a series of three-pulse protocols in the presence of Ca^{2+} 2 mM and after addition of Mg^{2+} 30 mM. Inward currents during test pulses are strongly depressed and slowed by

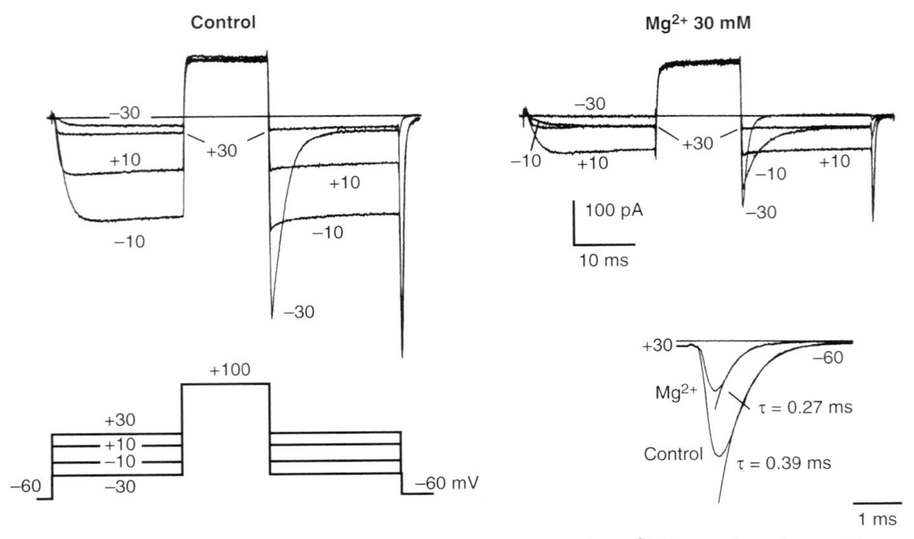

Fig. 6. Voltage-dependent block of high-voltage-activated calcium currents by Mg^{2+}. The overlapped current traces were obtained using the three-pulse protocol illustrated. The inset shows on an expanded time scale the tail currents on return to –60 mV from +30 mV at control and in Mg^{2+} 30 mM.

Mg^{2+}. However, outward currents at +100 mV are less affected, suggesting full activation of available channels and an effective clearing of blocking ions at this potential. There are two possible interpretations for the marked slowing of calcium currents between –30 and +30 mV. Either the high Mg^{2+} concentration changes channel gating by shifting the activation parameters towards more positive voltages, or the slow activation reflects unblocking of channels that were occupied by Mg^{2+} while deactivated at rest. In the latter case, membrane depolarisation would activate the channel at the same time as pushing out the blocking ion. If this process is slow enough, it may account for the slowing of channel activation. However, this hypothesis is unlikely for two reasons. First, channel unblocking is fast and at high voltages is barely resolved by the recording apparatus: there is no visible delay in the rising of the outward current at +100 mV (see fig. 6), suggesting that clearing of channels of Mg^{2+} must be very rapid at this potential (<0.2 ms). A fast unblock is also expected at lower potentials. Second, reblock of open channels by Mg^{2+} is very fast. On return to –30 and –10 mV from +100 mV, the tail currents do not show an instantaneous current equivalent to that of the activated and fully unblocked control currents. The reduced tail amplitude indicates that channel reblocking by Mg^{2+} must occur within the resolution of the measurement (<100–200 µs). Thus, the most plausible explanation for the slowing of channel gating is a screening effect of Mg^{2+} on surface charges, causing a positive shift and hence a slowing of voltage-dependent activation. Indeed, the voltage-dependence of $t_{½}$ and $1/\tau_{tail}$, indicative parameters of activation and deactivation kinetics, respectively, are altered by Mg^{2+} 30 mM (fig. 7). Both curves are shifted towards more positive potentials, and this accounts for the slow activation and fast deactivation measured between –30 and –10 mV. It also accounts for the acceleration of the tails on return to –60 mV from +30 mV (see fig. 6) where Mg^{2+} block is nearly abolished and the currents have the same steady-state value.

Overall, we can conclude that the kinetics of blocking and unblocking by Mg^{2+} are very fast. In addition, the observed slowing of current activation is primarily an effect on channel gating associated with an increased screening of surface charge.

In addition to channel gating, screening of surface charge may also affect ion permeation if localised charges near the channel mouth are able to exert electrostatic effects on ions entering the pore.[19,20] These local effects may be exhibited as voltage shifts of the current–voltage relationship in the presence of Mg^{2+}, and by correcting for these shifts the true voltage-dependence of Mg^{2+} block on calcium currents can be determined (see fig. 7). The instantaneous current–voltage curve derived from channel reblocking after a brief depolarisation to +100 mV in the presence of Mg^{2+} is reduced in amplitude and crosses the control current–voltage curve around +22 mV. This indicates that tail currents are reduced at potentials below +20 mV but are equal to or even larger than control tails at potentials ≥20 mV. The screening of the low-density local charges around the pore by Mg^{2+} produces a shift in voltage.[10,19] Compensation for this voltage shift is nearly impossible without knowing the exact density of negative charges around the pore. However, a minimum of an 8 mV shift to the left, to align the two current–voltage curves above

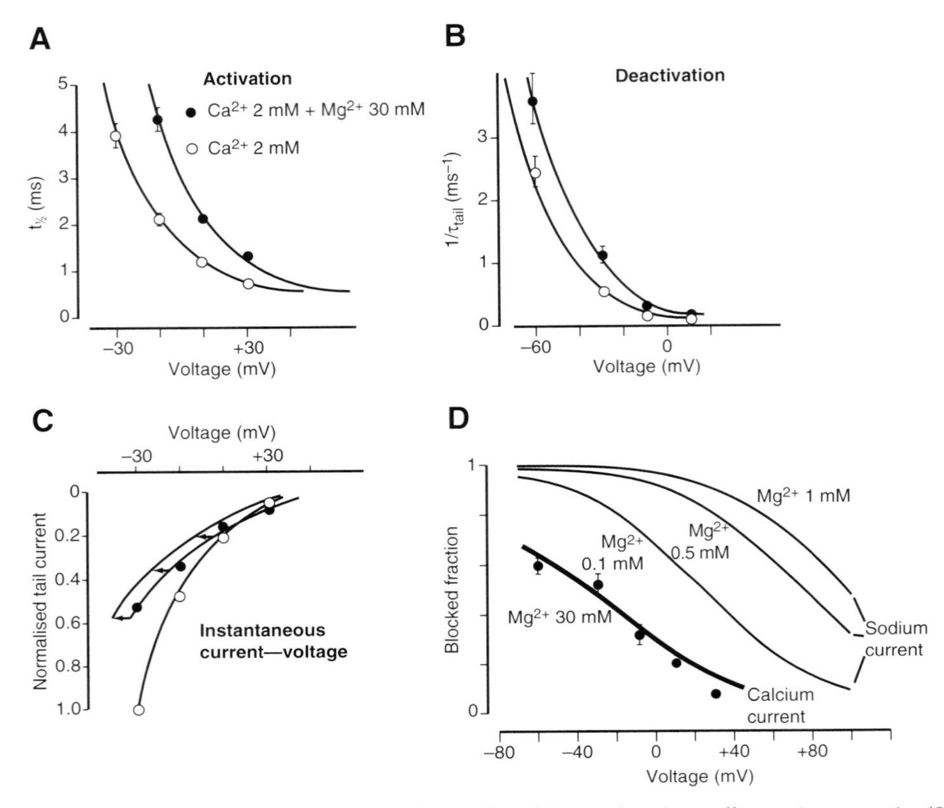

Fig. 7. Separation of surface charge effects on channel gating (A & B) from surface charge effects on ion permeation (C) induced by Mg^{2+}. Data are derived from 4 cells. Half-time to peak ($t_{½}$) was derived from the first test depolarisation, while $1/\tau_{tail}$ and the normalised current–voltage relationships were calculated from the time-course and amplitude of the tail current relaxation on return to the test potential. D) True voltage-dependence of Mg^{2+} block derived from the instantaneous current–voltage relationship after correction for an 8 mV shift. The thin curves were taken from figure 4 and represent the voltage-dependence of Mg^{2+} block on sodium currents.

+30 mV, is justified by the assumption that control tails cannot be smaller than Mg^{2+}-modified tails at very positive potentials. The corrected current–voltage curve then allows the voltage-dependence of Mg^{2+} block on calcium currents to be estimated, and this can be compared with the block of sodium currents (see fig. 7). Thus, after correction for the surface charge effects, depression of calcium currents in Ca^{2+} 2 mM requires a high concentration of Mg^{2+} (K_d = 18 mM at +10 mV), while sodium currents are blocked at Mg^{2+} concentrations some 3 orders of magnitude lower (K_d = 38 μM at −10 mV). Sodium currents require more positive potentials than calcium currents to be cleared of Mg^{2+} and require less negative voltages to be blocked. Thus, the presence of divalent versus monovalent ions markedly alters the ability of impermeant ions to block the channel.

Discussion

Most of the present data indicate that T-type and HVA (L- and N-type) calcium channels possess one binding site inside the pore that is the common locus for the binding of permeant ions (Ca^{2+}, Na^{+}), permeant blockers (Ca^{2+}, Cd^{2+}, Zn^{2+}, La^{3+}) and impermeant blockers (Mg^{2+}). This concept is supported by three lines of evidence.

1) Sodium currents are blocked by micromolar concentrations of Ca^{2+} and Mg^{2+}, revealing the presence of a high-affinity site in the pore.
2) Ca^{2+} and Mg^{2+} block is strongly voltage-dependent, suggesting that the blocking ion is localised inside the pore at a site that senses the membrane electrical field.
3) Point mutations of the channel sequence reveal only one site in the pore region that is responsible for high-affinity interactions with Ca^{2+}. The site for ion–channel interaction may be able to change the arrangement of its charges depending on the type of bound ion. This could explain the ability of Ca^{2+} to act as a permeant ion at millimolar Ca^{2+} concentrations but as a blocker at micromolar Ca^{2+} concentrations.

Nevertheless, in addition to the interactions between pore charges and ions, another structural property must influence ion movement through the pore. For example, although Mg^{2+} can reach its binding site inside the pore, it is unable to pass into the cell interior. One possible explanation is that Mg^{2+} has a slow dehydration rate and thus it may not completely lose its water-shell before entering the channel. One or two remaining water molecules may be sufficient to hinder the complete passage of the ion through the pore without preventing its entrance to the inner portion of the channel. This view is supported by the fact that Ni^{2+} and Co^{2+}, which like Mg^{2+} have small ionic radii and slow dehydration rates, are also impermeant blockers of calcium channels,[21,22] and that they bind to a more superficial site of the channel than either Ca^{2+} or La^{3+}.[23]

The observation that Mg^{2+} block of sodium currents through HVA channels occurs at concentrations about 3 orders of magnitude lower than those required to block calcium currents (K_d = 18 mM *vs* 38 μM) is similar to previous observations that barium currents are more sensitive to Mg^{2+} than are calcium currents.[18] Indeed, not only is the K_d of block very different, but voltage-dependence also varies. Thus, although unblock is only partial at +100 mV in the presence of Mg^{2+} 30 mM and Ca^{2+} 2 mM (see fig. 6), it is almost complete in the presence of Mg^{2+} 100 μM and Na^{+} 120 mM (see fig. 4). The opposite occurs on reblock of HVA currents: at Mg^{2+} concentrations near the K_d, full block of calcium currents requires much more negative potentials (less than –80 mV) than for full block of sodium currents (less than –40 mV).

The difference in voltage-sensitivity of Mg^{2+} block for Ca^{2+} and Na^{+} may result from the different affinity of the permeant ion for the pore charges. Ca^{2+} binds more tightly to the site than either Ba^{2+} or Na^{+} and thus more Mg^{2+} is required to displace Ca^{2+}. How much this action is related to ion–ion repulsion or to the local arrangements of pore charges is difficult to determine. Pure ion–ion interaction would not account for the different degree of channel unblocking observed following depolarisation to +100 mV when Ca^{2+} and Na^{+} are the permeant cations (see fig. 6 *vs* fig. 4). We favour the idea that Mg^{2+} block is strongly dependent on how the permeating ion affects the arrangements of the pore charges. In the presence of Ca^{2+}, the charges are more tightly bound to the permeant ion and hence less free to bind Mg^{2+}, while with Na^+ the charges are somewhat differently arranged and are free to bind Mg^{2+} with high affinity. In terms of ion entry and exit rates, this implies that while the exit rate is unlikely to be affected by the permeant ion ($K_{off} = 2.4 \times 10^3\ s^{-1}$ for Na^+ and $3.5 \times 10^3\ s^{-1}$ for Ca^{2+}) the entry rate will decrease dramatically from $K_{on} = 1 \times 10^8\ M^{-1}\ s^{-1}$ for Na^+ to $2 \times 10^5\ M^{-1}\ s^{-1}$ for Ca^{2+}.[9,10,24]

We have shown Mg^{2+} block of sodium currents to be equivalent for LVA and HVA channels (K_d = 30 and 38 μM, respectively). Preliminary data in our laboratory suggest that this is also true when the two channels carry calcium currents. In neuroblastoma IMR32 cells there is a comparable depression and shift in the current–voltage relationship of LVA and HVA currents in the presence of Mg^{2+} 60 mM and Ca^{2+} 10 mM, suggesting comparable surface charge screening and blocking effects of Mg^{2+} on both channels (Carbone, Carabelli, Bertodo and Zucker, unpublished observations). The reason for this lack of selectivity is unknown. However, it is unrelated to the slow rate of Mg^{2+} dehydration, since Ni^{2+}, which dehydrates 10 times more slowly than Mg^{2+}, is able to block T-type calcium channels more potently than L- and N-type channels[25] and also to discriminate between individual cloned calcium channels (α_{1A}, α_{1B}, α_{1C} and α_{1E}) and $\alpha_1\beta$ subunit combinations.[26]

Conclusions

Interaction of impermeant cations with ion permeation through calcium channels is a useful tool in the investigation of calcium channel structure and function. Impermeant cations such as Ni^{2+} help to distinguish calcium channel subtypes; others, such as Mg^{2+}, are unable to separate LVA from HVA channels, but their blocking potency is markedly altered when permeant divalent cations are replaced by monovalent cations.[5,27] Since permeability and blocking properties of calcium channels critically depend on the local arrangement of negative charges inside the pore, understanding of the charge interactions with ions will clarify how only some impermeant ions are able to selectively block one channel subtype. Such information may also facilitate the identification of new channel subtypes that cannot be readily classified as either low or high threshold.

Acknowledgements

This work was partially supported by NATO (grant no. CRG 0576/87 to E.C.).

References

1. Kostyuk PG, Mironov SL, Shuba YM. Two ion-selecting filters in the calcium of the somatic membrane of mollusc neurons. J Membr Biol 1983; 76: 83–93
2. Hess P, Tsien RW. Mechanism of ion permeation through calcium channels. Nature 1984; 309: 453–6
3. Almers W, McCleskey EW. Non-selective conductance in calcium channels of frog muscle: calcium selectivity in a single-file pore. J Physiol 1984; 353: 585–608
4. Fukushima Y, Hagiwara S. Currents carried by monovalent cations through calcium channels in mouse neoplastic B lymphocytes. J Physiol 1985; 358: 255–84

5. Lux HD, Carbone E, Zucker H. Na^+ currents through low-voltage-activated Ca^{2+} channels of chick sensory neurones: block by external Ca^{2+} and Mg^{2+}. J Physiol 1990; 430: 159–88
6. Heinemann SH, Terlau H, Stuhme W, et al. Calcium channel characteristics conferred on the sodium channel by single mutations. Nature 1992; 356: 441–3
7. Yang J, Hellinor PT, Sather WA, et al. Molecular determinants of Ca^{2+} selectivity and ion permeation in L-type Ca^{2+} channels. Nature 1993; 366: 158–61
8. Ellinor PT, Yang J, Sather WA, et al. Ca^{2+} channel selectivity at a single locus for high-affinity Ca^{2+} interactions. Neuron 1995; 15: 1121–32
9. Lansman JB, Hess P, Tsien RW. Blockade of Ca current through single calcium channels by Cd^{2+}, Mg^{2+} and Ca^{2+}: voltage and concentration dependence of calcium entry into the pore. J Gen Physiol 1986; 88: 321–47
10. Kuo C-C, Hess P. Block of the L-type Ca^{2+} channel pore by external and internal Mg^{2+} in rat phaechromocytoma cells. J Physiol 1993; 466: 683–706
11. Armstrong CM, Neyton J. Ion permeation through calcium channels: a one-site model. Ann N Y Acad Sci 1992; 635: 18–25
12. Mironov SL. Conformational model for ion permeation in membrane channels: a comparison with multi-ion models and applications to calcium channel permeability. Biophys J 1992; 63: 485–96
13. Swandulla D, Armstrong CM. Calcium channel block by cadmium in chicken sensory neurons. Proc Natl Acad Sci U S A 1989; 86: 1736–40
14. Winegar BD, Lansman JB. Voltage-dependent block by zinc of single calcium channels in mouse myotubes. J Physiol 1990; 425: 563–78
15. Lansman JB. Blockade of current through single calcium channels by trivalent lanthanide cations: effect of ionic radius on the rates of ion entry and exit. J Gen Physiol 1990; 95: 679–96
16. Thévenod F, Jones SW. Cadmium block of calcium current in frog sympathetic neurons. Biophys J 1992; 63: 162–8
17. Kostyuk PG, Mironov SL, Doroshenko PA, et al. Surface charges on the outer side of mollusc neuron membrane. J Membr Biol 1982; 70: 171–9
18. Wilson DL, Morimoto K, Tsuda Y, et al. Interaction between calcium ions and surface charge as it relates to calcium currents. J Membr Biol 1983; 72: 117–30
19. Zhou W, Jones SW. Surface charge and calcium channel saturation in bullfrog sympathetic neurons. J Gen Physiol 1995; 105: 441–62
20. Kuo C-C, Hess P. A functional view of the entrances of L-type Ca^{2+} channels, estimates of the size and surface potential at the pore mouths: Neuron 1992; 9: 515–26
21. Fukuda J, Kawa K. Permeation of manganese, cadmium, zinc, and beryllium through calcium channels of an insect muscle membrane. Science 1977; 196: 309–11
22. Mlinar B, Enyeart JJ. Block of current through T-type calcium channels by trivalent metal cations and nickel in neural rat and human cells. J Physiol 1993; 469: 639–52
23. Winegar BD, Kelly R, Lansman JB. Block of current through single calcium channels by Fe, Co and Ni: location of the transition metal binding site in the pore. J Gen Physiol 1991; 97: 351–67
24. Pusch M. Open-channel block of Na^+ channels by intracellular Mg^{2+}. Eur Biophys J 1990; 18: 318–26
25. Carbone E, Swandulla D. Neuronal calcium channels: kinetics, blockade and modulation. Prog Biophys Mol Biol 1989; 54: 31–58
26. Zamponi GW, Bourinet E, Snutch TP. Nickel block of a family of neuronal calcium channels: subtype- and subunit-dependent action at multiple sites. J Membr Biol 1996; 151: 77–90
27. Carbone E, Lux HD, Carabelli V, et al. Ca^{2+} and Na^+ permeability of high-threshold Ca^{2+} channels and their voltage-dependent block by Mg^{2+} ions in chick sensory neurones. J Physiol 1997; 504: 1–15

Limitations of Ni^{2+} ions as a tool for discrimination between high- and low-threshold calcium channels

Gerald W. Zamponi,[1] Emmanuel Bourinet,[2] Terry P. Snutch[1]

[1] Biotechnology Laboratory, University of British Columbia, Vancouver, Canada; [2] Centre de Recherches en Biochimie Macromoléculaire, Centre National de la Recherche Scientifique, Montpellier, France

Most neurons express multiple types of voltage-gated calcium channels and it is probable that each has a unique role in physiological functions such as excitability, neurotransmitter release, gene expression and neurite outgrowth. Electrophysiological and pharmacological criteria have been used to classify calcium channels into T, L, N, P and Q types.[1–4] T-type calcium channels constitute a heterogeneous family of channels which activate at negative potentials (generally –70 to –40 mV) and show a transient (rapidly inactivating) response to voltage.[5–6] L-, N-, P- and Q-type calcium channels activate at more positive membrane potentials (typically greater than –30 mV) and exhibit overlapping electrophysiological and biophysical properties. At the molecular level, each calcium channel type is encoded by a distinct α_1 subunit (α_{1A}–α_{1E}) in combination with an α_2 subunit and any one of four types of β subunits (β_1–β_4).[7] The type of β subunit coexpressed dramatically affects the electrophysiological properties of the α_1 subunit, in particular the voltage-dependence of activation and the time-course of inactivation.[8,9] It is therefore difficult to classify native calcium currents and to assign cloned calcium channel α_1 subunits to their native counterparts based exclusively on activation range and channel kinetics. This issue is further complicated by the concept that the cytoplasmic environment of certain exogenous expression systems modifies the biophysical properties of some calcium channels.[10]

The pharmacological profiles of calcium channels has allowed a more definitive classification:[4,11] L-type channels are sensitive to dihydropyridines, N-type channels are blocked by the peptide ω-CTx-GVIA from the cone snail *Conus geographus* and P- and Q-type calcium channels are blocked with high affinity by peptides from the venom of the funnel web spider, *Agelonopsis aperta* (ω-Aga-IVA) and the cone snail *Conus magus* (ω-CTx-MVIIC).[12–14] Classically, Ni^{2+} ions are considered to preferentially block T-type calcium channels, and Ni^{2+} continues to be used as a discriminative tool to distinguish low-voltage-activated calcium channels from other calcium channel types. However, there is now evidence for additional calcium channel subtypes that do not fall precisely into one of the above categories. Some of these show a Ni^{2+} sensitivity comparable to that seen with native T-type calcium channels.[15] Furthermore, the action of Ni^{2+} appears to be dependent on a variety of factors. This raises some doubt as to the suitability of Ni^{2+} as an agent capable of distinguishing T-type calcium channels.

Effect of external Ni^{2+} ions on cloned neuronal Ca^{2+} channels

Block of calcium channels by divalent cations is widely believed to occur via physical occlusion of the channel pore. However, to date, the molecular mechanisms underlying the inhibitory actions of Ni^{2+} ions have been only sporadically addressed.[16,17] Since it is difficult to determine the action of blockers on native calcium channel subtypes under identical conditions, we have examined the effects of external Ni^{2+} ions on four major classes of cloned neuronal calcium channels transiently expressed in *Xenopus* oocytes. The data provide evidence that the action of Ni^{2+} ions is complex and cannot be explained by action at a single site. The effect of Ni^{2+} is likely to involve both pore block and an antagonistic effect on channel activation.[18]

Figure 1 depicts the effect of Ni^{2+} 100 μM on whole-cell α_{1E} barium currents recorded at various test potentials. Ni^{2+} caused a significant decrease in currents elicited at all potentials. Concomitantly, the current–voltage relationship was shifted towards more depolarising potentials such that while the peak α_{1E} current was at ~0 mV under control conditions, it was ~+20 mV in the presence of Ni^{2+} 100 μM. A further effect of Ni^{2+} was an apparent slowing of the time-courses of current activation and inactivation. Ni^{2+} also reduced the maximum slope conductance, g (as reflected in the slope of the decaying phase of the current–voltage relationship), without a significant effect on the extrapolated reversal potential (see fig. 1 (C)). Examination of current–voltage relationships over a range of Ni^{2+} concentrations showed that the effects of Ni^{2+} could be separated into two distinct components. First, a reduction in the maximum slope conductance of the channel in the presence of Ni^{2+} ions which we defined as 'nickel block', and second, a concentration-dependent shift of the half-activation potential towards more depolarised potentials which we refer to as a 'gating effect' of Ni^{2+}. Because of the superimposed shift in half-activation potential, the action of Ni^{2+} appears highly voltage-dependent, producing a 50% inhibition of α_{1E} currents at a concentration of 10 μM at very negative potentials, but requiring a concentration of almost 300 μM to block half of the current at the plateau of the activation curve. Furthermore, because the action of Ni^{2+} appears to arise from a combination of block and gating effects, the dose-dependence of the total Ni^{2+} action produces a voltage-dependent Hill coefficient, yielding Hill coefficients well below 1 at negative potentials, and of approximately 1 at the plateau of the activation curve where shifts in voltage potential are not detected.[18]

Dose-dependence of Ni^{2+} block

The dose-dependence of Ni^{2+} block on four classes of neuronal calcium channels was determined from the Ni^{2+}-dependence of the maximum slope conductance (fig. 2 (A)). The data are fitted with simple hyperbolas, suggesting that Ni^{2+} block occurs as a bimolecular reaction between Ni^{2+} and the channel complex. The affinities of Ni^{2+} for the various channel subtypes spanned approximately one order of magnitude, with the L-type calcium channel α_{1C} being the most effectively blocked, followed by $\alpha_{1E} > \alpha_{1A} > \alpha_{1B}$. Figure 2 (B) demonstrates the dose-dependence of the effect of Ni^{2+} on the half-activation potential. The plot of the shift in half-activation potential as a function of Ni^{2+} concentration is described by a simple saturation curve suggesting that Ni^{2+} may affect the half-activation potential by binding with 1:1

A

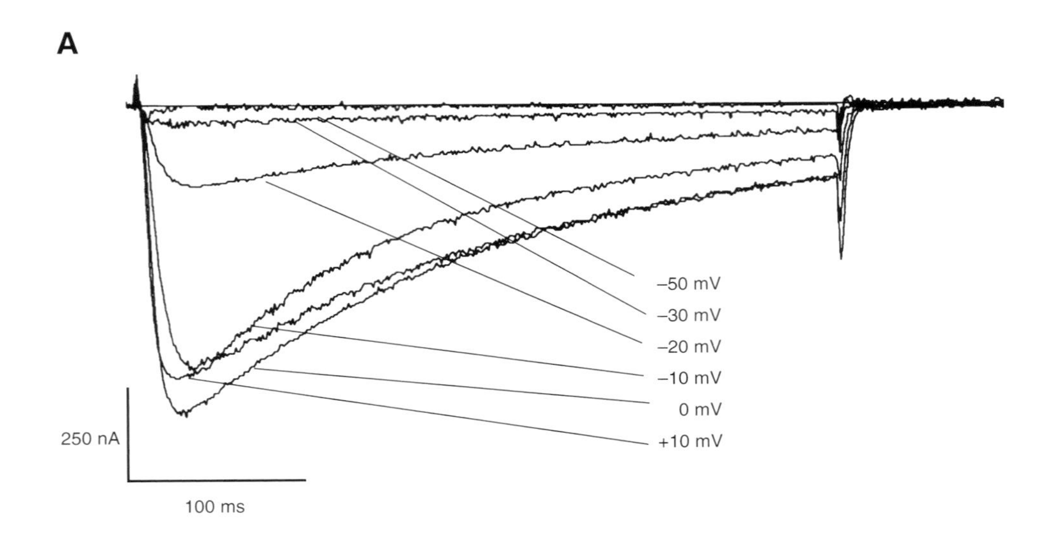

B

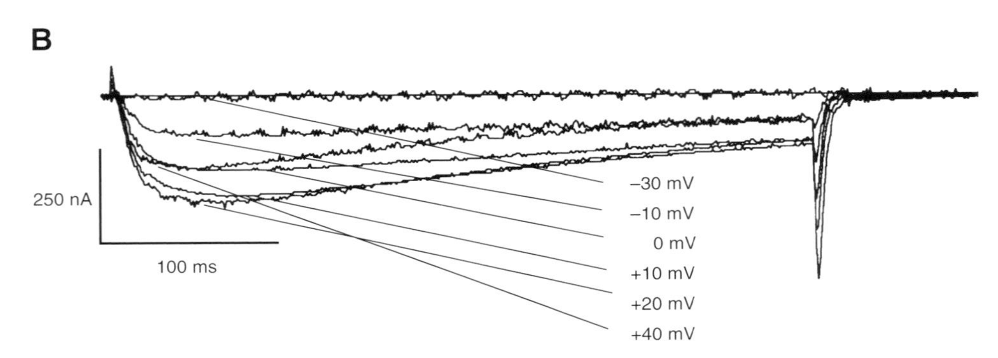

C

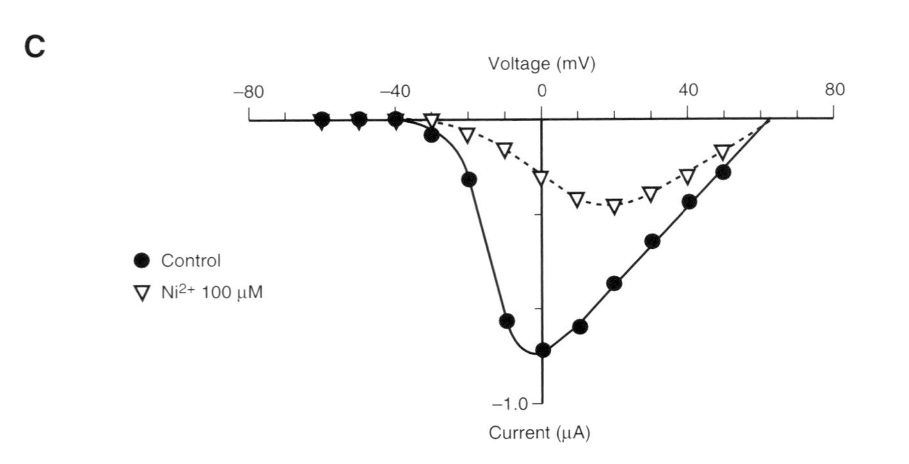

Fig. 1. A & B) Whole-cell currents recorded under voltage clamp from a Xenopus oocyte *expressing* $\alpha_{1E}\alpha_{2B}\beta_{1b}$ *in the absence (A) and presence (B) of* Ni^{2+} *100 μM from a holding potential of −100 mV.*[21] *C) Current–voltage relationship obtained from panels A and B. Data were fitted with the equation* $I = \{1/(1 + \exp(V_{½} - V)/S)\}(V - E_{rev})g$, *where g is the maximum slope conductance, V is the test potential,* E_{rev} *is the reversal potential, S is the slope factor and* $V_{½}$ *is the half-activation potential. The fitting parameters were as follows: control:* $V_{½} = -13.3$ *mV,* $g = 13.6$ *μS,* $E_{rev} = 62.0$ *mV,* $S = 4.3$ *mV;* Ni^{2+}: $V_{½} = 4.8$ *mV,* $g = 8.2$ *μS,* $E_{rev} = 65$ *mV,* $S = 9.5$ *mV.*

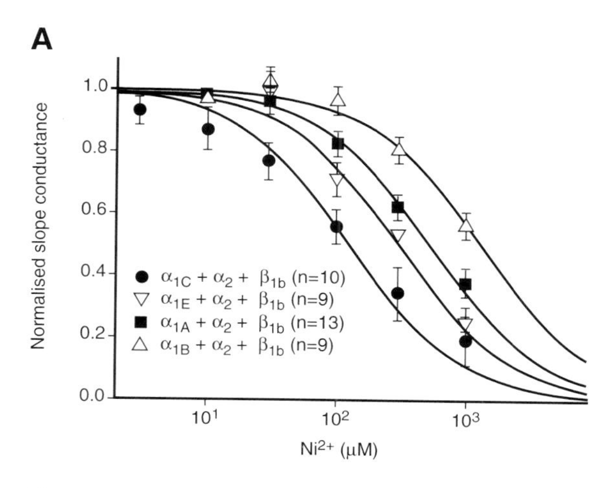

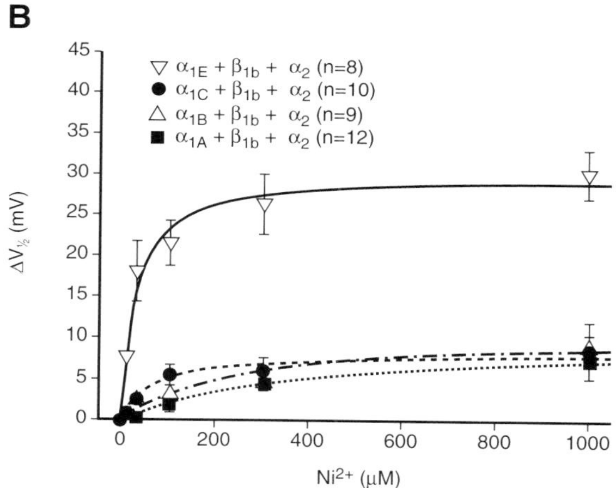

Class	$\alpha_{1E}\beta_{1b}\alpha_{2B}$	$\alpha_{1C}\beta_{1b}\alpha_{2B}$	$\alpha_{1B}\beta_{1b}\alpha_{2B}$	$\alpha_{1A}\beta_{1b}\alpha_{2B}$
K_i (μM)	27.8	59.5	207.5	348.9
Max (mV)	29.9	8.7	10.7	10.1

Fig. 2. A) Dose–response of the effect of Ni^{2+} on the maximum slope conductance as determined by fits to current–voltage relationships for four classes of calcium channel α_1 subunits (coexpressed with β_{1b} and α_{2B}). The curves were fitted with simple hyperbolas with an arbitrary Hill coefficient of 1. K_d values were: α_{1C} 127.6 μM; α_{1E} 303.0 μM; α_{1A} 535.0 μM; α_{1B} 1337.6 μM. B) Dose-dependence of the shift in half-activation voltage for four major classes of neuronal calcium channel α_1 subunits coexpressed with β_{1b} and α_{2B}. The curves were fitted with saturation isotherms, using the equation $\Delta V_{½} = max/(1 + K_i/[Ni^{2+}])$, where $\Delta V_{½}$ is the absolute shift in half-activation voltage as a function of Ni^{2+} concentration, max is the maximal shift, and K_i is the equilibrium dissociation constant for Ni^{2+}. The fitting parameters are shown at the bottom of the figure.

stoichiometry to a saturable site at the extracellular side of the channel. The effect was most pronounced for α_{1E}, with the other calcium channel subtypes affected to a lesser degree. In addition, the steepness of the rising phase of the isotherm was greatest for α_{1E}, suggesting that the putative Ni^{2+} binding site on α_{1E} exhibits a higher affinity compared with the analogous sites on the other calcium channel types. Overall, these data indicate that the Ni^{2+}-induced shifts in the half-activation potential are subtype-specific, both in absolute magnitude and concentration-dependence. Qualitatively, the relative order of blocking affinities did not parallel the Ni^{2+} concentrations required to produce a half-maximal shift in half-activation potential (compare panels A & B in fig. 2). Of particular note, for α_{1E} the half-activation potential shift was half maximal at a Ni^{2+} concentration of 29 μM, while 10-fold higher concentrations were required to reduce the maximum slope conductance by 50%. This result suggests that block and the shifts in half-activation potential probably occur via distinct mechanisms. This is supported by two additional pieces of evidence. First, for α_{1A} and α_{1E}, elimination of the β subunit resulted in an increase in Ni^{2+} blocking affinity, whereas the concentrations required to produce a half-maximal effect on activation of α_{1E} were not altered. For α_{1A}, the type of β subunit coexpressed did not affect Ni^{2+} block, but it did influence the magnitude of the voltage shift, with β_{2a} producing the largest shifts, followed by β_4 and β_{1b}.[20] Second, block and the effect on gating were differentially sensitive to the type of permeant ion and to the external permeant ion concentration.[18] Overall, these data indicate that Ni^{2+} inhibits calcium channels via two distinct mechanisms. First, Ni^{2+} blocks the channel in a 1:1 interaction which may occur within the permeation pathway, and second, it increases the threshold for channel activation. The overall action of Ni^{2+} is governed by a combination of these processes and results in α_{1E} being the most effectively inhibited overall but not the most effectively blocked. It is apparent that when comparing the blocking action of Ni^{2+} among different calcium channel isoforms, it is crucial to choose the appropriate experimental conditions.

A similar consideration applies to the use of Ni^{2+} ions to assign cloned calcium channels to their native counterparts. Because of the highly dynamic action of Ni^{2+} (i.e. the dependence of the two Ni^{2+} effects on holding potential, β subunit coexpression, the type and concentration of permeant ion), the apparent Ni^{2+} affinity may vary dramatically. For example, with α_{1E}, changing only a single parameter can result in an apparent 10- to 50-fold change in Ni^{2+} affinity.

A further consideration is that the complex action of Ni^{2+} at two distinct sites could, under certain circumstances, produce biphasic dose–response curves in spite of the presence of only one species of calcium channel. Figure 3 is a simulation of this potential behaviour where the Ni^{2+} affinity for the gating site has been arbitrarily set at 8 μM and the blocking affinity at 550 μM. The maximal shift was chosen as 15 mV, and the half-activation potential in the absence of Ni^{2+} was set to –13 mV. At a test potential of 0 mV, a combined action of Ni^{2+} on both the gating site and a pore blocking site would produce a biphasic dose–response curve with a clear plateau at Ni^{2+} concentrations of about 50 μM. Thus, a biphasic dose–response curve to the effect of Ni^{2+} ions does not necessarily imply the presence of two distinct populations of channels. Additional information such as single-channel recordings may be required to confirm such a contention.[15]

Ni^{2+} ions are not the only divalent cations able to induce depolarising shifts in current–voltage relationships. For example, in rat dorsal root ganglion, Hg^{2+} 2 μM

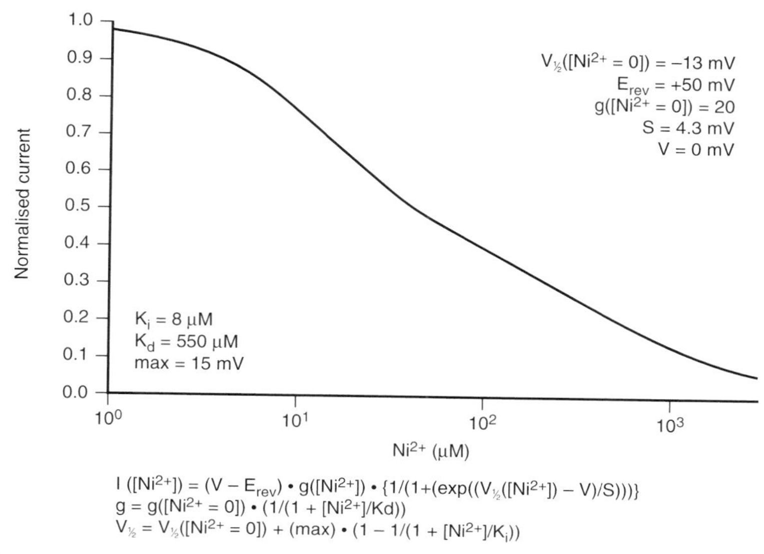

$$I([Ni^{2+}]) = (V - E_{rev}) \cdot g([Ni^{2+}]) \cdot \{1/(1+(\exp((V_{½}([Ni^{2+}]) - V)/S)))\}$$
$$g = g([Ni^{2+} = 0]) \cdot (1/(1 + [Ni^{2+}]/Kd))$$
$$V_{½} = V_{½}([Ni^{2+} = 0]) + (max) \cdot (1 - 1/(1 + [Ni^{2+}]/K_i))$$

Fig. 3. Simulation of a dose–response curve of Ni^{2+} block. The curves were constructed using the equation for $I([Ni^{2+}])$, normalised to $I([Ni^{2+} = 0])$. The parameters used were as follows: $V_{½}([Ni^{2+} = 0])$ = half-activation potential in the absence of Ni^{2+}; E_{rev} = reversal potential; $g([Ni^{2+} = 0])$ = maximum slope conductance in the absence of Ni^{2+}; S = Boltzmann slope factor; V = test potential; K_i = equilibrium dissociation constant for Ni^{2+} binding to the gating site; K_d = equilibrium dissociation constant for Ni^{2+} pore block; max = total voltage shift at saturating Ni^{2+} concentrations.

induced a 15 mV shift in the activation curve for high-voltage-activated (HVA) calcium currents.[19] Similarly, Al^{3+} ions caused shifts in current–voltage properties of HVA calcium channels, while neither Zn^{2+} nor Pb^{2+} exhibited this effect.[20] Depolarising shifts in current–voltage properties have also been reported for block of molluscan neuronal L-type calcium channels by Ni^{2+}, Co^{2+} and Cd^{2+}.[21] In contrast, no similar effect was observed for *Aplysia* neuronal HVA calcium currents at concentrations as high as 20 μM,[19] or for doe-1 channels in the presence of Ni^{2+} 30 μM,[22] suggesting that the mechanism responsible for the shift in the current–voltage relationship is not conserved among all types of calcium channels. Finally, Ca^{2+} ions have also been shown to cause depolarising shifts in current–voltage properties, and there is evidence that this effect may occur via binding to a specific site linked to the gating machinery.[23]

Affinities of different channel types for Ni^{2+}

If we assume that Ni^{2+} block occurs via binding within the pore, our data suggest that the α_{1C} L-type calcium channel pore exhibits the highest affinity for Ni^{2+}, while the pore of the α_{1B} N-type calcium channel possesses a 13-fold lower affinity. According to current permeation models, the most crucial pore structures for binding divalent ions are four glutamate residues which are conserved across all types of neuronal calcium channels.[24,25] Since blocking affinities for individual calcium channel subtypes span more than one order of magnitude, it is likely that either the orientation of the glutamic acid residues differs among the channel subtypes, or that there are additional amino acid residues which are important for permeation and divalent ion block of calcium channels. This is supported by recent data describing unique permeation characteristics of the α_{1E} calcium channel.[26]

In summary, it appears that the action of Ni^{2+} on calcium channels is complex and cannot be described by action at a single site. This complexity suggests that it may be difficult to use Ni^{2+} block as an unequivocal criterion to classify calcium channels as either low threshold (T type) or high threshold.

References

1. Bean BP. Classes of calcium channels in vertebrate cells. Annu Rev Physiol 1989; 51: 367–84
2. Hess P. Calcium channels in vertebrate cells. Annu Rev Neurosci 1990; 13: 337–56
3. McClesky EW. Calcium channels: cellular roles and molecular mechanisms. Curr Opin Neurobiol 1994; 4: 304–12
4. Zhang J-F, Randall AD, Ellinor PT, et al. Distinctive pharmacology and kinetics of cloned neuronal calcium channels and their possible counterparts in mammalian CNS neurons. Neuropharmacology 1993; 32: 1075–88
5. Bean BP. Two kinds of calcium channels in canine atrial cells. J Gen Physiol 1985; 86: 1–30
6. Akaike N, Kostyuk PG, Osipchuk YV. Dihydropyridine-sensitive low-threshold calcium channels in isolated rat hypothalamic neurones. J Physiol 1989; 412: 181–95
7. Stea A, Soong TW, Snutch TP. Voltage-gated calcium channels. In: North RA, editor. Handbook of receptors and channels. Boca Raton, Fla.: CRC Press, 1995: 113–51
8. Stea A, Dubel S, Pragnell M, et al. A β subunit normalizes the electrophysiological properties of a cloned N-type calcium channel α_1 subunit. Neuropharmacology 1993; 32: 1103–16
9. Olcese R, Qin N, Schneider T, et al. The amino terminus of a calcium channel β subunit sets rates of channel inactivation independently of the subunit's effects on activation. Neuron 1994; 13: 1433–8
10. Dzhura I, Kostyuk P, Lyubanova O, et al. Expression of low-voltage activated Ca^{++} channels from rat brain neurons in *Xenopus* oocytes. Neuro Report 1994; 5: 1960–2
11. Randall A, Tsien RW. Pharmacological dissection of multiple types of Ca^{2+} channel currents in rat cerebellar granule neurons. J Neurosci 1995; 15: 2995–3012
12. Bean BP. Nitrendipine block of cardiac calcium channels: high affinity binding to the inactivated state. Proc Natl Acad Sci U S A 1984; 81: 6288–92
13. Droogmans G, Callewaert G. Ca^{2+}-channel current and its modification by the dihydropyridine agonist Bay K 8644 in isolated smooth muscle cells. Pflugers Arch 1986; 406: 259–65
14. Adams ME, Myers RA, Imperial JS, et al. Toxityping rat brain calcium channels with ω-toxins from spider and cone snail venoms. Biochemistry 1993; 32: 12566–70
15. Tottene A, Moretti A, Pietrobon A. Functional diversity of P-type and R-type calcium channels in rat cerebellar neurons. J Neurosci 1996; 16: 6353–63
16. Winegar BD, Kelly R, Lansman JB. Block of current through single calcium channels by Fe, Co, and Ni. J Gen Physiol 1991; 97: 351–67
17. Mlinar B, Enyeart JJ. Block of current through T-type calcium channels by trivalent metal cations and nickel in neural rat and human cell lines. J Physiol 1993; 469: 639–52
18. Zamponi GW, Bourinet E, Snutch TP. Nickel block of a family of neuronal calcium channels. Subtype and subunit-dependent action at multiple sites. J Membr Biol 1996; 151: 77–90
19. Pekel M, Platt B, Buesselberg D. Mercury (Hg^{2+}) decreases voltage-gated calcium channel currents in rat DRG and *Aplysia* neurons. Brain Res 1993; 632: 121–6
20. Buesselberg D, Platt B, Michael D, et al. Mammalian voltage-activated calcium channel currents are blocked by Pb^{2+}, Zn^{2+}, and Al^{3+}. J Neurophysiol 1994; 1: 1491–7
21. Byerly L, Chase PB, Stimers J. Permeation and interaction of divalent cations in calcium channels of snail neurons. J Gen Physiol 1985; 85: 491–518
22. Ellinor PT, Zhang JF, Randall AD, et al. Functional expression of a rapidly inactivating neuronal calcium channel. Nature 1993; 363: 455–8
23. Zamponi GW, Snutch TP. Evidence for a specific site for modulation of calcium channel activation by external calcium ions. Pflugers Arch 1996; 431: 470–2
24. Yang J, Ellinor PT, Sather WA, et al. Molecular determinants of Ca^{2+} selectivity and ion permeation in L-type Ca^{2+} channels. Nature 1993; 366: 158–61
25. Ellinor PT, Yang J, Sather WA, et al. Ca^{2+} channel selectivity at a single locus for high affinity Ca^{2+} interactions. Neuron 1996; 15: 1121–32
26. Bourinet E, Zamponi GW, Stea A, et al. Neuronal α_{1E} calcium channels display permeation characteristics similar to low voltage-activated channels. J Neurosci 1996; 16: 4983–93

Section 2

Biological roles in diverse cell types

Introduction

This group of chapters gather together several perspectives on the physiological contributions of T-type calcium channels in various cell systems, including cardiac, smooth and skeletal muscle as well as neurons and endocrine cells. T-type channels can support electrogenesis of repetitive activity as well as provide Ca^{2+} entry for the regulation of secretion.

Lei et al. reassess the role that T-type channels play in generating cardiac rhythm, elegantly combining theoretical and experimental approaches. Their modelling studies in rabbit sinoatrial node cells point to discrepancies between the demonstrated importance of T-type channels for pacemaker activity and existing descriptions of their voltage-dependent kinetics. Indeed, direct experiments demonstrated considerable overlap between inactivation and activation curves that was not seen in previous experiments, successfully accounting for the contribution by T-type channels. **Han et al.** review experiments from the laboratory of the late Thomas W. Smith, who made a presentation at the symposium and who will be sorely missed. They have studied the participation of T-type current in pacemaker activity of rabbit atrioventricular node cells and arrhythmogenic potentials in ventricular cells of cardiomyopathic (CM) hamster. T-type channels provided a substantial contribution to the intrinsic rhythm. T-type current was sharply increased in CM cells, related in large part to a shift in their activation properties to more negative potentials. **Richard and Nargeot** describe properties of T- and L-type currents in vascular smooth muscle cells (VSMCs) and show their general resemblance to their counterparts in other systems, including an ability to support steady Ca^{2+} influx ('window current'). They also take up the fascinating question of whether T-type currents might be important in controlling cell proliferation. So far, however, attempts at finding T-type channel expression in proliferating VSMCs *in vivo* (e.g. after balloon injury) have not been successful.

The focus shifts to neuronal preparations in the remaining chapters in this section. **Johnston et al.** point out that there exist 'low voltage-activated' (LVA) channels other than T type. For example, CA3 hippocampal pyramidal cells express currents that activate at relatively negative potentials but display pharmacology expected for L-type channels, including inhibition by nimodipine and calciseptine and potentiation by BayK8644. These LVA L-type channels contribute to resting Ca^{2+} influx. Patch-clamp recordings from dendrites reveal channel activity with the properties of classical T-type calcium channels; such channel activity may be recruited by naturally occurring synaptic depolarisations. **Huguenard** provides a lucid review of LVA calcium channels in central neurons and their role in low-threshold spiking. He summarises the clear evidence for the existence of two varieties of T-type currents: (i) a 'classical' T-type current, prominent in ventrobasal relay neurons of the thalamus, with properties largely similar to those described in heart, smooth muscle and certain cell lines (GH_3, NG108); and (ii) a more slowly inactivating T-type current (T_s type), with kinetics and ionic properties similar to those found for expressed α_{1E} subunits.

Beam describes T-type calcium channels in excitable cells important for motor activity. In general, T-type channels are particularly adept at supplying Ca^{2+} flux since they activate more readily and deactivate more slowly than other channels. Skeletal muscle expressed T-type channels with classical properties, but only during early neonatal development. A similar change occurred in the T-type currents of motoneurons. There are significant distinctions to be made between the underlying channel molecules, as judged by selective effects of antisera from patients with Eaton–Lambert myasthenic syndrome, which reduce T-type currents (and HVA currents) in motoneurons but not in muscle. **Frischknecht and Randall** studied floor plate cells, a class of cells key for CNS development. The only calcium channel activity was an LVA current with kinetic and ionic properties of classical T-type current. The strong possibility that emerges from their work is that T-type channels are targets of modulators and in turn control the release of chemoattractant molecules during development. This is an intriguing system, worthy of additional study. **Barrett et al.** provide some of the best evidence for a role of T-type channels in regulating the production of steroid hormone and, ultimately, its secretion. Working with adrenal glomerulosa cells, they have shown that angiotensin controls T-type calcium channel activation via two signalling pathways, involving the G protein G_i on one hand, and the multifunctional Ca^{2+}/CaM kinase CaMKII on the other. **Rossier et al.** also focus on secretion of steroid hormone from adrenal glomerulosa cells. They found that while steroidogenesis is closely tied to T-type calcium channel activity, bulk cytoplasmic Ca^{2+} is correlated with opening of L-type calcium channels, with little or no relationship to T-type channels. They raise the interesting possibility that Ca^{2+} influx through T-type channels may somehow exert a preferential impact on mitochondrial Ca^{2+} and the biochemical steps it controls.

What role do T-type calcium channels play in cardiac pacemaker activity?

Ming Lei, Hilary Brown, Denis Noble

University Laboratory of Physiology, University of Oxford, Oxford, UK

Summary

The role of the T-type calcium channels in cardiac pacemaker activity has been reassessed. Existing kinetic data show no significant overlap between the activation and inactivation curves for the channel, so that during the pacemaker depolarisation the channels become inactivated before they can be activated. Incorporating this kinetic data into a single sinus node cell model confirms the prediction that there would be no T-type channel contribution to the speed of the pacemaker depolarisation. Using the permeabilised-patch technique on single rabbit sinoatrial node cells we have shown that a combined ramp–step protocol, in which the steps are preceded by a ramp that mimics the pacemaker depolarisation, does reveal a significant T-type channel current. Conventional step protocols also reveal that the inactivation curve is less steep than reported previously. When this kinetic data is incorporated into the sinoatrial node cell model, block of T-type calcium channels is predicted to slow rhythm by around 10%, which is comparable to that resulting from therapeutic levels of mibefradil.

Introduction

Calcium channels play a major role in the generation of natural pacemaker activity in the heart.[1] The most dramatic demonstration of this lies in the observation that the sinoatrial node region continues to beat even when the rest of the heart is arrested by blockade of the fast sodium channels with tetrodotoxin (TTX). The upstroke of the action potential in the sinoatrial node is almost entirely dependent on L-type calcium channels, which also play a role in the last third or so of the pacemaker depolarisation when it reaches the foot of the activation curve for these channels.

In contrast, the functional role of T-type calcium channels has been less certain. On the one hand, Ni^{2+} ions produce a significant (5–15%) slowing of sinoatrial node rhythm. If Ni^{2+} is selective for T-type calcium currents, this suggests a modulating role of moderate importance for these channels in pacemaker activity. It is therefore surprising that when the kinetics of T-type calcium currents[2] are incorporated into the single sinus cell model of the OXSOFT HEART program (Oxsoft Ltd, Oxford, UK), the predicted time-course of these currents shows this role to be exceedingly small and these channels to have a negligible contribution to pacemaker activity. The reason for this result is also obvious. The activation and inactivation curves in the results obtained by Hagiwara et al. show so little overlap that during the slow pacemaker depolarisation T-type calcium channels become fully inactivated before they have time to become activated.[2]

This matter clearly needs reinvestigation, and there are several possible explanations for this inconsistency. First, it is conceivable that step voltage-clamp results constitute a poor basis for quantitative prediction of the current during the more natural voltage changes associated with pacemaker depolarisation. That would be true if the history of the voltage changes was important in determining the kinetic behaviour (e.g. if the rate coefficients for activation and deactivation did not depend uniquely on the instantaneous membrane potential). The second possibility is that the experimental results of Hagiwara et al. have some systematic problem that has led them to seriously underestimate the region of overlap between the activation and inactivation curves.[2] Both questions are tackled experimentally in this paper. We have also used the results obtained to recompute the contribution of T-type calcium current to pacemaker activity.

Results using a combined ramp–step voltage-clamp protocol

The first possibility can be investigated by using a different voltage-clamp protocol from the standard step voltage pulses from constant holding potentials. The best protocol for this purpose is to impose the step clamps after first clamping the membrane to a ramp voltage change that closely mimics the pacemaker depolarisation. Since the latter approximates to a slowly rising ramp, this will produce a situation in which the subsequent steps will reveal the availability of the current following a history of changes in potential similar to that of the pacemaker depolarisation itself.

The experiments were carried out in isolated single sinus node cells from the rabbit using a whole-cell clamp via amphotericin-permeabilised patches.[3] The initial ramp was imposed from a starting voltage of –65 mV, with the ramp taking 75 ms to reach a voltage of –45 mV. Step voltage pulses of 125 ms duration were then applied to various voltages between –40 and +20 mV. The cells were treated with TTX 30 μM to block any sodium current, and nisoldipine 300 nM to block any L-type calcium current.

Panel A of figure 1 shows the results obtained. Clearly there is a significant transient inward current following each step depolarisation. Panel B shows the relationship between the peak inward current and the membrane potential during the voltage-clamp step. The maximum current is around –130 pA and the reversal potential is around +20 mV. The current inactivates rapidly (within about 30 ms). These are characteristics consistent with the current being T-type. The inward current is reversibly blocked by Ni^{2+} 40 μM (data not shown).

These results clearly show a significant availability of T-type calcium channels towards the end of the pacemaker depolarisation. The channels are therefore not fully inactivated at this time.

Steady-state activation and inactivation curves

Next, attempts were made to ascertain whether this result is attributable to a failure of step voltage protocols to predict the results of ramp protocols or whether the

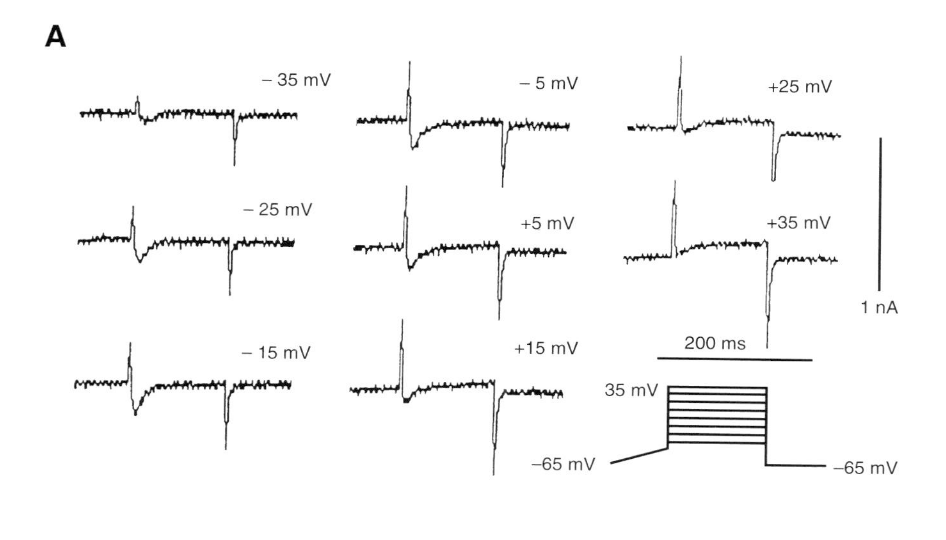

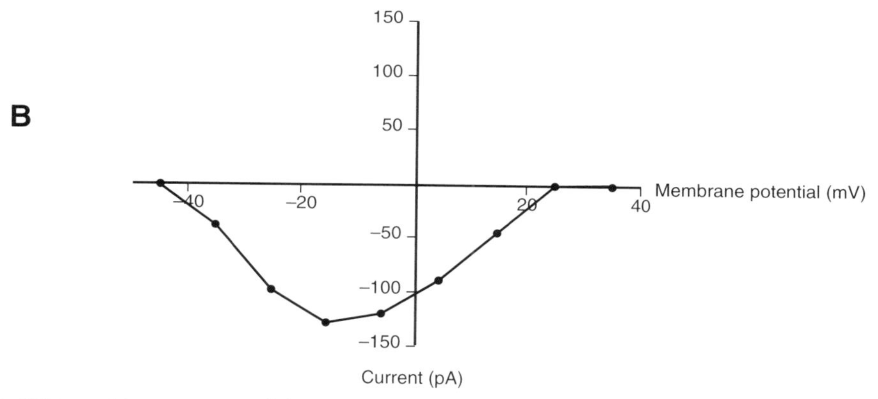

Fig. 1. A) T-type calcium current recorded in response to square depolarising clamp pulses to the potentials indicated given after a 75 ms voltage-clamp ramp, rising at 0.27 mV/ms from –65 to –45 mV. Interpulse 500 ms, in the presence of tetrodotoxin 30 μM and nisoldipine 300 nM. Amphotericin-permeabilised patch whole-cell recording. B) Current–voltage curve for T-type calcium current from the same cell.

voltage-dependence of activation or inactivation is different from that estimated by Hagiwara et al.[2] The steady-state activation of T-type calcium current was obtained by measuring the amplitude of inward currents during step depolarisations from a holding potential of –80 mV to test potentials ranging between –70 and +20 mV. The steady-state inactivation curve was obtained using a double voltage pulse protocol with varying holding potentials followed by a test clamp to –40 mV. Results are plotted in figure 2 (A). Panel B of figure 2 shows the results of Hagiwara et al. for comparison.[2] Results were fitted with a Boltzmann distribution of the form:

$$a = 1/(1 + \exp([V_{mem} - V_{½}]/k))$$

where a = fraction of channels available, V_{mem} = membrane potential and $V_{½}$ = half-activation potential.

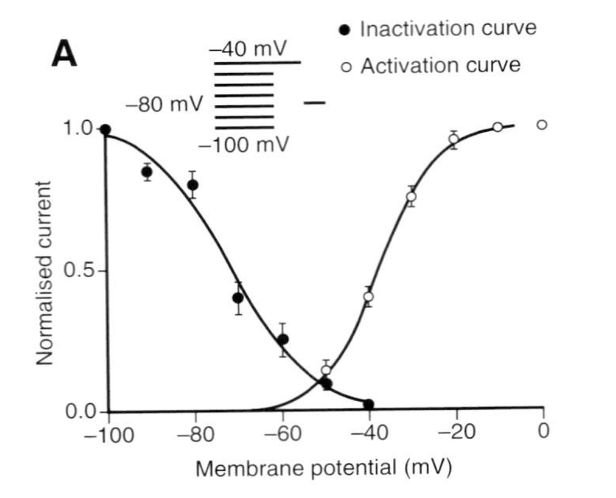

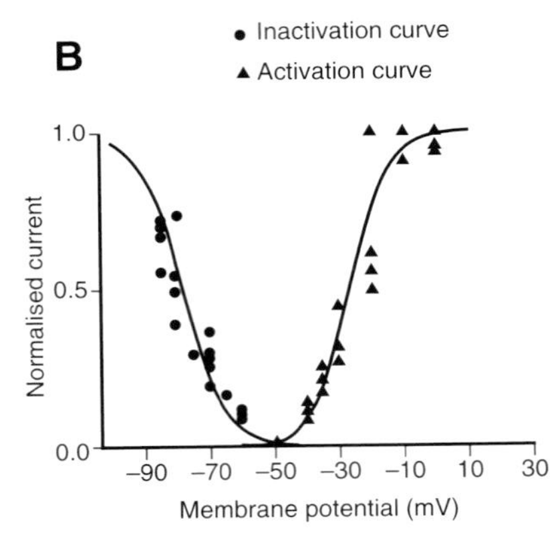

Fig. 2. A) Activation– (d_T) and inactivation– (f_T) voltage relationships for T-type calcium current ($I_{Ca,T}$) in sinoatrial node cells. d_T determined by voltage square pulses (inset) from the holding potential of –80 mV to various potentials. Peak current was normalised during the test potential to +20 mV ($I_{Ca,T}/I_{Ca,Tmax}$). f_T was determined with a double-pulse protocol (inset) and peak currents were normalised during test potential to –40 mV ($I_{Ca,T}/I_{Ca,Tmax}$). Averaged data were fitted by Boltzmann's distribution equation. B) Comparable results from Hagiwara et al.[2]

Between the two sets of data, the results for the activation curves are similar. However, those obtained for the inactivation curve are significantly different.

The half-potential in our results was –71 mV, compared with –75 mV in those of Hagiwara et al.[2] The largest difference, however, lies in the slope factor k, which was 9 mV in our results, compared with 6.1 mV in those of Hagiwara et al.[2] The consequences of this difference are very significant indeed, as they fall within the range of potentials relevant to pacemaker depolarisation.

Reconstructions using a computer model of the sinoatrial node

Activation and inactivation curves may be used to estimate the steady-state current that would be expected to flow through the T-type calcium channels at various potentials. This has been done using the OXSOFT HEART program (version 4.6). Figure 3 (A) shows the activation and inactivation curves fitted by the program to the results of Hagiwara et al.[2] and to our own. The steady-state current that would be expected to flow through the T-type calcium channels has also been computed. There is virtually no region of overlap in the curves determined by Hagiwara et al., and the steady-state current is negligible over the whole voltage range. In the steady state, therefore, as one moves in the depolarising direction the channels become fully inactivated before they can be opened. Since the pacemaker depolarisation shifts the voltage smoothly and relatively slowly, it is not surprising that computation using these activation and inactivation curves showed no contribution of T-type calcium current to pacemaker activity. In contrast, with the curves fitted to the results reported here, there is significant overlap between the activation and inactivation curves. This indicates a significant steady-state current in the pacemaker range.

Panel B of figure 3 shows the results obtained after application of the computer program to mimic the combined ramp–step protocol used to obtain some of our

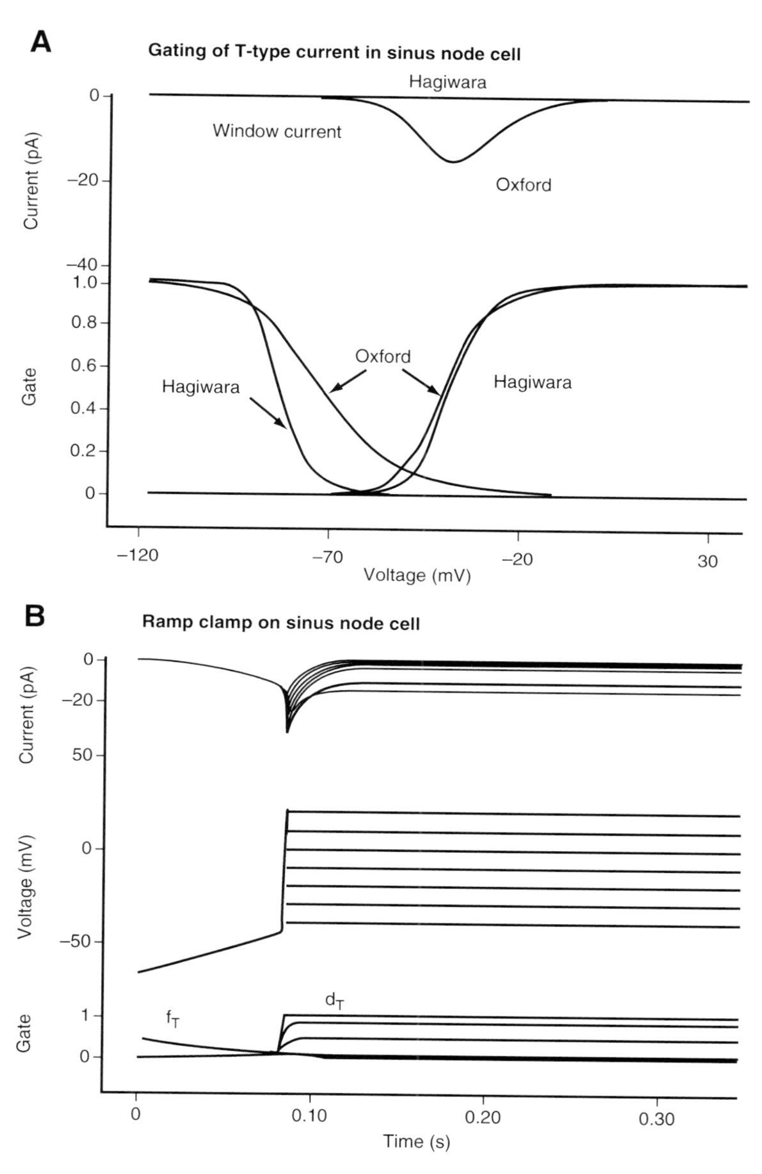

Fig. 3. A) Activation and inactivation curves computed from the OXSOFT HEART program from data of Hagiwara et al.[2] and from data obtained in the present paper. B) Reconstruction of combined ramp–step voltage-clamp protocol using the OXSOFT HEART program. d_T = activation–voltage relationship; f_T = inactivation–voltage relationship.

experimental results. As the steps are applied at the end of the ramp, T-type calcium current is clearly available and the amplitudes are similar to those recorded experimentally (thus answering the second of the questions posed earlier (see p. 104)). There is no need to assume that the history of membrane potentials makes a significant difference to the instantaneous kinetics of the channels in order to reconstruct the ramp–step protocol results, as the computations simply use the activation and inactivation curves obtained in straightforward step-clamp experiments. This is convenient, as it makes computation of the role of T-type calcium current in pacemaker activity easier than it might otherwise have been.

Panel B of figure 4 shows a computation of sinus node pacemaker activity with and without the T-type calcium current. The kinetics of this current were set to the

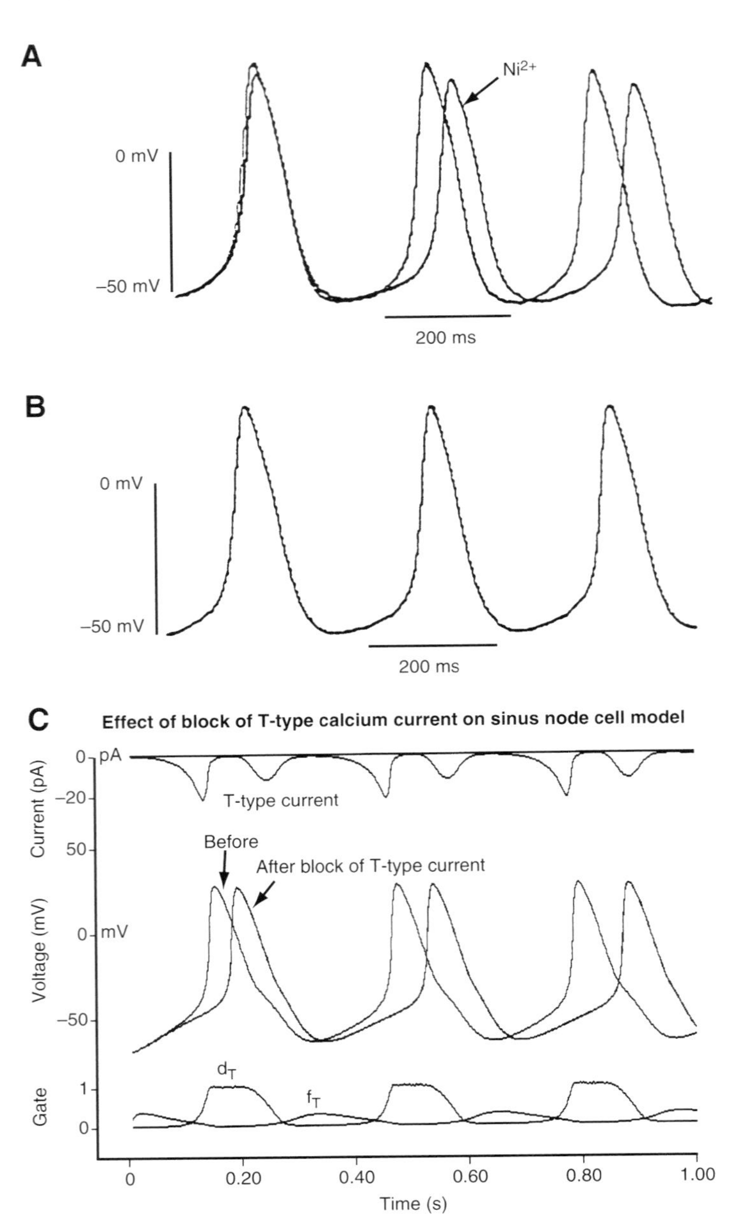

Fig. 4. A) Effect of $NiCl_2$ 40 μM on spontaneous activity of sinoatrial (SA) node cell: superimposed action potentials before and after application of Ni^{2+} 40 μM for 5 min. The diastolic depolarisation rate was decreased and cycle length was prolonged. B) Near-full recovery shown after a 5 min wash. C) OXSOFT HEART model: computation of spontaneous activity in the SA node cell model with results from the present paper. d_T = activation–voltage relationship; f_T = inactivation–voltage relationship.

experimental data obtained in the present work. The current generated by this channel clearly does have a significant effect on frequency. Removing the current from the model reduces the frequency by around 8%, which is very similar to the experimentally determined effect of Ni^{2+} (see fig. 4 (A)).

Conclusions

The main conclusion of this paper is that T-type calcium channels do play a significant modulating role in natural pacemaker activity in the heart. Their presence increases frequency by around 10%. A blocker of these channels would therefore be expected to produce moderate slowing of heart rate.

A second conclusion is that this contribution can be computed from the observed global kinetics of T-type calcium current without the assumption that step and ramp protocols have different effects on the instantaneous kinetics.

It is still unclear as to why the inactivation curves obtained in the present study and in that of Hagiwara et al.[2] are so different. This is puzzling since Hagiwara et al. also observed slowing of pacemaker activity when T-type calcium current was blocked by Ni^{2+}. These authors did not attempt to compute the time-course of T-type calcium current during the pacemaker depolarisation from their own data, but it is clear from our results that this would have revealed a discrepancy. An obvious possibility that might provide an explanation is that the experimental techniques used differ between studies in some significant way. Most importantly, in our study we minimised cell dialysis by using amphotericin-permeabilised patches. It is conceivable that without this precaution the channel properties are affected by run-down as metabolites and ions are changed following application of the patch electrode (e.g. as occurs in the case of the hyperpolarisation-activated channel, I_f).

References

1. Irisawa H, Brown HF, Giles W. Cardiac pacemaking in the sinoatrial node. Physiol Rev 1993; 73: 197–227
2. Hagiwara N, Irisawa H, Kameyama M. Contribution of two types of calcium currents to the pacemaker potentials of rabbit sino-atrial node cells. J Physiol (Lond) 1988; 395: 233–53
3. Lei M, Brown HF, Noble D. Contribution of T-type calcium current to the pacemaker depolarisation of rabbit isolated SA node cells. J Physiol 1995; 487P: 148–9P

Functions of T-type calcium channels in rabbit atrioventricular node and cardiomyopathic hamster ventricle

Xinqiang Han, Luyi Sen, Thomas W. Smith

Cardiovascular Division, Brigham and Women's Hospital, Harvard Medical School, Boston, Massachusetts, USA

Summary

Transmembrane calcium channels control Ca^{2+} entry from the extracellular space. Two distinctive types of calcium channels have been identified in the heart: L type and T type. Ca^{2+} entering through the L-type channels is essential in triggering Ca^{2+} release from internal stores and initiating myocardial contraction. The role of Ca^{2+} entering through the T-type channels in the heart, however, has not been well defined in either physiological or pathological conditions. We studied the T-type current in freshly isolated single cells from the rabbit atrioventricular node and compared the L- and T-type calcium currents in myocytes from the genetically determined cardiomyopathic (CM) hamster heart using the whole-cell patch-clamp technique. T-type calcium current was recorded in the spindle-like cells that manifested spontaneous pacemaker activity (120 $\pm$ 26 beats/min; n=7) from the rabbit atrioventricular node. Low concentrations of Ni^{2+} (50 μM), which preferentially block T-type calcium current, significantly decreased the pacemaker frequency (82 $\pm$ 13 beats/min; n=7). These results suggest that T-type calcium channels participate in conducting electrical signals through the atrioventricular node. To elucidate the role of calcium current in the pathogenesis of myopathy, L- and T-type currents were measured in myopathic and normal control ventricular myocytes from age-matched hamster hearts. Both L- and T-type calcium currents were present in CM and normal cells. L-type current density was the same in CM and normal control myocytes. However, the mean density of T-type current in CM cells was significantly higher than in normal cells (CM, 12.3 $\pm$ 1.8 pA/pF; normal, 5.8 $\pm$ 1.1 pA/pF; n=8; $p<0.01$). T-type calcium current in CM cells was activated and inactivated at more negative potentials than in cells from normal hamster hearts. These findings demonstrate no abnormality of the dihydropyridine-sensitive voltage-dependent L-type calcium channel. In contrast, the observed abnormalities in T-type calcium channel function in CM hamster myocytes suggest that this alteration may be related to the pathogenesis of Ca^{2+} overload and arrhythmias in this genetically determined form of cardiomyopathy.

Introduction

Ca^{2+} ions entering the cell through the sarcolemmal calcium channels in the heart are essential in triggering Ca^{2+} release from internal stores and initiating contraction (excitation–contraction coupling). In electrical terms, the currents generated by influx of Ca^{2+} through the calcium channels contribute to the plateau of the action potential in the working myocardium.[1] By the early 1980s, evidence had mounted to suggest that cardiac calcium channels might differ from those found in various non-cardiac cells.[2,3] The existence of both L- and T-type calcium channels in the heart has been well established since the mid-1980s.[4–6]

While the distributions, properties and functions of the L-type calcium channels have been studied extensively over the past two decades, much is still to be learnt about the cardiac T-type channels that activate and inactivate 'transiently'.[1,7] The T-type calcium channel has not been cloned from the heart. However, current through this type of channel has been found in myocytes from non-diseased guinea-pig ventricle, canine atrium, ventricle and Purkinje fibre, frog atrium and sinus venosus, rabbit sinoatrial node and ventricle, and chick embryonic ventricle.[1] The amplitude of T-type calcium current ranges from approximately 10% of L-type current in guinea-pig ventricle to >100% of L-type current in chick embryonic ventricle. T-type calcium current is not stimulated by cAMP elevation (including β-agonists) or protein kinase A activation, and is not sensitive to the classic calcium channel blockers (e.g. verapamil, diltiazem, nifedipine) at the concentrations normally used. However, T-type current may be stimulated by growth hormone (GH) as well as agents that release diacylglycerol (e.g. angiotensin II (Ang II), endothelin-1, phospholipase C, phorbol esters) and is blocked by low concentrations of Ni^{2+} ions, amiloride, tetramethrin,[8] U-88779E,[9] and more selectively by mibefradil (Ro 40-5967).[10]

The physiological functions of T-type calcium current have yet to be defined. There is some evidence that as a result of its low activation threshold T-type current may contribute to the pacemaker activity in rabbit sinoatrial node[8] and 'latent pacemaker' activity in feline atrium.[11] T-type calcium current may also participate in regulation of cell growth and proliferation, since its amplitude (relative to L-type calcium current) is higher during development than in adulthood in both heart and skeletal tissues. In addition, stimulation of cell growth by GH or growth factors such as endothelin-1, Ang II and phorbol esters coincides with the stimulation of T-type calcium current in these cells. Whether T-type calcium channels play a role in triggering the sarcoplasmic reticulum (SR) calcium release or SR calcium loading remains unresolved.[7]

T-type calcium channel expression may be changed in diseased mammalian myocardium. T-type calcium current is not present in the normal adult feline ventricle. However, long-standing pressure-overload-induced hypertrophy induces T-type channel expression in myocytes isolated from feline left ventricle.[12] Re-expression of T-type calcium current may make hypertrophied myocardium more prone to spontaneous action potentials and increase the likelihood for arrhythmias in partially depolarised hypertrophied myocardium.

The cardiomyopathic (CM) Syrian hamster is known to develop a genetically determined cardiomyopathy, with development of progressive and ultimately fatal congestive heart failure. The myocardium of the CM hamster (Bio 14.6 strain) shows evidence of intracellular Ca^{2+} overload, and it has been suggested that excess free intracellular Ca^{2+} plays an important role in the pathogenesis of this disease. It has long been postulated that increased influx of Ca^{2+} via voltage-sensitive calcium channels may cause Ca^{2+} overload. However, the underlying mechanism by which heart cells of the CM hamster become overloaded with Ca^{2+} remains unknown.[13]

To study the physiological function of T-type calcium channels in normal mammalian heart further, and to elucidate the role of both L- and T-type channels in the pathogenesis of cardiomyopathy, we recorded action potentials and whole-cell calcium currents in single cells isolated from the normal adult rabbit atrioventricular node, CM hamster and age-matched control hamster ventricles. We report here that T-type calcium current was present in the spindle-like atrioventricular nodal cells and may influence the electrical excitation and conduction in the atrioventricular node. Both L- and T-type calcium channels were present in ventricular myocytes from CM (Bio 14.6 strain, 200–300 days old) and age-matched control (FIB) hamsters. The mean density of T-type calcium current in CM cells was significantly higher (>2-fold) than in normal cells, whereas the density of L-type calcium current remained the same in both groups. Thus, Ca^{2+} entry into the myocytes via T-type current may play an important pathogenic role in this cardiomyopathy model.

Methods

Rabbit atrioventricular nodal cell isolation

The technique used for isolation of single atrioventricular nodal cells was as described previously.[14] In brief, heparinised rabbits weighing 1–3 kg were anaesthetised with pentobarbital, then sacrificed by a blow to the neck. Hearts were quickly excised and Langendorff-perfused at 37 °C with:

i) bicarbonate-buffered Tyrode solution for 3 min to wash out the blood
ii) Ca^{2+}-free Tyrode solution for 8 min
iii) enzyme-containing (collagenase 12.5 U/ml; Yakult, Tokyo), Ca^{2+}-free Tyrode solution for a further 10 min.

Small segments of the atrioventricular node were excised from the intact hearts and the surrounding tissues were removed under a dissecting microscope. The final preparations (about 3×4 mm^2) were cut into four pieces and stirred at 37 °C in Ca^{2+}-free, HEPES-buffered Tyrode solution containing collagenase 500 U/ml (Sigma, Type I) and bovine serum albumin 0.1% (Sigma, Fraction V). Cells were collected, centrifuged at 140 g for 5 min and stored at 4 °C in modified KB solution (potassium glutamate 90 mmol/L; oxalate 10 mmol/L; KCL 25 mmol/L; KH_2PO_4 10 mmol/L; taurine 20 mmol/L; EGTA 0.5 mmol/L; HEPES 5 mmol/L; glucose 10 mmol/L; $MgCl_2$ 1 mmol/L; pH 7.2).

Hamster ventricular myocyte isolation

Eight-month-old Bio 14.6 CM and FIB control hamsters were obtained from Bio-breeders (Fitchburg, Massachusetts, USA). Normal and CM hamsters were anaesthetised with ether, and the hearts were rapidly removed. After cannulation of the aorta, the hearts were perfused at a rate of 5 ml/min with oxygenated Krebs-Henseleit (K-H) bicarbonate-buffered solution containing NaCl 118 mmol/L, KCl 4.7 mmol/L, $CaCl_2$ 0.6 mmol/L, $MgSO_4$ 1.2 mmol/L, KH_2PO_4 1.2 mmol/L, $NaHCO_3$ 25 mmol/L and glucose 15 mmol/L at 37 °C for 8 min to wash out the blood. The hearts were then perfused for a further 5 min with a similar solution that contained no $CaCl_2$. Collagenase (0.03%) was added and perfusion continued for an additional 25 min. The ventricular muscle was removed from the perfusion apparatus, cut into 3 mm^3 pieces and placed in a 10 ml flask containing collagenase 0.03%, hyaluronidase 0.015%, trypsin 0.0015%, deoxyribonuclease 0.0015%, and $CaCl_2$ 1 mmol/L in K-H buffer. The flask was shaken at 37 °C for 15 min, and the tissue pieces were transferred to Ca^{2+}-free enzyme buffer with bovine serum albumin 2.0%. Tissue pieces were mechanically dissociated by gently triturating 10–15 times with a 5 ml pipette (tip diameter 3 mm). The isolated myocytes were filtered through Nitex mesh (Tetko, New York, USA) and collected in a centrifuge tube. Cells were centrifuged twice at 500 rpm for 1 min in Ca^{2+}-free K-H buffer to remove the dissociation enzymes. The isolated cells were resuspended in Ca^{2+} 0.6 mmol/L solution. Myocytes were transferred to coverslips coated with collagen. The morphology by phase-contrast microscopy of isolated myocytes from CM and normal hamster was indistinguishable.

Recording methods and data acquisition

In experiments assessing the action potential changes in the rabbit atrioventricular nodal cells, the nystatin-perforated (0.3 mg/ml) patch recording technique was used.[14] The pipette solution contained potassium aspartate 110 mmol/L, KCl 30 mmol/L, NaCl 6 mmol/L, $MgCl_2$ 1 mmol/L and HEPES 5 mmol/L. The pH was adjusted to 7.2 with KOH. The DC resistance of the microelectrode was 1–3 MΩ and recordings were made at 32.5 °C. The conventional suction microelectrode in the whole-cell configuration was applied to record both L- and T-type calcium current.[15] In these experiments, the pipette solution included caesium aspartate 135 mmol/L, caesium-EGTA 10 mmol/L, HEPES 10 mmol/L, sodium phosphocreatine 3 mmol/L, ATP 4 mmol/L, $MgCl_2$ 5 mmol/L and EGTA 10 mmol/L at pH 7.2. A liquid junction potential of approximately –10 mV was corrected electronically. The electrode resistance was between 1 and 2 MΩ, and after compensation the series resistance was <3 MΩ. Recordings were made at 22–24 °C. Data were discarded from experiments in which run-down of L-type calcium current was >10%. An Axon amplifier (Axopatch 1C; Axon Instruments, Foster City, California, USA) was used for voltage clamp. Protocol generation, data acquisition and storage were controlled by an IBM/AT computer (Compaq) and a 12-bit A/D converter with the use of pCLAMP 6.0 software (Axon Instruments, Foster City, California, USA). Data were filtered at 3 kHz and analysed off line. Cell capacitance was calculated by dividing the area under a capacitative transient by the voltage step used to induce it (from –80 to –75 mV).

Statistical analysis

Statistical analysis was performed by ANOVA or paired t-test where appropriate. Results were expressed as mean ± SD; p values <0.05 were considered significant.

Results

We first studied whether T-type calcium current could be recorded from rabbit atrioventricular nodal cells. In these experiments, only those spindle-shaped cells that exhibited spontaneous activity were used. A test depolarisation to –30 mV from a holding potential of –50 mV (fig. 1 (A)) only activated a small inward L-type calcium current (a). In the same cell, a test pulse from –90 mV to –30 mV elicited a much larger inward current (b) that was subsequently blocked by Ni^{2+} 50 µmol/L (c). Using the same protocol, we compared the amplitudes of peak L- and T-type calcium current in the same atrioventricular nodal cell (see fig. 1 (B)). T-type current was activated by the same protocol as in panel A of figure 1, and L-type current was activated by depolarisation to 0 mV from a holding potential of –40 mV. The Ni^{2+}-sensitive T-type calcium current was 18 ± 7% of L-type current (n=6).

As a result of its low threshold, the presence of T-type calcium current in the atrioventricular nodal cells may suggest that the role of this current lies in pacemaker generation or in the conduction of electrical excitation. This was tested in experiments in which only cells that showed a relatively fast pacemaker frequency were used. Ni^{2+} at a concentration of 50 µmol/L significantly decreased the frequency of the spontaneous action potentials (SAP) and inhibited the phase 4 spontaneous depolarisation (fig. 2). In 7 cells, the SAP frequency was 120 ± 26 beats/min in the absence of Ni^{2+} and 82 ± 13 beats/min after Ni^{2+} application (p<0.05).

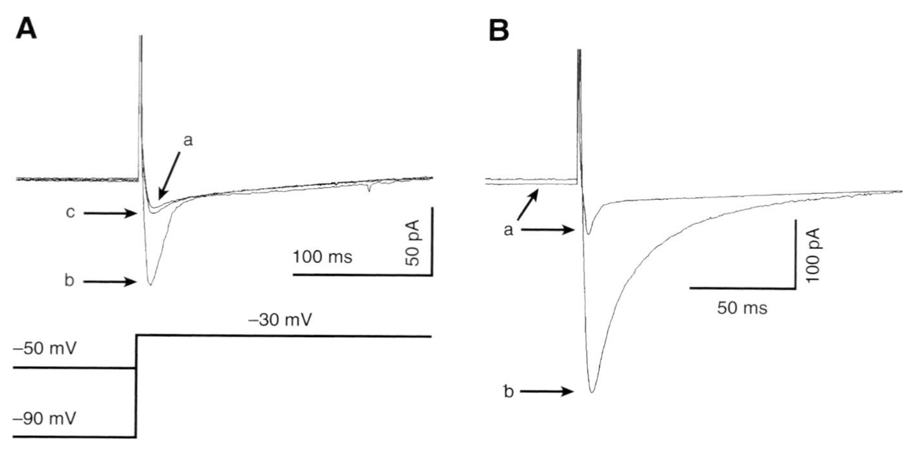

Fig. 1. T-type calcium current in rabbit atrioventricular nodal cells. A) Superimposed current traces (top) and the activation protocol. Traces a and b were elicited by depolarisation to –30 mV from a holding potential of –50 and –90 mV, respectively. Trace c was obtained in the presence of Ni^{2+} 50 µmol/L and was generated by the same protocol as for trace b. B) Superimposed current traces showing T- (a) and L-type calcium current (b) in the same cell. L-type current was activated from –40 to 0 mV and T-type current from –90 to –30 mV.

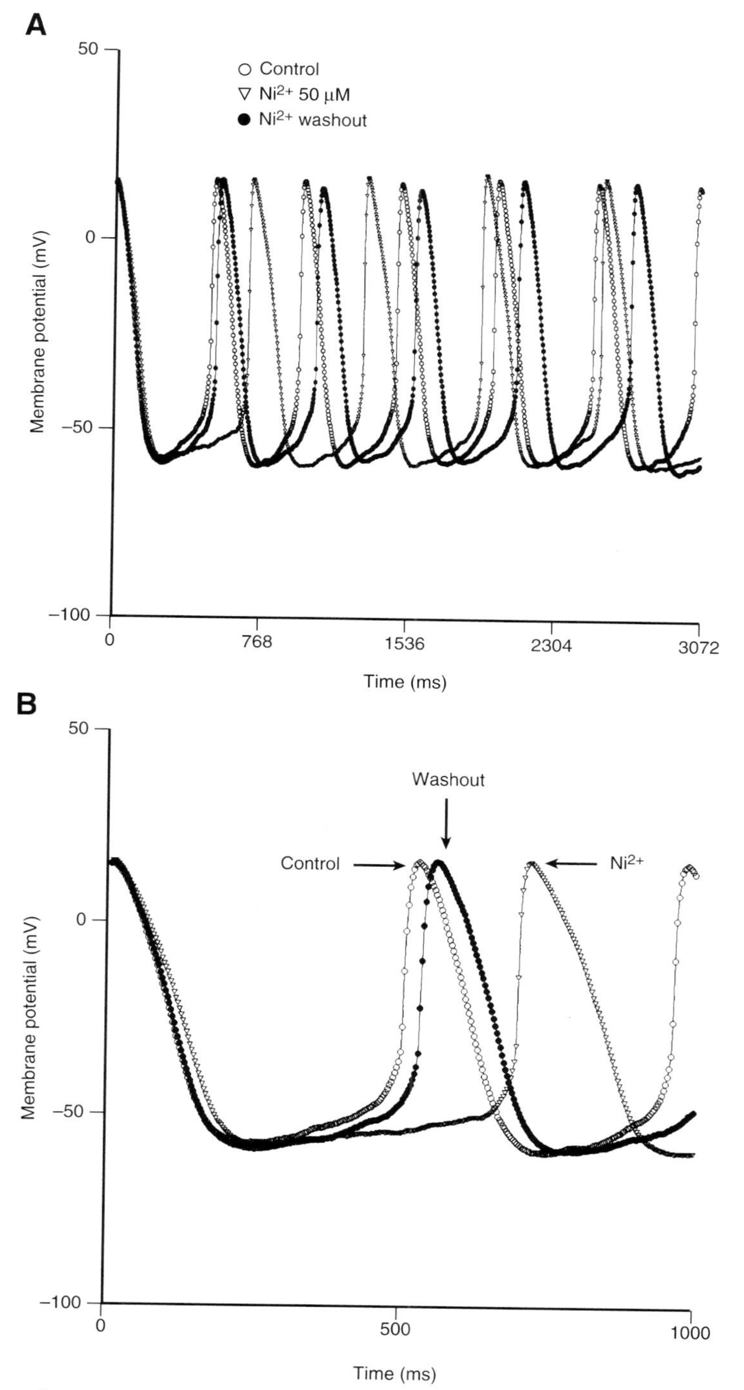

Fig. 2. Effects of Ni^{2+} 50 μmol/L on the frequency of spontaneous action potentials recorded in single atrioventricular (AV) nodal cells. A) Superimposed spontaneous action potentials recorded under control, Ni^{2+} application and washout of Ni^{2+} in a single AV nodal cell. B) Action potentials from panel A illustrated in extended time-scale. Ni^{2+} inhibited the frequency of spontaneous action potential and pacemaker activity (phase 4 depolarisation) without significantly affecting the maximum diastolic potential or the action potential amplitude.

Detailed studies of T-type calcium current in cells from normal and CM hamster ventricles were performed.[13] Both L- and T-type current could be recorded from normal and CM cells using the same protocol as described above (fig. 3 (A)). In CM cells, T-type calcium current was a regular observation. However, in some normal cells (5 of 25), no T-type current was detectable. The two inward currents differed not only in their kinetics and dependence on holding potential but also in their sensitivity to Ni^{2+} 40 mmol/L or nifedipine 1 µmol/L (see fig. 3 (B)). Panel C of figure 3 shows

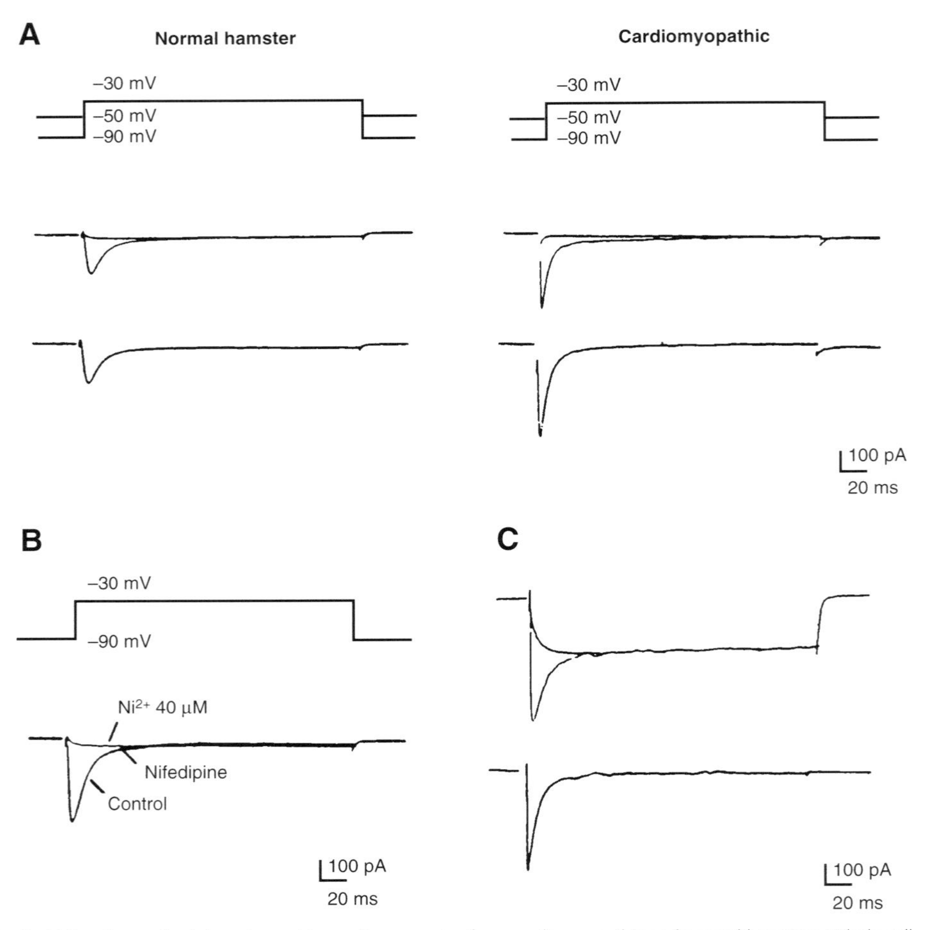

Fig. 3. A) Two types of calcium channel in cardiac myocytes from cardiomyopathic and normal hamsters. Whole-cell currents carried by Ba^{2+} (20 mmol/L) are shown in response to voltage-clamp steps to –30 mV. Two currents elicited from holding potentials of –50 and –90 mV are superimposed (upper traces). The extra component of current activated from the more negative holding potential is shown as the difference between the two current traces (lower traces). The capacitance of the normal cell shown was 141 pF and for the myopathic cell was 145 pF. B) Effects of Ni^{2+} and nifedipine on the T-type calcium current in cardiomyopathic myocytes. Transient barium current elicited from a holding potential of –90 mV is shown. T-type currents before and during administration of nifedipine 10 µmol/L were completely superimposable. However, Ni^{2+} 40 µmol/L completely abolished the T-type current. The same effect was found in normal cells (data not shown). Solutions and patch-clamp methods are the same as in panel A. C) Effects of the dihydropyridine calcium channel agonist (+)PN 202-791 on two types of calcium currents. The figure shows superposition of whole-cell barium currents elicited from two holding potentials. The same myopathic cell is shown as in panel A. Exposure to (+)PN 202-791 1 mM selectively increased the L-type current without effect on the T-type current. Lower trace is T-type current isolated by subtracting the current of –50 mV holding potential from the current of –90 mV holding potential. The same effect was observed in normal cells.

that the dihydropyridine calcium channel agonist (+)PN 202-791[16] selectively increased the maintained current component but had no effect on the transient current in CM cells. Similar results were found in normal cells (data not shown). T-type calcium current was not changed by tetrodotoxin (TTX) 30 μmol/L in either normal or CM cells.[5] However, TTX completely blocked sodium current in both CM and normal cells (data not shown).

The peak T-type calcium current was larger in myocytes from CM versus normal hamsters, while the cells from normal and CM hamster hearts had similar cell capacitance (see fig. 3 (A)). We compared the density of L- and T-type calcium currents, since the mean cell capacitance was significantly greater in CM myocytes (presumably because of cell hypertrophy) than that in age-matched normal myocytes.[17] With Ba^{2+} 20 mmol/L as the charge carrier, the density of T-type calcium current in CM cells was significantly higher than that in normal cells (12.3 ± 1.8 pA/pF and 5.8 ± 1.1 pA/pF, respectively; n=8; $p<0.01$) (fig. 4). The current–voltage relationship of T-type calcium current was shifted in a hyperpolarising direction when compared to the normal cells. Maximal T-type current was activated at –30 mV in normal cells and at –40 mV in the CM cells. These results indicate that there is a substantial increase in the density of T-type calcium current in cardiac myocytes from the CM hamsters.

In contrast, L-type calcium current density (holding potential, –50 mV; test potential, –10 mV) remained unchanged in CM and normal cells (17.8 ± 1.5 *vs* 18.6 ± 2.1 pA/pF,

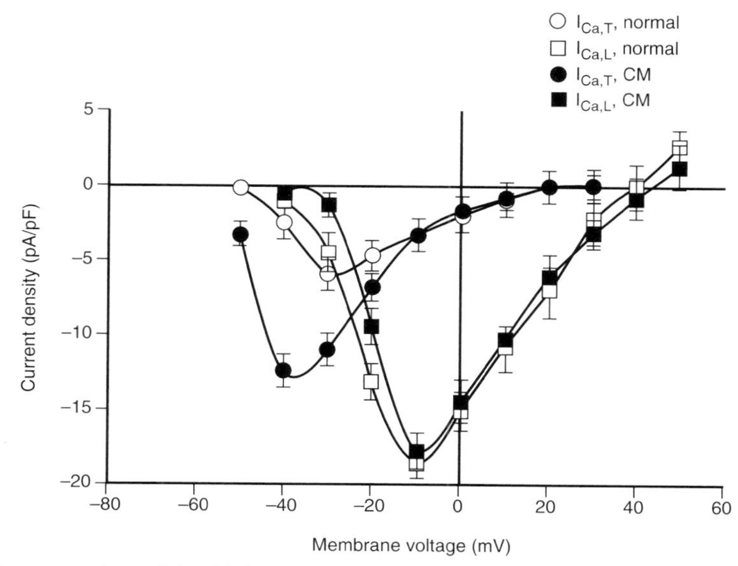

Fig. 4. Peak current–voltage relationship for two types of calcium channels in ventricular myocytes from normal and cardiomyopathic (CM) hamsters. T-type calcium current ($I_{Ca,T}$) density is plotted for normal and CM cells. The current was obtained at various test potentials from holding potentials of –90 and –50 mV. $I_{Ca,T}$ was identified by subtracting observed currents elicited from a holding potential of –50 mV from values observed using a holding potential of –90 mV. L-type calcium current ($I_{Ca,L}$) density is shown for normal and CM cells. The current was obtained at various test potentials from a holding potential of –50 mV. Calcium currents were measured as peak inward currents in reference to zero current. Each point demonstrates a mean value ± SEM of the current density (n=8) of each calcium channel type. Cell capacitance was measured from the capacitative current elicited by a small step depolarisation.

respectively; n=8; $p>0.4$). The current–voltage relationship of L-type calcium current showed an apparent threshold at –40 mV, a maximum at –10 mV and an apparent reversal potential at +40 mV in both CM and age-matched normal controls. There was no statistically significant difference in each test potential-induced current change in CM or normal cells. These results demonstrate that there was no measurable difference in the properties of L-type calcium current in ventricular myocytes from CM versus normal hamsters.

The kinetic properties of L- and T-type calcium current were compared further in CM and normal myocytes. In figure 5 (A), superimposed traces of T-type current were obtained from various holding potentials to a test potential of –30 mV. Panel B of figure 5 shows superimposed traces of L-type calcium current elicited at +20 mV from varying holding potentials. L- and T-type calcium currents were normalised and plotted against the membrane potentials in panels C and D of figure 5. The degree of steady-state inactivation and activation revealed a sigmoidal relationship with voltage. The steady-state activation parameter was obtained by normalising the peak conductance with the maximum available conductance as follows:

$$d_{\infty} = g_{Ca}/g_{Ca,max} = I_{Ca}/g_{Ca}\,(V_{mem} - E_{rev})$$

where g_{Ca} is the peak conductance, $g_{Ca,max}$ the maximum value of g_{Ca}, I_{Ca} the peak calcium current, V_{mem} the membrane potential and E_{rev} the reversal potential of the calcium current.[5] E_{rev} was assumed to be the zero-current potential in the current–voltage relationship. The continuous curves in panels C and D of figure 5 were calculated according to:

$$y_{\infty} = [1 + \exp(V_{mem} - V_{½})/S]^{-1}$$

where y is either steady-state inactivation or steady-state activation, $V_{½}$ is the potential to give a half value, and S is the slope factor that defines the steepness of the curve. The inactivation and activation parameters were fitted well by the Boltzmann function. T-type calcium current in CM cells inactivated at more negative holding potentials and was half inactivated at –88.7 ± 0.8 mV. In comparison, normal cells were half inactivated at –76.8 ± 0.6 mV (n=6; $p<0.01$). The slope factor of the steady-state inactivation curve was 9.0 ± 0.8 mV in CM cells and 6.1 ± 0.6 mV in normal cells. The steady-state inactivation curve of T-type calcium current in CM myocytes was thus shifted by approximately 12 mV negative to that in normal cells, whereas its activation curve was shifted by 8 mV negative ($V_{½}$ = –53.1 ± 0.4 mV in CM cells and –43.2 ± 0.7 mV in normal cells). However, L-type calcium current revealed similar slope factors of steady-state inactivation and activation, as well as half-inactivated and activated potentials in CM (11.3 ± 0.8 mV and 9.9 ± 0.4 mV, –25.6 ± 0.9 mV and –4.3 ± 0.4 mV, respectively) and normal cells (10.2 ± 0.7 mV and 9.2 ± 0.5 mV, –25.3 ± 0.8 mV and –4.5 ± 0.5 mV, respectively; n=6; $p>0.1$).

Figure 6 (A) shows peak current–voltage relationships recorded from 5 normal and 5 CM cells in Ca^{2+} 5 mmol/L and then after substituting extracellular Ca^{2+} with equimolar Ba^{2+}. Similar to the observations made in other tissues,[5,18] Ba^{2+}

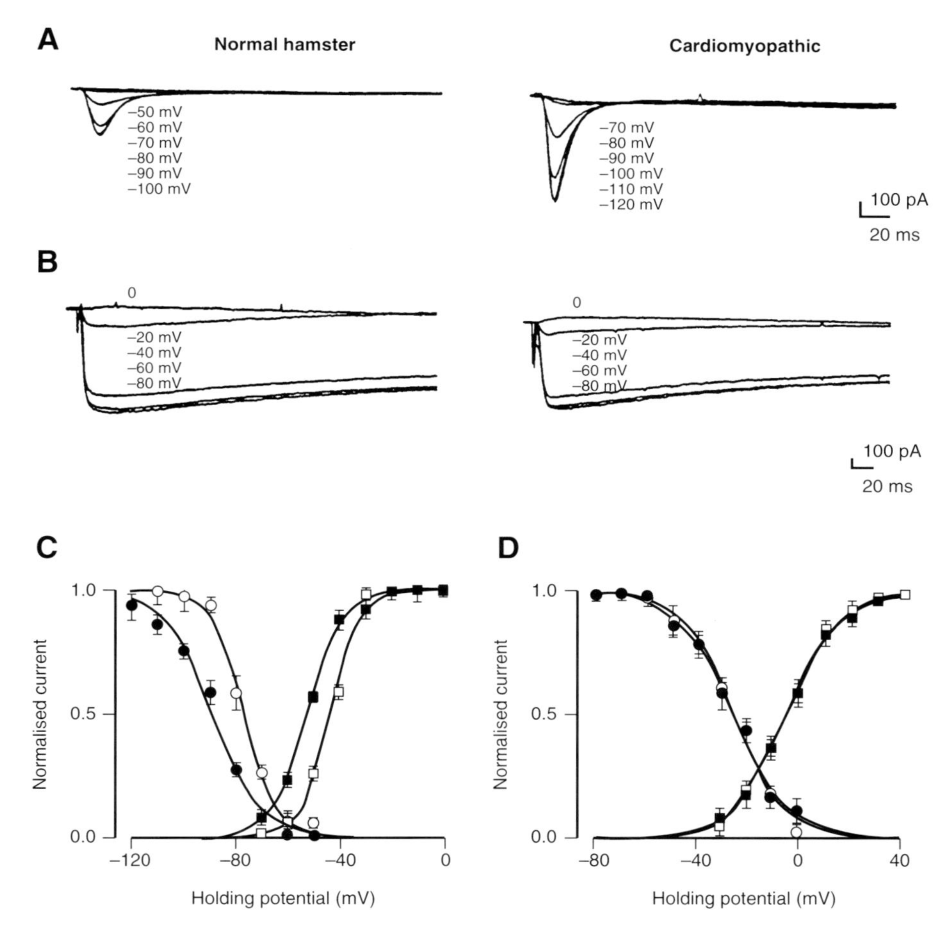

Fig. 5. A) T-type calcium current from cardiomyopathic (CM) and normal hamster cells. The currents were elicited by a test pulse of 2 s duration to –30 mV from various holding potentials. T-type current was isolated by subtraction as in panel A of fig. 3. B) Superimposed traces of L-type calcium currents from CM and normal cells. The currents were elicited at +20 mV from various holding potentials. C) Voltage-dependence of inactivation and activation of transient inactivating currents in normal (○, □) and CM myocytes (●, ■). The inactivation of T-type current was obtained by measuring Ca^{2+}-activated current at –30 mV from various holding potentials. The calcium current was normalised to the peak current elicited from a holding potential of –140 mV. The results (○, ●) were plotted against holding potentials and fitted to the Boltzmann equation. The activation (■, □) of T-type current was obtained by measuring peak T-type current elicited at various test potentials from a holding potential of –90 mV. The smooth curve was drawn according to the Boltzmann equation. D) Voltage-dependence of inactivation and activation of slowly inactivating currents in normal (○, □) and CM (●, ■) myocytes. Inactivation (○, ●) and activation (■, □) of slowly inactivating current were obtained as described in panel B. For steady-state inactivation, currents were elicited by a test pulse to +20 mV. For activation, current was obtained from a holding potential of –50 mV.

substitution greatly augmented L-type calcium current and slowed its decay. The changes induced by different charge carriers were identical in both normal and CM cells. As shown in panels B–D of figure 6, L-type current amplitudes are unaffected by CM cells, regardless of the external divalent, whereas the density of this current is consistently increased by more than 2-fold in all cases.[13] This suggests that Ca^{2+} and Ba^{2+} are about equally able to permeate through the T-type calcium channel in both normal and CM cells.

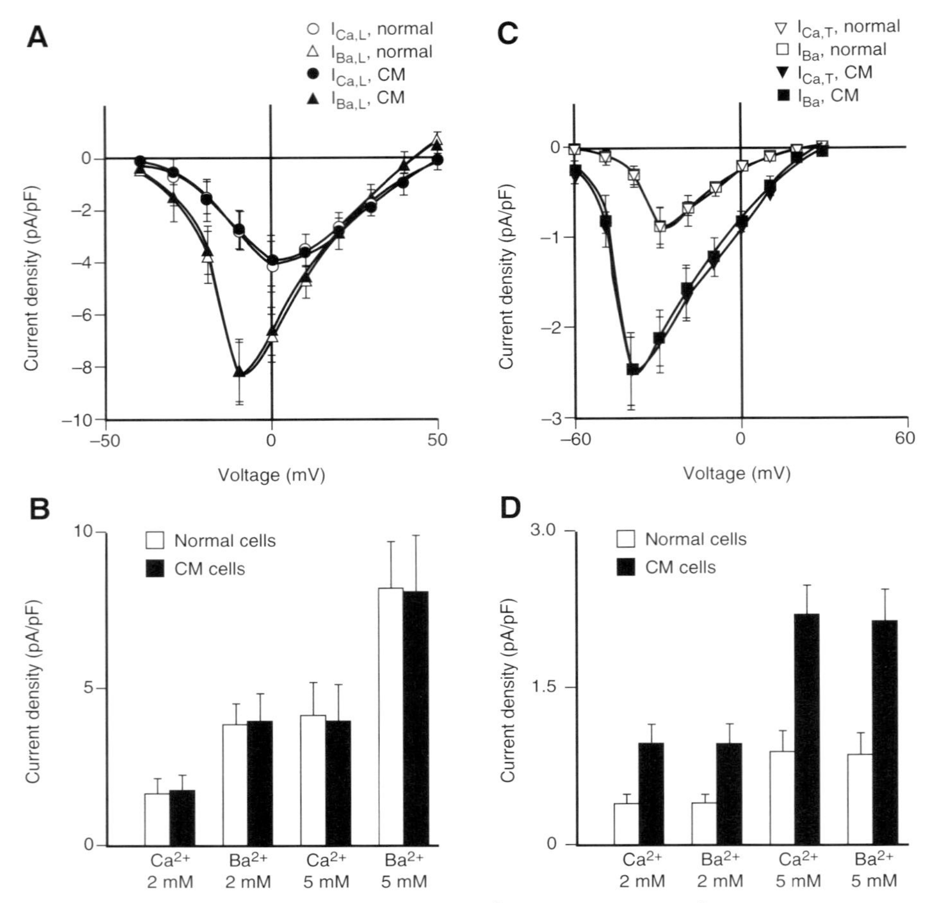

Fig. 6. A) Peak current–voltage relation for L-type current in Ca^{2+} 5 mmol/L ($I_{Ca,L}$) and Ba^{2+} 5 mmol/L ($I_{Ba,L}$) in the same normal or CM cells shown in figure 5. Values in Ca^{2+} 5 mmol/L were obtained 6 min before changing to Ba^{2+} 5 mmol/L. The current was obtained at various test potentials from a holding potential of –50 mV. Each point demonstrates a mean value ± SEM of the current density (n=5). B) Mean values ± SEM of the current densities of the L-type channel carried by Ca^{2+} or Ba^{2+} 2 and 5 mmol/L in normal and CM cells (n=8). Currents were measured after leak-subtraction at the peak of the current–voltage relationship in normal cells. C) Peak current–voltage relationship for T-type current in Ca^{2+} 5 mmol/L ($I_{Ca,T}$) and Ba^{2+} 5 mmol/L (I_{Ba}) in the same normal or CM cells. The current was obtained at various test potentials from holding potentials of –90 and –50 mV. T-type current was identified by subtracting observed currents elicited from a holding potential of –50 mV from values observed using a holding potential of –90 mV. Each point demonstrates a mean value ± SEM of the current density (n=5). D) Mean values ± SEM of T-type current density carried by Ca^{2+} or Ba^{2+} 2 and 5 mmol/L in normal and CM cells (n=8). Currents were measured after leak-subtraction at the peak of the current–voltage relationship in normal cells.

Discussion

The physiological role of the T-type calcium channel has yet to be clearly defined. The highest density of T-type channels is found in cells that do not have a well-developed T-tubular system, such as nodal cells and embryonic cardiac myocytes.[7,19] The low threshold of T-type calcium current is suited for participation in pacemaker generation.[20] The present experiments suggest that rabbit atrioventricular nodal cells express T-type calcium channels and that modulation of T-type current may affect the pacemaker generation and electrical conduction through this region.

Although this is the first report to focus on a comparison of both T- and L-type calcium channel properties in CM and normal hamster cardiac myocytes, these experimental observations should be considered in the context of other studies of the properties of cardiac myocytes from the CM hamster. Other authors have reported that calcium channel antagonists, when administered *in vivo*, preserve contractile function in myopathic hearts.[21,22] While these studies employed drugs thought to act chiefly or entirely on L-type calcium channels, a number of coronary and peripheral vascular (as well as myocardial) sites of action of calcium channel antagonists could contribute to the effect. Thus, we do not view the present observations as contradicting a direct effect of verapamil on myocytes.[23]

The L-type current densities we observed in normal and myopathic cells are quantitatively lower than that reported by an early study,[24] possibly because of the different animal ages and different experimental conditions. The shift observed in T-type calcium channel voltage-dependencies of inactivation and activation might partially counteract the effect of an increase in T-type calcium current density at the normal resting potential. However, as we have shown (fig. 4 and 6), even with 42% channel inactivation, the density of the T-type calcium current in CM cells is still 2.3-fold higher than that in normal cells. At a –80 mV holding potential, T-type calcium current was still 1.8-fold higher in CM versus normal cells. This significant increase in T-type current density could not be completely abolished by the observed voltage shift in inactivation. Interestingly, this shift in voltage-dependencies could move the voltage range for the T-type window current toward the resting potential.[25] This abnormality might promote spontaneous beating or arrhythmias in CM tissue.[26]

The experimental data presented herein permit several conclusions to be drawn regarding calcium homeostasis in the Bio 14.6 CM hamster heart. The L-type calcium channels show no demonstrable abnormality as judged by whole-cell clamp studies, confirming our finding of no appreciable difference in numbers of dihydropyridine binding sites in cells from the same source.[23] The lack of change in affinity for a dihydropyridine ligand is also consistent with the absence of any major change in the structure of the channel, at least in the dihydropyridine binding domain. Although no difference in sodium current density was observed between CM and age-matched normal cells, we cannot exclude the possibility that there was abnormal sodium channel expression, since the present study was conducted with only 40 mmol/L of Na^+ in the extracellular solution. Measurement of sodium current with more physiological extracellular Na^+ is needed to compare sodium current density and kinetics in this experimental model.

Our results indicate that there is considerably increased T-type calcium current density in cardiac myocytes from CM hamsters and that these channels show abnormal activation and inactivation kinetics. Overexpression of the T-type calcium channel is likely to be a cellular response (proliferative response to increased workload of the myocardium during development of cardiomyopathy. This change in T-type calcium channel properties may be a clue to the pathogenic process, but its role in

Ca^{2+} overload is not clear. The abnormal T-type calcium channel properties in this genetically determined cardiomyopathy suggest that this alteration may contribute to the pathogenesis of Ca^{2+} overload as a consequence of enhanced transsarcolemmal Ca^{2+} influx through this pathway. The increase of T-type calcium current might also contribute to the abnormalities in electrophysiological properties and arrhythmogenic potential in this form of cardiomyopathy.

Acknowledgements

This study was supported by National Institutes of Health grants HL-36141 and HL-52320 to Dr T.W. Smith.

References

1. McDonald TF, Pelzer S, Trautwein W, et al. Regulation and modulation of calcium channels in cardiac, skeletal, and smooth muscle cells. Physiol Rev 1994; 72: 365–507
2. Hagiwara S, Byerly L. Calcium channels. Annu Rev Neurosci 1981; 4: 69–125
3. Tsien RW. Calcium channels in excitable cell membranes. Annu Rev Physiol 1983; 45: 341–58
4. Nilius B, Hess P, Lansman JB, et al. A novel type of cardiac calcium channel in ventricular cells. Nature 1985; 316: 443–6
5. Bean BP. Two kinds of calcium channels in canine atrial cells. J Gen Physiol 1985; 86: 1–30
6. Mitra R, Morad M. Two types of calcium channels in guinea pig ventricular myocytes. Proc Natl Acad Sci U S A 1986; 83: 5340–4
7. Katz AM. Calcium channel diversity in the cardiovascular system. J Am Coll Cardiol 1996; 28: 522–9
8. Hagiwara N, Irisawa H, Kameyama M. Contribution of two types of calcium currents to pacemaker potentials of rabbit sino-atrial node cells. J Physiol (Lond) 1988; 395: 233–53
9. Im HK, Im WB, Tsuzuki K. Selective block of transient Ca channel current in mouse neuroblastoma cells by U-88779E. J Pharmacol Exp Ther 1993; 265: 529–35
10. Mishra SK, Hermsmeyer K. Selective inhibition of T-type Ca^{2+} channels by Ro 40-5967. Circ Res 1994; 75: 144–8
11. Zhou Z, Lipsius SL. T-type calcium current in latent pacemaker cells isolated from cat right atrium. J Mol Cell Cardiol 1994; 26: 1211–19
12. Nuss HB, Houser SR. T-type Ca^{2+} current is expressed in hypertrophied adult feline left ventricular myocytes. Circ Res 1993; 73: 777–82
13. Sen L, Smith TW. T-type Ca^{2+} channels are abnormal in genetically determined cardiomyopathic hamster hearts. Circ Res 1994; 75: 149–55
14. Han X, Kobzik L, Balligand J-L, et al. Nitric oxide synthase (NOS3)-mediated cholinergic modulation of Ca^{2+} current in adult rabbit atrioventricular nodal cells. Circ Res 1996; 78: 998–1008
15. Hamill O, Marty A, Neher E, et al. Improved patch clamp techniques for high-resolution current recording from cells and cell-free membrane patches. Pflugers Arch 1981; 391: 85–100
16. Hof RP, Ruegg A, Hof A, et al. Stereoselectivity at the calcium channel: opposite action of the enantiomers of a 1,4-dihydropyridine. J Cardiovasc Pharmacol 1985; 7: 689–93
17. Sen L, O'Neill M, Marsh JD, et al. Myocyte structure, function and calcium kinetics in the cardiomyopathic hamster heart. Am J Physiol 1990; 259: H1533–43
18. Shorofsky SR, January CT. L- and T-type Ca^{2+} channels in canine cardiac Purkinje cells: single-channel demonstration of L-type Ca^{2+} window current. Circ Res 1992; 70: 456–64
19. Bogdanov KY, Ziman BD, Spurgeon HA, et al. L- and T-type calcium currents differ in finch and rat ventricular cardiomyocytes. J Mol Cell Cardiol 1995; 27: 2581–93
20. Irisawa H, Brown HF, Giles WR. Cardiac pacemaking in the sino-atrial node. Physiol Rev 1993; 73: 197–227
21. Rouleau JL, Chuek LHS, Hollosi G, et al. Verapamil preserves myocardial contractility in the hereditary cardiomyopathy of the Syrian hamster. Circ Res 1982; 50: 40–8
22. Sole MJ, Liew CC. Catecholamines, calcium and cardiomyopathy. Am J Cardiol 1988; 62: 20–4G
23. Sen L, O'Neill M, Marsh JD, et al. Inotropic and calcium kinetic effects of calcium channel agonist and antagonist in isolated cardiac myocytes from cardiomyopathic hamsters. Circ Res 1990; 67: 599–608
24. Rossner KL. Calcium current in congestive heart failure of hamster cardiomyopathy. Am J Physiol 1991; 260: H1179–86
25. Hirano Y, Fozzard HA, January CT. Characteristics of L- and T-type Ca^{2+} currents in canine cardiac Purkinje cells. Am J Physiol 1989; 256: H1478–92
26. January CT, Chau V, Makielski JC. Triggered activity in the heart: cellular mechanisms of early after-depolarisation. Eur Heart J 1991; 12: 4–9

T-type calcium currents in vascular smooth muscle cells: a role in cellular proliferation?

Sylvain Richard, Joël Nargeot

Centre de Recherches de Biochimie Macromoléculaire, Centre National de la Recherche Scientifique, Montpellier, France

Summary

Transmembrane voltage-gated calcium channels constitute the main route for Ca^{2+} entry in vascular smooth muscle cells (VSMCs). VSMCs can express two distinct types of calcium current: L type, which plays a central role in the development and maintenance of contractile tone, and T type, the physiological role of which is more obscure. It was first suggested that T-type calcium current had a role in the pacemaker activity of spontaneously contractile primary-cultured azygos vein VSMCs. However, there is also evidence that T-type calcium current is expressed in relation to cell dedifferentiation and proliferation of arterial myocytes grown in vitro. *T-type calcium current is absent in freshly isolated differentiated arterial myocytes (e.g. rat aortic myocytes, human coronary and aortic myocytes) but appears when cells are primary-cultured. The expression of T-type calcium current is transient and parallels proliferation and concomitant loss of contractility of cells. T-type calcium current disappears when confluence is reached. The expression of T-type calcium current is related to cell-cycling activity. T-type calcium current is expressed predominantly during the G_1–S phase of the cell cycle. It is not expressed when cells are quiescent (in the G_0 phase induced by serum deprivation). Therefore one possible role of T-type calcium channels may be gene activation, necessary for cell replication and growth.*

The contractile activity of vascular smooth muscle cells (VSMCs) is modulated by the concentration of free cytosolic Ca^{2+}. The passage of extracellular Ca^{2+} across the highly resistant plasma membrane into the cytoplasmic compartment in response to hormonal or electrical stimuli is important. Ca^{2+} enters via a finite number of ion-selective channels. Voltage-gated calcium channels constitute the main route and therefore have a major role in the development and maintenance of contractile tone. These channels open primarily in response to changes in membrane potential that can be brought about through agonist–receptor stimulation by hormones and neurotransmitters. In contrast to neurons, VSMCs express only two major types of calcium current: the L type and the T type, also often referred to as 'low-voltage-activated current'. Although L-type calcium current plays a central role in excitation–contraction coupling, the role of T-type calcium current is more obscure. In this review, we focus on T-type current and, more specifically, on its possible role in the proliferation of VSMCs.

T-type calcium current in vascular smooth muscle cells

T-type calcium channels have been found in a wide variety of excitable and non-excitable cells.[1–5] It is highly probable that they represent heterogeneous subgroups of calcium channels with significant differences in functional properties.[2,3] L- and

T-type calcium channels have distinct electrophysiological and pharmacological properties. During voltage-clamp depolarisation, T-type calcium current is characterised by a fast decay, whereas that of L-type current is slower (fig. 1 (A)). Overall, they differ in their activation thresholds and voltage-dependent availabilities for opening (i.e. current as a function of the resting cell membrane potentials; see fig. 1 (B)). At physiological concentrations of extracellular Ca^{2+}, L-type calcium current activates at depolarisations greater than or equal to –30 mV, whereas T-type calcium current begins to activate at much more negative voltages (~–60 mV), as illustrated in panels A and B of figure 1. L-type calcium current is fully available at the resting membrane potential of –50 mV, whereas T-type calcium current requires more negative potentials (see fig. 1 (B)). In addition to differing unitary conductances, T- and L-type calcium channels have clearly distinct regulatory and pharmacological properties. For example, L-type calcium current is the preferred target for synthetic ligands (widely referred to as 'calcium antagonists' and including dihydropyridines, phenylalkylamines and benzothiazepines). In contrast, there is a lack of specific ligands for T-type calcium current, but the new compound mibefradil (Ro 40-5967), which selects T-type current, presents some very interesting perspectives.[6–8]

T-type calcium channels are found in various types of VSMC isolated from veins and arteries. T-type calcium current was first recorded in primary-cultured VSMCs isolated from neonatal rat azygos and adult rat portal veins,[9,10] freshly isolated saphenous vein VSMCs[11] and from rat tail artery and rabbit ear and mesenteric arteries.[12–16] T-type calcium current has also been recorded in primary-cultured myocytes[17–24] and in A7R5 and A10 cell lines[25,26] derived from rat aorta. However, it is worth noting that high concentrations of Ba^{2+} are often required to detect T-type currents. The subdivision of the global calcium channel current within T and L components may also have been oversimplified in some studies.[27] This may be particularly true for some types of VSMC, recorded immediately after isolation, which clearly lack T-type calcium current. This is the case for VSMCs isolated from rat aorta[21,23] and from both rabbit and human coronary arteries,[23,28] although T-type current has been found in freshly isolated VSMCs from the rabbit ear artery and guinea-pig coronary artery.[12,27,29] Differences in the nature of myocytes from various sources (different tissues, species and sizes), and variations in recording conditions and physiological states could also account in part for this variability. It could be argued that the enzymatic procedure damages the T-type calcium channel protein. However, in aortic VSMCs, we have noted that: (i) T-type calcium current can be recorded consistently in neonatal rat ventricular cells dispersed using the same enzymes (unpublished observations), (ii) cultured cells can still express T-type calcium current following enzymatic treatment, and (iii) of major interest, there is a clear correlation between cell-cycling activity during proliferation and the expression of T-type calcium current (see p. 126).

Possible role(s) of T-type calcium current in VSMCs

There is a general agreement that tension of arterial smooth muscle is highly sensitive to L-type selective calcium channel inhibitors.[30] L-type current is consistently

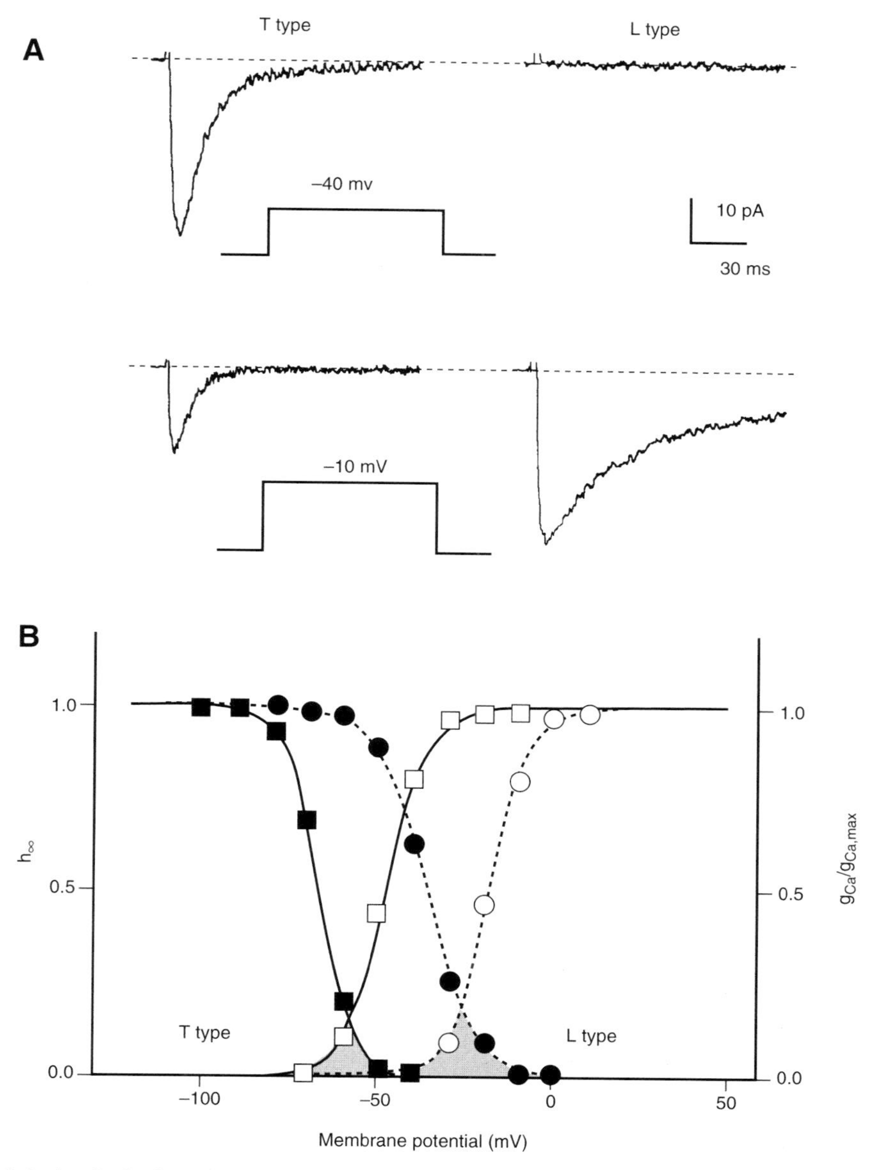

Fig. 1. T- ($I_{Ca,T}$) and L- ($I_{Ca,L}$) type calcium currents recorded separately in two different cultured rat aortic myocytes. Currents were recorded from a holding potential of –100 mV in extracellular Ca^{2+} 1.5 mM. Experimental procedure as described previously.[23] A) Waveforms of $I_{Ca,T}$ and $I_{Ca,L}$ recorded at test depolarisations of –40 mV and –10 mV in two distinct cells. Note that a depolarisation to –40 mV evokes a large $I_{Ca,T}$ but no $I_{Ca,L}$. Note also the distinct time-course of decay of $I_{Ca,T}$ and $I_{Ca,L}$. B) Voltage-dependence of steady-state availability (h_∞: ■, ●) and the normalised conductance ($g_{Ca}/g_{Ca,max}$: ○, □) to voltage relationships of $I_{Ca,T}$ (■, □) and $I_{Ca,L}$ (●, ○). Curves were plotted from currents recorded in the cells shown in panel A (complete current–voltage and steady-state inactivation curves). The fitted curves were obtained using the equation $g_{Ca} = g_{Ca,max}/(1 + \exp[(V - V_{½})/k])$, where $V_{½}$ is the voltage at which g_{Ca} is half maximal and k the slope factor for the conductance increase. $V_{½}$ = –47 mV (k = 5.7) for $I_{Ca,T}$ and $V_{½}$ = –17 mV (k = 5.5) for $I_{Ca,L}$. The voltage-dependence of steady-state inactivation (h_∞) was studied using a double-pulse protocol consisting of a 5 s conditioning prepulse from the holding potential of –100 mV (see inset). Current amplitude was normalised to that in the absence of a conditioning prepulse. $I_{Ca,T}$ was evoked at a test pulse of –40 mV and $I_{Ca,L}$ at a test pulse of 0 mV. The fitted curves for h_∞ were obtained using the equation $h_\infty = 1/(1 + \exp[(V - V_{½})/k])$, where $V_{½}$ is the voltage at which g_{Ca} is half inactivated and k is the slope factor for voltage-dependence. $I_{Ca,T}$ and $I_{Ca,L}$ are half inactivated at –66 mV (k = –4.9) and –35 mV (k = –7.2), respectively. Note the distinct 'windows' (overlap between h_∞ and $g_{Ca}/g_{Ca,max}$ to voltage relationships) for $I_{Ca,T}$ and $I_{Ca,L}$.

the predominant calcium current in most VSMC types investigated. Although this suggests that T-type calcium current is not of primary importance in excitation–contraction coupling, it is nevertheless worth noting that T-type calcium current is often detected in highly contractile vessels, such as small resistance arteries.[12,13,14,29] It is interesting that 30% of cells isolated from rat renal arteries exhibit large T-type calcium current at physiological extracellular Ca^{2+} concentrations,[31] but no correlation with contractile activity has been demonstrated so far. A large T-type calcium current is also expressed in spontaneously contracting primary-cultured azygos vein VSMCs, but its presence is more likely to be related to pacemaking activity.[32] Several lines of evidence indicate that both rat aortic and human coronary VSMCs grown in primary culture express T-type calcium current during *in vitro* proliferation. In past years we and others have studied the possibility that expression of T-type calcium current may be associated with the proliferative state of the VSMCs in arteries.

T-type calcium current and proliferation

Primary cultures of rat aortic VSMCs express both L- and T-type calcium currents, with these currents being seen even at physiological extracellular Ca^{2+} concentrations (see fig. 1). As in other cell types, L- and T-type calcium currents are distinguished by their kinetics of decay, activation thresholds, current–voltage relationship and voltage-dependent steady-state inactivation. The 'window' currents, arising from overlap of the activation and steady-state inactivation curves for the two types of conductance, are also quite different (see fig. 1). It should be noted that the window current for T-type calcium current is close to the resting membrane potential of VSMCs (generally between –40 and –55 mV). Such a window current could generate a significant steady-state, continuous entry of Ca^{2+} in this range of potentials. It is interesting to note that T-type calcium current in rat aortic VSMCs is relatively sensitive to calcium channel blockers.[16,17,20,21,24] One implication is that the use of dihydropyridines and other (so-called) L-type specific blockers to identify the target(s) of these molecules at the tissue level may be critical. A second implication is that T-type calcium current is a potential target for some of the calcium channel blockers used clinically. Indeed, even if these drugs are intrinsically more selective for L-type calcium current, it should be kept in mind that the effect of some of them on T-type current is also voltage-dependent (i.e. enhanced by membrane depolarisation). Therefore, the block of T-type current may be as important as the block of L-type current at the resting membrane potentials of VSMCs.[20,21]

The first suggestion of a link between the proliferation of aortic VSMCs and the expression of T-type calcium current was made by Akaike and co-workers.[17] From the observation that with prolongation of the period of cell culture (between 5 and 15 days) the population of cells with T-type calcium current decreases and the population of cells with L-type current increases, these investigators concluded that 'as the cells proliferate, the population with [T-type calcium current] decreases'. However, this was probably not the right conclusion because it assumed that there is no change between the time of cell plating and day 5. In fact, the expression of

T-type current is transient.[24] At the time of dissociation and plating in culture, the aortic myocytes in normal arteries of mature animals are differentiated and remarkably quiescent (fig. 2). They are in a contractile state and express only L-type calcium current,[21,33] as represented in figure 2. T-type calcium current is not detected, even in the presence of high concentrations of extracellular Ca^{2+}. When plated for primary culture, the cells attach onto the bottom of the culture dish and spread out during the first 48–72 hours after enzymatic isolation and seeding. During this time, they slowly convert into a proliferative, synthetic state and start to proliferate under the stimulation of the mitogenic agents contained in the serum. When seeded at an initial density of 2.10^4/ml in the presence of serum 1%, proliferative activity is at its highest 7–8 days after plating and decreases thereafter, stopping when cell confluence is reached (see fig. 2). The expression of T-type calcium current parallels the transient proliferation and loss of contractility of the cells and disappears at confluence (see fig. 2). The cell population is not homogeneous with respect to the expression of T- and L-type calcium currents.[17,19,22,24] This heterogeneity delineates several cell subpopulations:

i) cells exhibiting only T-type calcium current
ii) cells exhibiting only L-type calcium current
iii) cells exhibiting both L- and T-type calcium currents.[19,24]

Our demonstration of the presence of two subtypes of L-type calcium current with distinct electrophysiological properties, sensitivity to the dihydropyridine nicardipine and regulation by β-adrenergic stimulation[21,22] indicates that the situation is probably more complicated.

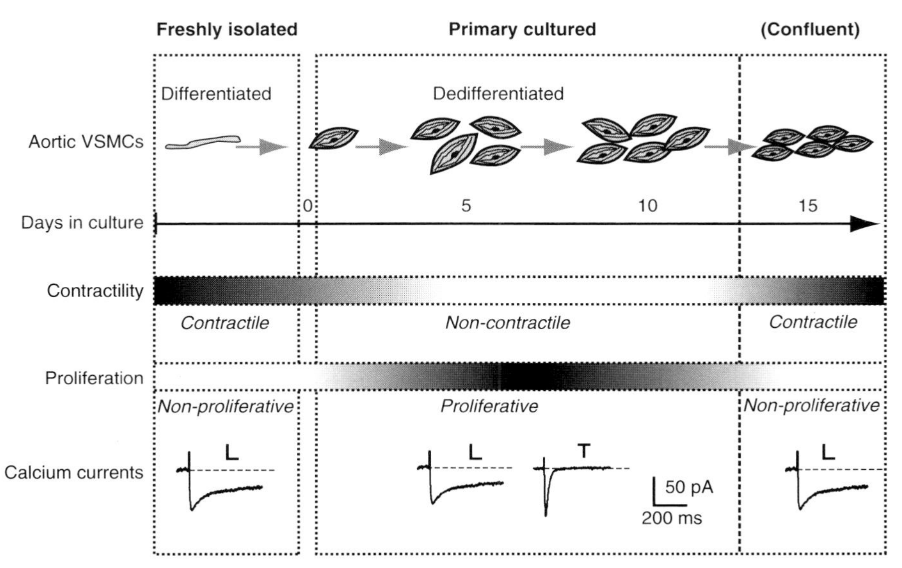

Fig. 2. Schematic of the phenotypic modulation of the expression of T-type calcium current in rat aortic vascular smooth muscle cells (VSMCs). The well-differentiated, contractile and freshly isolated myocytes express only L-type calcium current. The expression of T-type calcium current in cultured myocytes is transient and parallels the proliferative activity of dedifferentiated cells. T-type calcium current disappears at confluence.[24]

T-type calcium current and cell cycling

VSMCs reproduce by duplicating their contents and then dividing in two. The DNA in the nucleus is replicated only during a limited portion of the full time interval (approximately 20 hours) between two mitotic events; this is called the S (synthesis) phase (fig. 3). Between the end of the M (mitosis) phase and the S phase, there is one interval known as the G_1 phase (G for gap) and a second interval, known as the G_2 phase, which separates the end of the S phase from the next M phase. As pointed out above, the proliferative cell population is heterogeneous. Cell-cycle duration can vary slightly from cell to cell as cells are asynchronous. A simple technique to obtain synchronous populations is to manipulate the culture conditions. The cells can be exposed to a drug that interferes with a specific step in the cycle and halts all cells at this point. For example, after 48 hours' exposure to hydroxyurea, a well-known polymerase blocker which stops proliferation by halting the cells at the G_1–S border (see fig. 3), most of the cells express only T-type calcium current and only a few express L-type current.[22] This finding was recently corroborated by Kuga and co-workers in an elegant study based on an immunocytochemical analysis of cell-cycle-specific nuclear antigens after electrophysiological recordings in individual cells.[19] Small T-type calcium current was also detected in association with L-type current in the G_1 phase.[19] Serum deprivation is another manipulation which renders the cells quiescent (in the G_0 phase) and favours cell redifferentiation (see fig. 3). In these conditions, the predominant current is L type,[19,22] as expected from experiments performed in well-differentiated, freshly isolated cells.[22,33] In contrast to the expression of T-type calcium current, the expression of L-type current is much less dependent on cell-cycling activity (see fig. 3), despite possible variations in density.[19]

The data reviewed above allow us to establish a link between T-type calcium current and cell-cycling activity of proliferative aortic VSMCs.[17,19,22,24] Cells that exhibit T-type calcium current correspond to those in the G_1/S phases (see fig. 3). At present, the precise role of this type of current is unclear. It is also unclear how it is activated (whether T-type calcium channels generate a small window current or whether they are gated by oscillations of cell membrane potential during the G_1/S phases of cell cycling. It is possible that 'window' calcium currents close to the normal resting potential of VSMCs could provide the cell with a very small but continuous Ca^{2+} influx that activates a specific transduction pathway and triggers a function other than contraction. This function could be gene activation during the S phase. Indeed, intracellular Ca^{2+} is a key messenger of cell-cycle control, but the specific pathways regulating the concentration of intracellular Ca^{2+} have not yet been elucidated. In contrast to what has been proposed for cardiac cells,[34] it seems unlikely that T-type calcium current is involved in the regulation of protein synthesis, because the total protein content of proliferating cells increases more or less continuously throughout the cycle (i.e. is interrupted only briefly by mitosis).

The hypothesis of a role for T-type calcium channels in a signal transduction pathway that regulates cell proliferation and growth is attractive. This hypothesis is not

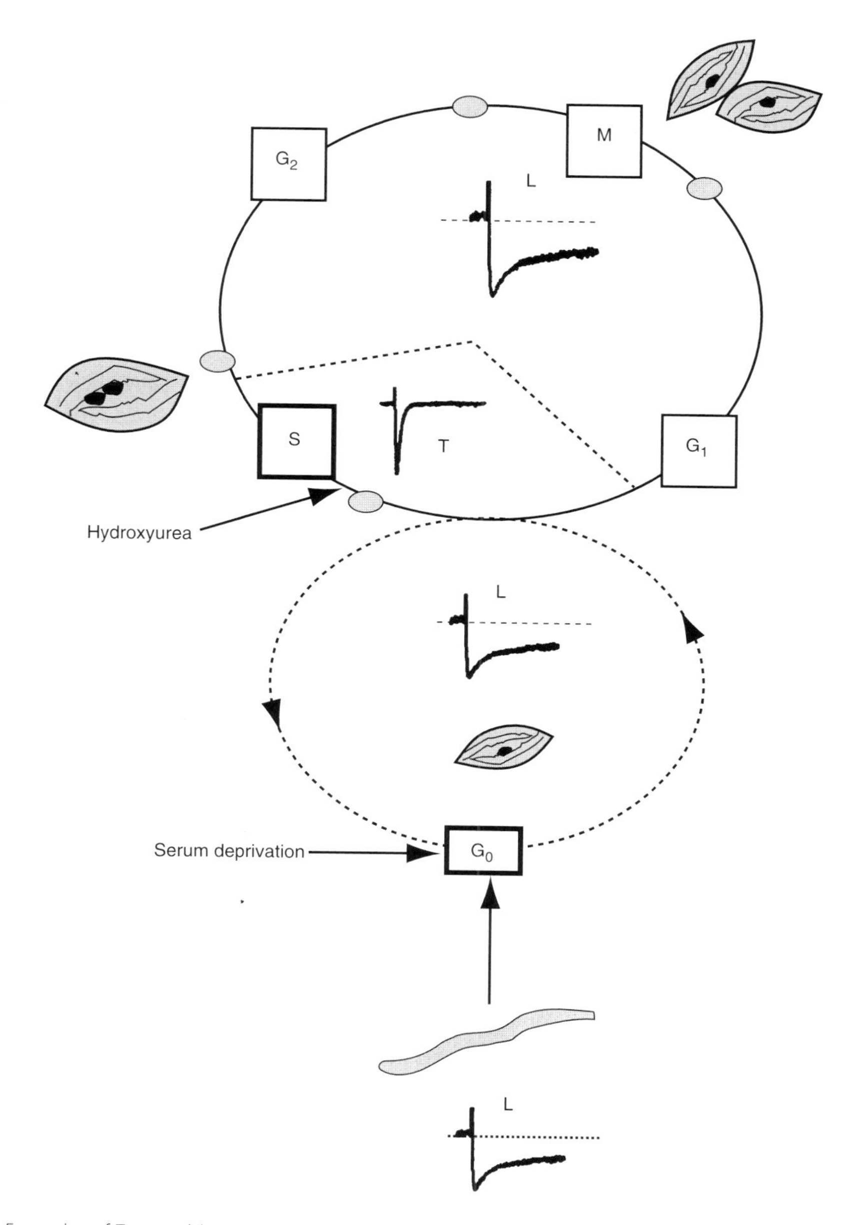

Fig. 3. Expression of T-type calcium current depends upon the phase of the cell cycle. Hydroxyurea halts the cycle at the G_1–S border, where cells express predominantly T-type calcium current. During quiescence, promoted by serum deprivation, cells express L-type calcium current only as the freshly isolated myocytes.[19,22]

unique for VSMCs. It has also been proposed for neuronal cells and for both cardiac and skeletal myocytes, which express T-type calcium current at early stages of development or during pathology. In cardiac cells, for example, T-type current is highly expressed at the embryonic stage,[35] under the influence of growth factors[36] and during hypertrophy.[37] This phenomenon has also been shown in a model of genetic cardiomyopathy.[38] Interestingly, VSMC growth, proliferation and contraction are implicated in the pathogenesis and progression of atherosclerosis, hypertension and restenosis after angioplasty. As discussed in this review, primary cultures of aortic VSMCs provide an interesting model to evaluate the role of T-type calcium current in these diseases. However, at present, the extrapolation for *in vivo* conditions needs further evaluation. Attempts in our laboratory to evidence T-type calcium current in naturally proliferative cells *in vivo* have failed. This is the case for aortic myocytes freshly isolated from neonatal rats[33] and from the neointima formed after arterial injury (de-endothelialisation) with a balloon catheter in adult rats (unpublished observations). Cell proliferation *in vivo* and *in vitro* may be very different. Proliferation depends critically upon cellular environment and particular factors. For example, if the rate of proliferation and/or percentage of proliferative cells is lower *in vivo* than *in vitro*, the probability of recording cells in the S phase of the cell cycle would also be lower. The rate of cellular proliferation *in vitro* is highly dependent on serum concentration and on the nature of mitogenic factors. In addition, myocytes freshly isolated from the tissue are greatly influenced *in vivo* by endogenous factors such as those related to the presence of endothelium. Nevertheless, the recent finding that the selective T-type calcium channel blocker mibefradil prevents proliferation of VSMCs after de-endothelialisation of rat carotid artery provides indirect evidence that T-type calcium channels may participate in the proliferative process *in vivo*.[39]

Conclusion

Much remains to be learned about the physiology of T-type calcium channels in VSMCs. Their role may not be unique. They are expressed in spontaneously beating veins (where they seem to be involved in pacemaking activity), in high-resistance arteries and in proliferative cells (where they could activate a particular function related to cell cycle). In this latter case, one possible role of T-type calcium current could be gene activation, necessary for cell replication and growth. As previously demonstrated in cardiac and skeletal muscles and in neurons, T-type calcium current could be involved in the normal proliferation-dependent growth of vessels in the early stages of development. However, T-type current could also be involved in abnormal states in proliferation-dependent pathology. Although this needs to be demonstrated *in vivo*, it seems reasonable to hypothesise that T-type calcium current controls key events dictated by the physiology (and/or pathology) of VSMCs. The control of this specific calcium pathway by selective calcium channel blockers may therefore have potential therapeutic implication. From a clinical standpoint, the most important members of the calcium channel family are the L-type calcium channels, which bind the dihydropyridines, phenylalkylamines and benzothiazepines used to treat cardiovascular disorders including hypertension, cardiac arrhythmia and coronary artery disease. However, the newly developed compound mibefradil, which is clearly selective for T- over L-type calcium current, has interesting properties in cardiovascular disease that may be related in part to the modulation of T-type calcium current.[6–8] Beyond its important therapeutic potential, this compound provides a useful tool to study more specifically the role and structure of T-type calcium channels.

Acknowledgements

We thank Drs A. Kumar and M. Mangoni for helpful comments on the manuscript and Drs G. Carnac, P. Travo, D. Neveu and J.F. Quignard for their participation in some of the experiments mentioned in this review. This work was supported by the French MENESR (ACCSV9), Association Française contre les Myopathies and Fondation de France.

References

1. Bean BP. Classes of calcium channels in vertebrate cells. Ann Rev Physiol 1989; 51: 367–84
2. Chen C, Hess P. Mechanism of gating of T-type calcium channels. J Gen Physiol 1990; 96: 603–30
3. Huguenard JR. Low-threshold calcium currents in central nervous system neurons. Ann Rev Physiol 1996; 58: 329–48
4. Kuryama H, Kitamura K, Nabata H. Pharmacological and physiological significance of ion channels and factors that modulate them in vascular tissues. Pharmacol Rev 1995; 47: 387–573
5. Tsien RW, Lipscombe D, Madison DV, et al. Multiple types of neuronal calcium channels and their selective modulation. Trends Neurosci 1988; 11: 431–8
6. Ertel EA. Mibefradil (Ro 40-5967) is a selective blocker of myocardial T-type vs. L-type Ca channels. Biophys J 1996; 70: A315
7. Merke G, Zong XG, Flockerzi V, et al. The Ca^{2+} channel blocker Ro 40-5967 blocks differently T-type and L-type Ca^{2+} channels. J Pharmacol Exp Ther 1994; 271.3: 1483–8
8. Mishra SK, Hermsmeyer K. Selective inhibition of T-type Ca^{2+} channel by Ro 40-5967. Circ Res 1994; 75: 144–8
9. Loirand G, Pacaud P, Mironneau C, et al. Evidence for two distinct calcium channels in rat vascular smooth muscle cells in short term primary culture. Pflugers Arch 1986; 407: 566–8
10. Serebryakov V, Takeda K. Voltage-dependent calcium current and the effects of adrenergic modulation in rat aortic smooth muscle cells. Philos Trans R Soc Lond B Biol Sci 1992; B337: 37–47
11. Yatani A, Seidel CL, Allen J, et al. Whole-cell and single-channel calcium currents of isolated smooth muscle cells from saphenous vein. Circ Res 1987; 60: 523–33
12. Benham CD, Hess P, Tsien RW. Two types of calcium channels in single smooth muscle cells from rabbit ear artery studied with whole-cell and single-channel recordings. Circ Res 1987; 61 (Suppl.): 10–6
13. Bean BP, Sturek M, Puga A, et al. Calcium channels in muscle cells isolated from rat mesenteric arteries: modulation by dihydropyridine drugs. Circ Res 1986; 59: 229–35
14. Ohya Y, Abe I, Fujii K, et al. Voltage-dependent Ca^{2+} channels in resistance arteries from spontaneously hypertensive rats. Circ Res 1993; 73: 1090–9
15. Wang R, Karpinski E, Pang KT. Two types of calcium channels in isolated smooth muscle cells from rat tail artery. Am J Physiol 1989; 256: H1361–8
16. Worley JF, Deitmer JW, Nelson MT. Single nisoldipine-sensitive calcium channels in smooth muscle cells isolated from rabbit mesenteric artery. Proc Natl Acad Sci U S A 1986; 83: 5746–50
17. Akaike N, Kanaide H, Kuga T, et al. Low-voltage-activated calcium current in rat aorta smooth muscle cells in primary culture. J Physiol 1989; 416: 141–60
18. Bodin P, Richard S, Travo C, et al. Responses of subcultured rat aortic smooth muscle myocytes to vasoactive agents and KCl-induced depolarization. Am J Physiol 1991; 260: C151–8
19. Kuga T, Kobayashi S, Hirakawa Y, et al. Cell cycle-dependent expression of L- and T-type Ca^{2+} currents in rat aortic smooth muscle cells in primary culture. Circ Res 1996; 79: 14–9
20. Kuga T, Sadoshima JI, Tomoike H, et al. Actions of Ca^{2+} antagonists on two types of Ca^{2+} channels in rat aorta smooth muscle cells in primary culture. Circ Res 1990; 67: 469–80
21. Neveu D, Nargeot J, Richard S. Two high-voltage activated, dihydropyridine-sensitive Ca^{2+} channel currents with distinct electrophysiological and pharmacological properties in cultured rat aortic myocytes. Pflugers Arch 1993; 424: 45–53
22. Neveu D, Quignard JF, Fernandez A, et al. Differential β-adrenergic regulation and phenotypic modulation of voltage-gated calcium currents in rat aortic myocytes. J Physiol (Lond) 1994; 479 (Pt 2): 171–82
23. Quignard JF, Frapier JM, Harricane MC, et al. Voltage-gated calcium channel currents in human coronary myocytes: regulation by cyclic GMP and NO. J Clin Invest 1997; 99: 185–93
24. Richard S, Neveu D, Carnac G, et al. Differential expression of voltage-gated Ca^{2+} currents in cultivated aortic myocytes. Biochim Biophys Acta 1992; 1160: 95–104
25. Fish RD, Sperti G, Colucci WS, et al. Phorbol ester increases the dihydropyridine-sensitive calcium conductance in a vascular cell line. Circ Res 1988; 62: 1049–54
26. Friedman ME, Suarez-Kurtz G, Kaczorowski GJ, et al. Two calcium currents in a smooth muscle cell line. Am J Physiol 1986; 250: H699–703

27. Aaronson PI, Bolton TB, Lang RJ, et al. Calcium currents in single isolated smooth muscle cells from the rabbit ear artery in normal-calcium and high-barium solutions. J Physiol 1988; 405: 57–75
28. Matsuda JJ, Volk KA, Shibata EF. Calcium currents in isolated rabbit coronary arterial smooth muscle myocytes. J Physiol 1990; 427: 657–80
29. Ganitkevich VY, Isenberg G. Stimulation-induced potentiation of T-type Ca^{2+} channel currents in myocytes from guinea-pig coronary artery. J Physiol 1991; 443: 703–25
30. Nelson MT, Standen NB, Brayden JE, et al. Noradrenaline contracts arteries by activating voltage-dependent calcium channels. Nature 1988; 336: 382–5
31. Gordienko DV, Clausen C, Goligorski M. Ionic currents and endothelin signaling in smooth muscle cells from rat resistance arteries. Am J Physiol 1994; 266: F325–41
32. Sturek M, Hermsmeyer K. Calcium and sodium channels in spontaneously contracting vascular smooth muscle cells. Science 1986; 233: 475–8
33. Quignard JF, Grazzini E, Guillon G, et al. Absence of calcium channels in neonatal rat aortic myocytes. Pflugers Arch 1996; 431: 791–3
34. Katz AM. Calcium channel diversity in the cardiovascular system. J Am Coll Cardiol 1996; 28: 522–9
35. Bkaily G, Sculptoreanu A, Jacques D, et al. Apamin, a highly potent fetal L-type Ca^{2+} current blocker in single heart cells. Am J Physiol 1992; 262: H463–71
36. Xu X, Best PM. Increase in T-type calcium current in atrial myocytes from adult rats with growth hormone-secreting tumors. Proc Natl Acad Sci U S A 1990; 87: 4655–9
37. Nuss HB, Houser SR. T-type Ca^{2+} current is expressed in hypertrophied adult feline left ventricular myocytes. Circ Res 1993; 73: 777–82
38. Sen L, Smith TW. T-type Ca^{2+} channels are abnormal in genetically determined cardiomyopathic hamster hearts. Circ Res 1994; 75: 149–55
39. Schmitt R, Clozel JP, Iberg N, et al. Mibefradil prevents neointima formation after vascular injury in rats: possible role of the blockade of the T-type voltage-operated calcium channel. Arterioscler Thromb Vasc Biol 1995; 15: 1161–5

Physiology, pharmacology and function of LVA calcium channels in hippocampal pyramidal neurons

Daniel Johnston, Robert B. Avery, Jeffrey C. Magee

Division of Neuroscience, Baylor College of Medicine, Houston, Texas, USA

Central neurons possess multiple types of voltage-gated calcium channels,[1,2] and these channels are classified as either low-voltage-activated (LVA) or high-voltage-activated (HVA).[2,3] LVA channels can be opened by small depolarisations that are below the threshold for action potential generation.

Until recently, the only member of the LVA group has been the T-type calcium channel. Single-channel recordings from guinea-pigs suggest that T-type calcium channels are particularly abundant on hippocampal CA3 pyramidal neurons, relative to neurons from area CA1 or the dentate gyrus.[1] LVA channels may be involved in the depolarising envelope that underlies neuronal burst firing in these cells.[4,5] It has been suggested that burst firing originates in the dendrites of CA3 neurons.[6]

Hippocampal pyramidal neurons have extensive dendritic arborisations that receive tens of thousands of excitatory synaptic inputs. It is now recognised that these dendrites exhibit active properties that allow action potentials generated in the axon near the cell body to back-propagate into the dendrites. Action potentials in the dendrites open both LVA and HVA calcium channels and cause an increase in intracellular Ca^{2+} concentrations[7] that may play a role in the induction of various forms of long-term synaptic plasticity.[8,9] Dendritic LVA channels may also contribute to the shape of excitatory postsynaptic potentials (EPSPs) in dendrites and/or may participate in local signalling.

In this chapter, several recent studies devoted to the physiology, pharmacology and function of LVA calcium channels in hippocampal pyramidal neurons will be reviewed. The first study involved the investigation of whole-cell calcium currents in acutely dissociated CA3 pyramidal neurons.[10] Two components of the LVA calcium current, a transient and a steady-state component, were found. These could be distinguished by their physiological and pharmacological properties. In another study, T-type (and R-type) calcium channels were found to be prominently located in the dendrites of CA1 pyramidal neurons.[11] Moreover, the T-type calcium channels could be opened by EPSPs producing a localised increase in intracellular Ca^{2+} concentrations.[12,13] Because approximately half of the T-type calcium channels are inactivated at rest, inhibitory postsynaptic potentials (IPSPs) can modulate the number of T-type calcium channels activated by the EPSPs. These results suggest a prominent role for T-type calcium channels in synaptic integration and firing behaviour of pyramidal neurons in the hippocampus.

Methods

Acutely dissociated cell preparation

Details of the methods are given in Avery and Johnston.[10] Briefly, transverse hippocampal slices of 500 μm thickness were cut from 7- to 14-day-old rats in ice-cold, oxygenated dissecting saline. Slices were incubated in a solution in which papain (10 U/ml; Worthington Biochemical, Lakewood, New Jersey, USA), cysteine (5 mM), EDTA (1 mM) and mercaptoethanol (0.5 mM) were added to 5 ml of the dissecting saline. Cells were isolated by gently triturating the tissue through a series of 4 or 5 fire-polished Pasteur pipettes.

Conventional whole-cell recordings were made from isolated CA3 neurons bathed in external solutions containing a normal concentration of extracellular Ca^{2+} (2 mM).[10] For changing solutions the cell was positioned in the outlet stream of a multi-inlet microperfusion pipette, which allowed exchange of the solution bathing the cell within a few seconds. For all drug applications, the control saline included the drug vehicle.

Intact slice preparation

Hippocampal slices (300–400 μm) were prepared with a Vibratome from 6- to 8-week-old Sprague-Dawley rats.[11] The slices were incubated in a submerged holding chamber for at least 30 min at 35 °C and stored at room temperature (22 °C) for the remainder of the experiment (<6 hours). A Zeiss Axioskop, fitted with × 40 water-immersion objective and differential interference contrast (DIC) optics, was used to view slices. Light in the infrared range (740 nm) was used in conjunction with a contrast-enhancing Newvicon camera to resolve the dendritic arbors.

Cell-attached and whole-cell recordings were made from dendrites and somata of identified CA1 pyramidal neurons.[13–15] For the cell-attached patch recordings, the resting membrane potential (–60 to –70 mV) was determined either by later rupture of the patch to whole-cell recording mode or by simultaneous voltage recordings from the soma with a second whole-cell patch pipette (Axoclamp 2A amplifier; Axon Instruments, Foster City, California, USA). For focal extracellular stimulation, a glass pipette (tip diameter 10 μm) or a single etched platinum wire (tip diameter <1 μm) was placed near the dendrite under study.

Results

Acutely dissociated CA3 neurons

Using whole-cell recordings from isolated neurons, we established a protocol to measure drug effects on LVA and HVA currents. We functionally defined LVA channels as those channels that could be activated by a subthreshold stimulus. LVA currents were evoked by holding at –80 mV and stepping to –50 mV for 600 ms (fig. 1). To compare the pharmacology of the two LVA components, we further subdivided the LVA current and measured the inactivating and non-inactivating phases. The non-inactivating current was measured as the amplitude of the current

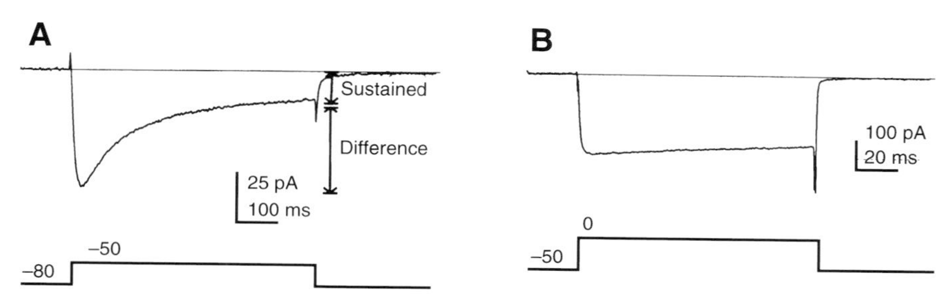

Fig. 1. Measurement of different components of the calcium current. A) Low-voltage-activated currents were evoked by holding at –80 mV and depolarising to –50 mV. Mean amplitude of the difference component = 34 ± 19 pA; mean amplitude of the sustained component = 23 ± 11 pA (n=68). B) High-voltage-activated (HVA) currents were isolated by holding at –50 mV and stepping to 0 mV. Mean HVA current peak = 224 ± 125 pA (n=63).[10]

remaining at the end of a 600 ms step and was called the sustained component. The amplitude of the inactivating component was estimated as the difference between the peak of the LVA current and the sustained current (the difference component).

At higher concentrations Cd^{2+} is a non-selective calcium channel blocker. However, LVA currents have shown less susceptibility to lower concentrations of Cd^{2+} than HVA currents.[16,17] The effect of different concentrations of Cd^{2+} on whole-cell calcium currents is shown in figure 2 (A). At each concentration Cd^{2+} blocked the HVA current

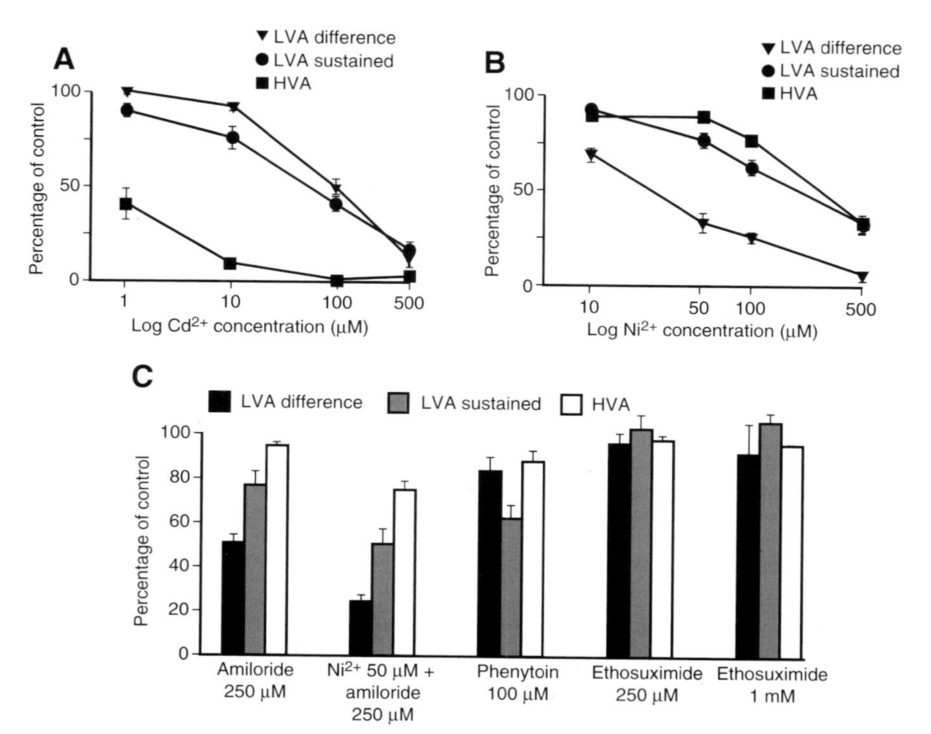

Fig. 2. Pharmacology of low-voltage-activated (LVA) currents. A) Dose–response relationship (mean ± SEM) for Cd^{2+} for the measured current components. Current amplitudes are normalised to the estimated baseline amplitude. B) Dose–response relationship for Ni^{2+} for the measured current components. C) Summary of data for effects of putative T-type calcium channel blockers. HVA = high-voltage-activated.[10]

(IC_{50} <1 μM) more strongly than the LVA current; the two components of the LVA current shared a similar sensitivity to Cd^{2+} (IC_{50} ≈100 μM). Although the block was less for the LVA components, one cannot necessarily conclude that Cd^{2+} has a lower affinity for LVA channels. Because HVA currents were measured at 0 mV but LVA currents were measured at –50 mV, the differential effects of Cd^{2+} could be related, at least in part, to voltage-dependence of the Cd^{2+} block.[18,19]

Ni^{2+} is the most commonly used antagonist of T-type calcium channels and has been used to probe their physiological function.[20] The effect of different concentrations of Ni^{2+} on whole-cell calcium currents is shown in panel B of figure 2. At any given concentration, Ni^{2+} was more effective in blocking the inactivating component of the LVA current than the sustained LVA or HVA currents, and thus appears to preferentially block the channels responsible for the LVA difference component. The LVA difference component was more sensitive to Ni^{2+} than the other current components, with an IC_{50} of 10–50 μM. The LVA sustained and HVA components were similarly sensitive to Ni^{2+}, with IC_{50} values of 100–500 μM.

We tested a number of other drugs that have been reported to have effects on T-type currents in different preparations.[10] We found that amiloride was selective for the LVA difference current and phenytoin for the LVA sustained component, whereas ethosuximide had no effect on any of the calcium currents examined. As shown in panel C of figure 2, amiloride, either alone or with Ni^{2+}, most strongly blocked the LVA difference component. Phenytoin (100 μM) affected all components but had its greatest effect on the LVA sustained component. Ethosuximide, at concentrations up to 1 mM, had no effect on any current component.

The LVA difference and sustained currents appeared to result from different channel types. This conclusion was further supported by results in which we found that nimodipine and calciseptine, two drugs that act on L-type channels, selectively blocked the sustained component, whereas BayK8644, an L-type channel agonist, selectively enhanced the sustained component. On the other hand, ω-CTx-MVIIC, a toxin that blocks N- and P-/Q-type channels, had no effect on either component of the LVA current.[10] These results suggest that the LVA sustained current is brought about by an L-like channel that is active at potentials near rest, and that the LVA difference current is most likely caused by a T-type calcium channel.

Fura-2 imaging of intracellular Ca^{2+} concentrations[21] was used to test the hypothesis that the sustained current is active at rest. Hyperpolarisations from near the resting potential decreased the intracellular Ca^{2+} concentration. This decrease was blocked by nimodipine but not by Ni^{2+}, which supports the conclusion that the sustained LVA current results from an L-type channel that is open near the resting potential.

Dendritic recordings from slices

Calcium channel activity was recorded from cell-attached patches on the soma and on apical dendrites from near the soma to distances greater than 300 μm away (the maximum length of CA1 apical dendrites is approximately 400 μm) (fig. 3).

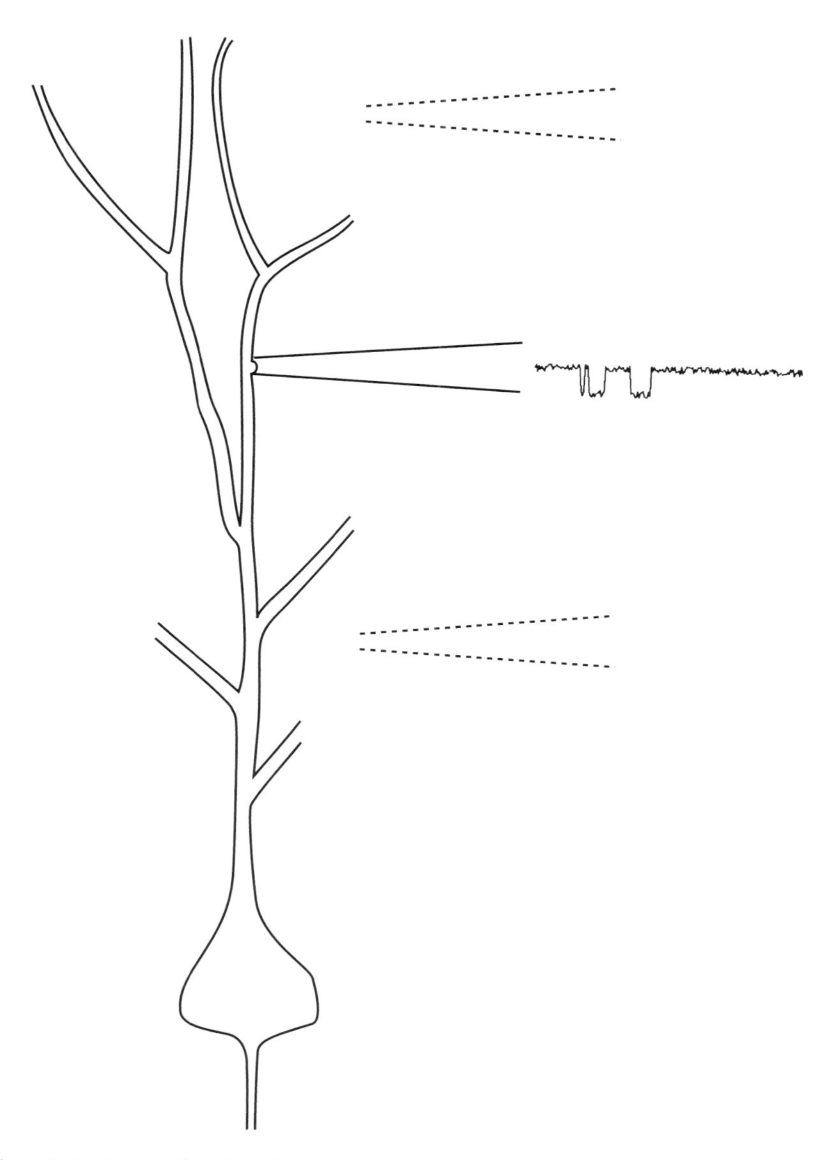

Fig. 3. Cell-attached patch recordings from CA1 pyramidal neurons. Recordings were made from patches from hippocampal slices in which the dendrites were visualised using infrared differential interference contrast and videomicroscopy. Patches were made along the dendrites at different distances from the soma as indicated. (See also Magee and Johnston.[11])

Although many types of calcium channels were identified, the two most frequently observed channels on dendrites more than 100 μm from the soma were a small-conductance LVA channel and a medium-conductance HVA channel (which was characterised as the 'R' type). Channel activity was recorded with either Ba^{2+} 20 mM or Ba^{2+} 110 mM in the pipette (fig. 4). Panel A of figure 4 shows consecutive sweeps of LVA calcium channel activity following step depolarisations from –85 mV to –15 mV, with the concentration of Ba^{2+} in the recording solution being 110 mM.

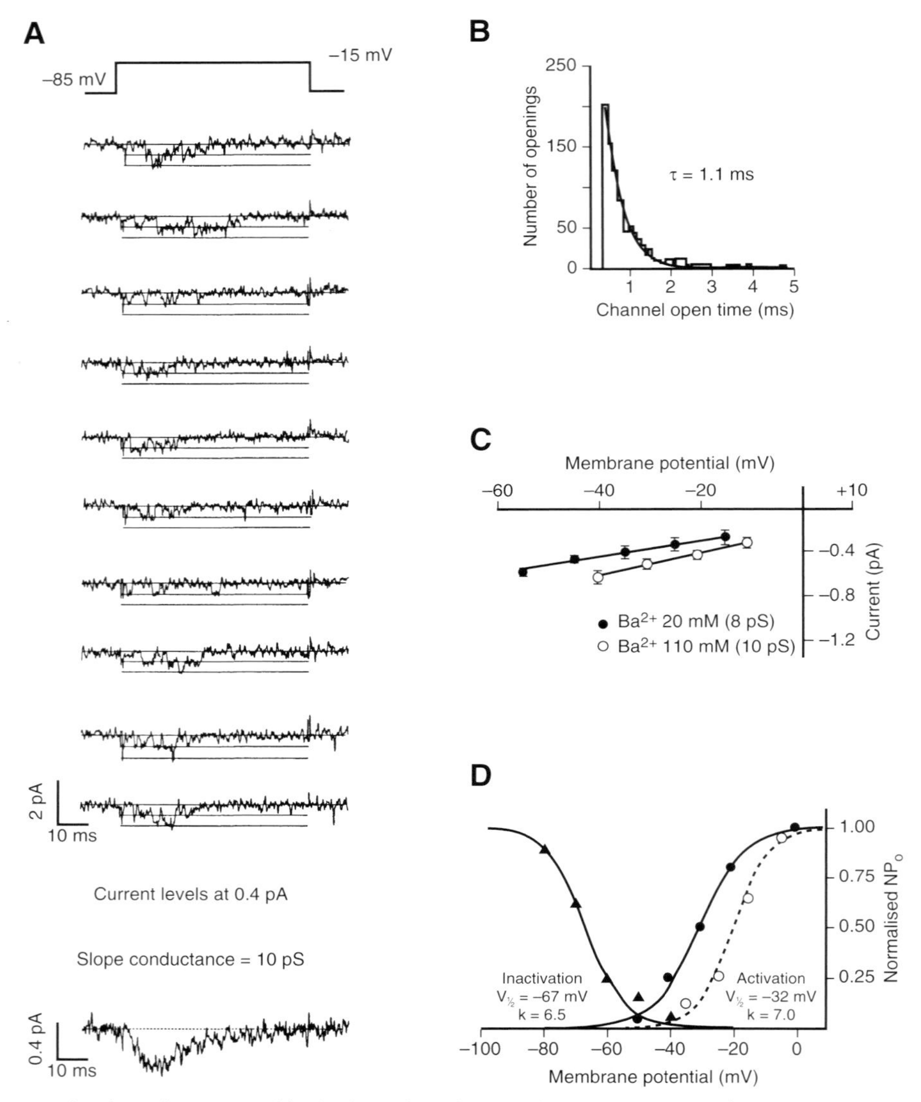

Fig. 4. Dendritic low-voltage-activated (LVA) calcium channel activity. A) Consecutive sweeps of LVA small slope conductance (10 pS) calcium channel activity following step depolarisations from –85 mV to –15 mV. Recordings were analogue-filtered at 2 kHz and were later digitally refiltered at 1 kHz for display. B) Channel open-time histogram for same patch as in panel A. Raw recordings, analogue-filtered at 2 kHz, were used for determination of channel open times. C) Unitary current amplitude plotted as a function of membrane potential for patches recorded with Ba^{2+} 20 mM (n=27) or 110 mM (n=16). D) Representative steady-state activation and inactivation plots for dendritic LVA calcium channels recorded in $BaCl_2$ 20 mM. $V_{½}$ = half-activation and -inactivation voltages; k = slope factors; ○ = activation range for the LVA channel activity shown in panel A (Ba^{2+} 10 mM; $V_{½}$ = –19 mV, k = –6.5).[11]

Channel openings began with command pulses to around –30 mV, and the observed channel had a small slope conductance (10 pS). The ensemble average (104 traces) in the bottom trace demonstrated significant inactivation during a 60 ms depolarisation. The open-time distribution (see fig. 4 (B)) was best fit by a single exponential function with a time constant of 1.1 ms, which demonstrated that the LVA channels had a relatively prolonged mean channel open time. In panel C of figure 4, the linear regression lines have a slope of 8 pS (Ba^{2+} 20 mM) and 10 pS (Ba^{2+} 110 mM). Current versus voltage plots demonstrate these channels to be LVA calcium channels that activate near the resting potential and are partially inactivated at rest. These channels were insensitive to nimodipine or ω-CTx-MVIIC but were blocked by amiloride 0.5 mM and Ni^{2+} 50 μM. Overall, they had characteristics expected of T-type calcium channels. In contrast, the HVA medium-conductance channel recorded from dendrites had properties similar to the R-type channel (not shown).[11,22]

In other experiments, double patch-clamp recordings were made from CA1 pyramidal neurons (whole-cell on the soma and cell-attached on the dendrite). EPSPs were evoked by Schaffer collateral stimulation; these dendritic EPSPs opened single calcium channels in dendrite patches (fig. 5). Voltages displayed in panels A and B of figure 5 are patch holding potentials. The initial capacity current has been subtracted using the average of traces with no channel activity. Traces in panels B and C of figure 5 were digitally refiltered at 0.5 kHz. Recordings in panels A–C of figure 5 were 260, 120 and 150 μm, respectively, from the soma. The maximal fractional open time, NP_o, was calculated from:

$$NP_o = t_o/t$$

where N = number of channels in a patch, P_o = probability of a single channel being open during the EPSP, t_o = time during the trace that a channel is open and t = total EPSP duration. The minimum number of channels in a patch was estimated by dividing the maximum channel current overlap by the unitary current amplitude.[13]

The characteristically prolonged single-channel openings of LVA calcium channels were most often observed near the peak and/or falling phases of the EPSPs. EPSP-activated channel openings displayed the small unitary current amplitude and slope conductance characteristic of T-type calcium channels. EPSPs with a peak amplitude of 10 mV (at the site of recording) were necessary for activation of the calcium channels, whereas EPSPs that were just below the threshold of action potential generation (20–25 mV at the site of recording) were able to activate LVA channels with near-maximal fractional open time.

We also explored the amount of steady-state inactivation of these channels near rest. From a holding potential of 10–15 mV depolarised from rest (which should approximately counter the effects of charge screening by the Ba^{2+} 20 mM solution in the pipette), EPSP-activated LVA channel activity was relatively infrequent (see fig. 5 (C)). A 4 s hyperpolarising prepulse prior to synaptic stimulation increased the opening of calcium channels in a voltage-dependent manner (see fig. 5 (C & D)). This suggests that a high proportion of LVA channels are inactivated at the resting voltage and that membrane hyperpolarisation and subsequent channel deinactivation are necessary for channel activation to occur with EPSPs. The observed EPSP activation of LVA calcium channels suggests that these channels could play a critical role in the mediation of the influx of Ca^{2+} into dendrites during subthreshold synaptic activation.[12] This role of LVA channels would, however, be particularly prominent in the case of EPSPs occurring after hyperpolarising IPSPs or spike-mediated after-hyperpolarisations.

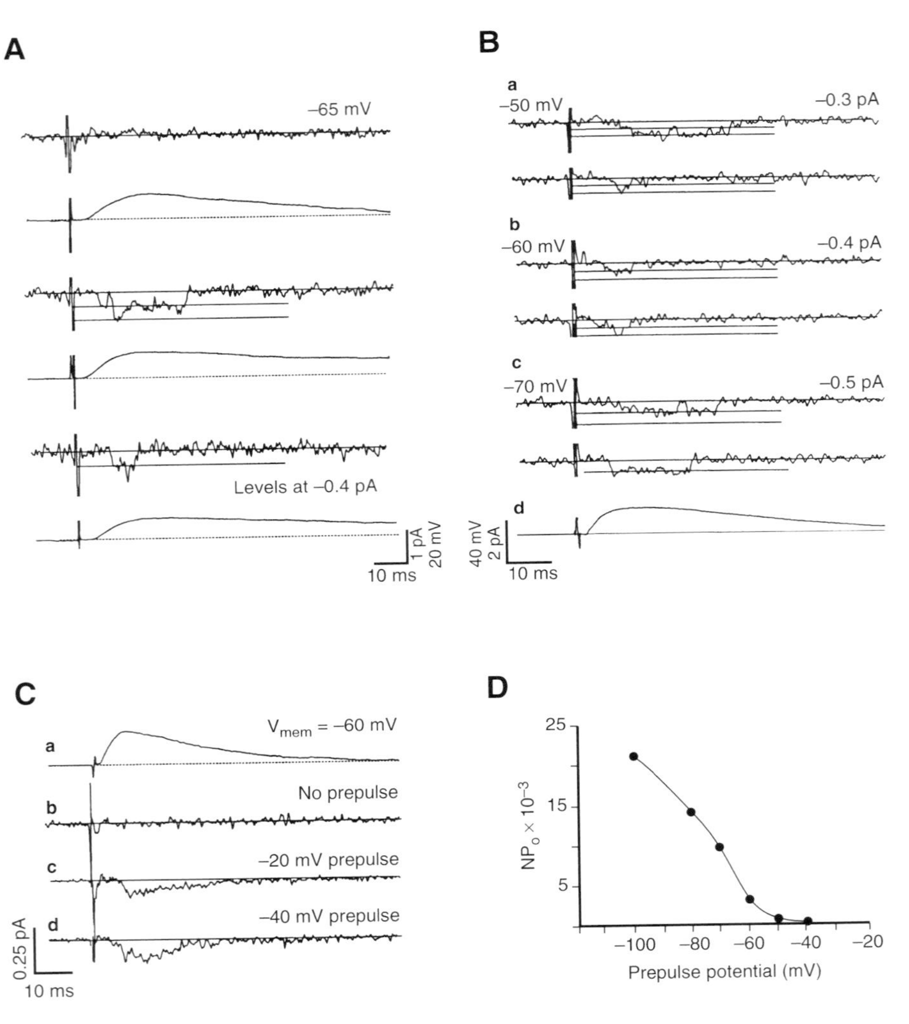

Fig. 5. Subthreshold synaptic activation of low-voltage-activated (LVA) calcium channels. A) Consecutive sweeps of dendrite-attached patch recordings with patch held at resting potential (V_{mem}) (top traces) showing calcium channel activation by subthreshold excitatory postsynaptic potentials (EPSPs). Bottom traces are somatic voltage simultaneously recorded by a second whole-cell electrode. B) Dendrite-attached patch recordings demonstrating the voltage-dependence of EPSP-activated unitary current amplitudes when the patch is held (a) 15 mV depolarised, (b) 5 mV depolarised and (c) 5 mV hyperpolarised of V_{mem}. Two traces containing openings were selected from consecutive sweeps and illustrated for each voltage. Slope conductance of EPSP-evoked channel activity was 10 pS, compared with 8 pS when activated by voltage steps; (d) average of 5 EPSPs recorded from the dendrite immediately following rupture of patch. C) Hyperpolarising prepulses increase the EPSP activation of LVA calcium channels: (a) integral of EPSP-induced capacitive current showing EPSP time-course; (b) ensemble average of 50 consecutive current traces showing minimal EPSP channel without the prepulse; (c) ensemble average of 60 consecutive current traces showing increased EPSP channel activation following a 4 s prepulse of –20 mV; (d) ensemble average of 60 consecutive current traces showing maximal EPSP channel activation following a 4 s prepulse of –40 mV. Patch was returned to a holding potential that was 10 mV depolarised from V_{mem} 400 ms after hyperpolarising prepulse. D) Maximal fractional open time (NP_o) for EPSP-activated LVA calcium channel activity plotted against prepulse potential amplitude.[13]

Discussion

Hippocampal pyramidal neurons possess two types of LVA calcium current: a transient current with the same physiology and pharmacology as those reported for T-type calcium channels, and a sustained or steady-state current with properties similar to those of L-type channels (except for its negative range of activation). It is not clear whether the sustained component is generated via the same L-type channels as those studied previously at more positive potentials or via a separate channel. It should be noted, however, that the use of physiological concentrations of Ca^{2+} in this study should result in a more negative voltage range for activation than in other studies that used high concentrations of Ba^{2+} or Ca^{2+} as the charge carrier.[10,23] The function of the sustained LVA current in these neurons is also unclear, but imaging studies from intact neurons have demonstrated that it contributes to resting intracellular concentrations of Ca^{2+}.[21]

The dendritic recordings of single calcium channels suggest that the T-type calcium channel may play a prominent role in dendritic function. This channel appears to have a higher density in dendrites than in the soma, is activated by subthreshold EPSPs and can produce a localised influx of Ca^{2+} in the vicinity of subthreshold synaptic input.[12] The activity of the channel during synaptic events is also dramatically increased by prior hyperpolarisation, such as might result from IPSPs, or after-hyperpolarisations following action potentials. The importance of this channel in synaptic integration may therefore vary from moment to moment depending on the prior activity of the dendrites.

References

1. Fisher RE, Gray R, Johnston D. Properties and distribution of single voltage-gated calcium channels in adult hippocampal neurons. J Neurophysiol 1990; 64: 91–104
2. Llinas R, Yarom Y. Properties and distribution of ionic conductances generating electroresponsiveness of mammalian inferior olivary neurones *in vitro*. J Physiol (Lond) 1981; 315: 569–84
3. Carbone E, Lux HD. A low voltage-activated calcium conductance in embryonic chick sensory neurons. Biophys J 1984; 46: 413–18
4. Destexhe A, Contreras D, Steriade M, et al. *In vivo*, *in vitro*, and computational analysis of dendritic calcium currents in thalamic reticular neurons. J Neurosci 1996; 16: 169–85
5. Jahnsen H, Llinas R. Ionic basis for the electroresponsiveness and oscillatory properties of guinea-pig thalamic neurones *in vitro*. J Physiol (Lond) 1984; 349: 227–47
6. Wong RKS, Prince DA, Basbaum AI. Intradendritic recordings from hippocampal neurons. Proc Natl Sci U S A 1979; 76: 986–90
7. Christie BR, Eliot LS, Ito KI, et al. Different Ca^{2+} channels in soma and dendrites of hippocampal pyramidal neurons mediate spike-induced Ca^{2+} influx. J Neurophysiol 1995; 73: 2553–7
8. Christie BR, Magee JC, Johnston D. The role of dendritic action potentials and Ca^{2+} influx in the induction of homosynaptic long-term depression in hippocampal CA1 pyramidal neurons. Learn Mem 1996; 3: 160–9
9. Magee JC, Johnston D. A synaptically-controlled, associative signal for Hebbian plasticity in hippocampal neurons. Science 1997; 275: 209–13
10. Avery RB, Johnston D. Multiple channel types contribute to the low voltage-activated calcium current in hippocampal CA3 pyramidal neurons. J Neurosci 1996; 16: 5567–82
11. Magee JC, Johnston D. Characterization of single voltage-gated Na^+ and Ca^{2+} channels in apical dendrites of rat CA1 pyramidal neurons. J Physiol (Lond) 1995; 487: 67–90
12. Magee JC, Christofi G, Miyakawa H, et al. Subthreshold synaptic activation of voltage-gated Ca^{2+} channels mediates a localized Ca^{2+} influx into the dendrites of hippocampal pyramidal neurons. J Neurophysiol 1995; 74: 1335–42

13. Magee JC, Johnston D. Synaptic activation of voltage-gated channels in the dendrites of hippocampal pyramidal neurons. Science 1995; 268: 301–4
14. Stuart GJ, Dodt HU, Sakmann B. Patch-clamp recordings from the soma and dendrites of neurones in brain slices using infrared video microscopy. Pflugers Arch 1993; 423: 511–8
15. Stuart GJ, Sakmann B. Active propagation of somatic action potentials into neocortical pyramidal cell dendrites. Nature 1994; 367: 69–72
16. Mogul DJ, Fox AP. Evidence for multiple types of Ca^{2+} channels in acutely isolated hippocampal CA3 neurones of the guinea-pig. J Physiol (Lond) 1991; 433: 259–81
17. Ozawa S, Tsuzuki K, Iino M, et al. Three types of voltage-dependent calcium current in cultured rat hippocampal neurons. Brain Res 1989; 495: 329–36
18. Brown AM, Tsuda Y, Wilson DL. A description of activation and conduction in calcium channels based on tail and turn-on current measurements in the snail. J Physiol (Lond) 1983; 344: 549–83
19. Byerly L, Chase PB, Stimers JR. Calcium current activation kinetics in neurones of the snail *Lymnaea stagnalis*. J Physiol (Lond) 1984; 348: 187–207
20. Hagiwara N, Irisawa H, Kameyama M. Contribution of two types of calcium currents to the pacemaker potentials of rabbit sino-atrial node cells. J Physiol (Lond) 1988; 395: 233–53
21. Magee JC, Avery RB, Christie BR, et al. Dihydropyridine-sensitive, voltage-gated Ca^{2+} channels contribute to the resting intracellular Ca^{2+} concentration of hippocampal CA1 pyramidal neurons. J Neurophysiol 1996; 76: 3460–70
22. Randall A, Tsien RW. Pharmacological dissection of multiple types of Ca^{2+} channel currents in rat cerebellar granule neurons. J Neurosci 1995; 15: 2995–3012
23. Hille B. Ionic channels of excitable membranes. Sunderland, Mass.: Sinauer Associates, 1992

Heterogeneity of LVA calcium currents in thalamic neurons and their functional role in burst firing

John R. Huguenard

Department of Neurology and Neurological Sciences, Stanford University School of Medicine, Stanford, California, USA

Summary

Certain classes of neurons within the CNS are capable of firing robust Ca^{2+}-dependent burst responses. Low-voltage-activated (T-type) calcium channels, with their unique biophysical properties, are particularly well suited to activate the generator potential that underlies burst responses. The thalamus, an area expressing high levels of T-type channels, is one of the most prominent areas for burst generation in the mammalian forebrain. Various T-type channels lead to distinct forms of burst generation in neurons of different thalamic nuclei; however, all T-type channel subtypes respond to blockade by the succinimide class of antiepileptic drugs. Blockade of T-type channels leads to reduced burst-firing capability and a reduced ability to sustain synchronous network discharges in the thalamus. This is the likely mechanism of antiepileptic drug action.

Introduction

The mechanisms by which neurons express different action potential firing patterns has been a topic of great interest in recent years.[1,2] Experiments performed in preparations such as brain slices and neuronal cultures have provided some insight into the properties of ion channels that lead to patterned responses, including phasic (or burst) discharges, delayed firing, and adapting and non-adapting repetitive firing responses. High-frequency burst discharges are prominent events in neurons of several forebrain areas, including the thalamus, the inferior olive, some cortical areas and the hypothalamus. In the early 1980s, several studies from Llinás's laboratory were particularly influential in developing the concept of Ca^{2+}-dependent burst firing in thalamic and inferior olive neurons.[3–6] Here it was apparent that appropriate hyperpolarising conditioning pulses resulted in rebound activation characterised by a 20–50 ms generator potential, termed the 'low-threshold spike', or LTS. The LTS, which could trigger a high-frequency burst of Na^{+}-dependent action potentials, was shown to be Ca^{2+}-dependent since it was not blocked by the sodium channel poison tetrodotoxin, yet was abolished by replacing extracellular Ca^{2+} with Co^{2+}. Furthermore, the time-course of the LTS was unaffected by substituting Ba^{2+} for Ca^{2+}. The authors correctly surmised that K^{+}-dependent repolarisation was not involved, but rather that the kinetic properties of a unique channel, the low-threshold calcium channel, were largely responsible for LTS generation.

LVA currents and burst firing in thalamic relay neurons

Recent voltage-clamp studies in thalamic relay neurons[7–10] have identified the burst-promoting ionic current, which has many similarities with a unique calcium current described in sensory neurons, termed either the 'low-voltage-activated' (LVA),[11] 'transient' (T),[12] slowly deactivating[13] or fast [14] calcium current. In our studies in thalamic neurons, acute isolation resulted in semi-truncated cells that were electrotonically compact and were thus suitable for detailed voltage-clamp studies. Absolute peak LVA current averaged 350 pA,[7] and the ratio of peak LVA to high-voltage-activated (HVA) currents was >1.[7] Thus, the LVA current tends to dominate the physiology of relay neurons. The results of recent voltage-clamp experiments with neurons in brain slice preparations suggest that the absolute values of LVA current amplitude in intact neurons can be much higher (several nanoamperes of peak current; not shown) than in those that have been isolated and truncated (<0.5 nA). This suggests that there is significant dendritic localisation of LVA channels in thalamic relay neurons. Similarly, in hippocampal CA1 neurons it has been suggested that LVA channels are predominantly localised in dendrites.[15] This idea is based on the fact that the LVA steady-state inactivation curve is particularly hyperpolarised and that LVA amplitude was progressively decreased by dendritic lesions. Single-channel recordings from apical dendrites in CA1 cells also support a primarily dendritic localisation.[16]

The high-quality voltage clamp that is possible in isolated cells (fig. 1) has allowed a relatively complete kinetic and pharmacological characterisation of this current.[7,17] Recently, we performed Hodgkin–Huxley type analysis of this current[18] and were able to reproduce all the essential features of thalamic burst firing.[19] Some prominent features of LVA current in relay cells include a slow deactivation (see fig. 1 (B)) similar to that seen in sensory neurons,[13] rectification of the instantaneous current–voltage curve that is consistent with the Goldman–Hodgkin–Katz equation (see fig. 1 (C & D)), Ca^{2+}-dependence (see fig. 1 (E)), similar permeability to Ba^{2+} and Ca^{2+} (fig. 2 (D)),[17] modest sensitivity to Ni^{2+}, Cd^{2+} and amiloride blockade, and inhibition by antiepileptic succinimide compounds.[17,20–24]

Functionally, the LVA current in thalamic and sensory neurons shares a number of properties with the sodium current originally identified in squid giant axon by Hodgkin and Huxley.[25] For example, the rates of macroscopic activation and inactivation are strongly voltage-dependent, and the time-course of the current is described by a sigmoidal activation and exponential inactivation.[7,18] Thus, the LVA current seems to serve a similar function to the sodium current, i.e. the production of regenerative responses. The specifics of the Ca^{2+} and Na^{+} responses clearly differ, especially in terms of spike threshold (approximately –60 mV for LTS *vs* –45 mV for Na^{+} spikes), duration (20–80 ms *vs* 1 ms), and height (30–40 mV *vs* 80–100 mV). However, one feature, shared by sodium currents and LVA calcium currents, that leads to the promotion of regenerative responses is voltage-dependent activation. In both cases, the rate of activation is relatively slow near spike threshold and increases with depolarisation.[7,25] Thus, the onset of the response may be characterised by

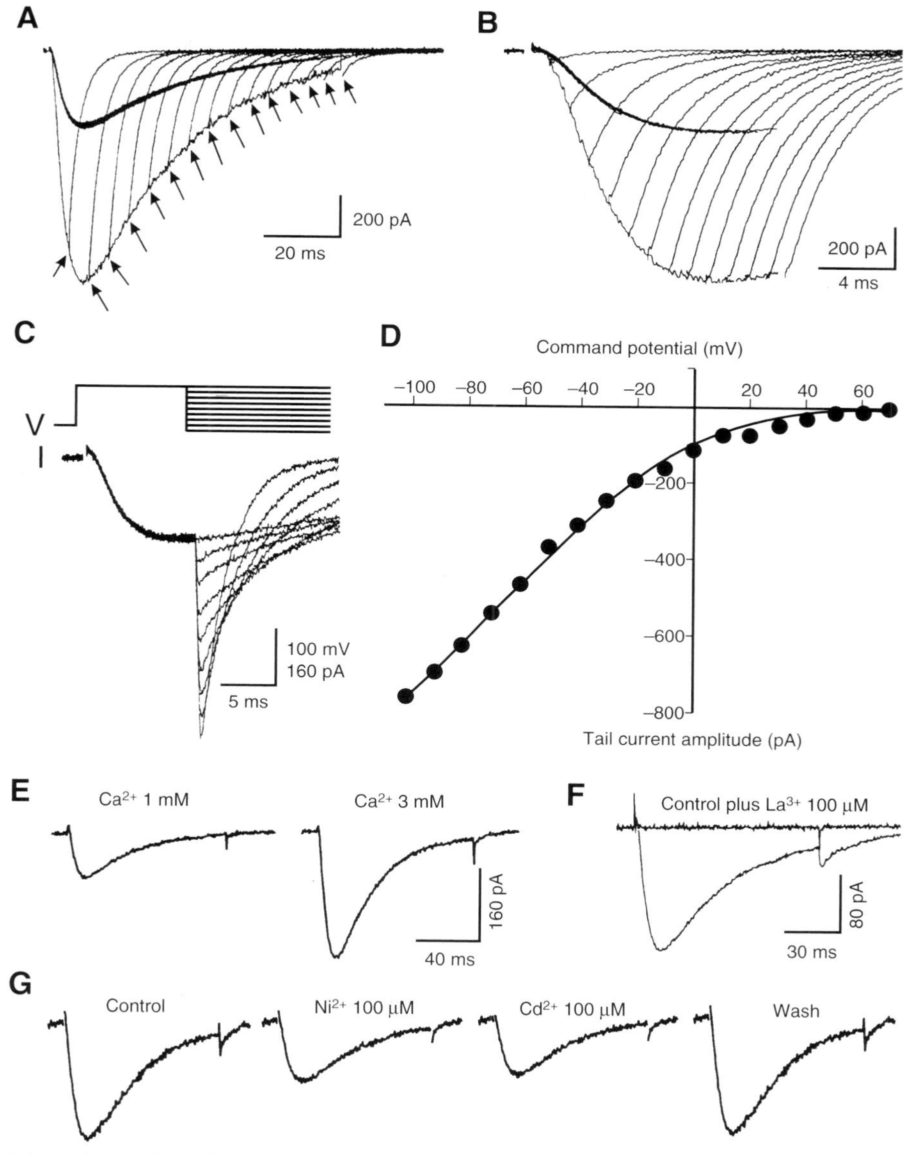

Fig. 1. Low-voltage-activated (LVA; T-type) calcium currents in thalamic relay neurons. A & B) Voltage clamp can be well controlled during activation of T-type currents in acutely isolated thalamic neurons. Currents were activated by step depolarisations to –40 mV. In this family of P/4 leak-subtracted current traces, the depolarisations were interrupted at various intervals (5, 10, 15 ms, etc., in panel A and 1, 2, 3 ms, etc., in panel B) and the membrane potential returned to –80 mV. The envelope of the peak tail current amplitudes (arrowheads) closely matches the time-course of the scaled (~ × 3) LVA current, indicating that: (i) a single population of channels (i.e. calcium channels) is likely activated by the depolarisations; (ii) the voltage clamp is capable of controlling the voltage in the neuron and can do so on the order of 0.2 ms; (iii) tail current amplitudes accurately reflect the number of LVA channels opened during the depolarising command. C & D) LVA channels are rectifying rather than ohmic, consistent with the Goldman–Hodgkin–Katz constant field equation. In this experiment LVA currents were activated by a 10 ms step to –30 mV. This was followed by steps to potentials in the range of –110 to +70 mV to obtain an instantaneous current–voltage (I–V) curve. Example leak-subtracted traces for tail potentials in the range of –120 to –30 mV are shown. Panel D shows the amplitude of the peak tail current versus tail current potential. The smooth curve is derived from the constant field equation with extracellular Ca^{2+} 3 mM, intracellular Ca^{2+} 10 nM and a permeability of 168×10^{-9} cm/s. E & F) LVA currents in thalamic

(continued overleaf)

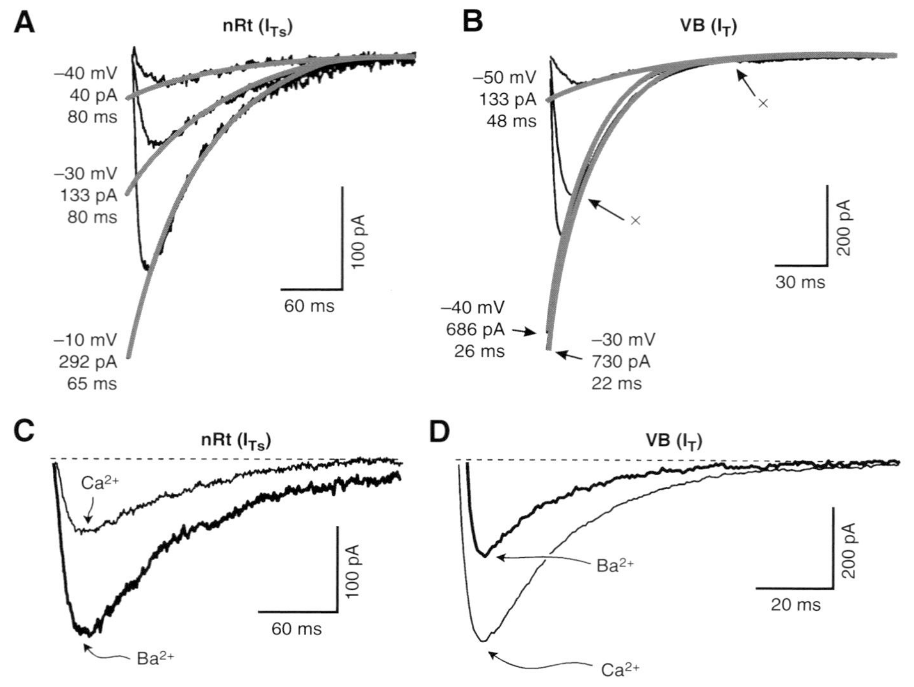

Fig. 2. Low-voltage-activated (LVA) currents vary in neurons of different thalamic nuclei. A) Inactivation kinetics of the slow T-type current (I_{Ts}) found in thalamic reticular neurons (nRt). Three traces are shown at command potentials of –40, –30 and –10 mV. The terminal portions of each trace are fitted with single exponential decay curves (grey lines). Numbers to the left of each curve refer to the command potential, the initial (t_0) current level and the time constant of inactivation (in ms). NB: the currents become incrementally larger with more depolarised command potentials, but the rate of inactivation is relatively insensitive to voltage. B) A family of depolarisation-activated 'standard' T-type currents (I_T) in a ventrobasal (VB) relay neuron, with fitted decay curves as in panel A. In this case the curves cross each other (×), mainly because the larger currents obtained with stronger depolarising steps are more rapidly inactivating than those activated with weak depolarisations. NB: different time bases for panels A and B. C & D) LVA currents evoked upon depolarising step commands to –30 mV with Ca^{2+} or Ba^{2+} 3 mM as the charge carrier. NB: in nRt cells the LVA current is increased in amplitude (thick line) when Ba^{2+} is substituted on an equimolar basis with Ca^{2+} (panel C). This was true at all potentials within the activation range of I_{Ts}. By contrast, in relay cells the LVA current was decreased with Ba^{2+} as the charge carrier (panel D).

opening of a few channels, which leads to further depolarisation and progressively faster opening of channels. The net result is a rapidly progressive, regenerative spike that tends to be 'all or nothing'.[24]

We recently examined the conditions leading to graded LTS generation.[26] In these experiments, both depolarisation from rest and transient hyperpolarisation resulted in LTSs or burst responses that were robust, i.e. they could be reproduced with a wide range of conditioning pulses. Contrary to expectation, graded responses that varied in amplitude as a continuous function of conditioning potential were not obtained

(Fig. 1 continued)
relay neurons are Ca^{2+}-dependent. Increasing extracellular Ca^{2+} from 1 to 3 mM (divalent ion concentration kept constant at 3 mM with Mg^{2+}) increases the amplitude of the current (panel E), and the non-specific calcium channel antagonist La^{3+} abolished the current (panel F). G) LVA currents in relay neurons are relatively insensitive to Ni^{2+} blockade. Ni^{2+} 100 µM reduces LVA by only about 50%. At this concentration it also inhibits HVA calcium currents by ~30–40% and is therefore not a good selective blocker. By comparison, Cd^{2+} 100 µM blocks the current by about 50%, but this concentration blocks high-voltage-activated currents nearly completely. Intracellular solution: TRIS PO_4 110 mM; EGTA 11; $MgCl_2$ 2 mM; $CaCl_2$ 0.5 mM; ATP 4 mM; extracellular solutions: TEAC 155 mM; $CaCl_2$ 3 mM; HEPES 10 mM.

from the steady-state inactivation curve.[7] Rather, a discontinuous function was obtained, in which the most depolarised conditioning potentials resulted in failures, whereas less depolarised potentials produced all-or-nothing responses. Once threshold was reached, a full-blown LTS resulted. Partial blockade of LTS channels by succinimides did not alter the response *per se*, but it did reduce the probability of obtaining such a response with a given stimulation.[24] These results can be explained by the regenerative nature of the LTS and the fact that LTSs can be initiated near the resting membrane potential, which is near the minimal activation range for LVA current.[7] When the current clamp protocol was altered so that the activation step was an active depolarisation of about 10 mV rather than a passive return to resting membrane potential, the resultant LTSs were very clearly graded.[26] In this case, the LTS was activated by a voltage transient that approached the level required for 50% maximal activation of LVA currents.[7] Thus, the stimulus forced activation of the regenerative event, and the size of the event was a reasonable proxy for LVA channel availability. This approach provides a reliable method of characterising pharmacological effects on LVA channels in mature intact neurons, with which voltage-clamp studies are impractical.[26]

Several kinetic properties of the LVA current produce functional constraints of burst firing. The steady-state inactivation function results in most LVA channels being inactivated at rest, and hyperpolarisation beyond –70 mV is necessary to significantly remove inactivation. Thus, neuromodulators that can regulate membrane potential within this range strongly influence burst firing capability[27] and the ability of relay neurons to behave as linear input–output devices. The time constant for recovery from inactivation (deinactivation) is quite slow. At body temperature (37 °C), the time constant is approximately 80 ms at –80 mV.[7] Although recovery rate becomes faster with increased hyperpolarisation,[7,18] these negative potentials are rarely achieved *in vivo*,[28] and the effective refractory period limits the rate of repetitive burst firing to about 12 Hz or less. Thus, during thalamic spindle oscillations, which occur as a result of phasic inhibitory synaptic potentials, most relay cells are not capable of closely following the 8–12 Hz network oscillation.[28] Significant overlap in the steady-state inactivation and activation curves in the voltage range between –70 and –60 mV suggests the existence of a window current. An interesting physiological consequence of high LVA channel density is the expression of a region of negative slope conductance in the steady-state current–voltage curve in some thalamic neurons. In these cells, small negative deflections can lead to regenerative membrane hyperpolarisation produced by inactivation of a resting inward current.[29] These results indicate that persistent activation of LVA channels can lead to tonic depolarising current and Ca^{2+} entry.

Heterogeneity of LVA currents in thalamic relay versus reticular neurons

LVA burst responses in thalamic neurons can be quite varied, with some of the most striking differences being observed between relay[30,31] and reticular neurons.[32–36]

The thalamic reticular neurons (nRt) are a group of interconnected GABAergic neurons that send inhibitory fibres into the dorsal thalamus to impinge on relay neurons.[37] In general, burst responses in nRt cells are much longer lasting and have higher intraburst frequencies than those in relay neurons.[17] In addition, the within-burst spikes in nRt cells have an accelerando–decelerando pattern,[24,38] while in relay neurons the pattern is predominantly decelerando.[24] Since *in vivo* intracellular recordings in cat nRt cells have shown that relatively strong hyperpolarisations are required for burst generation, it was proposed that LVA channels are primarily localised on dendritic membranes.[36] To address this issue, the LVA current in isolated rat nRt cells was evaluated using a voltage-clamp technique. Significant differences between this LVA current and that in relay neurons were found, particularly in terms of kinetic properties.[17] The kinetic differences observed can account for some but not all of the differences in burst firing patterns between relay and nRt cells.[39]

Although the LVA or T-type current in relay cells [7] has many similarities with that in sensory neurons,[11–14] the LVA or T_s-type current in nRt cells displayed significantly slower activation and inactivation kinetics. The kinetic and pharmacological properties of the two currents are presented in table 1. These currents share a number of properties that distinguish them from HVA calcium currents,[17] most prominently their putative function (burst generation), insensitivity to Ca^{2+}-dependent inactivation or metabolic run-down, relative insensitivity to Cd^{2+}, their modest sensitivity to Ni^{2+} and amiloride, blockade by antiepileptic succinimide compounds[17,20,22,24] and their lack of sensitivity to dihydropyridines and ω–CTx-GVIA. In terms of voltage-dependent kinetics, both currents can be well-approximated with the Hodgkin–Huxley m^2h formalism, and the steady-state inactivation functions are almost identical. However, most other kinetic features differ, and these differences appear to be critically linked to the differences in burst firing in the two cell types.

Important kinetic differences include a more depolarised activation range for T_s-type current than for T-type current. This leads to a more depolarised threshold for LTS generation in nRt cells, such that Ca^{2+} and Na^+ spike thresholds are very similar.[40] The rate of ensemble current inactivation is one of the most striking differences. The inactivation rate of T_s-type current is not only slower than that for T-type current – it is almost *voltage-independent*, which contrasts with the strong voltage-dependence of T-type current (see fig. 2 (A & B)). Thus, a family of T-type current traces at different command potentials demonstrates clear crossing points (see fig. 2 (B)), while a similar family of T_s-type current traces tend to show parallel inactivation and do not cross (see fig. 2 (A)). In contrast, the rate of deinactivation, or recovery from inactivation, is voltage-dependent for both forms of T-type current, yet overall it is about twice as slow for T_s-type current. Deactivation, as measured by tail currents, tends to be faster for the latter. For example, at –80mV T_s-type current deactivates with a time constant of about 2.5 ms, compared with a value of about 7 ms for T-type current.[17] Thus, T-type current may be regarded as 'slowly deactivating'[13] in that it deactivates much more slowly than HVA calcium currents (τ_{tail} <0.5 ms[13]). Overall, voltage-independence of inactivation, along with a high apparent Ba^{2+}:Ca^{2+}

Table 1. Comparison of properties of low-voltage-activated (LVA) or T-type current in relay cells versus LVA or T_s-type current in thalamic reticular neurons

Property	T type	T_s type
Kinetics		
Model	m^2h	m^2h
Steady-state inactivation (h_∞)	$V_{½} = -81$ $k = 4.4\ mV^{-1}$	$V_{½} = -78$ $k = 5.0\ mV^{-1}$
Steady-state activation (m_∞)	$V_{½} = -59$ $k = 5.2\ mV^{-1}$	* $V_{½} = -50$ $k = 7.4\ mV^{-1}$
Inactivation rate	60 – 28 ms –60 to –20 mV Voltage-dependent	* 90 – 80 ms –60 to –20 mV * Voltage-independent
Activation rate	5 – 1 ms –50 to –20 mV Voltage-dependent	* 12 – 4 ms –50 to –20 mV Voltage-dependent
Deinactivation rate	260 ms at –90 mV Voltage-dependent	* 590 ms at –90 mV Voltage-dependent
Miscellaneous		
Function	Burst firing	Burst firing
Metabolic stability	Stable	Stable
Ba^{2+}:Ca^{2+} permeability ratio	0.66	* 1.5
Pharmacology†		
Amiloride	~400 μM	~400 μM
Ni^{2+}	~150 μM	~150 μM
Cd^{2+}	~150 μM	~150 μM
Methylphenylsuccinimide	~3 mM	~3 mM
Nimodipine (1 μM)	No effect	No effect
BayK8644 (1 μM)	No effect	No effect
ω-CTx-GVIA (0.5 μM)	No effect	No effect

Symbols and abbreviations: $V_{½}$ = half-activation/inactivation potential; * differences between the two currents; † approximate EC_{50} values.

permeability ratio (see fig. 2 (C)), sets T_s-type current apart from most other forms of LVA current.[41]

While kinetic differences in LVA current certainly contribute to differences in LTS generation, other factors are also important. For example, other voltage-gated channels may be involved in shaping the response, and the complex electrotonic structure of a neuron may influence spike patterns.[42] In a theoretical study we have shown that T_s-type current will lead to prolonged bursts in nRt cells, but in order to reproduce the accelerando–decelerando spike pattern T_s-type channels must be concentrated in dendritic membranes.[39] Indeed, experiments in isolated nRt cells indicated a relatively low density of T_s-type channels in somatic membranes.[17] By analogy, a similar situation may also occur in neurons of the lateral habenula. The cells have the interesting physiological response of repetitive burst firing triggered by single, brief, hyperpolarising current pulses.[43] The properties of LVA currents in these cells were intermediate between T_s- and T-type currents of thalamic neurons. For example, the inactivation rate displayed both slow and fast decay components.[44] The density of somatic LVA channels in lateral habenula cells was low, suggesting that (as with nRt cells) LVA channels may be concentrated in dendritic membranes.

This sort of localisation may promote intrinsic rhythm in neurons.[35,43] Thus, dendritic LVA channels trigger powerful and long-lasting bursts,[39] and the associated Ca^{2+} entry leads to activation of after-hyperpolarisations that deinactivate LVA channels and enable rebound burst firing.

The recently characterised rbE-II calcium channel possesses a number of properties that suggest that it is a member of the LVA family.[45] Notably, it can be activated by relatively weak depolarisations and is largely inactivated at normal neuronal resting potentials, especially when coexpressed with a β subunit.[45,46] Furthermore, in common with LVA channels in sensory neurons,[13,47,48] it is blocked by low levels of Ni^{2+}. However, it seems unlikely that this channel contributes to LTS generation, at least in thalamus, since Ni^{2+} does not seem to be a particularly effective antagonist of LVA currents in thalamic neurons.[7] In addition, while Cd^{2+} is an effective blocker of rbE-II channels,[45] the LTS in lateral geniculate neurons is relatively insensitive to this ion.[9] Furthermore, rbE-II is rapidly deactivating[46,49] and its metabolic stability is less[45,49] than that for the LVA current.[17] In the thalamus, although LVA currents are prominent,[7] rbE-II does not appear to be expressed at high levels.[45] Finally, although the voltage-dependence of rbE-II is clearly modified by coexpression with accessory subunits,[45,46] it appears that the kinetics of the current are more consistent with a functional role in the relatively persistent calcium current that would lead to sustained Ca^{2+} entry, rather than the transient and highly voltage-dependent calcium current that leads to LTS generation.[3,7]

Conclusions

The presence of a high density of LVA channels, especially in neuronal soma but also in dendrites, leads to paradoxical excitation of neurons. Transient hyperpolarisations, such as those produced by inhibitory postsynaptic potentials, removes inactivation of the channels and leads to regenerative Ca^{2+}-dependent burst firing. The regenerative responses are largely governed by the kinetic properties of the LVA channels. Cell-specific LVA channel forms, in conjunction with particular somatodendritic localisation, result in variations in burst responses. Pharmacological blockade of LVA channels can reduce the probability of obtaining burst responses and can therefore reduce network interactions that strongly depend on burst expression.

Acknowledgements

This work was supported by National Institutes of Health grants NS06477, NS12151, NS34774 from the National Institute of Neurological Disorders and Stroke, and the Pimley Research Fund.

References

1. Llinás R. The intrinsic electrophysiological properties of mammalian neurones: insights into central nervous system function. Science 1988; 242: 1654–64
2. Connors BW, Gutnick MJ. Intrinsic firing patterns of diverse neocortical neurones. Trends Neurosci 1990; 13: 99–104

3. Jahnsen H, Llinás R. Electrophysiological properties of guinea-pig thalamic neurones: an *in vitro* study. J Physiol (Lond) 1984; 349: 205–26
4. Jahnsen H, Llinás R. Ionic basis for the electroresponsiveness and oscillatory properties of guinea-pig thalamic neurones *in vitro*. J Physiol (Lond) 1984; 349: 227–47
5. Llinás R, Yarom Y. Properties and distribution of ionic conductances generating electroresponsiveness of mammalian inferior olivary neurones *in vitro*. J Physiol (Lond) 1981; 315: 569–84
6. Llinás R, Yarom Y. Electrophysiology of mammalian inferior olivary neurones *in vitro*. Different types of voltage-dependent ionic conductances. J Physiol (Lond) 1981; 315: 549–67
7. Coulter DA, Huguenard JR, Prince DA. Calcium currents in rat thalamocortical relay neurones: kinetic properties of the transient, low-threshold current. J Physiol (Lond) 1989; 414: 587–604
8. Crunelli V, Lightowler S, Pollard CE. A T-type Ca^{2+} current underlies low-threshold Ca^{2+} potentials in cells of the cat and rat lateral geniculate nucleus. J Physiol (Lond) 1989; 413: 543–61
9. Hernandez-Cruz A, Pape H-C. Identification of two calcium currents in acutely dissociated neurones from the rat lateral geniculate nucleus. J Neurophysiol 1989; 61: 1270–83
10. Suzuki S, Rogawski MA. T-type calcium channels mediate the transition between tonic and phasic firing in thalamic neurones. Proc Natl Acad Sci U S A 1989; 86: 7228–32
11. Carbone E, Lux HD. A low voltage-activated, fully inactivating Ca channel in vertebrate sensory neurones. Nature 1984; 310: 501–2
12. Nowycky MC, Fox AP, Tsien RW. Three types of neuronal calcium channel with different calcium agonist sensitivity. Nature 1985; 316: 440–3
13. Swandulla D, Armstrong CM. Fast-deactivating calcium channels in chick sensory neurones. J Gen Physiol 1988; 92: 197–218
14. Fedulova SA, Kostyuk PG, Veselovsky NS. Two types of calcium channels in the somatic membrane of new-born rat dorsal root ganglion neurones. J Physiol (Lond) 1985; 359: 431–46
15. Karst H, Joëls M, Wadman WJ. Low-threshold calcium current in dendrites of the adult rat hippocampus. Neurosci Lett 1993; 164: 154–8
16. Magee JC, Johnston D. Synaptic activation of voltage-gated channels in the dendrites of hippocampal pyramidal neurones. Science 1995; 268: 301–4
17. Huguenard JR, Prince DA. A novel T-type current underlies prolonged Ca^{2+}-dependent burst firing in GABAergic neurones of rat thalamic reticular nucleus. J Neurosci 1992; 12: 3804–17
18. Huguenard JR, McCormick DA. Simulation of the currents involved in rhythmic oscillations in thalamic relay neurones. J Neurophysiol 1992; 68: 1373–83
19. McCormick DA, Huguenard JR. A model of the electrophysiological properties of thalamocortical relay neurones. J Neurophysiol 1992; 68: 1384–400
20. Coulter DA, Huguenard JR, Prince DA. Specific petit mal anticonvulsants reduce calcium currents in thalamic neurones. Neurosci Lett 1989; 98: 74–8
21. Coulter DA, Huguenard JR, Prince DA. Characterization of ethosuximide reduction of low-threshold calcium current in thalamic neurones. Ann Neurol 1989; 25: 582–93
22. Coulter DA, Huguenard JR, Prince DA. Differential effects of petit mal anticonvulsants and convulsants on thalamic neurones: calcium current reduction. Br J Pharmacol 1990; 100: 800–6
23. Coulter DA, Huguenard JR, Prince DA. Mechanism of block of thalamic 'T'-type Ca^{2+} channels by petit mal anticonvulsants. Exp Brain Res 1991; 20: 201–4
24. Huguenard JR, Prince DA. Intrathalamic rhythmicity studied *in vitro*: nominal T current modulation causes robust anti-oscillatory effects. J Neurosci 1994; 14: 5485–502
25. Hodgkin AL, Huxley AF. A quantitative description of membrane current and its application to conduction and excitation in nerve. J Physiol (Lond) 1952; 117: 500–44
26. Smith SD, Huguenard JR. The specific T-type Ca^{2+} channel blocker U92032 reduces synchronous phasic discharge in thalamus [abstract]. Epilepsia 1996; 37 Suppl. 5: 116
27. McCormick DA, Bal T. Sensory gating mechanisms of the thalamus. Curr Opin Neurobiol 1994; 4: 550–6
28. Steriade M, Llinás R. The functional states of the thalamus and the associated neuronal interplay. Physiol Rev 1988; 68: 649–742
29. Williams SR, Turner JP, Toth TI, et al. Voltage and temporal amplification in thalamocortical (TC) neurones – experimental studies [abstract]. Neurosci Abstr 1995; 21: 104
30. Deschênes M, Roy JP, Steriade M. Thalamic bursting mechanism: an inward slow current revealed by membrane hyperpolarization. Brain Res 1982; 239: 289–93
31. Llinás R, Jahnsen H. Electrophysiology of mammalian thalamic neurones *in vitro*. Nature 1982; 297: 406–8
32. Llinás R, Giejo-Barrientos E. *In vitro* studies of mammalian thalamic and reticularis thalami neurones. In: Bentivoglio M, Spreafico R, editors. Cellular thalamic mechanisms. Amsterdam: Elsevier, 1988: 23–33
33. Domich L, Oakson G, Steriade M. Thalamic burst patterns in the naturally sleeping cat: a comparison between cortically projecting and reticularis neurones. J Physiol (Lond) 1986; 379: 429–49
34. McCormick DA, Prince DA. Acetylcholine induces burst firing in thalamic reticular neurones by activating a potassium conductance. Nature 1986; 319: 402–5
35. Avanzini G, de Curtis M, Panzica F, et al. Intrinsic properties of nucleus reticularis thalami neurones of the rat studied *in vitro*. J Physiol (Lond) 1989; 416: 111–22
36. Mulle C, Madariaga A, Deschênes M. Morphology and electrophysiological properties of reticularis thalami neurones in cat: *in vivo* study of a thalamic pacemaker. J Neurosci 1986; 6: 2134–45

37. Jones EG. The thalamus. New York: Plenum, 1985
38. Steriade M, Domich L, Oakson G. Reticularis thalami neurones revisited: activity changes during shifts in states of vigilance. J Neurosci 1986; 6: 68–81
39. Destexhe A, Contreras D, Steriade M, et al. *In vivo*, *in vitro* and computational analysis of dendritic calcium currents in thalamic reticular neurones. J Neurosci 1996; 16: 169–85
40. McCormick DA, Wang Z. Serotonin and noradrenaline excite GABAergic neurones of the guinea-pig and cat nucleus reticularis thalami. J Physiol (Lond) 1991; 442: 235–55
41. Huguenard JR. Low-threshold calcium currents in central neurones. Annu Rev Physiol 1996; 58: 329–48
42. Mainen ZF, Sejnowski TJ. Influence of dendritic structure on firing pattern in model neocortical neurones. Nature 1996; 382: 363–6
43. Wilcox KS, Gutnick MJ, Christoph GR. Electrophysiological properties of neurones in the lateral habenula nucleus: an *in vitro* study. J Neurophysiol 1988; 59: 212–25
44. Huguenard JR, Gutnick MJ, Prince DA. Properties of low threshold calcium current in neurones isolated from the lateral habenula of the rat. J Neurophysiol 1993; 70: 158–66
45. Soong TW, Stea A, Hodson CD, et al. Structure and functional expression of a member of the low voltage-activated calcium channel family. Science 1993; 260: 1133–6
46. Olcese R, Qin N, Schneider T, et al. The amino terminus of a calcium channel β subunit sets rates of channel inactivation independently of the subunit's effect on activation. Neurone 1994; 13: 1433–8
47. Fox AP, Nowycky MC, Tsien RW. Kinetic and pharmacological properties distinguishing three types of calcium currents in chick sensory neurones. J Physiol (Lond) 1987; 394: 149–72
48. Carbone E, Lux HD. Kinetics and selectivity of a low-voltage-activated calcium current in chick and rat sensory neurones. J Physiol (Lond) 1987; 386: 547–70
49. Bourinet E, Zamponi GW, Stea A, et al. The α_{1E} calcium channel exhibits permeation properties similar to low-voltage-activated calcium channels. J Neurosci 1996; 16: 4983–93

Ca^{2+} entry through T-type channels of nerve and muscle

Kurt Beam

Department of Anatomy and Neurobiology, Colorado State University, Fort Collins, Colorado, USA

Introduction

Presented here is a review of the results of work conducted in the Colorado State University Department of Anatomy and Neurobiology on T-type calcium currents. This work includes an analysis of the developmental expression of T-type calcium current in skeletal muscle and spinal motoneurons, effects of calcium channel antagonists and serum from human patients with Eaton–Lambert myasthenic syndrome, and the role of T-type calcium channels in causing changes in intracellular Ca^{2+}.

Developmental changes in T-type calcium current expression in skeletal muscle

Our initial experiments on developmental regulation of calcium currents were prompted by the observation of a slow-activating, L-type calcium current in adult skeletal muscle. The slow activation and the fact that excitation–contraction coupling in skeletal muscle does not require the entry of extracellular Ca^{2+} made it difficult to understand the function of this calcium current. Our working hypothesis was that the slow L-type calcium current was vestigial in adult muscle and only functionally important earlier in development. To address this issue, we applied the whole-cell patch-clamp technique to single fibres obtained by enzymatic dissociation of flexor digitorum brevis (FDB) muscles from rats of varying postnatal age.[1,2] Neonatal FDB fibres displayed two calcium currents: in addition to the slow L-type current, which activated at high voltages, there was a low-voltage-activated (LVA) transient current. With Ca^{2+} 10 mM as the extracellular divalent cation, the LVA current activated at potentials of at least –50 mV, peaked in 10–20 ms and decayed back to baseline in 50–100 ms. This current was maximal for test potentials of about –20 mV and was completely inactivated by a 1 s prepulse to about –30 mV. In myotubes, where transient LVA calcium currents are also present,[3,4] cell-attached recordings revealed that the underlying channels have a unitary conductance of ~9 pS in Ba^{2+} 110 mM.[5] These macroscopic and microscopic properties are similar to those that were reported for T-type currents in cardiac atrial[6] and ventricular[7] cells and sensory neurons.[8]

In neonatal (1–5 days old) rat FDB fibres, the density of peak T-type calcium current (1.4 pA/pF) was quite significant compared to that of the slow L-type current (3.6 pA/pF). The T-type current decreased in size during postnatal development, becoming undetectable in fibres from animals >3 weeks of age.[2] By contrast, the density of the slow L-type current increased substantially during postnatal development, reaching 16.4 pA/pF by 6 weeks postnatally. At about the same time as the publication of a paper by Beam and Knudson,[2] very similar results were reported for mouse FDB fibres by Gonoi and Hasegawa.[9] The results with developing muscle fibres argued against our initial hypothesis, that the L-type current was vestigial in adult muscle fibres. Moreover, the results provided an additional conundrum, that of the function of the T-type current in neonatal muscle fibres: in neonatal FDB muscle, excitation–contraction coupling was still functional after blocking all calcium currents by addition of extracellular Cd^{2+}.[10]

The results summarised above raise questions not only about the function of T-type current in developing skeletal muscle, but also about the regulatory influences that cause it to disappear. The *in vivo* environment is not required for the expression of T-type calcium channels in muscle, since T-type currents are present in myotubes obtained by primary culture of myoblasts harvested from embryonic or neonatal mice.[3,4] T-type currents are also present in myotubes obtained by primary culture of satellite cells, the quiescent muscle precursor cells present in muscle tissue of adult animals (Beam, unpublished observations). With respect to the factors controlling the disappearance of T-type currents during *in vivo* development, the experiments of Gonoi and Hasegawa eliminate a number of possibilities.[9] When muscles were denervated and maintained *in vivo*, denervation in young animals (i.e. when T-type calcium currents were still present) did not prevent T-type currents from disappearing, nor did denervation in older animals cause them to reappear. However, muscle fibres removed from young animals and kept in tissue culture for almost 3 weeks continued to have a T-type current density similar to that present at the time of removal. Moreover, fibres removed from older animals and kept in culture began to re-express T-type current after about 2 weeks. Since satellite cells adhere to isolated FDB fibres, the reappearance of T-type channels after long-term culture may have been a result of the proliferation of satellite cells followed by their fusion into the FDB fibres.[11] In any case, a hypothesis to account for the results of Gonoi and Hasegawa[9] is to suppose that:

i) there is a humoral factor(s) present *in vivo* which controls the expression of T-type calcium channels
ii) this factor disappears during postnatal development
iii) this same factor is present in tissue-culture media.

It is tempting to speculate that this factor might be growth hormone (GH), since T-type current density is increased in atrial myocytes from rats with GH-secreting tumours.[12]

Developmental changes in T-type calcium current expression in spinal motoneurons

An important developmental event in spinal motoneurons is naturally occurring cell death: about half of the initial population of spinal motoneurons dies during embryonic days E6–E9 in chicks and E13–E18 in mice.[13] After the period of cell death is over, individual motoneurons have overlapping synaptic outputs (i.e. individual muscle fibres receive synaptic input from several motoneurons). The supernumerary synapses are eliminated from E9 to E21 in chicks and during postnatal days P0–P21 in mice.[13] To determine whether there are changes in calcium current expression that are associated with these developmental changes in motoneurons, we labelled motoneurons by using the lipophilic dye di-I as originally described by Honig and Hume.[14] The di-I was either injected into limb muscles or applied to the cut end of the sciatic nerve. Subsequently, the spinal cord was removed and enzymatically dissociated. The dissociated cells were placed in primary tissue culture, and di-I-labelled cells were analysed by means of whole-cell patch clamp 12–24 hours later.

Using the techniques summarised above, we were able to analyse calcium currents in motoneurons isolated from chicks at E4 (when axons arrive at the periphery and thus the earliest time when dye labelling is possible), E6 (immediately before the onset of cell death) and E11 (a couple of days after the end of cell death).[15] We also succeeded in measuring calcium currents in motoneurons isolated from mice at E14 (when axons arrive at the periphery and early during the period of cell death), P1–P3 (after cell death and at the onset of synapse elimination) and P7–P8 (part way through the period of synapse elimination).[16,17] It proved very difficult to isolate viable motoneurons from chicks older than E11 or mice older than P8. The chick and mouse motoneurons displayed both T-type and high-voltage-activated (HVA) calcium currents. Under comparable recording conditions, the motoneuronal T-type calcium currents had voltage-dependence and kinetics similar to those of T-type calcium currents in developing skeletal muscle (see pp. 153–4).

In chick motoneurons, peak T-type current density decreased from 3.6 pA/pF at E4 to 0.9 and 0.4 pA/pF at E6 and E11, respectively, while the density of peak HVA calcium current increased from 3.7 pA/pF to 9.6 and 13.4 pA/pF, respectively.[15] In mouse motoneurons, T-type calcium current density decreased from 0.7 pA/pF at E14 to 0.4 and 0.2 pA/pF at P1–P3 and P7–P8, respectively, whereas the HVA calcium current density changed little from E14 (13.0 pA/pF) to P1–P3 (9.8 pA/pF) but increased substantially from P1 to P3 to a value of 38.6 pA/pF at P7–P8.[16] Interestingly, the absolute density of both T-type calcium current (0.7 pA/pF) and HVA current (13.0 pA/pF) in E14 mouse motoneurons was similar to that of T-type calcium current (0.9 pA/pF) and HVA current (9.6 pA/pF) found in chick motoneurons at the comparable developmental stage (E6). In summary, robust changes in expression of HVA calcium current occurred prior to the onset of cell death (chick) and during the initiation of synapse elimination (mouse); motoneuronal T-type calcium currents were appreciable in size only very early in development. Since neuromuscular activity has been shown to have a critical influence on both cell death and synapse elimination,[13] the changes in HVA currents seem reasonable since these currents are likely to be involved in synaptic transmission. However, the role of T-type calcium currents in developing motoneurons remains obscure (just as in developing skeletal muscle).

Similarities and differences between T-type calcium currents in myotubes and motoneurons

As initially described for T-type calcium currents in neuroblastoma cells,[18] amiloride blocked the T-type current in mouse myotubes,[19] chick motoneurons[15] and mouse motoneurons,[16] without affecting the HVA calcium currents to a great extent. The sensitivity to amiloride was similar for T-type calcium channels in myotubes (~75% reduction, by 0.3–1.0 mM) and chick motoneurons (~80% reduction, by 1.0 mM); however, the mouse motoneuronal T-type calcium current appeared to be less sensitive (~50% reduction, by 1–2 mM). Although, the sensitivity to amiloride suggests that the muscle and nerve T-type calcium channels are related, experiments with serum from patients with the autoimmune disorder Eaton–Lambert syndrome suggest the opposite conclusion. Specifically, 24 hours' incubation with serum from four patients with Eaton–Lambert syndrome significantly reduced T-type currents in cultured mouse motoneurons but not in mouse myotubes or cardiomyocytes.[20] Although this differential effect may result from differences in channel turnover and/or accessibility to antibodies, it also may mean that the subunit composition of T-type calcium channels differs in motoneurons and muscle. Since T-type currents in skeletal muscle are unaffected by knockout of the gene encoding the calcium channel β_1 subunit,[21] it seems unlikely that T-type calcium channels contain this subunit.

Although the effects of Eaton–Lambert syndrome sera suggest that there are biochemical differences between neuronal and muscle T-type calcium channels, they also suggest that there are commonalities between neuronal calcium channels. In particular, sera from three of the four Eaton–Lambert syndrome patients tested reduced both T-type and HVA currents in mouse dorsal root ganglion (DRG) neurons, and sera from all four patients reduced HVA currents in mouse motoneurons.[20,22]

Ca^{2+} entry through T-type calcium channels

In addition to observing developmental changes in calcium currents in motoneurons, we also found changes in the waveform of the action potential.[23] Thus, the question arose as to how alterations in the action potential might affect calcium currents through T-type and HVA calcium channels. To address this issue, we used action potential waveforms as voltage-clamp command signals applied to chick DRG neurons via a whole-cell patch pipette.[24] DRG neurons were used because they have much larger calcium currents than motoneurons. Since the calcium current measured with an action potential waveform would have contributions from both T-type and HVA calcium channels, it was necessary to have a method to dissect the contributions of the two channel types. Figure 1 illustrates a method based upon the use of amiloride. The voltage-clamp commands (either conventional square steps or action potential waveforms) are shown in the top row of the figure. The second row illustrates the resulting calcium currents measured under control

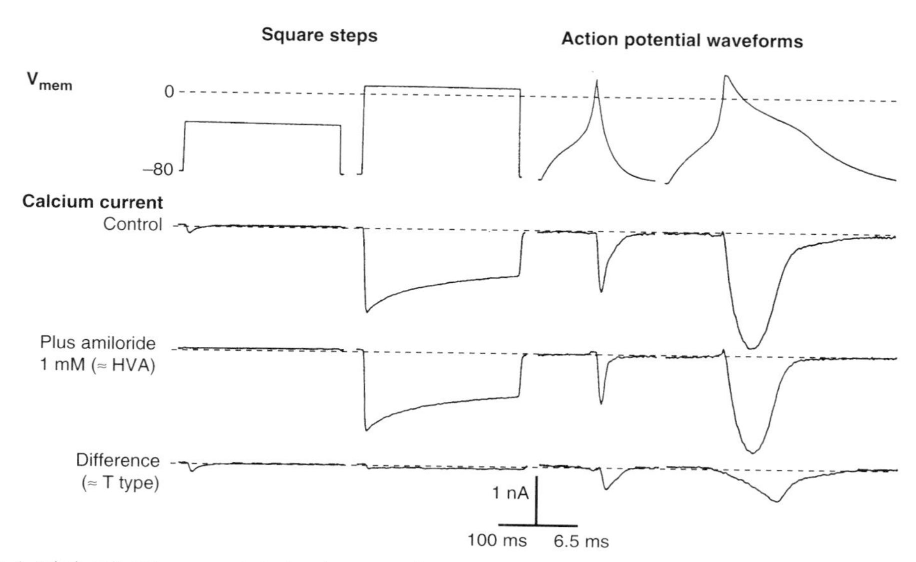

Fig. 1. Whole-cell calcium currents in dorsal root ganglion neurons elicited by voltage-clamp command steps to –30 mV (first column) or +10 mV (second column), or by a voltage-clamp command having the time-course of an action potential waveform of brief (third column) or long (fourth column) duration. The bath and pipette solutions were designed to block ionic currents, except for those arising from calcium channels. HVA = high-voltage activated; V_{mem} *= membrane potential. (Reproduced with permission, copyright Cell Press.[24])*

conditions, and the third row shows the currents measured in the presence of amiloride 1 mM. The bottom row illustrates the currents obtained by subtraction of the current in amiloride from the control current for each kind of voltage-clamp command. Under the assumption that amiloride specifically blocks T-type current, the currents in the third and fourth rows should represent the contribution of HVA and T-type channels, respectively. A step command to –30 mV (first column) elicited a small transient current, which was blocked almost completely by amiloride, so that the 'difference' current was almost the same as the control current. A step command to +10 mV (second column) elicited a much larger calcium current that had both transient and sustained components under control conditions and which was little affected by amiloride, so that the 'difference' current was very small. Application of the same procedure to currents elicited by the action potential waveforms (third and fourth columns) revealed that T-type channels contributed substantially to the total current, especially for the briefer of the two action potentials. In fact, Ca^{2+} entry through T-type channels (determined by integration) for the brief action potential was nearly equal to the entry through HVA channels. Thus, the calcium currents elicited by step commands give one an erroneous expectation about the relative Ca^{2+} entry through T-type and HVA calcium channels in response to a physiological stimulus, an action potential.

Similar results were obtained when the dissection of currents was accomplished using Cd^{2+} 35 μM, which preferentially blocks HVA calcium channels. The current in the presence of Cd^{2+} had a time-course and amplitude similar to that of the 'difference' currents obtained with amiloride. The difference between the control current and the current in the presence of Cd^{2+} had an amplitude and time-course similar to those of currents measured in the presence of amiloride. The apparently disproportionate contribution of T-type calcium channels to Ca^{2+} entry in response to an action potential can be explained by (i) the lower threshold of T-type channels compared with HVA channels, and (ii) the much slower deactivation of T-type channels.[25] The slow deactivation has the consequence that the largest contribution of T-type channels comes during the falling phase of the action potential.

In dysgenic myotubes, we were able to evaluate directly the changes in cytoplasmic Ca^{2+} produced by Ca^{2+} entry through T-type channels.[19] This was possible because T-type channels are the only type of calcium channel appreciably expressed in many dysgenic myotubes, although dysgenic myotubes may also express a rapidly activating L-type calcium current.[26] Activation of T-type channels in dysgenic myotubes caused measurable changes in cytoplasmic Ca^{2+} that were roughly proportional to the amplitude of the elicited current (fig. 2). Quite likely, even larger changes in cytoplasmic Ca^{2+} would have resulted if the stimulus had been an action potential rather than the step commands that were used in this experiment. However, the Ca^{2+} entry in response to an action potential appears to be insufficient to trigger contraction of myotubes since dysgenic myotubes expressing only T-type channels do not contract in response to brief electrical stimulation.[27]

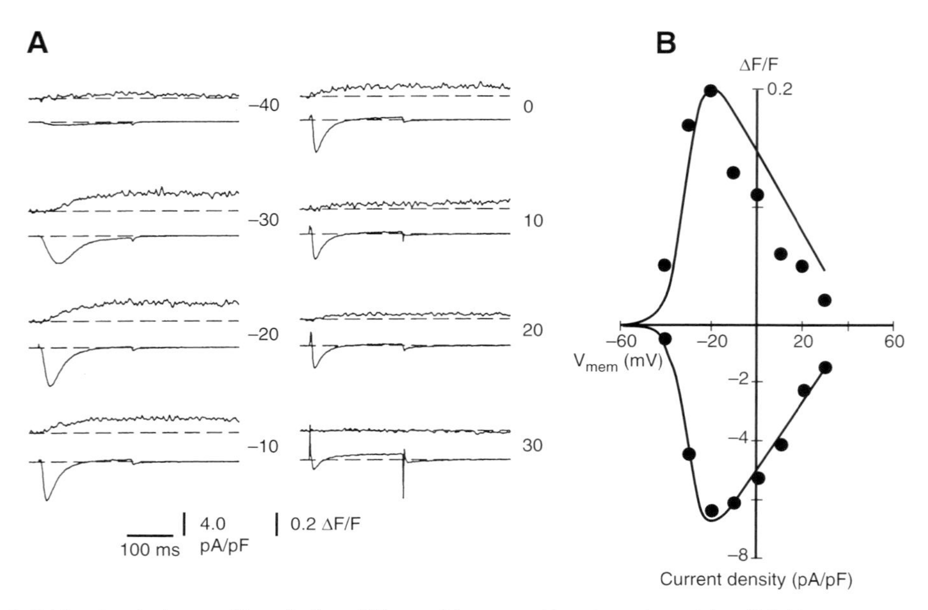

Fig. 2. Calcium transients caused by activation of T-type calcium current in a dysgenic myotube. A) Calcium currents (lower trace of each pair) and calcium transients (upper trace of each pair) elicited by the indicated test depolarisations. The whole-cell patch-clamp technique was used to measure ionic current and the cell was loaded with Ca^{2+} indicator by including the potassium salt of Fluo-3 in the patch pipette. Changes in fluorescence were monitored with a photomultiplier apparatus and ionic current with conventional patch-clamp circuitry. B) Voltage-dependence of calcium current and Ca^{2+}-induced increase in Fluo-3 fluorescence. F = Farads; V_{mem} = membrane potential. (Reproduced from the Journal of General Physiology by copyright permission of The Rockefeller University Press.[19])

Conclusions

T-type calcium currents are expressed at high density in developing skeletal muscle and spinal motoneurons, but the density rapidly falls with maturation to an undetectable level. Motoneuronal and muscle T-type currents have similar voltage-dependence and kinetics and are blocked by millimolar concentrations of amiloride. However, T-type channels in the two tissues may have a different molecular composition since they are differentially affected by serum from patients with Eaton–Lambert myasthenic syndrome. Because they have a lower voltage threshold for activation and deactivate more slowly than HVA calcium channels, T-type calcium channels can contribute disproportionately to the calcium current elicited by an action potential. Activation of T-type channels in myotubes produces easily measured changes in cytoplasmic Ca^{2+}. None the less, activation of T-type channels does not appear to produce sufficient Ca^{2+} entry to cause muscle contraction.

Because they are expressed at high levels and have properties that facilitate production of large calcium currents during action potentials, T-type channels must have important cellular roles. However, these roles remain obscure. It seems likely that identification of the molecular composition of T-type channels and the use of 'knockout' mice will be very helpful in elucidating these roles.

References

1. Beam KG, Knudson CM. Calcium currents in embryonic and neonatal mammalian skeletal muscle. J Gen Physiol 1988; 91: 781–98
2. Beam KG, Knudson CM. Effect of postnatal development on calcium currents and slow charge movement in mammalian skeletal muscle. J Gen Physiol 1988; 91: 799–815
3. Cognard C, Lazdunski M, Romey G. Different type of Ca^{2+} channels in mammalian skeletal muscle cells in culture. Proc Natl Acad Sci U S A 1986; 83: 517–21
4. Beam KG, Knudson CM, Powell JA. A lethal mutation in mice eliminates the slow calcium current in skeletal muscle cells. Nature 1986; 320: 168–70
5. Dirksen RT, Beam KG. Single calcium channel behavior in native skeletal muscle. J Gen Physiol 1995; 105: 227–47
6. Bean BP. Two kinds of calcium channels in canine atrial cells. J Gen Physiol 1985; 86: 1–30
7. Nilius B, Hess P, Lansman JB, et al. A novel type of cardiac calcium channel in ventricular cells. Nature 1985; 316: 443–6
8. Nowycky MC, Fox AP, Tsien RW. Three types of neuronal calcium channel with different calcium agonist sensitivity. Nature 1985; 316: 440–3
9. Gonoi T, Hasegawa S. Post-natal disappearance of transient calcium channels in mouse skeletal muscle: effects of denervation and culture. J Physiol 1988; 401: 617–37
10. Knudson CM, Jay SD, Beam KG. Developmental increase in skeletal muscle slow calcium current. Biophys J 1986; 49: 13a
11. Bischoff R. Proliferation of muscle satellite cells on intact myofibers in culture. Dev Biol 1986; 115: 129–39
12. Xu X, Best PM. Increase in T-type calcium current in atrial myocytes from adult rats with growth hormone-secreting tumors. Proc Natl Acad Sci U S A 1990; 87: 4655–9
13. Betz WJ. Motoneuron death and synapse elimination. In: Salpeter MM. The vertebrate neuromuscular junction. AR Liss: New York, 1987: 117–62
14. Honig MG, Hume RI. Fluorescent carbocyanine dyes allow living neurons of identified origin to be studied in long term cultures. J Cell Biol 1986; 103: 171–87
15. McCobb DP, Best PM, Beam KG. Development alters the expression of calcium currents in chick limb motoneurons. Neuron 1989; 2: 1633–43
16. Mynlieff M, Beam KG. Characterization of voltage-dependent calcium currents in mouse motoneurons. J Neurophysiol 1992; 68: 85–92

17. Mynlieff M, Beam KG. Developmental expression of voltage-dependent calcium currents in identified mouse motoneurons. Dev Biol 1992; 152: 407–10
18. Tang C-M, Presser F, Morad M. Amiloride selectively blocks the low threshold (T) calcium channel. Science 1988; 240: 213–15
19. García J, Beam KG. Calcium transients associated with the T-type calcium current in myotubes. J Gen Physiol 1994; 104: 1113–28
20. García KD, Beam KG. Reduction of calcium currents by Lambert–Eaton syndrome sera: motoneurons are preferentially affected and L-type currents are spared. J Neurosci 1996; 16: 4903–13
21. Strube C, Beurg M, Powers PA, et al. Reduced Ca^{2+} current, charge movement, and absence of Ca^{2+} transients in skeletal muscle deficient in dihydropyridine receptor β_1 subunit. Biophys J 1996; 71: 2531–43
22. García KD, Mynlieff M, Sanders DB, et al. Lambert–Eaton sera reduce low-voltage and high-voltage activated Ca^{2+} currents in murine dorsal root ganglion neurons. Proc Natl Acad Sci U S A 1996; 93: 9264–9
23. McCobb DP, Best PM, Beam KG. The differentiation of excitability in embryonic chick limb motoneurons. J Neurosci 1990; 10: 2974–84
24. McCobb DP, Beam KG. Action potential waveform voltage-clamp commands reveal striking differences between calcium entry via low and high voltage-activated calcium channels. Neuron 1991; 7: 119–27
25. Armstrong CM, Matteson DR. Two distinct populations of calcium channels in a clonal line of pituitary cells. Science 1985; 227: 65–7
26. Adams BA, Beam KG. A novel calcium current in dysgenic skeletal muscle. J Gen Physiol 1989; 94: 429–44
27. Adams BA, Beam KG. Contractions of dysgenic skeletal muscle triggered by a potentiated endogenous calcium current. J Gen Physiol 1991; 97: 687–96

T-type calcium channels in floor plate cells of the developing CNS

F. Frischknecht, A. Randall

Neurobiology Division, Medical Research Council Laboratory of Molecular Biology, Cambridge, UK

Summary

The cells of the floor plate region of the developing spinal cord and brain stem release chemoattractant and chemorepellent molecules and express specific cell-adhesion proteins that influence the outgrowth and trajectory of axons. We have investigated the electrophysiological properties of floor plate cells in tissue slices obtained from the embryonic and neonatal CNS. Floor plate cells possessed T-type calcium channels, but no other type. We hypothesise that activation of T-type calcium channels could trigger the release of chemoattractant molecules from floor plate cells.

Introduction

The Ca^{2+}-dependent release of bioactive molecules from eukaryotic cells is such a widespread phenomenon that it can be regarded as a fundamental biological process. In the mammalian CNS, this is a particularly widely exploited mechanism since it is crucial to the functioning of the large majority of synapses.

The regulated release of biologically active molecules in the CNS is not, however, confined to the presynaptic terminal. For instance, both glial cells and neurons participate in non-synaptic release of growth factors, cytokines and components of the extracellular matrix. One particularly interesting and important example of a non-neuronal release process in the CNS is the liberation of chemoattractant and chemorepellent molecules from the specialised neuroepithelial cells of the floor plate region of the developing spinal cord and brain stem.[1–5]

The floor plate is a ventral midline structure formed early in the developing CNS.[6] Before disappearing in early postnatal life, the floor plate seems to play a number of roles in the development of the CNS. These include dorso-ventral patterning, motor neuron induction and guidance of the axons of commissural neurons during their passage across the midline.[7–17]

The best candidates for the long-range chemoattractant/chemorepellent molecules which direct pioneering axons are the netrins,[2–4] the semaphorins[18] and sonic hedgehog.[1] When commissural axons reach the floor plate itself, additional axonal guidance may be provided by specific cell-adhesion molecules, such as F-spondin.[2–4,18–20]

There is some evidence that the release of floor plate chemoattractants occurs via a classical Ca^{2+}-dependent mechanism. For example, substance P receptor (i.e. NK_1-receptor) activation stimulates chemoattractant release apparently through an IP_3-dependent elevation of intracellular Ca^{2+}.[21,22] To date, however, analysis of floor plate function has mainly been carried out anatomically, biochemically and with cell and molecular biological techniques. To obtain further insights into the signalling processes involved in the Ca^{2+} homeostasis of floor plate cells, we initiated an electrophysiological study of the floor plate cells of neonatal and embryonic tissue slices. The results presented here demonstrate that floor plate cells possess a single class of voltage-activated calcium channel, the properties of which strongly suggest membership of the low-voltage-activated (LVA) T-type calcium channel family.

Methods

In order to study the electrophysiological properties of the floor plate, we developed two novel tissue slice preparations. The first, a brain-stem slice from postnatal day P0 rats, provided access to the floor plate on the ventral aspect of the aqueduct. The second preparation was a whole-body slice that included the brain stem and/or spinal cord of embryonic day E14 or E15 rats. In this latter preparation, the floor plate cells studied were those bordering the spinal central canal. The slices were prepared by standard means and remained viable for up to 3 days *ex vivo*. Confirmation of the presence and location of the floor plate in our slices was confirmed with immunostaining for the NK_1 receptor, a floor plate-selective marker (Frischknecht and Randall, unpublished observations).

For electrophysiological experiments, single tissue slices were transferred into a constantly perfused low-volume recording chamber, where they were secured in place with 31-gauge syringe needles. The chamber was mounted on the stage of an upright microscope equipped with infrared differential interference contrast (DIC) optics. This permitted visualisation of individual cells within tissue slices. Standard whole-cell patch-clamp recordings were made from cells of the floor plate region. Although cells of both neuronal and non-neuronal morphologies were studied, only the latter will be discussed here.

The standard extracellular solution for slice maintenance and the initiation of patch-clamp recordings was an aCSF of the following composition: NaCl 124 mM, $NaCO_3$ 26 mM, NaH_2PO_4 1.5 mM, KCl 3 mM, $CaCl_2$ 2 mM, $MgCl_2$ 1 mM and D-glucose 10 mM. This was equilibrated with O_2 95%/CO_2 5%. For the isolation of calcium currents, the aCSF was supplemented with TEAC 20 mM, and either $CaCl_2$ or $BaCl_2$ 2 mM or 10 mM was used as charge carrier. The electrode solution for calcium current recording was of pH 7.3 and 295 mOsm, and consisted of: $CsCH_3SO_4$ 108 mM, NaCl 10 mM, HEPES CsOH 24 mM, EGTA 9 mM, $MgCl_2$ 4.5 mM, ATP 4 mM and GTP 0.3 mM.

All voltage-activated currents were recorded both as raw data and as P/4 leak-subtracted traces; the latter are presented herein. Blocking molecules were applied via the constant perfusion of the recording chamber and were therefore presented to the tissue with some delay as a result of dead-time. This was characterised and has been accounted for in all figures shown.

Results

By far the largest currents in floor plate cells were those carried by K^+.[23] When these were eliminated with the solutions described above, small inactivating inward currents could be recorded in the large majority of floor plate cells. In Ca^{2+} 2 mM, the density of these currents averaged 8 ± 1 pA/pF in neonatal and 18 ± 4 pA/pF in embryonic floor plate cells. These currents were not blocked by the application of tetrodotoxin (TTX) 1 µM but, as shown in figure 1 (A), they were increased in amplitude 2.1-fold when extracellular Ca^{2+} 2 mM was replaced with Ba^{2+} 10 mM. This

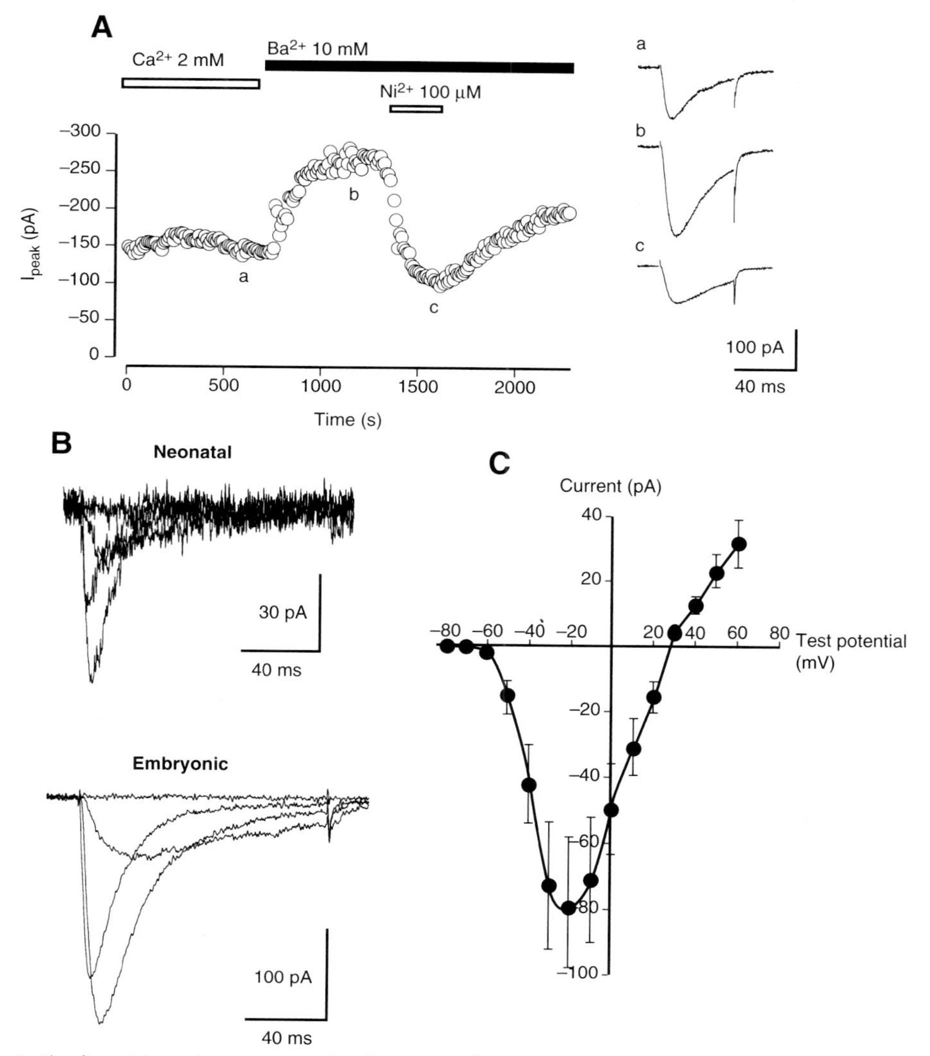

Fig. 1. A) Left: peak inward current versus time from an E14 floor plate cell. The cell was stepped from −80 to −20 mV every 10 s. The composition of the bathing aCSF was altered as indicated by the bars. Right: example sweeps comprising the average of the response to 5 consecutive depolarisations from the points indicated (a–c) on the left graph. B) Example sweeps taken from current–voltage series from a neonatal (top) and an embryonic (bottom) floor plate cell. The holding potential was −80 mV, and the currents were elicited at test potentials of −60, −40 , −20 and 0 mV. C) An average peak current–voltage relationship from 19 neonatal floor plate cells.

suggested strongly that these inward currents were carried by fluxes through a voltage-activated calcium channel.

In the presence of extracellular Ba^{2+} 10 mM, we made recordings of the inward current over a range of test potentials from both neonatal and embryonic floor plate cells. Examples of sweeps are shown in panel B of figure 1. When the data from neonatal cells were converted to standard current–voltage plots, U-shaped curves typical of calcium channel activation were generated (see fig. 1 (C)). The inward current first became detectable with depolarisation to potentials positive to –60 mV. On average, the peak of the current–voltage relationship was recorded close to –20 mV and the reversal potential occurred at around +30 mV. Very similar current–voltage relationships were generated from embryonic floor plate cells (data not shown). These curves suggested that the inward current was for the most part carried by an LVA or T-type calcium current. Indeed, standard analytical approaches revealed no evidence of any high-voltage-activated (HVA) components in the current–voltage relationship of any floor plate cell.

Taken together, the voltage range of activation of the inward current in floor plate cells, along with its potentiation upon exchanging Ba^{2+} 10 mM for Ca^{2+} 2 mM, suggested that the inward current arose from the activation of a T-type calcium current. In other systems, a variety of additional biophysical hallmarks distinguish T-type calcium channels from other calcium channels: these include a prevalence for rapid voltage-dependent inactivation, an equal ability to pass Ca^{2+} and Ba^{2+} ions and a more potent inhibition by Ni^{2+} than Cd^{2+}. The last two of these properties distinguish T-type calcium channels from the HVA L-, N-, P-, Q- and R-type calcium channels.[24]

Addressing the first of these parameters, in both neonatal and embryonic floor plate cells, exponential fits to the inactivation trajectory of the inward current revealed that the rate of current inactivation was both rapid and voltage-dependent. A plot of inactivation time constant against test potential from 7 neonatal cells is shown in figure 2 (A). At strong levels of depolarisation the time constant of inactivation approaches an asymptotic value of about 10 ms, slightly faster than that reported for T-type calcium channels elsewhere, but slower than that of TTX-sensitive and TTX-insensitive sodium channels.[25,26]

When an extracellular solution containing Ca^{2+} 10 mM was exchanged for one containing Ba^{2+} 10 mM, there was no change in the peak current amplitude measured at a test potential of –20 mV (see fig. 2 (B)). Application of either 40 or 120 µM of $NiCl_2$ produced a dose-dependent depression of the LVA inward current in floor plate cells. Pooled data from 5 cells revealed that Ni^{2+} 40 µM depressed the inward current at –20 mV by about 40% (see fig. 2 (C)). In contrast, $CdCl_2$ 100 µM produced little or no block of the inward current evoked at a test potential of –20 mV (see fig. 2 (D)). Removal of extracellular Ca^{2+} from the bathing medium and the addition of EGTA greatly depressed the inward current.[23]

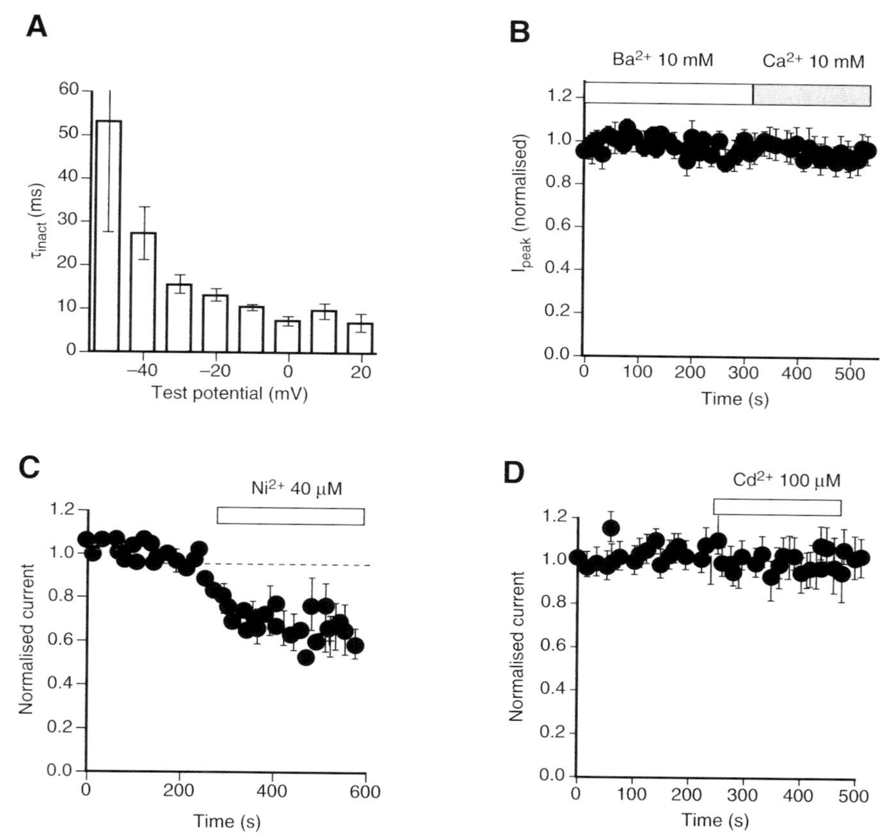

Fig. 2. A) Time constant of inactivation of the T-type current of floor plate cells vs test potential in the range –50 to +20 mV. Data pooled from 7 cells. B) Average change in amplitude caused by changing the bathing solution from one containing Ba^{2+} 10 mM to one containing Ca^{2+} 10 mM. Data from 5 cells, prior to averaging the current amplitude at each time-point for each cell, were normalised to the average value recorded in Ba^{2+}. C) Average block afforded by Ni^{2+} 40 mM of the current carried by Ba^{2+} 10 mM in 5 floor plate cells. Data processed as for panel B. D) As for panel C. Lack of inhibition afforded by Cd^{2+} 100 mM. Data from 5 floor plate cells.

Discussion

Our data clearly demonstrate the activation of a voltage-dependent inward current upon depolarisation of floor plate cells. In all respects, the properties of this current indicate that it arises from activation of LVA T-type calcium channels. Specifically, the current can be distinguished from both TTX-sensitive and TTX-insensitive sodium channels by its pharmacology, kinetics and, perhaps more importantly, its strong enhancement at all test potentials after increases in extracellular Ca^{2+} or Ba^{2+} concentrations. These observations clearly indicate that the current rises from some class of calcium channel. The extension of our classification to that of a T-type calcium channel comes from a range of additional observations. First, the channel clearly exhibits an LVA nature, since even in extracellular Ca^{2+} or Ba^{2+} 10 mM, currents are present at –50 mV (see fig. 1 (C)). Second, the channel is blocked by Ni^{2+} (40 μM) (see fig. 1 (C)) but is almost completely insensitive to Cd^{2+} (100 μM) (see fig. 2 (D)), which is a potent blocker (IC_{50} ≈1 μM) of all HVA channels.

In itself, the presence of a T-type calcium channel is obviously not sufficient to infer its participation in the developmental roles played by the floor plate. Indeed, our ongoing and future investigations will attempt to define the role of LVA calcium channels in floor plate function. In support of a role for T-type calcium channels in floor plate cells are both the resting membrane potential and the position of the steady-state inactivation curve. In both neonatal and embryonic tissues, the resting membrane potential is a few millivolts negative relative to the foot of the calcium channel activation curve.[23] At this potential, about half the T-type calcium channels are inactivated, but the other half remain able to open after a small membrane depolarisation. Indeed, the relative position of the activation and inactivation curves will provide a measurable 'window' current at a membrane potential only slightly depolarised from rest.

It is our expectation that the activation of the T-type calcium channel and the subsequent elevation of intracellular Ca^{2+} will lead to changes in a variety of floor plate cell activities. In this respect, it is important to ask whether activity of the calcium channel correlates with the release of chemoattractants. Although not generally implicated in fast synaptic neurotransmitter release, T-type calcium channels have been implicated in the slower release of aldosterone from the adrenal gland.[27] A Ca^{2+}-dependent control of chemoattractant release has already been suggested for the NK_1 receptor, which when activated in a subset of floor plate cells triggers chemoattractant release, presumably via activation of phospholipase C and elevation of cytosolic Ca^{2+} levels.[21,22]

The modulation by neurotransmitters of T-type calcium channels has not yet been investigated to any great extent.[28] Were this phenomenon to be extended to floor plate cells, where T-type calcium channels seem to provide the sole voltage-gated Ca^{2+} entry pathway, it could provide a mechanism by which activation of G-protein-coupled receptors could profoundly alter calcium homeostasis. A further cellular consequence of Ca^{2+} entry into floor plate cells might be changes in the expression of certain genes. In this way, control over proliferation, differentiation, metabolism, morphology and the receptor complement of cells could be exerted in the medium term.[29]

In conclusion, our work represents the first findings on the membrane physiology of floor plate cells. The presence of a voltage-activated calcium channel, in addition to a potassium channel, suggests that alterations in membrane potential (and thereby Ca^{2+} homeostasis) are likely to play a role in the developmental functions of these cells. Some caution is required in the interpretation of these findings, as our studies have concentrated on the floor plate of P0 and E14 rats. Although the channels present and other membrane properties are very similar at these two ages, it is important to note that the best understood roles of the floor plate are observed at approximately E10–E12. Although unlikely, it is possible that the electrophysiological properties of these cells at E12 are different from those at E14. It is notable, however, that the T-type calcium current is larger at E14 than at P0, and by extrapolation may be larger still at E12. Development of preparations in which very immature embryos can be studied electrophysiologically is clearly an important future step.

References

1. Marti E, Bumcrot DA, Takada R, et al. Requirement of 19K form of sonic hedgehog for induction of distinct ventral cell types in CNS explants. Nature 1995; 375: 322–5
2. Kennedy TE, Serafini T de le TJ, Tessier-Lavigne M. Netrins are diffusible chemotropic factors for commissural axons in the embryonic spinal cord. Cell 1994; 78: 425–35
3. Serafini T, Kennedy TE, Galko MJ, et al. The netrins define a family of axon outgrowth-promoting proteins homologous to *C. elegans* UNC-6. Cell 1994; 78: 409–24
4. Colamarino SA, Tessier-Lavigne M. The axonal chemoattractant netrin-1 is also a chemorepellent for trochlear motor axons. Cell 1995; 81: 621–9
5. Tessier-Lavigne M, Placzek M, Lumsden AGS, et al. Chemotrophic guidance of developing axons in the mammalian central nervous system. Nature 1988; 336: 775–8
6. Schoenwolf GC, Smith JL. Mechanisms of neuralation: traditional viewpoints and recent advances. Development 1990; 109: 243–70
7. Hatta K, Kimmel CB, Ho RK, et al. The cyclops mutation blocks specification of the floor plate of the zebrafish central nervous system. Nature 1991; 350: 339–41
8. Hirano S, Fuse S, Sohal GS. The effect of the floor plate on pattern and polarity in the developing central nervous system. Science 1991; 251: 310–3
9. van Straaten HWM, Hekking JW. Development of floor plate, neurons and axonal outgrowth pattern in the early spinal cord of the notochord-deficient chick embryo. Anat Embryol (Berl) 1991; 184: 55–63
10. Yamada T, Placzek M, Tanaka H, et al. Control of cell pattern in the developing nervous system: polarizing activity of the floor plate and notochord. Cell 1991; 64: 635–47
11. Ericson J, Thor S, Edlund T, et al. Early stages of motor neuron differentiation revealed by expression of homeobox gene islet-1. Science 1992; 256: 1555–60
12. Ruiz IAA, Jessell TM. Pintallavis, a gene expressed in the organizer and midline cells of frog embryos: involvement in the development of the neural axis. Development 1992; 116: 81–93
13. Goulding MD, Lumsden A, Gruss P. Signals from the notochord and floor plate regulate the region-specific expression of two *Pax* genes in the developing spinal cord. Development 1993; 117: 1001–16
14. Yamada T, Pfaff SL, Edlund T, et al. Control of cell pattern in the neural tube: motor neuron induction by diffusible factors from notochord and floor plate. Cell 1993; 73: 673–86
15. Hynes M, Poulsen K, Tessier-Lavigne M, et al. Control of neuronal diversity by the floor plate: contact-mediated induction of midbrain dopaminergic neurons. Cell 1995; 80: 95–101
16. Roelink H, Porter JA, Chiang C, et al. Floor plate and motor neuron induction by different concentrations of the amino-terminal cleavage product of sonic hedgehog autoproteolysis. Cell 1995; 81: 445–55
17. Jessel TM, Dodd J. Floor plate-derived signals and the control of neuronal cell pattern in vertebrates. Harvey Lect 1992; 86: 87–128
18. Messersmith EK, Leonardo ED, Shatz CJ, et al. Semaphorin III can function as a selective chemorepellent to pattern sensory projections in the spinal cord. Neuron 1995; 14: 949–59
19. Klar A, Baldassare M, Jessell TM. F-spondin: a gene expressed at high levels in the floor plate encodes a secreted protein that promotes neural cell adhesion and neurite extension. Cell 1992; 69: 95–110
20. Campbell RM, Peterson AC. Expression of a *lacZ* transgene reveals floor plate cell morphology and macromolecular transfer to commissural axons. Development 1993; 119: 1217–28
21. Heath MJS, Lints TJ, Lee CJ, et al. Functional expression of the tachykinin NK-1 receptor by floor plate cells in the embryonic rat spinal cord and brainstem. J Physiol 1995; 486: 139–48
22. De Felipe C, Pinnock RD, Hunt SP. Modulation of chemotropism in the developing spinal cord by substance P. Science 1995; 267: 899–902
23. Frischknecht F, Randall AD. Voltage- and ligand-gated ion channels in floor plate neuroepithelia of the rat. Neuroscience. In press
24. Zhang J-F, Randall AD, Ellinor PT, et al. Distinctive pharmacology and kinetics of cloned neuronal Ca^{2+} channels and their possible counterparts in mammalian CNS neurons. Neuropharmacology 1993; 32: 1075–88
25. Ogata N, Tabebayashi H. Kinetic analysis of two types of Na^{+} channels on rat dorsal root ganglia. J Physiol 1993; 466: 9–37
26. Zhang X, Phelan KD, Geller HM. A novel tetrodotoxin resistant sodium current from an immortalized neuroepithelial cell line. J Physiol 1996; 490: 17–29
27. Barrett PQ, Ertel EA, Smith MM, et al. Voltage gated calcium currents have two opposing effects on the secretion of aldosterone. Am J Physiol 1995; 268: 985–92
28. Kobrinsky EM, Pearson HA, Dolphin AC. Low- and high-voltage activated calcium channel currents and their modulation in the dorsal root ganglion cell line ND7-23. Neuroscience 1994; 58: 539–52
29. Ghosh A, Greenberg ME. Calcium signalling in neurones: molecular mechanisms and cellular consequences. Science 1995; 268: 239–47

Angiotensin II stimulates aldosterone secretion by two distinct mechanisms that modulate LVA T-type calcium channels

Paula Q. Barrett, Hong-Kai Lu, Robert J. Fern

Department of Pharmacology, University of Virginia School of Medicine, Charlottesville, Virginia, USA

Introduction

The adrenal glomerulosa cell, which resides in the cortex of the adrenal gland, is responsible for the synthesis and secretion of the steroid hormone aldosterone.[1] Aldosterone production is Ca^{2+}-dependent and is stimulated by angiotensin II (Ang II), adrenocorticotrophic hormone (ACTH) and by small changes in the extracellular K^+ concentration.[2–4] Unlike the vesicular secretion of peptide hormones, the Ca^{2+}-dependence of steroid hormone secretion is related not to Ca^{2+}-dependent vesicular fusion (as steroid hormones are not 'prepackaged' for export from the cell), but rather to the Ca^{2+}-dependent movement of cholesterol from the cytoplasm to the mitochondria.[5,6] This multistep process, which includes the cleavage of cholesterol esters by cholesterol esterase, the movement of free cholesterol from the cytosol to the mitochondria, the passage of cholesterol across the outer and the inner mitochondrial membranes and the conversion of cholesterol to pregnenolone by the side-chain cleavage enzyme, depends upon the availability of Ca^{2+}[3,7–9] and the generation of the steroidogenic activator regulatory protein (StAR).[10] Since pregnenolone production is the rate-limiting step in the synthesis and secretion of steroidogenic hormones,[1] and the availability of substrate (cholesterol) limits the activity of the side-chain cleavage enzyme, the regulation of aldosterone production resides primarily in the processes that control the movement of free cholesterol to this mitochondrial cytochrome P450.

The involvement of the T-type calcium channel in the Ca^{2+}-dependence of aldosterone production was suggested initially by the profound voltage-dependence of aldosterone secretion. In contrast to many endocrine cells that are stimulated solely by strong depolarisations, small changes in the extracellular K^+ concentration that depolarise the cells of the glomerulosa only weakly stimulate aldosterone production.[11,12] The raising of the extracellular K^+ concentration by as little as 1.5 mM (from 3.5 to 5 mM) stimulates the synthesis and secretion of aldosterone, with concentrations of 10–12 mM eliciting a maximal secretory response. Concentrations above 12 mM are less stimulatory.[13] Furthermore, studies using calcium channel-blocking drugs with different affinities for L- and T-type calcium channels have shown that although the intracellular Ca^{2+} concentration rises monotonically with K^+ depolarisation (from K^+ 3.5 mM to 40 mM), a high intracellular Ca^{2+} concentration inhibits aldosterone secretion.[14] At present, the physiological significance of the inhibition of secretion by a high intracellular Ca^{2+} concentration is unknown. However, physiological increases in the extracellular K^+ concentration that elevate intracellular Ca^{2+} only modestly stimulate aldosterone secretion, primarily by enhancing Ca^{2+} entry through low-voltage-activated calcium channels.[13–16].

Physiologically, Ang II is the most potent regulator of aldosterone secretion.[2] In the glomerulosa cell (as in many cell types), Ang II signals through its type 1 receptor, which catalyses the activation of at least two G proteins, G_i and G_q.[17,18] As a consequence, numerous signalling pathways are activated with the concomitant stimulation of multiple protein kinases (protein kinase C,[19–21] Ca^{2+}/calmodulin (CaM)-dependent protein kinase II (CaMKII),[22,23] soluble tyrosine kinases[24]) and the generation of $G\alpha$- and $G\beta\gamma$-signalling molecules that can themselves transduce primary effects.[25–27] Within the last 2 years our laboratory has demonstrated that Ang II utilises at least two distinct signalling pathways to regulate the activity of the T-type calcium channel. Activation of CaMKII[28] or G_i[29] shifts the voltage-dependence of the T-type calcium channel to increase the response of the channel at low voltages.

Channel regulation by CaMKII

Figure 1 (A) shows our original observations when the concentration of Ca^{2+} in the pipette was raised from 23 nM to 1.27 μM in the presence of calmodulin 0.2 μM. This manipulation induces an approximate 9 mV hyperpolarising shift in the voltage-dependence of activation of the T-type calcium channel, converting the half-potential of activation from –14 mV (at intracellular Ca^{2+} 23 nM) to –23 mV (at intracellular Ca^{2+} 1.27 μM).[28] Whether this effect of elevated Ca^{2+} concentration on T-type calcium channel activation is the consequence of CaMKII activity was investigated in subsequent studies.

Although CaMKII is encoded by four genes, each isoform of the kinase contains the same domain structure (see fig. 1 (C)): an N-terminal catalytic domain that is inhibited by interaction with an autoinhibitory region; an autoinhibitory domain whose conformation is regulated by CaM binding and phosphorylation; and a C-terminal association domain which promotes oligomerisation among kinase monomers.[30] To establish the involvement of CaMKII, the activity of the kinase was manipulated by altering CaM binding or by augmenting autoinhibition. Panel B of figure 1 shows results from a study in which CaM binding was altered by preincubation of the glomerulosa cells with KN-62.[28] This lipophilic inhibitor competes with CaM for its binding site on the kinase (see fig. 1 (C)). As shown, pretreatment with KN-62 3 μM prevents intracellular Ca^{2+} from shifting the voltage-dependence of activation of the T-type calcium channel. Thus, voltage-dependencies are equivalent in the presence and absence of elevated pipette Ca^{2+}. For comparison, the previously defined Ca^{2+}-shifted half-potential of activation is also shown (dotted line). The specificity of this action of KN-62 was demonstrated by showing that high pipette CaM concentrations compete with KN-62 for the relevant binding site on the kinase and restore the half-potential of activation to its previous Ca^{2+}-stimulated level.[28]

The requirement for CaM binding was demonstrated in additional studies.[28] CaMKII (290-309), a peptide that encodes for a region of the kinase that contains the

CaM binding domain, was used in the pipette solution to scavenge CaM as it became unbound and thus abolish activation by Ca^{2+}. Although the data show that this peptide fails to reverse activation stimulated by Ca^{2+} 1.27 μM, it reverses stimulation

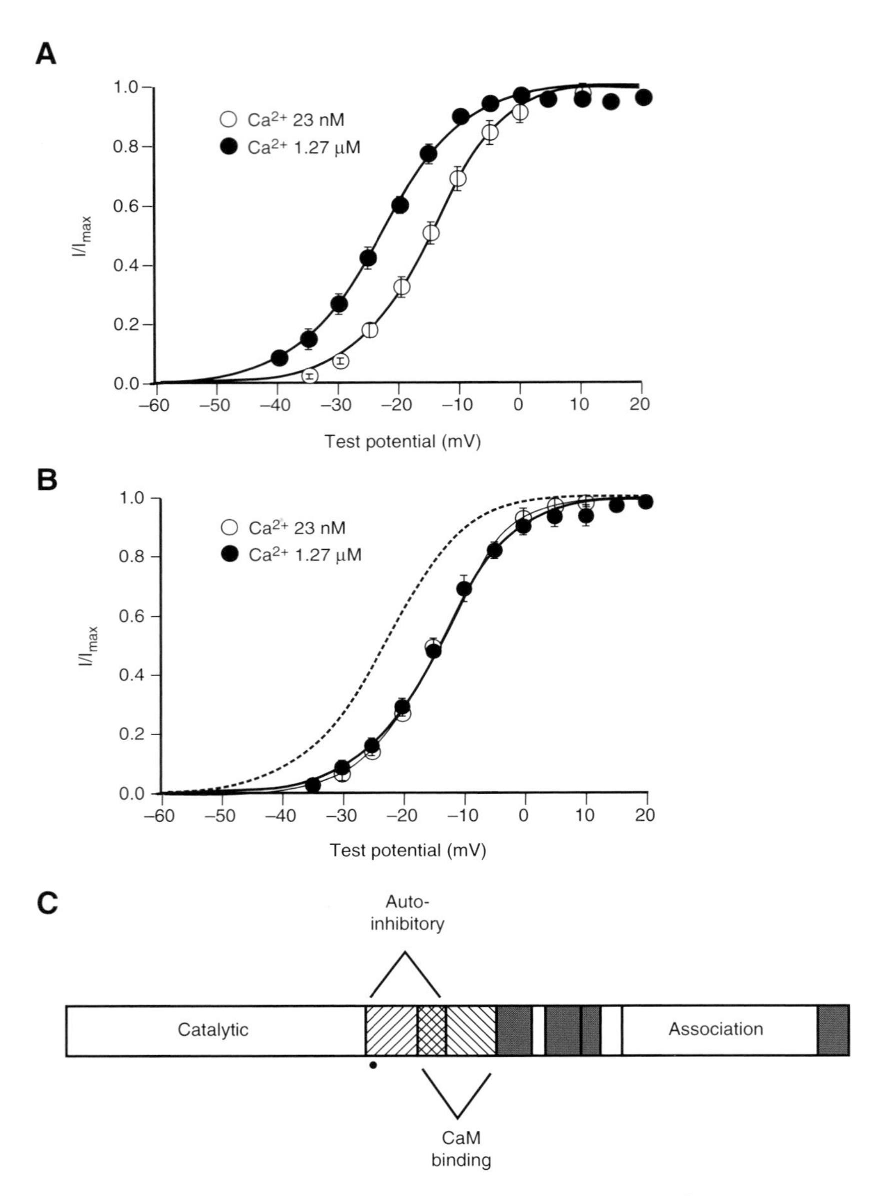

Fig. 1. Voltage-dependence of T-type calcium channel activation: effects of intracellular Ca^{2+} concentration and an organic inhibitor of CaMKII (calmodulin-dependent kinase II) (KN-62). Whole-cell currents were elicited during 10 ms test depolarisations, with Ca^{2+} 20 mM as the permeant ion, to variable potentials (test potential = –50 to +20 mV) from a holding potential of –90 mV (6 s). To isolate T-type calcium channel current, tail currents were elicited upon repolarisation (repolarisation potential = –50 mV) from test potentials in the pulse protocol mentioned above. Relative amplitude of the slowly deactivating component of tail current is plotted against test potential. Pipette Ca^{2+} was 23 nM or 1.27 μM. A) Control cells (n=10). B) Cells pretreated for 30 min with KN-62 3 μM (n=20). Broken line shows the Boltzmann relationship corresponding to Ca^{2+} 1.27 μM in panel A. C) Domain structure of CaMKII.

activated by a lower Ca^{2+} concentration (390 nM). This Ca^{2+}-dependence of the peptide's action is consistent with the observation that the rate of dissociation of CaM from the kinase is promoted by low Ca^{2+} concentration.[31] Thus, the ability of the peptide to scavenge CaM from the kinase should also be Ca^{2+}-dependent. These studies, in conjunction with the demonstrated requirement for a hydrolysable source of ATP, argue that phosphorylation and a Ca^{2+}- and CaM-dependent kinase activity underlie the change in gating behaviour elicited by elevations in intracellular Ca^{2+} concentration. We believe that this mechanism utilises CaMKII and operates during cell stimulation with Ang II, since the activity of this Ca^{2+}- and CaM-dependent kinase increases over the time-course of 1 hour in cells that have been stimulated with physiological levels (10–100 pM) of Ang II.[23]

Channel regulation by G_i activation

Our laboratory has demonstrated that Ang II regulates the activity of the T-type calcium channel by a mechanism that is independent of CaMKII activity.[29] In cells in which pipette calcium has been fixed at 150 nM (below the concentration required for the activation of CaMKII), Ang II selectively enhances T-type calcium channel current at negative potentials, effecting an approximate 10 mV hyperpolarising shift in the half-potential of activation (fig. 2 (A)). To further rule out the participation of CaMKII in this Ang II-induced shift in the half-potential of activation, we used CaMKII (281-302), a CaMKII peptide that duplicates the autoinhibitory domain, to inhibit the catalytic domain of the kinase. Panel B of figure 2 shows that the introduction of peptide 200 μM into the cell interior via the patch pipette blocks the shift in the half-potential of activation caused by Ca^{2+} 500 nM, yet fails to prevent the shift evoked by Ang II (see fig. 2 (C)). Thus, local rises in intracellular Ca^{2+}, produced by intracellular store depletion, that could activate CaMKII cannot account for the stimulatory effect of Ang II.

Whether this effect of Ang II on T-type calcium channel activation is the result of G_i activation was explored further in studies in which G-protein activation was precluded.[29] To establish the AT_1 receptor as the transducer of the change in channel current, losartan was used to prevent the Ang II-induced shift in the half-potential of activation. This AT_1-selective receptor antagonist abrogates the Ang II-induced shift in the half-potential of activation and rules out the participation of the AT_2 receptor, which is expressed abundantly in foetal and neonatal cells.[32] To verify the involvement of G_i/G_o in this change in channel current, pertussis toxin (PTX) was used to uncouple these G-protein subtypes from Ang II receptor activation. PTX pretreatment prevents the Ang II-induced shift in the half-potential of activation. Finally, to establish G_i as a possible transducer, a monoclonal antibody generated against recombinant $G_i\alpha$ was introduced into the cell via the patch pipette to block signal transduction. This antibody, which recognises all $G_i\alpha$ subtypes ($G_i\alpha_1$, $G_i\alpha_2$ and $G_i\alpha_3$) but not $G_o\alpha$, effectively blocks the Ang II-induced shift in the half-potential of activation. This action of the antibody is specific to G_i, as neither heat-treated antibody nor ascites fluid at equivalent protein concentrations prevented the Ang II-induced shift in the half-potential of activation.

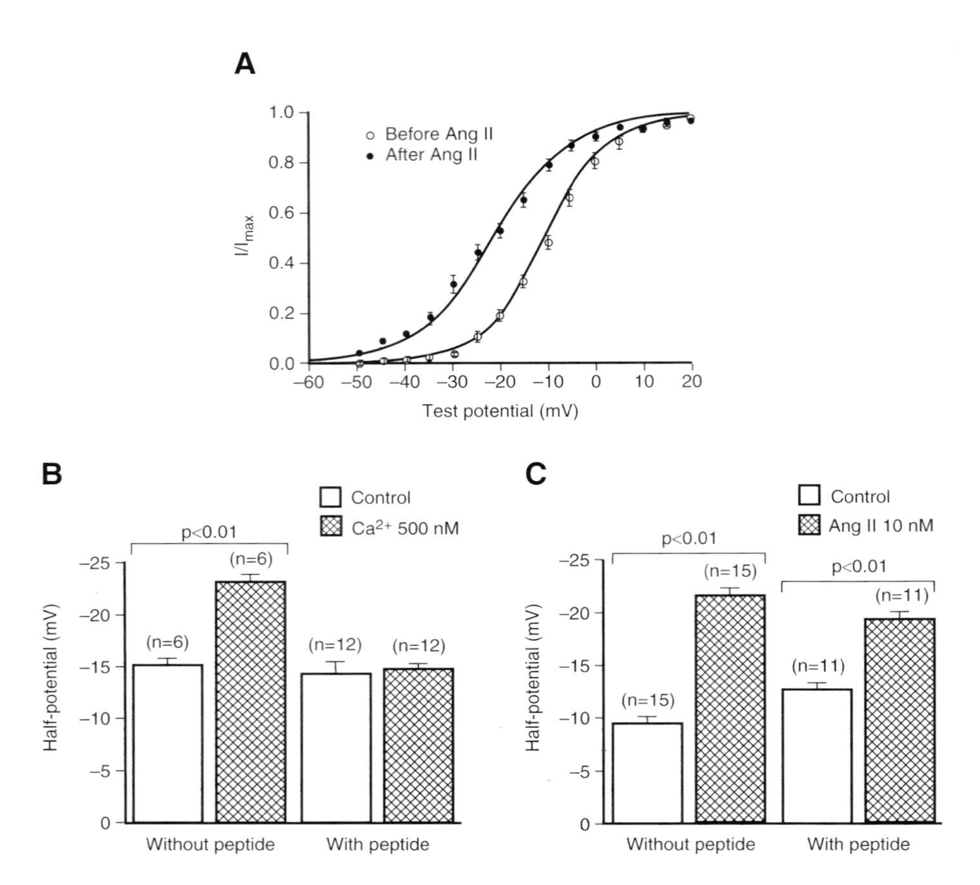

Fig. 2. Modulation of T-type calcium channel current by angiotensin II (Ang II): lack of CaMKII (calmodulin-dependent kinase II) mediation. A) Effect of Ang II on voltage-dependence of calcium channel activation. Relative amplitude of slowly deactivating component of tail current versus test potential before and after exposure to Ang II 10 nM. Pipette Ca^{2+} fixed at 150 nM. Data fitted by a Boltzmann distribution with control half-potential −10.6 mV and Ang II half-potential −21.7 mV (n=17). B & C) Effects of peptide inhibitor of CaMKII on the voltage-dependence of activation of T-type calcium channels. The half-potential of activation was determined from control or stimulated cells with or without CaMKII (281-302) 200 µM in the pipette solution. B) Cell stimulation with internal Ca^{2+} 500 nM (n=6; + peptide, n=12). Pipette Ca^{2+} was fixed at 23 nM in control cells. C) Cell stimulation with Ang II 10 nM (n=15; + peptide, n=11). Pipette Ca^{2+} was fixed at 150 nM in control cells.

These findings establishing a role for G_i are supported by reconstitution studies in which baculovirus-expressed AT_1 receptor was observed to couple to G_q and G_i but not G_o or G_s.[18] However, it should be pointed out that our studies do not indicate which G_i subunit is the putative regulator. Although the monoclonal antibody recognises only $G_i\alpha$, the participation of the $\beta\gamma$ subunit cannot be excluded because the antigenic epitope for this antibody has not been established. Thus, the monoclonal antibody may recognise $\beta\gamma$-coupled α (unactivated α) and hinder the generation of free $\beta\gamma$. The relative importance of α versus $\beta\gamma$ remains to be assessed. However, if Ang II stimulates T-type calcium channel current by a mechanism similar to that utilised by thyrotropin-releasing hormone (TRH) to stimulate L-type calcium channel current, the concomitant generation of activated $G_i\alpha$ and a soluble second messenger will be required for current stimulation.[33]

Importance of T-type calcium channel activity to aldosterone production

Although the role of the T-type calcium channel in supporting K^+-stimulated aldosterone production is well accepted, its importance in mediating aldosterone production stimulated by Ang II has been contested.[16,34–36] Nevertheless, figure 3 shows that T-type calcium channel activity is necessary to sustain aldosterone secretion stimulated by physiological concentrations of agonists. In these studies, glomerulosa cells were stimulated concomitantly with K^+ 5 mM and Ang II 100 pM, and the rate of aldosterone secretion during 30–60 min of stimulation was determined. This paradigm was chosen because the secretory rate during the sustained phase of an Ang II-induced secretory response should be maximally dependent on calcium channel activity and minimally affected by depletion of intracellular Ca^{2+} stores.

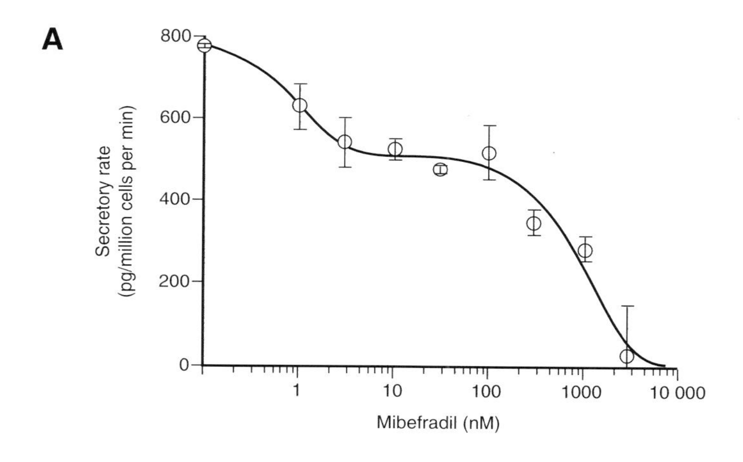

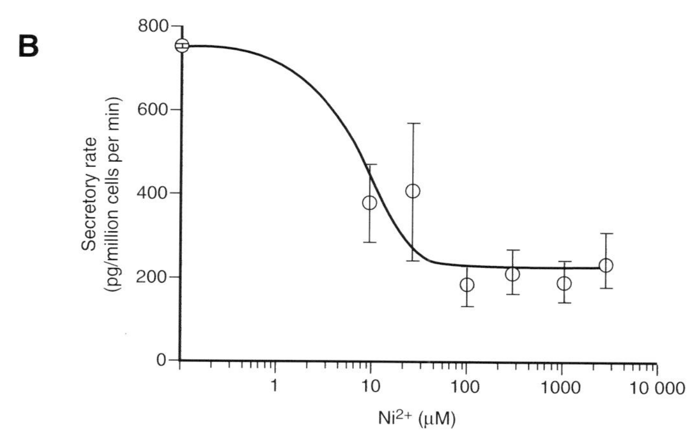

Fig. 3. Effect of T-type calcium channel inhibition on the rate of aldosterone secretion. Secretion evoked by costimulation with K^+ 5 mM and angiotensin II 100 pM was determined during 30–60 min of stimulation. Inhibitors were added during a maintained secretory response after 30 min of stimulation. Results (mean ± SE of 3 determinations) are representative of 6 similar studies using different cell isolates. A) Inhibition by mibefradil (1 nM to 10 μM). Data fitted by a biexponential distribution with IC_{50} 1.1 nM and 1.2 μM. B) Inhibition by Ni^{2+} (1 μM to 10 mM).

Panel A of figure 3 shows a complex dose-dependent inhibition of secretion by mibefradil. A 40% inhibition was seen with as little as 10 nM of mibefradil, with complete inhibition requiring a 1000-fold increase in the amount of drug. This two-site inhibition by mibefradil was observed in all experiments (n=6) in which mibefradil was freshly prepared. If, however, previously prepared stock solutions of mibefradil were used, only low-affinity inhibition was observed (n=5). For comparison, panel B of figure 3 shows that Ni^{2+}, a putative T-type calcium channel inhibitor, inhibits the sustained secretion of aldosterone at concentrations that are consistent with its block of calcium channels (<100 μM).[14,15] These data, obtained with a cationic and an organic inhibitor of the T-type calcium channel, argue strongly for the importance of calcium channel activity in sustaining aldosterone secretion evoked by physiological concentrations of Ang II.

Conclusion

In conclusion, our laboratory has demonstrated that the T-type calcium channel can be regulated by the activation of CaMKII and, quite independently, by G_i activation. At present, the manner in which these mechanisms interact is undefined. If the effects are additive, so that channel modulation is shifted by approximately 20 mV, then most of the secretory activity elicited by Ang II could result from channel modulation. If, however, each effect subserves the other, then modulation of T-type calcium channel activity would be only one component of the mechanism by which physiological concentrations of agonists stimulate aldosterone production. Nevertheless, given the marked inhibitory effects of mibefradil and Ni^{2+}, T-type calcium channel activity is a critically important determinant of the secretory activity studied under physiological paradigms.

Acknowledgement

This work was supported by National Heart, Lung and Blood Institute grant HL-36977 (P.Q.B.) and grant VHA-95-F-24 (H.-K.L.) from the Virginia Affiliate of the American Heart Association.

References

1. Kaplan NM. The adrenal glands. In: Griffin JE, Ojeda SR, editors. Textbook of endocrine physiology. New York: Oxford University Press, 1992: 247–75
2. Quinn SJ, Williams GH. Regulation of aldosterone secretion. Ann Rev Physiol 1988; 50: 409–26
3. Barrett PQ, Bollag WB, Islaes CM, et al. Role of calcium in angiotensin II-mediated aldosterone secretion. Endocr Rev 1989; 10: 496–518
4. Aguilera G. Factors controlling steroid biosynthesis in the zona glomerulosa of the adrenal. J Steroid Biochem Mol Biol 1993; 45: 147–51
5. Crivello JF, Jefcoate CR. Intracellular movement of cholesterol in rat adrenal cells. Kinetics and effects of inhibitors. J Biol Chem 1980; 255: 8144–51
6. Privalle CT, Crivello JF, Jefcoate CR. Regulation of intramitochondrial cholesterol transfer to side-chain cleavage cytochrome P-450 in rat adrenal gland. Proc Natl Acad Sci U S A 1983; 80: 702–6
7. Capponi AM, Lew PD, Jornot L, et al. Correlation between cytosolic free Ca^{2+} and aldosterone production in bovine adrenal glomerulosa cells. J Biol Chem 1984; 259: 8863–9

8. Bradley LM, Menachery AI, Brown EM, et al. Comparative effects of angiotensin II, potassium, adrenocorticotropin, and cyclic adenosine monophosphate on cytosolic calcium in rat adrenal cells. Endocrinology 1986; 119: 1010–19
9. Capponi AM, Lew PD, Valloton MBV. Quantitative analysis of the cytosolic free calcium dependency of aldosterone production in bovine glomerulosa cells. Biochem J 1987; 247: 335–40
10. Stocco DM, Clark BJ. Role of the steroidogenic acute regulatory protein (StAR) in steroidogenesis. Biochem Pharmacol 1996; 51: 197–205
11. Quinn SJ, Cornwall MC, Williams GH. Electrophysiological responses to angiotensin II of isolated rat adrenal glomerulosa cells. Endocrinology 1987; 120: 1581–9
12. Quinn SJ, Cornwall MC, Williams GH. Electrical properties of isolated rat adrenal glomerulosa and fasciculata cells. Endocrinology 1987; 120: 903–14
13. Barrett PQ, Isales CM, Bollag WB, et al. Ca^{2+} channels and aldosterone secretion: modulation by K^+ and atrial natriuretic peptide. Am J Physiol 1991; 261: F706–19
14. Barrett PQ, Ertel EA, Smith MM, et al. Voltage-gated calcium currents have two opposing effects on the secretion of aldosterone. Am J Physiol 1995; 268: C985–92
15. Cohen CJ, McCarthy RT, Barrett PQ, et al. Ca channels in adrenal glomerulosa cells: K^+ and angiotensin II increase T-type Ca channel current. Proc Natl Acad Sci U S A 1988; 85: 2412–16
16. Burnay MM, Python CP, Vallotton MB, et al. Role of the capacitative calcium influx in the activation of steroidogenesis by angiotensin-II in adrenal glomerulosa cells. Endocrinology 1994; 135: 751–8
17. Balla T, Baukal AJ, Eng S, et al. Angiotensin II receptor subtypes and biological responses in the adrenal cortex and medulla. Mol Pharmacol 1991; 40: 401–6
18. Graber SG, Figler RA, Garrison JC. Expression and purification of functional G protein α subunits using a baculovirus expression system. J Biol Chem 1992; 267: 1271–8
19. Nakano S, Carvallo P, Rocco S, et al. Role of protein kinase C on the steroidogenic effect of angiotensin II in the rat adrenal glomerulosa cell. Endocrinology 1990; 126: 125–33
20. Natarajan R, Stern N, Hseuh W, et al. Role of the lipoxygenase pathway in angiotensin-II mediated aldosterone biosynthesis in human adrenal glomerulosa cells. J Clin Endocrinol Metab 1994; 67: 584–91
21. Natarajan R, Lanting L, Xu L, et al. Role of specific isoforms of protein kinase C in angiotensin II and lipoxygenase action in rat adrenal glomerulosa cells. Mol Cell Endocrinol 1994; 101: 59–66
22. Fern RJ, Hahm MS, Lu HK, et al. Ca^{2+}/calmodulin-dependent protein kinase II activation and regulation of Ca^{2+} signaling in bovine adrenal glomerulosa cell. Am J Physiol 1995; 269: F751–60
23. Fern RJ. Ca^{2+}/calmodulin-dependent protein kinase II in the adrenal glomerulosa cell [doctoral thesis]. Charlottesville: University of Virginia, 1996
24. Bodart V, Ong H, DeLean A. A role for protein tyrosine kinase in the steroidogenic pathway of angiotensin II in bovine zona glomerulosa cells. J Steroid Biochem Mol Biol 1995; 54: 55–62
25. Hescheler J, Rosenthal W, Hinsch KD, et al. Angiotensin II-induced stimulation of voltage-dependent Ca^{2+} currents in an adrenal cortical line. EMBO J 1988; 7: 619–24
26. Rosenthal W, Herscheler J, Hinsch KD, et al. Cyclic AMP-independent, dual regulation of voltage-dependent Ca^{2+} currents by LHRH and somatostatin in a pituitary cell line. EMBO J 1988; 7: 1627–33
27. Diverse-Pierluissi M, Goldsmith PK, Dunlap K. Transmitter-mediated inhibition of N-type calcium channels in sensory neurons involves multiple GTP-binding proteins and subunits. Neuron 1995; 14: 191–200
28. Lu H-K, Fern RJ, Nee JJ, et al. Ca^{2+}-dependent activation of T-type Ca^{2+} channels by calmodulin-dependent protein kinase II. Am J Physiol 1994; 267: F183–9
29. Lu H-K, Fern RJ, Luthin D, et al. Angiotensin II stimulates T-type Ca^{2+} channel currents via activation of a G protein, Gi. Am J Physiol 1996; 271: C1340–9
30. Hanson PI, Schulman H. Neuronal Ca^{2+}/calmodulin-dependent protein kinases. Ann Rev Biochem 1992; 61: 559–601
31. Meyer T, Hanson PI, Stryer L, et al. Calmodulin trapping by calcium-calmodulin-dependent protein kinase. Science 1992; 256: 1199–202
32. Grady E, Sechi L, Griffin C, et al. Expression of AT_2 receptors in the developing rat fetus. J Clin Invest 1991; 88: 921–33
33. Gollasch M, Kleuss C, Hescheler J, et al. Gi2 and protein kinase C are required for thyrotropin-releasing hormone-induced stimulation of voltage-dependent Ca^{2+} channels in rat pituitary GH3 cells. Proc Natl Acad Sci U S A 1993; 90: 6265–9
34. Spat A, Balla I, Balla T, et al. Angiotensin II and potassium activate different calcium entry mechanisms in rat adrenal glomerulosa cells. J Endocrinol 1989; 122: 361–70
35. Ambroz C, Catt KJ. Angiotensin II receptor-mediated calcium influx in bovine adrenal glomerulosa cells. Endocrinology 1992; 131: 408–14
36. Rohacs T, Bago A, Deak F, et al. Capacitative Ca^{2+} influx in adrenal glomerulosa cells: possible role in angiotensin II response. Am J Physiol 1994; 267: C1246–51

Distinct functions of T- and L-type calcium channels during activation of aldosterone production in adrenal glomerulosa cells

Michel F. Rossier, Muriel M. Burnay, Alessandro M. Capponi

Division of Endocrinology and Diabetology, University Hospital, Geneva, Switzerland

Introduction

The activation of aldosterone secretion from adrenal glomerulosa cells in response to extracellular K^+ and angiotensin II (Ang II) clearly depends upon a sustained influx of Ca^{2+} into the cell.[1–3] However, at least three different types of calcium channel are thought to be involved in this influx: these are L- and T-type voltage-operated calcium channels, activated upon cell depolarisation, and the 'calcium release-activated calcium' (CRAC) channels, which open after depletion of intracellular Ca^{2+} stores by inositol 1,4,5-trisphosphate. The aim of the present study was to determine the different functions of L- and T-type calcium channels after a sustained stimulation of bovine glomerulosa cells by physiological concentrations (3–8 mM) of extracellular K^+. Using the patch-clamp method in the perforated patch configuration, combined with microfluorimetry of cytosolic Ca^{2+}, we have shown that L-type calcium channels are exclusively responsible for the sustained elevation of cytosolic Ca^{2+} observed after stimulation with extracellular K^+ or during a prolonged cell depolarisation. Conversely, aldosterone secretion appears closely related to T-type calcium channel activity. Moreover, when the activity of each channel type is selectively modulated by pharmacological agents or by protein kinase C, the cytosolic Ca^{2+} response to K^+ can be clearly dissociated from the steroidogenic response. This direct functional link between T-type calcium channel activity and steroidogenesis in adrenal glomerulosa cells indicates a model in which Ca^{2+} entering the cell through these channels bypasses the cytosol to activate the early intramitochondrial stages of aldosterone biosynthesis. Some of the results presented in this paper have also been published elsewhere.[4]

L-type calcium channels are exclusively responsible for the cytosolic Ca^{2+} response

The selectivity of various drugs for glomerulosa cell T- and L-type calcium channels has been determined previously with the patch-clamp technique in the whole-cell configuration. Both types of current were elicited by a gradual (ramp) depolarisation of the cell. This allowed us to separate them by means of their thresholds of activation (fig. 1). Indeed, because of their lower threshold of activation, T-type calcium channels opened first and caused an inward current, but inactivated rapidly when L-type calcium channels started to open. This approach enabled us to demonstrate that nifedipine, a dihydropyridine calcium antagonist, affects both currents but inhibits L-type calcium channels at much lower concentrations

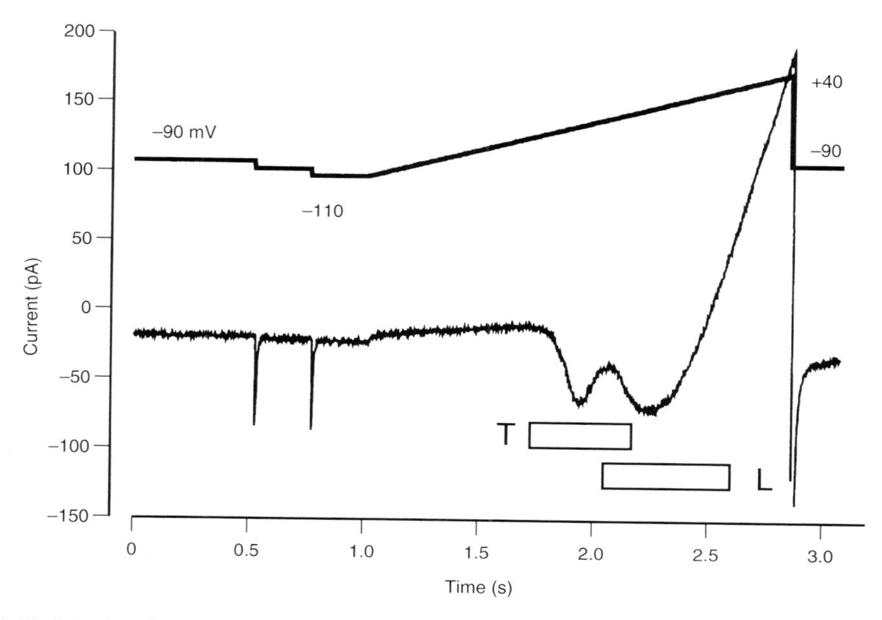

Fig. 1. Discrimination of T- and L-type calcium currents during depolarisation ramp. Whole-cell barium current was recorded under voltage-clamp conditions. A gradual cell depolarisation was applied from −110 to +40 mV (duration 1.8 s) to resolve the inward currents elicited upon opening of each type of channel. The voltage protocol is shown at the top of the trace. The approximate time during which each channel was activated is shown by boxes.

(IC_{50} = 50 nM, compared with 3 μM for T-type calcium channels).[4] In contrast, the Bayer agonist BayK8644 activated only L-type currents, and the antiepileptic drug zonisamide (ZNS; Dainippon Pharmaceutical, Osaka, Japan) showed a slight selectivity for inhibition of T-type calcium channels (IC_{50} = 300 μM, compared with 2 mM for L-type calcium channels).

We then analysed the correlation between the activity of each type of channel and the cytosolic Ca^{2+} concentration observed with sustained cell depolarisation. For this purpose, we combined the patch-clamp technique (perforated patch configuration) with microfluorimetry of Ca^{2+}. The presence of nystatin or amphotericin B in the patch pipette allowed us to record whole-cell currents without disturbing the cytosolic Ca^{2+} gradients. Variations in the concentration of cytosolic Ca^{2+} were monitored with the fluorescent probe Fluo-3. A gradual increase in concentration was seen during stepwise cell depolarisation from −100 to +20 mV, which started at −60 mV and reached a maximum value at −30 mV.[4] This response to cell depolarisation was completely abolished in the presence of nifedipine 1 μM and calciseptin 0.35 μM (two L-type calcium channel blockers which, by themselves, did not affect T-type currents in the same cell). This result therefore indicated that the response was related exclusively to activation of L-type calcium channels. This hypothesis was then confirmed by the observation that the concentration of cytosolic free Ca^{2+} was strongly correlated with L-type, but not T-type, calcium channel activity when each channel was selectively modulated with BayK8644, nifedipine or Ni^{2+}.

A sustained influx of Ca^{2+} through T-type calcium channels is theoretically possible because of the overlap of the activation and steady-state inactivation curves of the channel (fig. 2 (A & B)). However, it appears difficult to detect from cytosolic Ca^{2+} measurements. Because of the probability that a low percentage (<1%, as estimated from the activation and steady-state inactivation curves) of T-type calcium channels will be open during a prolonged period of stimulation with extracellular K^+, this

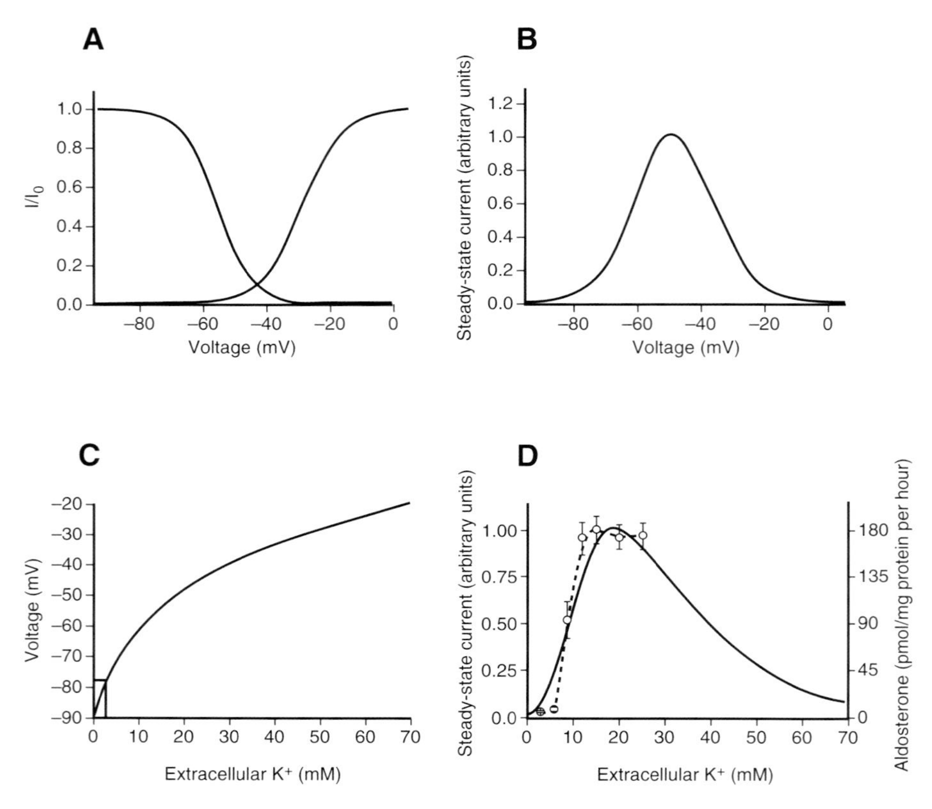

Fig. 2. Comparison of predicted steady-state current through T-type calcium channels and aldosterone secretion in response to extracellular K^+. A) Activation and steady-state inactivation of T-type channels. Voltage-dependent activation and inactivation of slowly deactivating currents in 75 bovine glomerulosa cells, voltage-clamped in the whole-cell configuration of the patch-clamp technique.[10] Current amplitudes fitted to Boltzmann's equation and normalised to the maximum of the function (I_0). Half-activation voltage and k for each curve were averaged to produce the figure. B) Steady-state current through T-type channels. Theoretical steady-state current determined as a function of voltage from Ohm's equation ($I_{stst} = g_{Ba}mh(V_{rev} - V)$, where I_{stst} = steady-state current, g_{Ba} = maximal barium conductance through T-type channels arbitrarily assigned a value of 1, m and h = proportions of open channels (I/I_0) determined from activation and inactivation curves shown in panel A, and V_{rev} = mean reversal potential (estimated as +50 mV). C) Relationship between extracellular K^+ concentration and membrane potential in glomerulosa cells. Extracellular K^+ values were converted to the corresponding membrane potential (voltage) predicted by the Goldman–Hodgkin–Katz equation ($V = (RT/F) \bullet \ln([K^+]_o + [(P_{Na}/P_K)\,[Na^+]_o]/[K^+]_i)$, where R = gas constant, T = absolute temperature, F = Faraday constant, $[K^+]_o$ = extracellular K^+ concentration, $[Na^+]_o$ = extracellular Na^+ concentration (150 mM), $[K^+]_i$ = intracellular K^+ concentration (160 mM), P_{Na}/P_K = relative Na^+:K^+ permeability (estimated as 0.037 in bovine glomerulosa cells).[12] D) Comparison of steady-state current through T-type channels and aldosterone secretion. Aldosterone secretion, in response to increasing concentrations of extracellular K^+, was determined in the cell culture medium by direct radioimmunoassay as described elsewhere.[4] Results collected from 23 independent experiments, performed in triplicate, were averaged and plotted as a function of $[K^+]_o$ (dotted line). Steady-state current (panel B) was also expressed as a function of $[K^+]_o$ after converting the voltage values with the function described in panel C. The aldosterone secretory rate scale was normalised to that of the steady-state current to facilitate comparison.

current is expected to be very small compared with the current flowing through L-type calcium channels.

Confirmation of the low amplitude of the steady-state current through T-type calcium channels was obtained by noise analysis, using the stationary fluctuation method (fig. 3).[5] A 'basal' noise of 1.52 pA^2 (variance of the recorded signal, filtered at 2 kHz and sampled at 10 kHz) was measured at –90 mV, under conditions where both L- and T-type calcium channels are expected to be closed. This noise was stable throughout the experiment and was not affected by the addition of nifedipine (500 nM) and Ni^{2+} (1 mM). Cell depolarisation to –20 mV, a potential at which T-type steady-state current is predicted to be very low (see fig. 2 (B)), elicited a substantial (~3.5 pA^2) increase in current noise. This was attributed mainly to the activation of L-type calcium channels. After inhibition of these channels with nifedipine 500 nM, the increase in current fluctuation upon depolarisation (to –40 mV) was 0.25 pA^2 (see fig. 3). This effect, although considerably smaller, was still statistically significant ($p<0.05$). Moreover, this response to depolarisation was abolished by Ni^{2+} 1 mM (known to be a potent inhibitor of T-type calcium channels) (see fig. 3 (inset)).

Because the variances are additive, it is possible to attribute the Ni^{2+}-sensitive increase in current variance that occurs upon depolarisation to the steady-state current through T-type calcium channels. Furthermore, with the probability of T-type calcium channel opening being very low during a sustained cell depolarisation to –40 mV, the mean steady-state current is approximately equal to the variance divided

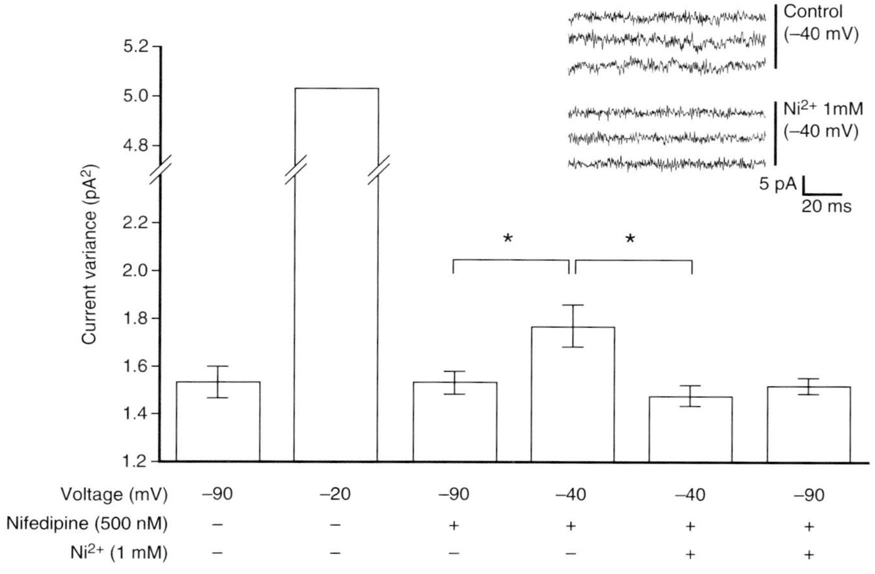

*Fig. 3. Noise analysis of the steady-state current flowing through L- and T-type channels. The noise of the cellular barium current (signal variance in pA^2) was determined in a bovine glomerulosa cell, voltage-clamped in the perforated patch configuration (with amphotericin B in the pipette). Data are means (± SEM) obtained from 10 consecutive 100 ms sweeps recorded every 20 s, filtered at 2 kHz and sampled at 10 kHz. Membrane potential values and channel antagonists are indicated below the chart. * $p<0.05$ (t-test). Inset shows an example of current recorded for noise analysis at –40 mV, in the absence (control) and the presence of Ni^{2+} 1 mM.*

by the unitary current.[5]. The unitary current (I) through an 8 pS (T-type calcium channel conductance, g) channel at –40 mV, with a measured reversal potential (V_{rev}) of +30 mV in this particular cell, is expected to be:

$$I = g(V - V_{rev}) = -0.56 \text{ pA}$$

The steady-state current at the same voltage is therefore estimated to be 0.45 pA, a value more than 100 times lower than the macroscopic T-type current (–51 pA) elicited in the same cell by a step depolarisation from –90 to –40 mV. The low amplitude of this steady-state current could explain the lack of contribution of T-type calcium channels to the cytosolic Ca^{2+} response to sustained stimulation with extracellular K^+. However, this contrasts strikingly with the crucial role of these channels in the regulation of steroidogenesis (see pp. 181 and 182).

The finding that L-type calcium channels are exclusively responsible for the response in cytosolic Ca^{2+} concentration observed upon a sustained cell depolarisation was quite surprising because it was believed that, at physiological concentrations (<8 mM), extracellular K^+ cannot depolarise the cell enough to reach the threshold of L-type calcium channel activation (see fig. 2 (C)). To demonstrate that L-type calcium channels are involved in this response, Fura-2-loaded cells were exposed to various pharmacological agents acting specifically on L-type calcium channels (nifedipine 50 nM, BayK8644 100 nM, CaS 700 nM) before being gradually depolarised by consecutive additions of KCl to the medium. This experiment clearly demonstrated that the K^+-induced response in cytosolic Ca^{2+} concentration was similarly affected by these agents at low and at high concentrations of the agonist, and therefore that a single type of calcium channel (pharmacologically consistent with L type) is responsible for the observed elevation in Ca^{2+} concentration.[4]

This suggests strongly that in glomerulosa cells the voltage window in which a steady-state current through L-type calcium channels can occur widens to include very negative membrane potentials (well below those required for a measurable channel activation).

T-type calcium channels control aldosterone secretion

The next question we addressed was whether aldosterone secretion is related to the concentration of cytosolic Ca^{2+}. For this purpose, we tested in parallel the effect of increasing concentrations of nifedipine, BayK8644 and ZNS on these parameters after stimulation with KCl 12 mM. As expected, nifedipine reduced the response of cytosolic free Ca^{2+} concentration to K^+ at all concentrations used (IC_{50} = 30 nM), but it clearly had a biphasic effect on aldosterone secretion. Indeed, at concentrations below 100 nM, nifedipine potentiated (up to 150% at 10 nM) rather than inhibited steroidogenesis.[4] The contrast was even more pronounced with BayK8644, which potentiated the cytosolic Ca^{2+} concentration response (increasing the Ca^{2+} levels by up to 210%, with an EC_{50} of 20 nM) and reduced steroid output by more than 60%. Finally, ZNS, at millimolar concentrations, almost completely prevented aldosterone secretion without significantly affecting the concentration of cytosolic Ca^{2+}. This study demonstrated that by using agents acting specifically on one type of calcium channel, it is possible to dissociate aldosterone production from cytosolic Ca^{2+} levels.

In contrast, K^+-induced aldosterone synthesis appeared to be significantly correlated with T-type (but not L-type) calcium channel activity when selective concentrations of nifedipine, nicardipine,[6] BayK8644, ZNS and tetrandrine[7] were used to modulate each channel activity individually. Similarly, mibefradil, a new non-dihydropyridine calcium antagonist[8] with a marked selectivity for T-type (as opposed to L-type) calcium channels in vascular smooth muscle cells,[9] inhibited the steroidogenic response to K^+ 12 mM completely, with an IC_{50} of 1.9 μM, a value consistent with the action of this drug on T-type calcium channels in glomerulosa cells (not shown).

Support for a direct role of T-type calcium channels in the control of aldosterone secretion is provided by the analysis of the sensitivity of secretion to extracellular K^+ (see fig. 2). In this experiment, we compared aldosterone secretion with the relative amplitude of the predicted steady-state current through T-type calcium channels at various K^+ concentrations. For this purpose, data were collected from 75 independent bovine glomerulosa cells, for which T-type calcium channel activation and steady-state inactivation curves were analysed as described in detail elsewhere.[10] The mean voltage at which half of the channels were activated was -28.9 ± 0.8 mV and the voltage at which half the channels were inactivated was -56.0 ± 1.0 mV, whereas the corresponding slope factors (k) were 6.62 ± 0.13 and 5.58 ± 0.28, respectively (see fig. 2 (A)). The predicted relative amplitude of the steady-state current at each voltage was then calculated from Ohm's law,[10] assuming a constant maximal conductance, g (when all T-type calcium channels are open), of 1.0 and a reversal potential measured at +50 mV (see fig. 2 (B)).

It is noteworthy that the steady-state current is never zero, even at the resting potential (estimated to be approximately –80 mV in glomerulosa cells[11]). However, this current is very low (<10% of the maximal amplitude) in the absence of stimulation with K^+. In order to compare the amplitude of the current with the steroidogenic response, we had to define in bovine adrenal glomerulosa cells the relationship that exists between the concentration of extracellular K^+ and the membrane potential (see fig. 2 (C)). For this purpose, extracellular K^+ concentrations were converted to equivalent membrane potentials (according to the Goldman–Hodgkin–Katz equation), with an assumed Na^+:K^+ permeability ratio of 0.037, as previously described for bovine glomerulosa cells.[12,13] This assumption allowed us to obtain a K^+ concentration–voltage relationship that predicted a resting potential (at extracellular K^+ 3 mM) of –77.5 mV, reasonably close to the resting potential measured with the current clamp technique by other investigators.[11,14,15] A comparison of the normalised aldosterone secretion obtained from 23 independent experiments with the predicted steady-state current (see fig. 2 (D)) revealed very close EC_{50}s ($\approx K^+$ 9 mM) for the action of K^+ on each parameter. This is concordant with a causal relationship between Ca^{2+} influx through T-type calcium channels and activation of steroidogenesis.

The phorbol ester PMA (phorbol 12-myristate 13-acetate) can be used to give another illustration of the dissociation of cytosolic Ca^{2+} from aldosterone synthesis and T-type calcium channel activity. Through the activation of protein kinase C, PMA has been shown to induce a significant positive shift (~7 mV) of the T-type calcium channel activation curve,[4,10] with no effect on the inactivation properties of this channel. As a consequence, the maximal amplitude of the steady-state current through these channels is reduced by approximately 40%. In contrast, PMA does not affect the cytosolic Ca^{2+} concentration maintained by extracellular K^+ 12 mM, which suggests that protein kinase C does not modulate L-type calcium channel activity. However, because aldosterone secretion is controlled by T-type calcium channels, it is also sensitive to PMA, which reduced K^+-induced steroidogenesis by 46%.[4] This inhibition by PMA appears to be secondary to its action on the channels, because the drug has no effect on aldosterone production induced by the Ca^{2+} ionophore ionomycin.

Discussion

In summary, it appears that upon slight but sustained depolarisation of the glomerulosa cell membrane by physiological concentrations of K^+, both T- and L-type calcium channels open together and allow Ca^{2+} into the cell (fig. 4). However, whereas the large amount of Ca^{2+} flowing through L-type calcium channels rapidly spreads throughout the cytosol and is therefore readily measurable with fluorescent

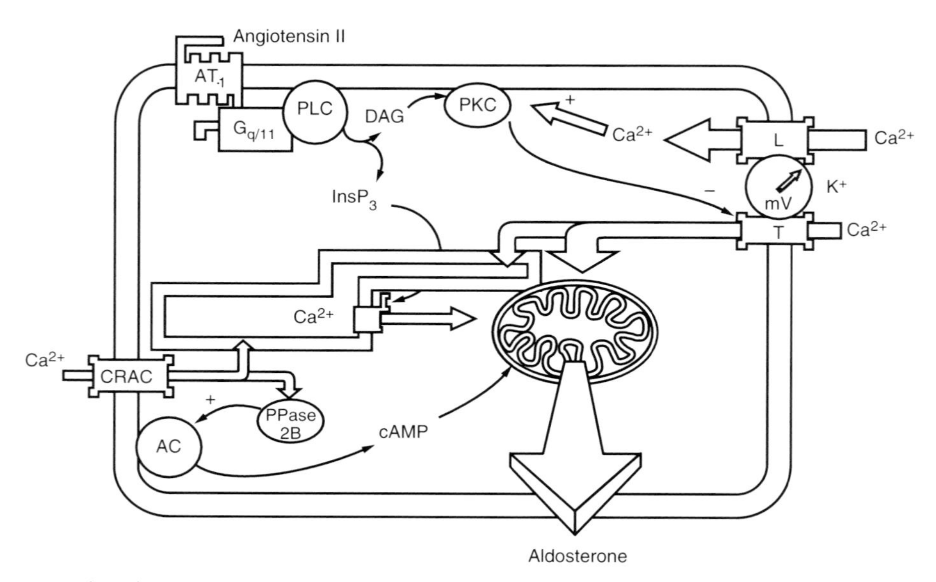

Fig. 4. Hypothetical intracellular mechanisms of K^+ and angiotensin II (Ang II) action in bovine adrenal glomerulosa cells. AC = adenylyl cyclase (type III); AT_1 = Ang II receptor of the AT_1 subtype; CRAC = calcium release-activated calcium channel; DAG = diacylglycerol; $G_{q/11}$ = heterotrimeric GTP-binding protein of the $G_{q/11}$ family; $InsP_3$ = inositol-1,4,5-trisphosphate; PKC = protein kinase C; PLC = phospholipase C_β; PPase 2B = protein phosphatase 2B (calcineurin); T and L = T- and L-type voltage-operated calcium channels.

probes, the less abundant Ca^{2+} entering the cell through T-type calcium channels is more effective in stimulating aldosterone secretion. The finding that L-type calcium channels are sensitive to very small cell depolarisations was surprising at first because these channels are generally considered to have a high threshold of activation (~–40 mV), and would therefore require at least 30 mM of K^+ to be activated (see fig. 2 (C)).

The sensitivity of the glomerulosa cell L-type calcium channels to much lower concentrations of K^+ could be explained by the expression in these cells of a particular subtype of L-type calcium channel, characterised by a pharmacology similar to that of the classical channel but opening at more negative potentials. This assumption is, however, in complete disagreement with the observed ability of a ramp of voltage to discriminate between T- and L-type macroscopic currents, as shown in figure 1. Another explanation is that the steady-state current (the only parameter relevant to cells lacking action potentials that undergo sustained stimulation with K^+) has characteristics that are not readily evident from the behaviour of the channel upon a large step or ramp depolarisation. Indeed, it would be very difficult to predict from the T-type calcium channel activation curve in panel A of figure 2 alone that, at –70 mV, the amplitude of the steady-state current is already at 20% of the maximum level (see fig. 2 (B)). Similar behaviour is conceivable for L-type channels in glomerulosa cells, but definitive proof requires further investigation.

The most significant finding of this study is that intracellular Ca^{2+} can have different functions depending on how (through which channel) it enters the cell. Similar variations in Ca^{2+} function have been observed in secretory cells; for example, in chromaffin cells, dihydropyridine-sensitive channels are apparently associated with exocytosis,[16] whereas neurotransmitter release at the synaptic ending is specifically regulated by N- (and P-) type calcium channels. A specific molecular interaction between the latter channels (at the cytosolic linker between repeats II and III of the α_1 subunit) and syntaxin,[17] a membranous protein that mediates vesicle docking and membrane fusion, is most important in the understanding of the 'specialisation' of calcium channels. Similarly, the triggering of Ca^{2+} release from the sarcoplasmic reticulum by the skeletal muscle L-type calcium channel is made possible by a molecular interaction of the L_{II-III} domain of α_1 with the ryanodine-sensitive channel.[18]

These observations suggest that a particular function for Ca^{2+} is associated with a particular localisation of the calcium channel in the plasma membrane, which in turn depends upon particular interactions of the channel with specialised cellular proteins. It could therefore be hypothesised that a similar interaction occurs with T-type calcium channels in glomerulosa cells. In this regard, the cytoskeleton, the integrity of which is necessary for an optimal steroidogenic function,[19] is an obvious candidate. Some cytoskeletal proteins could therefore be responsible for maintaining T-type calcium channels in the vicinity of mitochondria, where rate-limiting steps of aldosterone biosynthesis have been shown to be controlled by Ca^{2+}.[20] Alternatively, a colocalisation of T-type calcium channels with regions of the endoplasmic reticulum enriched with Ca^{2+}/Mg^{2+}-ATPase activity could be required for the intracellular transport of Ca^{2+} through the lumen of the organelle. Ca^{2+} would be subsequently released in a more central region of the cytoplasm (where steroidogenic mitochondria are found). The presence of this 'Ca^{2+} pipeline' should permit Ca^{2+} entering the cell through T-type channels to bypass the cytosol and reach the mitochondria directly.

In the present model, the role of the bulk cytosolic Ca^{2+} (triggered by L-type calcium channels) appears less important in steroidogenesis than previously believed, and the lack of a correlation between cytosolic Ca^{2+} concentration and acute aldosterone secretion observed upon selective inhibition of each type of channel[4] suggests other functions for cytosolic Ca^{2+}. Long-term stimulation with K^+ or Ang II is known to result in the increased expression of genes coding for P450 enzymes involved in aldosterone synthesis;[20] this nuclear action of Ca^{2+} might be linked to increased concentrations of this ion in the cytosol. Similarly, activation of protein kinase C by Ang II requires Ca^{2+} influx through a nitrendipine-sensitive pathway,[21] which suggests another possible role for cytosolic Ca^{2+} (see fig. 4).

Finally, as indicated earlier, a third pathway for Ca^{2+} entry that is activated exclusively by Ang II is also present in adrenal glomerulosa cells. This capacitative influx, linked to Ca^{2+} store depletion, is specifically responsible for the activation of cAMP production observed in bovine glomerulosa cells on stimulation with Ang II.[22] The colocalisation of CRAC channels with a Ca^{2+}-sensitive form of adenylyl cyclase (see fig. 4) appears, therefore, as a novel example of the functional compartmentalisation of the Ca^{2+} signal in this cell.

In conclusion, the determination of the specific function(s) of Ca^{2+} entering the cell through each channel is mandatory for the understanding of the reasons for the coexistence of several types of calcium channel in a single cell. In addition, because each pathway for Ca^{2+} entry appears to have a particular function, such studies should help to better predict the consequence of potential defects ('ion channel disease') in any particular channel, and to highlight the need for more selective calcium antagonist drugs.

Acknowledgements

M. Rossier is the recipient of a grant from the Professor Max Cloëtta Foundation, Zurich, Switzerland.

References

1. Barrett PQ, Bollag WB, Isales CM, et al. Role of calcium in angiotensin II-mediated aldosterone secretion. Endocr Rev 1989; 10: 496–518
2. Spät A, Enyedi P, Hajnoczky G, et al. Generation and role of calcium signal in adrenal glomerulosa cells. Exp Physiol 1991; 76: 859–85

3. Capponi AM, Python CP, Rossier MF. Molecular basis of angiotensin II action on mineralocorticoid synthesis. Endocrine 1994; 2: 579–86
4. Rossier MF, Burnay MM, Vallotton MB, et al. Distinct functions of T-type and L-type calcium channels during activation of bovine adrenal glomerulosa cells. Endocrinology 1996; 137: 4817–26
5. Hille B. 'Counting channels.' Ionic channels of excitable membranes. Sunderland, Mass.: Sinauer Associates, 1992: 315 ff.
6. Burnay MM, Python CP, Vallotton MB, et al. Role of the capacitative calcium influx in the activation of steroidogenesis by angiotensin II in adrenal glomerulosa cells. Endocrinology 1994; 135: 751–8
7. Rossier MF, Python CP, Capponi AM, et al. Blocking T-type calcium channels with tetrandrine inhibits steroidogenesis in bovine adrenal glomerulosa cells. Endocrinology 1993; 132: 1035–43
8. Clozel JP, Osterrieder W, Kleinbloesem CH, et al. Ro 40-5967: a new nondihydropyridine calcium antagonist. Cardiovasc Drug Rev 1991; 9: 4–17
9. Mishra SK, Hermsmeyer K. Selective inhibition of T-type calcium channels by Ro 40-5967. Circ Res 1994; 75: 144–8
10. Rossier MF, Aptel HBC, Python CP, et al. Inhibition of low threshold calcium channels by angiotensin II in adrenal glomerulosa cells through activation of protein kinase C. J Biol Chem 1995; 270: 15137–42
11. Quinn SJ, Cornwall MC, Williams GH. Electrical properties of isolated rat adrenal glomerulosa and fasciculata cells. Endocrinology 1987; 120: 903–14
12. Barrett PQ, Isales CM, Bollag WB. Calcium channels and aldosterone secretion: modulation by potassium and atrial natriuretic peptide. Am J Physiol 1991; 261: F706–19
13. Cohen CJ, McCarthy RT, Barrett PQ, et al. Calcium channels in adrenal glomerulosa cells: potassium and angiotensin II increase T-type calcium current. Proc Natl Acad Sci U S A 1988; 85: 2412–16
14. Natke Jr E, Kabela E. Electrical response in cat adrenal cortex: possible relation to aldosterone secretion. Am J Physiol 1979; 237: E158–62
15. Matsunaga H, Maruyama Y, Kojima I, et al. Transient calcium channel current characterised by a low threshold voltage in zona glomerulosa cells of rat adrenal cortex. Pflugers Arch 1987; 408: 351–5
16. Artalejo CR, Adams ME, Fox AP. Three types of calcium channel trigger secretion with different efficacies in chromaffin cells. Nature 1994; 367: 72–6
17. Sheng Z-H, Rettig J, Cook T, et al. Calcium-dependent interaction of N-type calcium channels with the synaptic core complex. Nature 1996; 379: 451–4
18. Tanabe T, Beam KG, Adams BA, et al. Regions of the skeletal muscle dihydropyridine receptor critical for excitation-contraction coupling. Nature 1990; 346, 567–9
19. Feuilloley M, Vaudry H. Role of the cytoskeleton in adrenocortical cells. Endocr Rev 1996; 17: 269–88
20. Capponi AM, Rossier MF. Regulation of aldosterone secretion. Curr Opin Endocrinol Diabetes 1996; 3: 248–57
21. Kojima I, Kawamura N, Shibata H. Rate of calcium entry determines the rapid changes in protein kinase C activity in angiotensin II-stimulated adrenal glomerulosa cells. Biochem J 1994; 297: 523–8
22. Burnay MM, Vallotton MB, Capponi AM, et al. Angiotensin II potentiates the adrenocorticotrophic hormone-induced cyclic AMP formation in bovine adrenal glomerulosa cells through a capacitative calcium influx. Biochem J. In press

Control of secretion in chromaffin cells from normal and spontaneously hypertensive rats

Lars Cleemann, Jing Fan, Martin Morad

Department of Pharmacology, Georgetown University Medical Center, Washington, District of Colombia, USA, and Mount Desert Island Biological Laboratory, Salsbury Cove, Maine, USA

Summary

Control of catecholamine secretion was studied in medullary chromaffin cells from spontaneously hypertensive Wistar-Kyoto rats and controls by simultaneously measuring whole-cell calcium currents, intracellular Ca^{2+} transients and single secretory events (using a carbon fibre microelectrode). The control of secretion by microdomains of calcium channels was indicated by the consistent finding that secretion was rapidly and directly related to calcium current but was largely insensitive to the much slower increase in intracellular Ca^{2+}. Spontaneously hypertensive rat (SHR) chromaffin cells had larger calcium currents and higher spontaneous rates of exocytosis than cells from control animals. The calcium channel blockers nifedipine and mibefradil both suppressed calcium current and secretion. Onset of the effect of nifedipine was rapid (<5 s), while mibefradil had slower onset and longer washout times. At 0.3 μM concentrations in SHR cells, mibefradil appeared to block basal and depolarisation-dependent catecholamine secretion more effectively than nifedipine.

Introduction

Adrenal medullary chromaffin cells contribute to the cardiovascular control of blood pressure by releasing catecholamines into the bloodstream. Secretion is thought to be controlled mainly by cholinergic stimulation that opens postsynaptic excitatory channels. This leads to depolarisation and sequential activation of sodium and calcium channels which results in Ca^{2+} influx and the triggering of vesicular fusion and exocytosis. It is also known, however, that internal Ca^{2+} stores in bovine chromaffin cells may be released by caffeine and histamines,[1,2] and that different types of calcium channel (T, L, N, P and Q) may differ in their effects on transmitter release.[3,4] These channels may also be differentially expressed in different animals. Furthermore, Ca^{2+} may be involved not only in the final exocytosis but also in the 'docking' of vesicles as a prerequisite for exocytosis.[5] Before evaluating the action of different calcium channel blockers in the rat chromaffin cell, it was therefore essential to examine the link between calcium current and secretion.

We hypothesised that adrenal calcium current and/or secretion might be altered in hypertension and that this might be examined in spontaneously hypertensive rats (SHRs). In its short life span, this stroke-prone rat strain develops many of the characteristics of essential hypertension, including increased levels of circulating catecholamines, increased blood pressure and hypertrophy of cardiac muscle and vascular smooth muscle.[6] Ventricular heart cells from this animal model have prolonged action potentials,[7] increased calcium current density[8] and increased secretion of brain natriuretic peptide (BNP).[9] The increase in cardiac calcium current density may in fact be a manifestation of cardiac hypertrophy, as such increases also occur when the disease is of renal origin[10] or is secondary to aortic stenosis.[11]

These observations lend support to the notion that calcium channels in the adrenal gland might serve as a therapeutic target in the treatment of hypertension. In this report, we examine the processes that control catecholamine secretion by chromaffin cells from SHRs and controls, and we test the effect of two calcium antagonists: a well-known calcium channel blocker (nifedipine) and a novel agent (mibefradil).

Simultaneous measurements of catecholamine secretion, membrane currents and intracellular Ca^{2+} transients

Primary cultures of rat chromaffin cells were prepared by a modification of a technique previously used for bovine chromaffin cells.[12] Secretion by individual cells was measured as discrete secretory events with a carbon fibre microelectrode[13] prepared from single filaments (6–8 μm diameter; Thornel, Greenville, South Carolina, USA) and insulated with polyethylene tubing (300 μm inner diameter). Suitable electrodes had low capacitance and conductance but strong rectification in both direction and, in characteristic potential regions, produced currents indicative of electrode processes such as hydrolysis of water and oxidation of catecholamines (about 200 pA in a test solution containing epinephrine 100 μM). It was anticipated that the circular tip of the carbon fibre electrode (6–8 μm diameter, surface area ~50 μm) would register only a small proportion of the total secretory event of the much larger chromaffin cell (15–30 μm diameter, surface area ~1000 μm, corresponding to membrane capacitance ~10 pF).

The oxidation currents recorded showed each secretory event as a spike of amplitude 5–300 pA and half-width 2–40 ms. The number, amplitudes and durations of spikes were determined by curve peeling.

A 'residual' level of secretory activity remained after the sequential removal of spikes, which may represent secretory events that take place at some distance from the carbon fibre electrode.

The secretory spikes were similar to the standard curve suggested by Chow and Rüden[14] and were characterised by a rapid upstroke and slow decay. Such a shape is predicted by a one-dimensional model of secretion where catecholamine is released instantaneously at the cell surface but must move by diffusion (D) some distance (d) before reaching the electrode and being oxidised at time t. The resulting set of curves have only two parameters: amplitude and Dt/d^2. This model is limited in that it accounts for neither the loss of catecholamine during diffusion to the electrode nor the slow release which sometimes precedes the rapid upstroke.[15]

After placement of the carbon fibre electrode on one side of the cell, a whole-cell voltage clamp[16] was applied from the other side (fig. 1 (C)) with a 3–5 MΩ microelectrode connected to a second amplifier (DAGAN model 8900).

Intracellular Ca^{2+} transients in whole-cell clamped cells were measured using fluorescent indicator dyes (Fluo-3, Calcium-green or Fura-2) dialysed through the patch pipette. Fluo-3 was excited with epi-illumination (Nikon objective, × 40, NA 1.4, oil immersion) with continuous blue light (488 nm wavelength) from an argon ion laser (Omnichrome; Chino, California, USA). Excitation above the cut-off wavelength of the barrier filter (510 nm) was detected with a photomultiplier tube. Fura-2 was excited at two alternating wavelengths (410 and 335 nm) with light from a mercury arc lamp chopped at 1200 Hz.[17] Pulsed fluorescence at wavelengths above 510 nm was detected with a single photomultiplier and was demultiplexed to yield two signals (corresponding to the two wavelengths of excitation) that were interlaced with the electrode measurements under the control of pCLAMP 6.0 software (Axon Instruments, Foster City, California, USA).

Regulation of secretion by calcium current

The putative link between calcium current and secretion was studied in whole-cell, clamped, cultured chromaffin cells from Wistar-Kyoto (WKY) rats. Ca^{2+} was measured as a possible intermediary step in this process. Figure 2 shows the responses produced by a 160 ms depolarisation from –60 to 0 mV (where calcium current is close to its

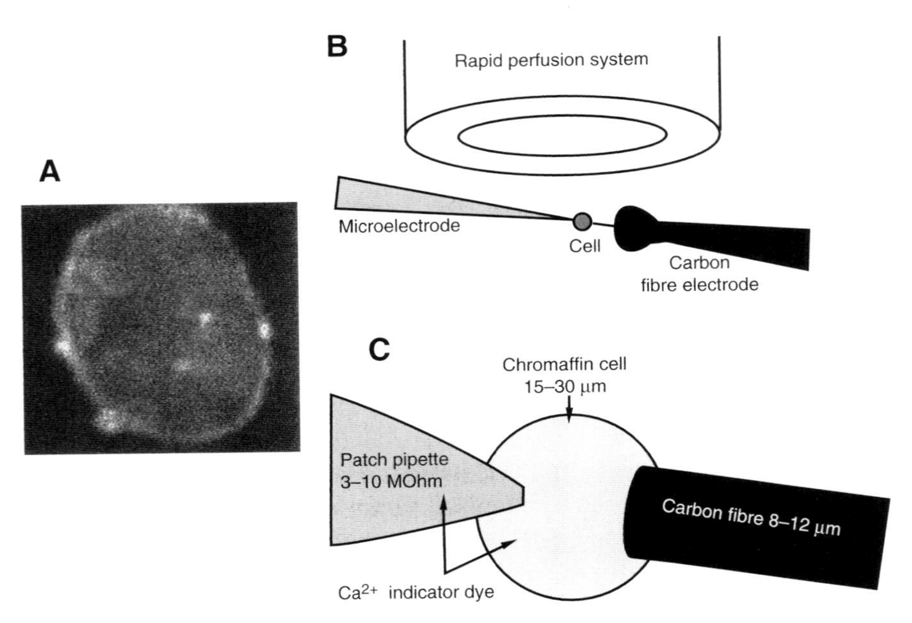

Fig. 1. A) Circular cross-section of a cultured, attached chromaffin cell stained with Fluo-3 and imaged with confocal microscopy (Noran, Oyssey XL). B) Schematic of a chromaffin cell under low-power magnification (× 10 objective) after positioning of the carbon fibre microelectrode, the patch microelectrode and the rapid perfusion system. C) Chromaffin cell and its environs under higher magnification (× 40) used in the final approach of the patch microelectrode to the cell.

maximal value). Sodium current was blocked with tetrodotoxin, and a prominent Ca^{2+}-activated potassium current was blocked by omitting extracellular K^+. This type of outward potassium current contributes to the generation of short action potentials under normal conditions and can also be blocked by apamine.[18] The remaining inward current (see fig. 2 (A)) has the characteristic voltage-dependence and slow inactivation kinetics of calcium currents found in chromaffin cells.[12]

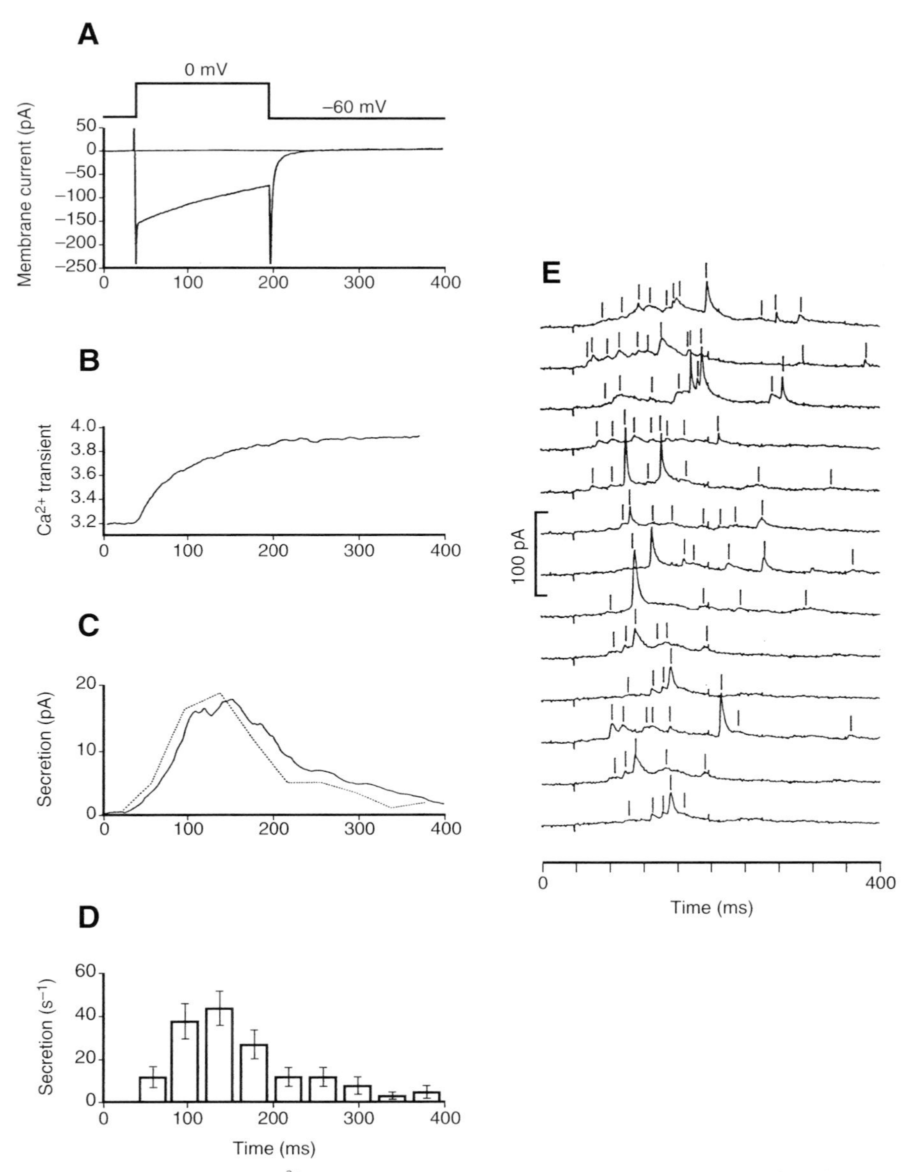

Fig. 2. Calcium current, intracellular Ca^{2+} transient and secretion in a voltage-clamped Wistar-Kyoto (WKY) rat chromaffin cell, voltage clamped from –60 to 0 mV for 160 ms 13 times at 20 s intervals. A) Calcium current. B) Intracellular Ca^{2+} transient. C) Filtered average of oxidation currents. D) Average frequency of secretory spikes in 80 ms bins (also shown by broken line in panel C). E) Individual recordings of oxidation current (short vertical lines indicate detected secretory spikes).

Panel B of figure 2 shows the intracellular Ca^{2+} transient recorded with Fluo-3 (K_d ~300 nM). This dye is very sensitive to Ca^{2+} but is not readily calibrated. The continued rise in the intracellular Ca^{2+} signal during the voltage-clamp pulse indicates that Ca^{2+} influx is maintained during the pulse. Unlike the other parameters, the intracellular Ca^{2+} transient did not fall rapidly after repolarisation. Panel E of figure 2 shows original tracings of the oxidation currents measured with a carbon fibre microelectrode. It is generally agreed that individual current spikes correspond to exocytosis of single secretory vesicles.

The stochastic nature of this process implies that multiple recordings are required for accurate measurement of secretion. In the experiment illustrated in figure 2, the depolarising pulse was repeated 13 times, and the time-course of secretion was estimated both from the average oxidation current (see fig. 2 (C)) and from the number of secretory spikes accumulated in bins of 40 ms duration (see fig. 2 (D)). The secretory spike rate rose rapidly and was near its maximum value 60 ms after depolarisation (i.e. in the bin centred at the 100 ms mark). Following repolarisation, the rate of secretion declined almost as rapidly. This behaviour was quite different from that of the intracellular Ca^{2+} transient. The two estimates of secretion were similar and differed only slightly with respect to the delay between calcium current and secretion. Panel C of figure 2 shows that the oxidation current (unbroken curve) rose and fell somewhat more slowly than the secretory spike rate (dotted curve). This may be attributable to the skewed appearance of individual secretory spikes and slower time-course of 'residual' secretion that remains after removal of detectable spikes.

To ascertain whether the reduced secretory rate above was associated with the timing of the calcium current or exhaustion of the pool of release-ready secretory vesicles, alternating clamp pulses of different durations were used (fig. 3). Results showed that the secretory response lasted as long as the depolarisation (50, 250 or 450 ms) and that the beginning of its decline coincided with repolarisation. The intracellular Ca^{2+} transients (see fig. 3 (B)), on the other hand, continued to rise during depolarisation, possibly approaching a saturation level. On the time-scale used in this illustration, intracellular Ca^{2+} transients showed only a small decline following repolarisation.

The current during the clamp pulse indicates that complete inactivation of calcium current occurs in about 500 ms. However, the tail currents were well maintained, which signified little calcium channel inactivation.

Figures 2 and 3 indicate that secretion lasts as long as the voltage-gated calcium current, but it is also conceivable that other Ca^{2+} transport mechanisms (e.g. Na^+/Ca^{2+} exchange) might play a role or that membrane depolarisation alone might have an effect. These possibilities were tested in the next series of experiments.

Figure 4 shows a comparison of the voltage-dependence of calcium current, intracellular Ca^{2+} transient and secretion in rat chromaffin cells. The cell was clamped

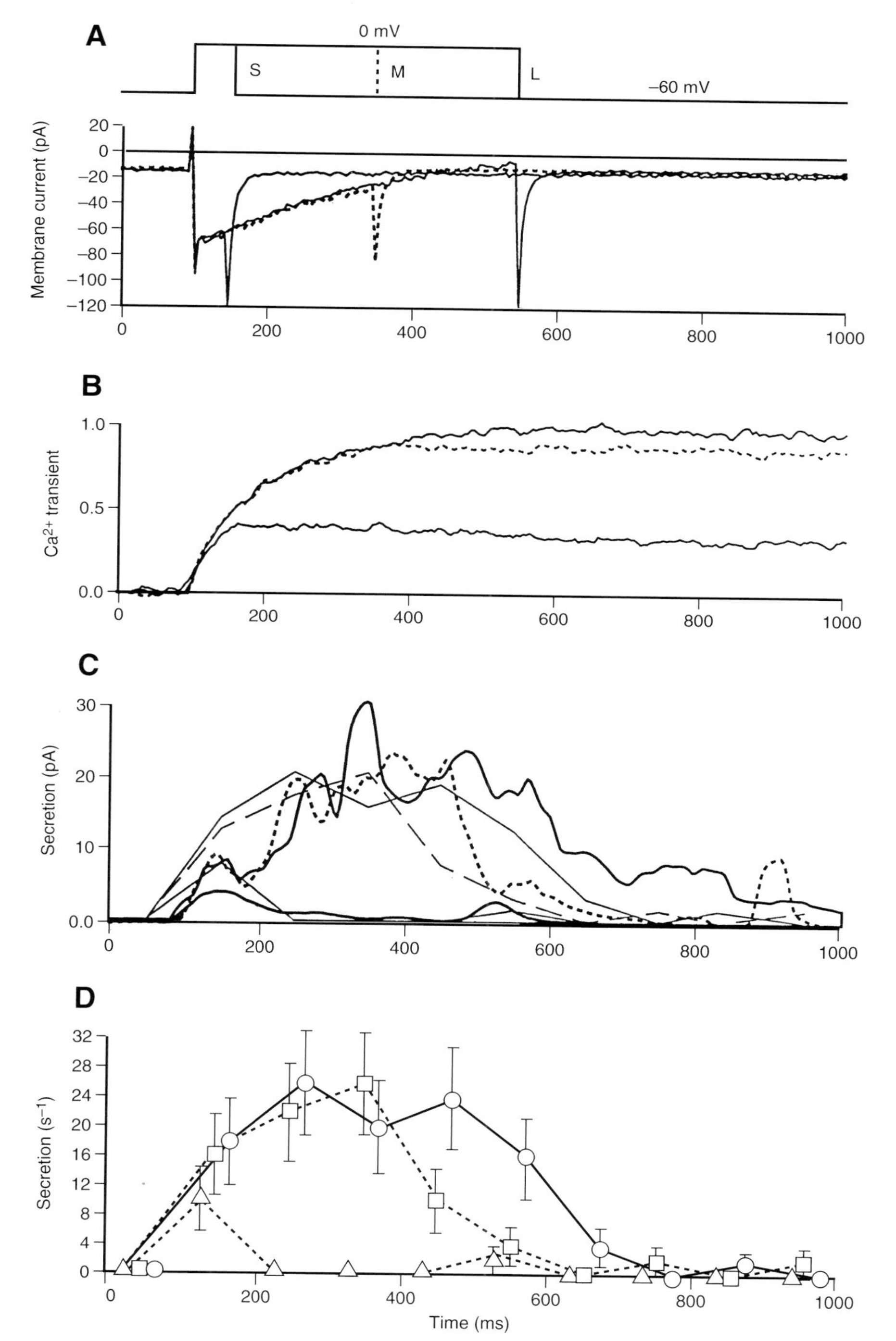

Fig. 3. Longer clamp pulses causing longer-lasting secretion. A chromaffin cell was depolarised repeatedly from −60 to 0 mV with clamp pulses of 50 (S), 250 (M) and 450 ms (L) duration. A) Calcium currents. B) Intracellular Ca^{2+} transients. C) Filtered secretory responses. Each plot shows average time-course corresponding to each of the three pulse durations. D) Secretory spike rate counted in bins of 100 ms duration (also shown by a thin line in panel C). Results from depolarisation of medium duration (M) shown by a broken line.

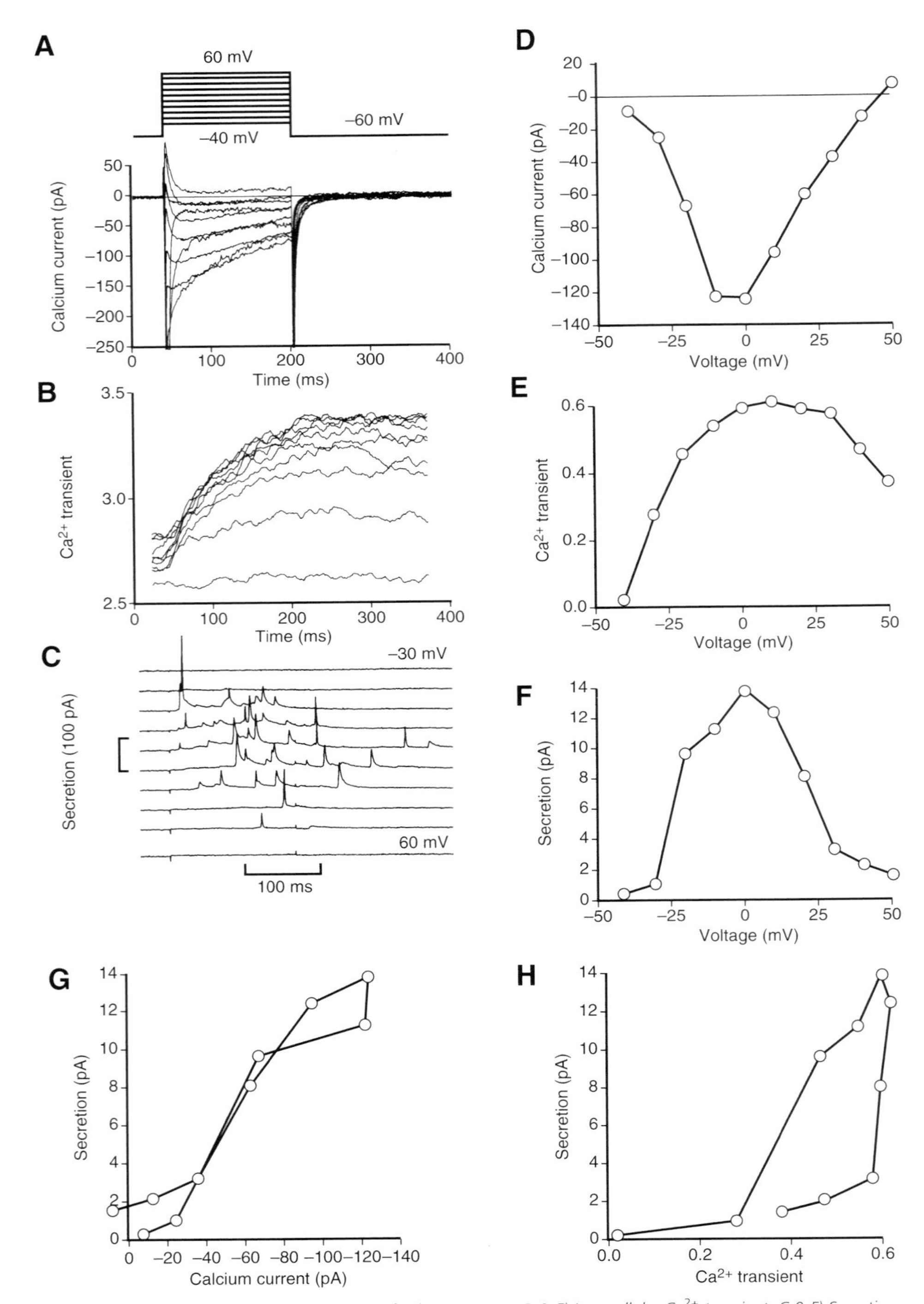

Fig. 4. A & D) Bell-shaped voltage-dependence of calcium current. B & E) Intracellular Ca^{2+} transient. C & F) Secretion. The cell was depolarised for 160 ms at 30 s intervals from –60 mV to different potentials in the range –30 to +60 mV. The bell-shaped voltage relationships (panels D–F) show the peak inward calcium current, uncalibrated intracellular Ca^{2+} transient and the integral charge of the oxidation current. G & H) Correlation of secretion with calcium current and intracellular Ca^{2+} transient.

at 30 s intervals to progressively increasing voltages (between –30 and +50 mV). Data from the original records (see fig. 4 (A–C)) were plotted and yielded similar bell-shaped voltage-dependence (see fig. 4 (D–F)). The voltage-dependence of secretion was particularly well correlated with that of calcium current (see fig. 4 (G)).

In contrast, the intracellular Ca^{2+} transients showed two distinct deviations. Secretion increased when plotted against intracellular Ca^{2+} transient (see fig. 4 (H)) and fell sharply at positive potentials, whereas the intracellular Ca^{2+} transient remained elevated. The first deviation is consistent with saturation of the indicator dye, but the second suggests considerable Ca^{2+} influx at +50 mV, where calcium current and secretion are either minimal or absent. Such Ca^{2+} influx might result from the entry of Ca^{2+} via the Na^+/Ca^{2+} exchanger.

The above results show that secretion is closely linked to entry of Ca^{2+} through the calcium channel. The secretion lasted as long as the calcium current (50–450 ms) (see fig. 2). Secretion stopped rapidly when the current was terminated by repolarisation, even though the intracellular Ca^{2+} concentration remained elevated for several seconds (see figs 2–4), probably at levels sufficient to bring Fluo-3 (K_m ~300 nM) close to saturation (see fig. 4 (H)). Proportionality between calcium current and secretion was observed either by changing the Ca^{2+} concentration or clamping to different potentials (see fig. 4). At more positive (50 mV) potentials, it is possible that Ca^{2+} enters the cell via routes other than the calcium channel (see fig. 4 (H)) but cannot trigger release from the cell in this way.

Thus, our findings suggest that Ca^{2+} triggers secretion by binding to a site close to the inner opening of the calcium channel, and that signalling occurs in a microdomain in which the Ca^{2+} concentration deviates significantly from the average Ca^{2+} concentration within the cell. Similar conclusions have been reached by other investigators working with bovine chromaffin cells.[19,20] In other respects, the control of secretion in cultured and voltage-clamped rat chromaffin cells may be different. For example, the block observed with substitution of Ba^{2+} for Ca^{2+} may be stronger than that seen in voltage-clamped bovine chromaffin cells.[21] Furthermore, though diverse caffeine- and histamine-sensitive intracellular Ca^{2+} stores have been identified in non-dialysed bovine chromaffin cells,[1] the present results indicate little or no internal Ca^{2+} release triggered by calcium currents or caffeine in rat chromaffin cells.

Calcium current and secretion in chromaffin cells from SHRs

In parallel experiments, we examined differences in secretion and calcium current between chromaffin cells from SHRs and control WKY rats.

Secretory activity was evaluated by measuring the basal rate of secretory spikes in non-dialysed cells constantly perfused with tyrode solutions containing Ca^{2+} (5 mM) and K^+ 0 or 5.3 mM. In some experiments, the differences were striking. Panel B of figure 5 shows spontaneous spikes generated by an SHR cell at a steady frequency. A control cell (see fig. 5 (A)) showed a much-reduced spike frequency. This finding was

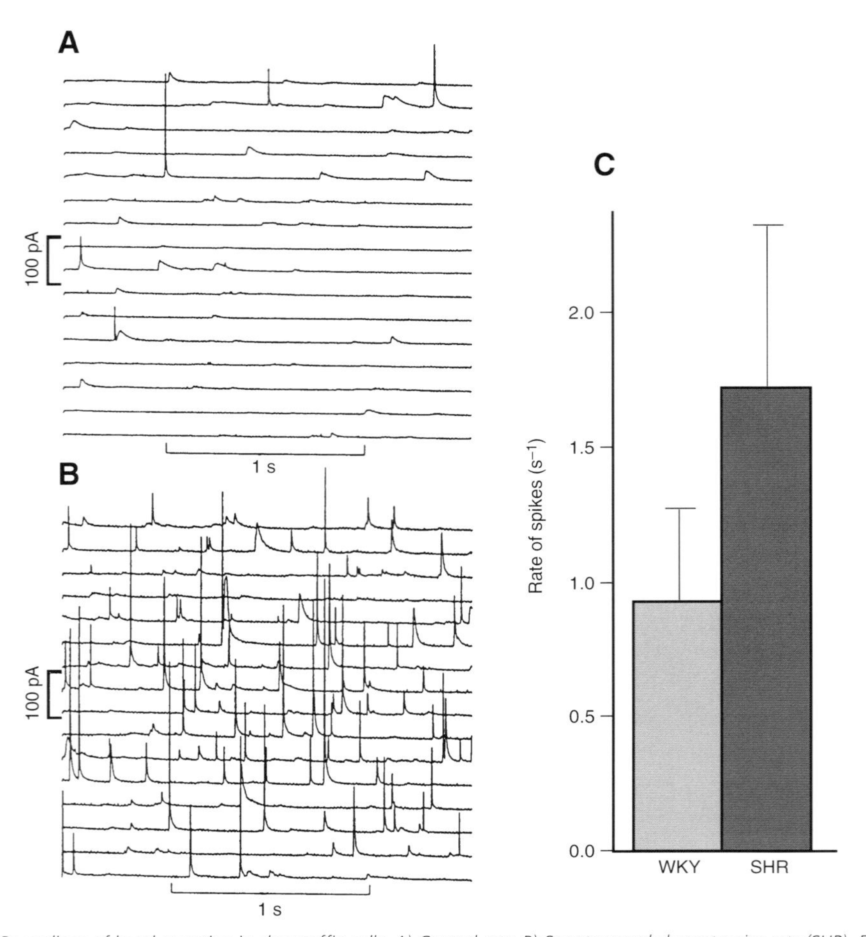

Fig. 5. Recordings of basal secretion in chromaffin cells. A) Control rats. B) Spontaneously hypertensive rats (SHR). Each panel shows the oxidation current in 16 consecutive 2 s tracings. C) Comparison of the average basal rate of secretory spikes in 6 control cells and 7 SHR cells. WKY = Wistar-Kyoto rats.

supported by the pooling of data from a number of successful experiments (see fig. 5 (C)). To confirm cell viability and the proper operation of the carbon fibre microelectrode, cells were required to produce a few healthy spikes of oxidation current over 1–2 min. We also excluded experiments where the placement of the microelectrode on the cell appeared to produce cell injury (i.e. a transient and rapidly fading high spike rate). Under these conditions, the rate of generation of spontaneous spikes was much higher in SHR than in WKY rat cells.

In another series of experiments, calcium currents in SHR and WKY cells were compared. Current magnitude was increased significantly when EGTA 10 mM was included in the dialysing solution. The voltage-dependence of calcium current was identical in the two types of cell (fig. 6), but the current magnitude in SHRs was twice that of controls. With 5 experiments in each group, the differences were highly significant. The measured currents were normalised in terms of membrane capacitance (C) (WKY: $C = 11.3 \pm 1.2$ pF; SHR: $C = 10.2 \pm 0.2$ pF).

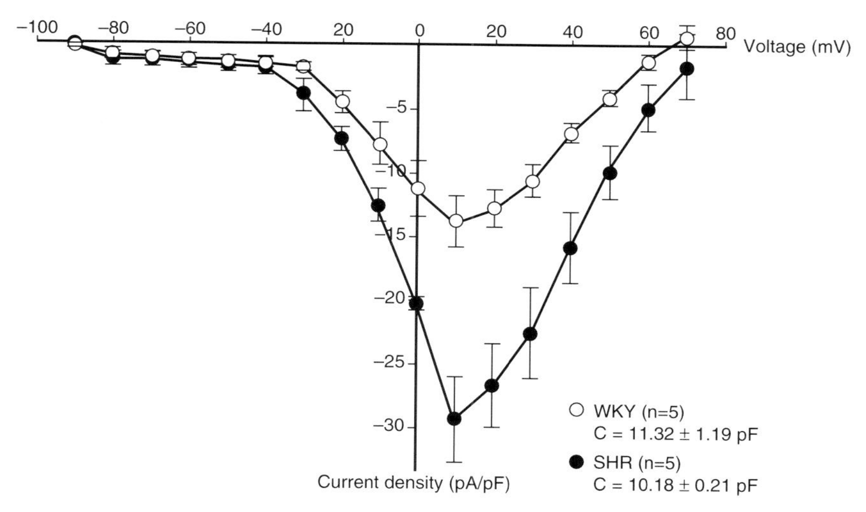

Fig. 6. Voltage-dependence of calcium current in chromaffin cells from control (Wistar-Kyoto; WKY) rats and spontaneously hypertensive rats (SHR). Each curve is the average of currents in 5 cells. The Ca^{2+} concentration of the internal solution was buffered with EGTA 10 mM (holding potential –90 mV; Ca^{2+} 5 mM). C = membrane capacitance.

These results indicate that calcium current and the basal rate of secretion are both increased by about 2-fold in chromaffin cells and that basal secretion is roughly proportional to the extracellular Ca^{2+}. However, it is unclear why the low basal secretion should be changed by approximately the same factor as the current.

The 2-fold increase in normalised calcium current density (pA/pF) measured in SHR chromaffin cells is comparable to the increases reported in normalised calcium current in ventricular myocytes from SHRs[8] and rats with renal hypertension.[10] The need to normalise current has been highlighted by the finding that cardiomyocytes hypertrophied by aortic stenosis had increased calcium current, but that this was in proportion to an increase in membrane capacitance (i.e. membrane area).[11]

Calcium channel blockers and secretion in chromaffin cells from normal rats and SHRs

Suppression of secretion by the calcium channel blockers nifedipine and mibefradil were measured and compared. Figure 7 illustrates the suppression of calcium current in SHR cells by these compounds at 10 μM concentration. Panels A and B of figure 7 show results from two representative cells, clearly illustrating differences in the time-course of action of the two drugs. When sampling every 20 s, the effect of nifedipine was fully developed from one depolarisation to the next, remained constant in the presence of the drug, and was rapidly and nearly completely reversible (see fig. 7 (A)). The effect of mibefradil, on the other hand, continued even when current was measured by successive depolarisations over a period of 1–3 min (see fig. 7 (A & B)). The addition of nifedipine to mibefradil produced a rapid additional current suppression. Washout of both compounds produced a rapid recovery that corresponded to the removal of nifedipine, and a much slower recovery associated with washout of

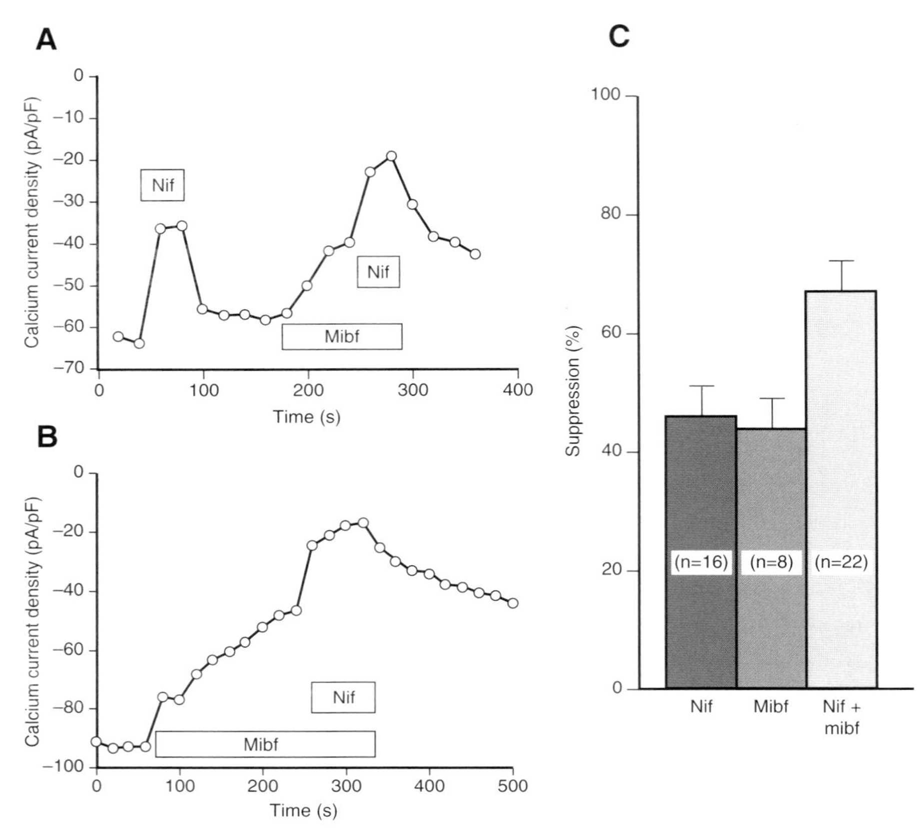

Fig. 7. Suppression of calcium current by nifedipine (Nif) and mibefradil (Mibf) in spontaneously hypertensive rat chromaffin cells. A) Suppression of calcium current by nifedipine 10 µM. B) Suppression by mibefradil 10 µM. C) Average suppression of calcium current by the two drugs applied separately and in combination. Calcium current was measured 50–80 ms after depolarisation from –60 mV to avoid any contamination by sodium current (holding potential –90 mV; Ca^{2+} 5 mM; EGTA 5 mM).

mibefradil. Indeed, in typical voltage-clamp experiments which lasted from 5 to 30 min and inevitably involved some current 'run-down', the effect of mibefradil was not allowed to develop fully and was never completely reversed.

To obtain a quantitative measure of the effect of mibefradil, we measured the effect of the drug on the suppression of calcium current after 2–5 min exposure. Under these conditions we found that the average current suppression by both drugs was about 45% (see fig. 7 (C)). When both drugs were used in combination, the effect was significantly greater (~70%).

The effects of 10 µM of nifedipine or mibefradil on secretion was tested in WKY cells (figs 8 & 9). Figure 8 (A & B) shows the rapid, partial and reversible suppression of current by nifedipine in dialysed cells from normal rats. Somewhat surprisingly, the simultaneously measured intracellular Ca^{2+} transients were only slightly reduced (see fig. 8 (B & D)). This cannot be explained entirely by saturation of the indicator dye (Calcium-green-1: 0.05 mM) since the initial slope of intracellular Ca^{2+} transients was

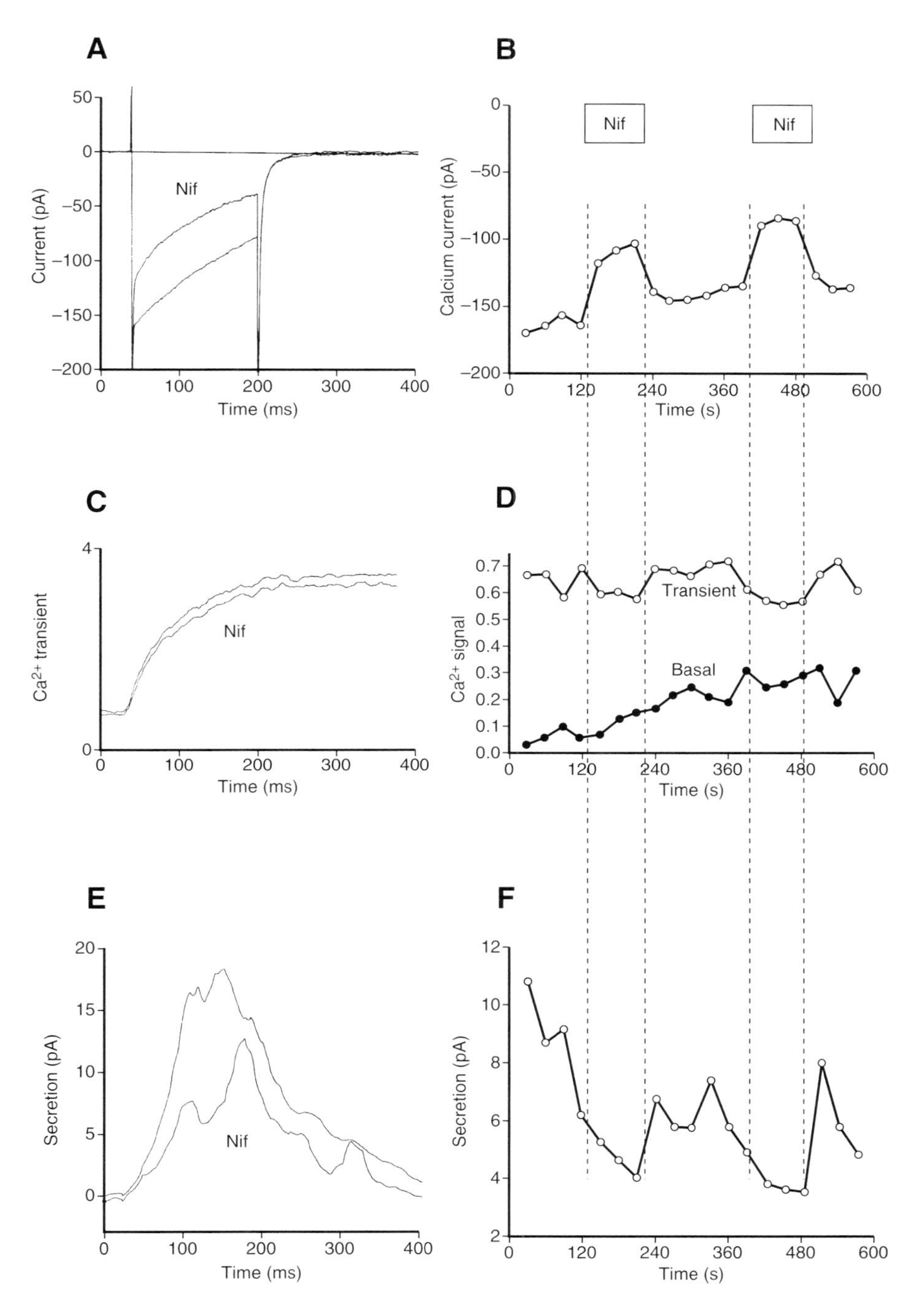

Fig. 8. Effect of nifedipine (Nif) on calcium current, intracellular Ca^{2+} transient and secretion in a chromaffin cell from the Wistar-Kyoto (WKY) rat. Nifedipine 10 μM was applied and washed out twice. The cell was depolarised every 30 s from –60 to 0 mV with pulses of 160 ms duration. A) Membrane current. B) Time-course of drug-induced effects on calcium current. C) Intracellular Ca^{2+} transient. D) Time-course of drug-induced effects on Ca^{2+} transient. E) Secretion. F) Time-course of drug-induced effects on secretion. Both basal and transient fluorescence intensities were plotted in panel D. The secretion in F is the average oxidation current measured in the 400 ms time slots used in the recordings. Traces A, C and F are averages of recordings made in the presence and absence of nifedipine (holding potential –60 mV; Ca^{2+} 5 mM; membrane capacitance 16 pF).

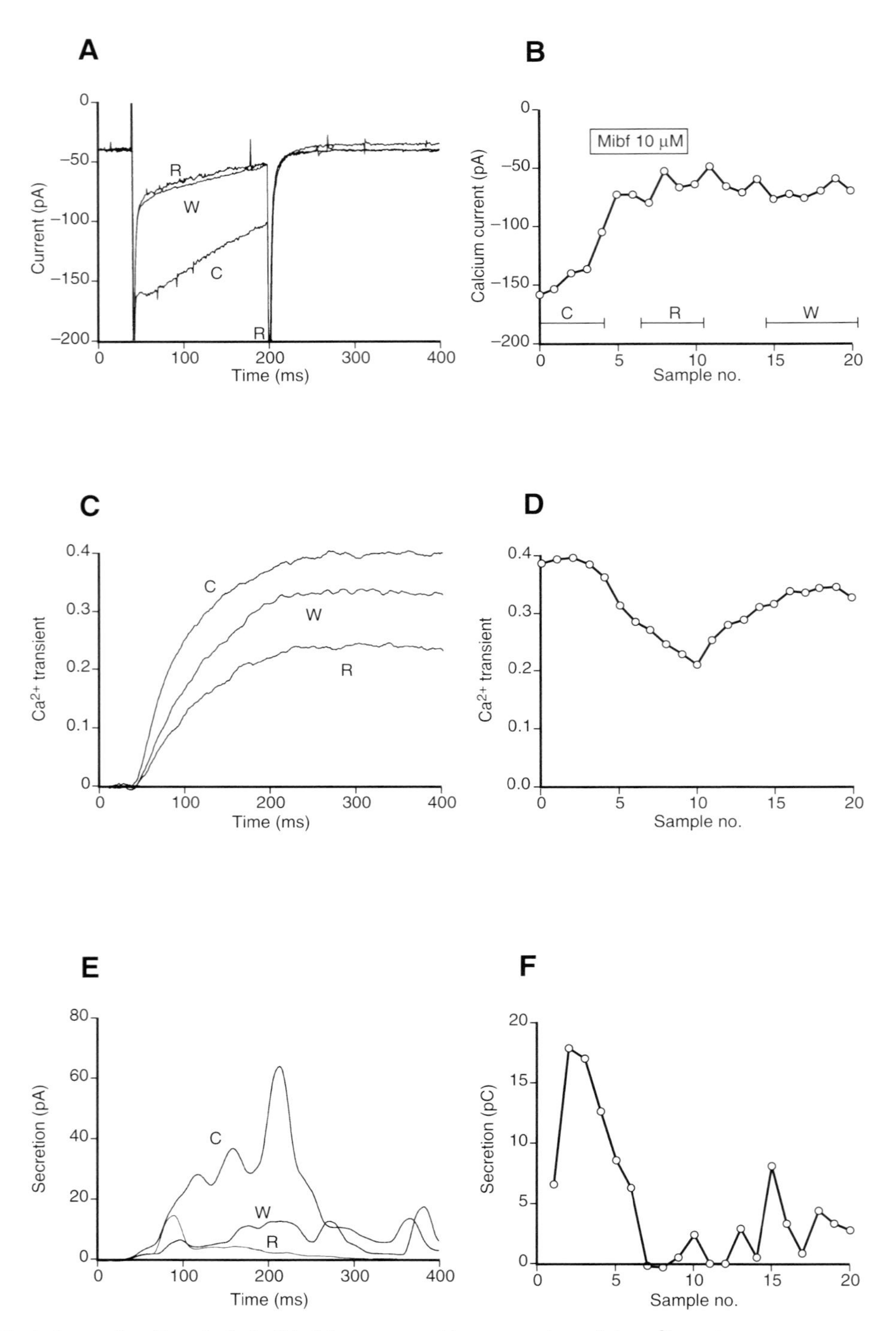

Fig. 9. Suppressive effect of mibefradil (Mibf) 10 μM on calcium current, intracellular Ca^{2+} transient and secretion in the spontaneously hypertensive rat chromaffin cell. A & B) Membrane current. C & D) Intracellular Ca^{2+} transients. E & F) Oxidation current. Parameters were measured before (C), during (R) and after (W) application of mibefradil and averaged from the measurements indicated in panel B (holding potential –60 mV; Ca^{2+} 5 mM; Calcium-green-1 0.2 mM; capacitance 18 pF).

also rather insensitive to the drug. Secretion (see fig. 8 (C & D)) was, however, suppressed to a similar degree as calcium current. Indeed, it appeared that secretion was often reduced more than current but that the effect developed gradually over 2–3 depolarisations.

The slow onset of action of mibefradil is illustrated in figure 9. The suppression of current developed over 1 min and, on washout, calcium current showed very little recovery (see fig. 9 (A & B)). The suppression of intracellular Ca^{2+} transient, however, was gradual but quite substantial and nearly completely reversible. The secretory response closely followed the time-course of calcium current suppression, showing a gradual onset and partial recovery (see fig. 9 (E & F)). Maximal suppression appeared to be nearly complete but is naturally subject to the random variations associated with the quantal release process.

The magnitude and time-course of the suppression of secretion in these experiments were consistent with calcium current suppression. Considering the strong suppression of secretion by nifedipine and mibefradil, it is noteworthy that these drugs are used in very high (probably saturating) concentrations. We therefore proceeded to measure the effect of mibefradil at much lower concentrations.

Extensive series of experiments in which the effects of mibefradil 0.03 μM on voltage-clamped SHR cells were tested produced inconclusive results. The decline in calcium current and secretion continued to be closely related, but drug effects were difficult to distinguish from those attributed to current run-down. At 10-fold higher concentrations, however, mibefradil suppressed calcium current by 50% and reduced the frequency of secretory spikes.

In non-dialysed SHR cells, the secretory response to 0.3 μM of mibefradil and nifedipine was tested by measuring the basal secretion rate and secretion produced by depolarisation induced by exposure of the cells to KCl 60 mM for 4 s (fig. 10). The basal rate of secretory spiking was low in these cells; nevertheless, spikes were completely absent in the presence of the drug (see fig. 10 (A)). The bursts of secretory spiking produced by KCl depolarisation were less intense but longer lasting than those produced by voltage-clamp depolarisations of 0.05–0.45 s duration. It was noted that mibefradil not only reduced the frequency of secretory spikes but also strongly suppressed the electrical charge carried by these spikes (see fig. 10 (B & C)). This was related to the decrease in the amplitude of individual spikes (see fig. 10 (E)), and not to the shortening of spike duration (see fig. 10 (D)). As in other cases, recovery after washout of the drug was incomplete. In the same experiment, nifedipine had little or no effect on the basal rate of secretion. Results of 8 similar experiments showed a consistent trend towards suppression of basal secretion by mibefradil that was equal to or larger than that seen with nifedipine.

These findings indicate that mibefradil is an effective blocker of secretion in chromaffin cells from SHRs and normal rats and that it produces similar levels of

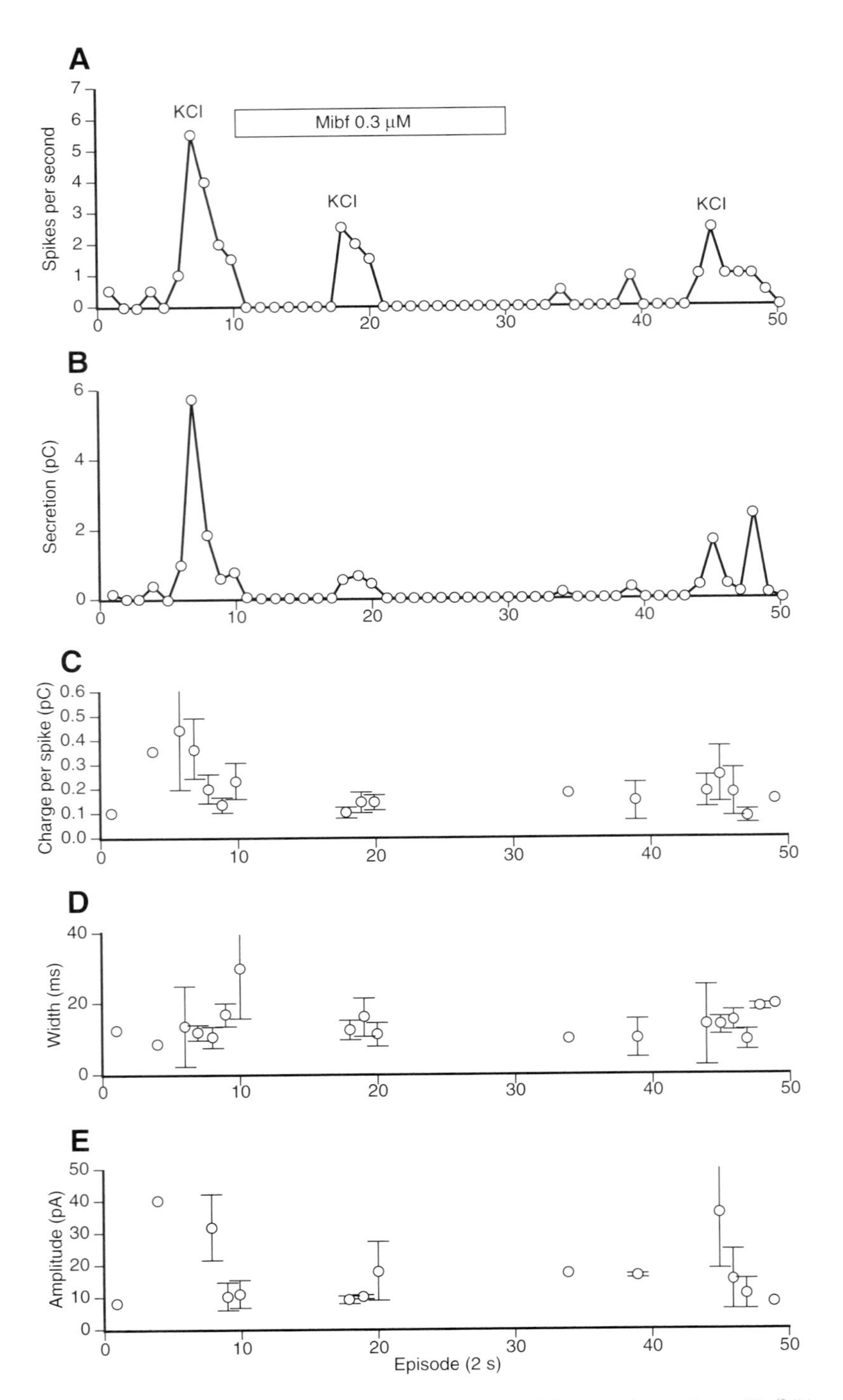

Fig. 10. Suppression of basal and KCl-induced secretion in the spontaneously hypertensive rat chromaffin cell by mibefradil (Mibf). A continuous recording of basal secretion was interrupted by 4 s depolarisations with KCl 60 mM before, during and after exposure to mibefradil 0.3 μM. The secretion was determined at 2 s intervals. A) Frequency of spikes. B) Charge carried by these spikes. The appearance of the individual spikes is indicated by (C) their average charge, (D) duration at half height and (E) amplitude (non-dialysed cell; Ca^{2+} 5 mM).

block at 10 and 0.3 μM concentrations (see figs 8 & 9). The similar effects of 10 and 0.3 μM concentrations suggest that the K_d of the suppressive effect of mibefradil must be <0.3 μM. The two drugs have distinct time-courses of effect, and their effects on calcium current are additive, even at saturation concentrations (see fig. 7). This suggests that they have different sites of action on the calcium channel.

Use of single cultured cells for pharmacological studies of secretion

The present studies show that the carbon microelectrode can be used to study the pharmacology of single voltage-clamped or non-dialysed rat chromaffin cells from normal rats and SHRs. Aided by computerised analysis of oxidation currents, we explored different ways of quantifying secretory responses.

It is possible that the residual secretion current (which remains after removal of the larger spikes) may reflect the relatively large number of exocytotic events that do not occur directly under the tip of the carbon fibre. This method may therefore improve the accuracy of this estimation. Alternatively, the changes in the shape of individual secretory spikes may indicate control of secretion by factors other than the rate of exocytosis.[22,23]

Adrenal secretion in hypertension

This cellular research in an animal model has explored the possibility that adrenal secretion may be elevated in the hypertensive state and that the block of specific adrenal calcium channels may serve to reduce this secretion. This was done by firmly establishing the control of secretion by calcium current, showing that calcium current and spontaneous secretion are both elevated in SHR cells, and through the finding that both can be reduced by nifedipine and mibefradil. The link between calcium current and spontaneous secretion in SHR cells was investigated further by determining whether the calcium current-induced release was also enhanced in SHR cells (compared to control rats). It may also be of interest (from a mechanistic perspective) to establish the dose-dependency of the effects of the drugs on calcium current and secretion, to examine their effects on calcium channels of different types and to study their combined effect on secretion. The wider relevance of these results could be explored by application of the techniques described to other models of hypertension.

Acknowledgements

This work was supported by National Institutes of Health grant HL RO1 16152.

References

1. Cheek TR, Barry YA, Berridge MJ, et al. Bovine adrenal chromaffin cells contain an inositol 1,4,5-triphosphate-insensitive but caffeine-sensitive Ca^{2+} store which can be regulated by intraluminal free Ca^{2+}. Biochem J 1991; 275: 697–701

2. Liu PS, Lin YJ, Kao LS. Caffeine-sensitive calcium stores in bovine adrenal chromaffin cells. J Neurochem 1991; 56: 172–7
3. Artalejo CR, Adams ME, Fox AP. Three types of Ca^{2+} channel trigger secretion with different efficacies in chromaffin cells. Nature 1994; 367: 72–6
4. Lopez MG, Albillos A, de la Fuente MT, et al. Localized L-type calcium channels control exocytosis in cat chromaffin cells. Pflugers Arch 1994; 427: 348–54
5. Neher E, Zucker RS. Multiple calcium-dependent processes related to secretion in bovine chromaffin cells. Neuron 1993; 10: 21–30
6. Owens GK. Influence of blood pressure in development of aortic smooth muscle in spontaneously hypertensive rats. Hypertension 1987; 9: 178–87
7. Hayashi H, Shibata S. Electrical properties from cardiac membrane of spontaneously hypertensive rats. Eur J Pharmacol 1974; 27: 255–359
8. Sorbera LA, Morad M. Defects in G_1 regulatory protein leads to upregulation of cardiac Ca^{2+} current. Biophys J 1993; 64: A204
9. Ogawa Y, Nakoa K, Mukoyama M, et al. Natriuretic peptides as cardiac hormones in normotensive and spontaneously hypertensive rats. Circ Res 1991; 69: 491–500
10. Keung EC. Calcium current is increased in isolated adult myocytes from hypertrophied rat myocardium. Circ Res 1989; 64: 753–63
11. Scamps F, Mayoux E, Charlemagne D, et al. Calcium current in single cells isolated from normal and hypertrophied rat heart. Circ Res 1990; 67: 199–208
12. Gandia L, Garcia AG, Morad M. ATP modulation of calcium channel in chromaffin cells. J Physiol 1993; 470: 55–72
13. Leszcyszyn DJ, Jankowky JA, Viveros OH, et al. Secretion of catecholamines from individual adrenal medullary chromaffin cells. J Neurochem 1991; 56: 1855–63
14. Chow RH, van Rüden L, Neher E. Delay in vesicle fusion revealed by electrochemical monitoring of single secretory events in adrenal chromaffin cells. Nature 1992; 356: 60–3
15. de Toledo GA, Fernandez-Chacon R, Fernandez JM. Release of secretory products during transient vesicle fusion. Nature 1993; 363: 554–8
16. Hamill OP, Marty A, Neher E, et al. Improved patch-clamp technique for high resolution current recording from cells and cell free membrane patches. Pflugers Arch 1981; 191: 88–100
17. Cleemann L, Morad M. Role of Ca^{2+} channel in cardiac excitation–contraction coupling: evidence from Ca^{2+} transients and contraction. J Physiol 1991; 432: 283–312
18. Neely A, Lingle CJ. Two components of calcium activated potassium current in rat adrenal chromaffin cells. J Physiol 1992; 453: 97–131
19. Robinson IM, Finnegan JM, Monck JR, et al. Colocalization of calcium entry and exocytotic release sites in adrenal chromaffin cells. Proc Natl Acad Sci U S A 1995; 92: 2474–8
20. Augustine GJ, Neher E. Calcium requirements for secretion in bovine chromaffin cells. J Physiol 1992; 450: 247–71
21. van Rüden L, Garcia AG, Lopez MG. The mechanism of Ba-induced exocytosis from single chromaffin cells. FEBS Lett 1993; 336: 48–52
22. Pihel K, Travis ER, Birges R, et al. Exocytotic release from individual granules exhibits similar properties at mast and chromaffin cells. Biophys J 1996; 71: 1633–40
23. Jankowski JA, Finnegan JM, Wightman RM. Extracellular ionic composition alters kinetics of vesicular release of catecholamines and quantal size during exocytosis at adrenal medullary cells. J Neurochem 1994; 63: 1739–47

Section 3

Molecular biological approaches to calcium channel diversity

Introduction

The chapters in this section provide an excellent overview of the molecular basis of calcium channel function, first of voltage-gated calcium channels classified as high-voltage activated (HVA), and then of low-voltage-activated (LVA) T-type channels. Interactions between various calcium channel subunits and splice variants all play a part in generating diverse patterns of behaviour. Binding interactions between specific regions of calcium channels and other cellular signalling molecules are described in considerable detail.

Catterall et al. used antibodies specific for individual members of the α_1 subfamily to localise the various types of α_1 subunits to particular regions of the brain and subregions of neurons. Molecular interactions between class A (P/Q type) and class B (N type) α_1 subunits and various intracellular signalling proteins were characterised. Signalling from G proteins centres around conserved motif in the cytoplasmic loop I–II while interactions with components of the exocytotic machinery (SNARE proteins) involve the 'synprint site' in loop II–III. **Harpold et al.** present a highly detailed analysis of splice variants of the α_{1E} subunit and their effect on interactions with ancillary subunits such as β subunits. The two splice variants α_{1E-1} and α_{1E-3}, differing only in loop II–III, gave rise to whole currents with very different inactivation kinetics – not if expressed alone, but only when coexpressed with ancillary subunits. This indicates that the influence of the ancillary subunits can be isoform-specific. In a separate study, a cell line containing only T-type channels was shown to contain an $\alpha_2\delta$ subunit. **Liu and Campbell** focus on recent experiments that clarify how the β subunit contributes to the overall properties of calcium channels. A lucid review is given on the biochemical and molecular genetic properties of β subunits and their sites of interaction with α_1 subunits. Interestingly, the regions of the α_1 subunit that interface with β subunits (loop I–II and possibly loop II–III; see above) are also implicated in the reception of signals from G proteins, ryanodine receptors and SNARE proteins. **Zühlke et al.** have found that naturally occurring splice variants of the human α_{1C} subunit exhibit radically different inactivation properties. Splice variant $\alpha_{1C,77}$ displays slow and incomplete voltage-dependent inactivation but abundant Ca^{2+}-dependent inactivation; on the other hand, splice variant $\alpha_{1C,86}$ shows fast and complete inactivation but little Ca^{2+}-dependence. Thus, $\alpha_{1C,86}$ bears some of the earmarks of a T-type calcium channel, although not the property of low-voltage activation. **Bourinet et al.** characterise the class E α_1 subunit in some detail, focusing on the issue of whether its properties can be equated to those of T-type or R-type calcium channels found in neurons. One similarity found between α_{1E} and T-type channels is that macroscopic currents carried by Ca^{2+} exceed those supported by equal concentrations of Ba^{2+}, somewhat reminiscent of properties of LVA T-type channels. At the single-channel level, the unitary conductance with either charge carrier is ~11–12 pS. The overall conclusion is that α_{1E} behaves more like a T-type channel than do α_1 subunits of classes A, B, C or D, although clear contrasts with classical T-type channels have emerged. **Birnbaumer et al.** emphasise that

β subunit interactions with the pore-forming α_1 subunit are not strictly limited to one region of α_1: studies with the yeast two-hybrid approach and GST fusion proteins implicate the C terminus in addition to the loop I–II site originally defined by Campbell's group. An endogenous β subunit was found in *Xenopus* oocytes. In addition, there is evidence for the possibility that there can be more than one β subunit per α_1 subunit, in contrast to the 1:1 stoichiometry proposed by others. **Dolphin** summarises work from her laboratory demonstrating the diversity of T-type calcium currents, based on a comparison between rat sensory neurons and a sensory neuron–neuroblastoma hybrid cell line (ND7-23). The cell line displays a mix of rapidly and slowly inactivating T-type channels. α_{1E} subunits transiently expressed in COS-7 cells show properties similar to R-type current, except for their responsiveness to the spider toxin ω-Aga-IVA, traditionally thought of as a specific inhibitor of P-/Q-type channels. **Rock et al.** studied α_{1E} subunits stably expressed in HEK293 cells and compared their current-carrying properties to those of stably expressed α_{1B} subunits and native T-type and R-type channels. Both class E and class B α_1 subunits give rise to HVA currents, unlike T-type channels, in agreement with previous studies. As a useful example of pharmacological analysis, the currents supported by α_{1E} were strongly inhibited by the spider toxin ω-Aga-IIIA, much more so than T-type calcium channels. Finally, **Perez-Reyes et al.** review their very recent discovery of a novel α_1 subunit, designated α_{1G}, that exhibits all the earmarks expected for a classic T-type calcium channel when expressed in *Xenopus* oocytes, including the characteristic kinetic patterns (slow deactivation, crossing-current records evoked by a series of increasingly strong depolarising steps) and single-channel behaviour (characteristic bursts of openings, slope conductance of ~8 pS in isotonic Ca^{2+} or Ba^{2+}). The class G α_1 subunit is a distant relative of both the ABE and SCD subfamilies that have received intense study up to now. In many ways, this is a discovery that the field has long been waiting for.

Localisation and function of brain calcium channels

William A. Catterall, Ruth E. Westenbroek, Stefan Herlitze, Charles T. Yokoyama

Department of Pharmacology, University of Washington, Seattle, Washington, USA

Introduction

Calcium channels in the brain are complexes consisting of an α_1 subunit (190–250 kDa), $\alpha_2\delta$ subunits (disulphide-linked dimers of 140 and 27 kDa) and a β subunit (55–72 kDa).[1–5] The different physiological and pharmacological properties of the various calcium channel subtypes (L, N, P, Q, R and T types)[6,7] are thought to be determined primarily by their α_1 subunits. Five distinct α_1 subunits, designated α_{1A} to α_{1E}, are expressed in the brain.[8,9] These α_1 subunits fall into two groups based on their amino acid sequences and tissue distribution. The α_{1C} and α_{1D} subunits share in common more than 75% of amino acid residues with the α_1 subunits of L-type calcium channels in skeletal muscle and are expressed at high levels in peripheral tissues, including cardiac and smooth muscle (α_{1C}) and endocrine tissue (α_{1D}). Thus, these α_1 subunits are components of L-type calcium channels in both neuronal and non-neuronal cells.[7–9] In contrast, α_{1A}, α_{1B} and α_{1E} subunits display more than 70% similarity with each other in their amino acid sequences, but only about 40% similarity with α_{1C} and α_{1D} subunits, and are expressed at their highest levels in neurons.[7–9] In this article we review research from this laboratory which focuses on the biochemical properties, subcellular localisation and functional specialisation of these related neuronal α_1 subunits.

Toxin binding

High-affinity binding of toxins and drugs that specifically block the various types of calcium channel provides the principal method of identification of channel proteins. L-type calcium channels are specifically labelled by dihydropyridine calcium channel antagonists, N-type calcium channels by ω-CTx-GVIA and P-/Q-type calcium channels by ω-CTx-MVIIC.[10] This approach also provides a sensitive method for identifying the calcium channels encoded by the α_1 subunit cDNAs. We prepared antibodies against unique predicted peptide sequences in the large intracellular loop connecting domains II and III (L_{II-III}) and the —COOH termini of the α_1 subunits, the two most divergent regions of the various α_1 subunits that have been cloned to date. We then used these antibodies to immunoprecipitate rat brain α_1 polypeptides specifically radiolabelled by binding of dihydropyridines or toxin derivatives.[11–15] Comparison of the different radiolabelled ligand–channel complexes precipitated by each antibody allowed us to identify the calcium channel type containing the α_1 subunit against whose amino acid sequence the antibody was directed. A summary of results from such immunoprecipitation experiments is presented in figure 1. Antibodies directed

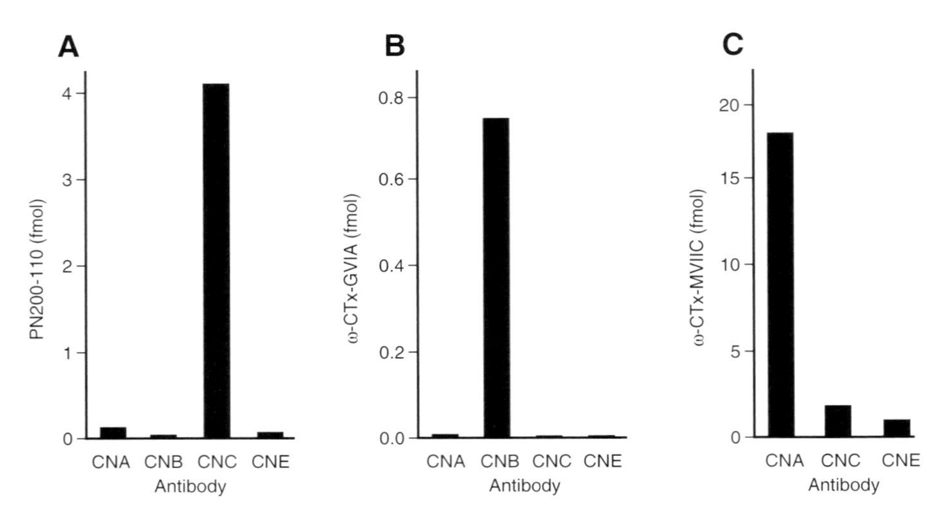

Fig. 1. Specific immunoprecipitation of partially purified calcium channel subtypes from brain membranes by site-directed antipeptide antibodies. L-type calcium channels were specifically labelled with [^{3}H]PN200-110, N-type calcium channels with [^{125}I]ω-CTx-GVIA and P-/Q-type calcium channels with [^{125}I]ω-CTx-MVIIC.[11,15,22] Antipeptide antibodies were directed against unique amino acid sequences in L_{I-II} of the various α_1 subunits. Immunoprecipitation by non-immune IgG was used as a control. CNA–CNE represent antipeptide antibodies against α_{1A}–α_{1E}, respectively.

against α_{1C} polypeptide precipitate L-type calcium channels labelled by dihydropyridines, antibodies against α_{1B} polypeptides precipitate N-type calcium channels labelled by ω-CTx-GVIA, and antibodies against α_{1A} polypeptides precipitate P-/Q-type calcium channels labelled by ω-CTx-MVIIC, whereas antibodies against α_{1E} polypeptides do not recognise any of the drug- or toxin-labelled calcium channels. This approach provided the first evidence that the α_{1B} subunit is associated with N-type calcium channels[11] and confirmed the identity of the α_1 subunits of L-type and P-/Q-type calcium channels revealed initially by cDNA expression and electrophysiological recording techniques. Calcium channels containing α_{1E} subunits are not labelled by the available drug or toxin probes,[15] in keeping with the hypothesis that they contribute to the residual (R-type) calcium current which remains when other calcium channels are blocked by a combination of dihydropyridines, ω-CTx-GVIA and ω-CTx-MVIIC. The functional properties of calcium channels containing α_{1E} subunits expressed in *Xenopus* oocytes resemble those of low-voltage-activated (LVA) calcium channels in that they show relatively rapid inactivation, slow deactivation, negative voltage-dependent activation and inactivation, and comparable permeabilities to Ba^{2+} and Ca^{2+} ions.[9]

Biochemical properties

Using this same panel of specific antibodies, we have identified the α_1 polypeptides in immunoblots and assessed their size, heterogeneity and phosphorylation by specific protein kinases, as summarised in table I. As shown for the α_1 subunits of L-type calcium channels in skeletal muscle, heart and brain,[16-19] the α_{1B} subunits of N-type calcium channels are present in brain in two principal size forms of 240 and

Table I. Biochemical properties of α_1 subunits

Subunit	Size form (kDa)[a]	Protein kinase			
		A	G	C	CaMKII
α_{1A}	220	++	–	–	ND
	190	+	+	+	ND
	160	–	–	–	ND
α_{1B}	240	++	++	+	++
	220	+	+	+	+
α_{1C}	220	++	++	+	+
	190	–	+	+	+
α_{1E}	245/255	++	+	+	+

[a] Estimated by SDS-PAGE in acrylamide gel 5%. Estimates in acrylamide gels 6% differ slightly.

Abbreviations: CaMKII = calmodulin kinase II; ND = not determined; – = not phosphorylated; +, ++ = extent of phosphorylation.

220 kDa, respectively, which differ in their —COOH termini.[20] The larger isoform is recognised by specific antibodies against the —COOH-terminal sequence and is therefore of full length. Both forms are phosphorylated by cAMP-dependent protein kinase and protein kinase C, but the full-length form is phosphorylated more effectively by Ca^{2+}/calmodulin (CaM)-dependent kinase II.[20] This suggests that these two size forms may be differentially regulated by second-messenger pathways which activate protein phosphorylation.

The α_{1E} subunits are present in two size forms with closely similar molecular masses of approximately 245 and 255 kDa, respectively, and both forms are rapidly phosphorylated by cAMP-dependent protein kinase and more weakly by protein kinase C, cGMP-dependent protein kinase and Ca^{2+}/CaM kinase II. The α_{1B}, α_{1C} and α_{1E} subunits are all phosphorylated in hippocampal slices as well as in samples of membrane proteins precipitated from brain extracts,[21] suggesting that they are substrates for multiple protein kinases in intact neurons.

α_{1A} subunits are considerably more varied in their biochemical properties than other α_1 subunits. Immunoblots of immunopurified α_{1A} subunits reveal a family of polypeptides ranging in size from 250 to 160 kDa.[22] The 250, 220 and 190 kDa polypeptides are all recognised by antibodies directed against the —NH_2- and —COOH-terminal sequences encoded by the cDNAs and therefore represent alternate splice products differing in internal amino acid sequences.[22] These different α_1 polypeptides are also differentially phosphorylated by cAMP-dependent protein kinase, cGMP-dependent protein kinase and protein kinase C.[22] In addition, α_{1A} subunits with two distinct isoforms of L_{II-III} have been cloned from rat and rabbit (designated rbA and BI, respectively).[23] Experiments with specific antibodies show that both these L_{II-III} isoforms are present in rat and rabbit brain and are associated with distinct size forms of α_{1A} subunits.[23] The large number of α_{1A} polypeptide isoforms revealed by molecular mass determination is surprising and suggests that an even larger number will be revealed by higher-resolution analysis of alternatively spliced isoforms at the level of cDNA and protein sequence.

Subcellular localisation

Immunocytochemical analysis of the localisation of different calcium channel α_1 subunits using the panel of specific antipeptide antibodies described above has yielded information on the cellular and subcellular distribution of distinct types of calcium channels. Surprisingly, most of these calcium channel types are expressed at readily detectable levels in the major classes of neurons in the cerebral cortex, hippocampus and cerebellum.[12–15] However, there are characteristic differences in the subcellular localisation of these α_1 subunits within individual neurons. L-type calcium channels recognised by a monoclonal antibody directed against their $\alpha_2\delta$ subunits are primarily localised in the cell bodies and proximal dendrites of central neurons, although these channels are also detected more distally on the dendrites.[1,24]

In keeping with this distribution, α_{1C} and α_{1D} subunits identified with specific antipeptide antibodies are also located primarily on the cell body and proximal dendrites.[14] However, they differ in their fine distribution: the α_{1D} subunit is relatively evenly distributed over the neuronal cell body and proximal dendrites and is present at higher density at the base of major dendrites, while the α_{1C} subunit is clustered in large patches measuring 1–2 μm on the cell body and dendrites,[14] as illustrated in figure 2. Immunocytochemical analysis shows that these clusters are located on the postsynaptic membrane, often coincident with postsynaptic densities of asymmetric, glutamatergic synapses.[25] The close association with glutamate receptors suggests a possible structural and functional connection between these receptors and L-type calcium

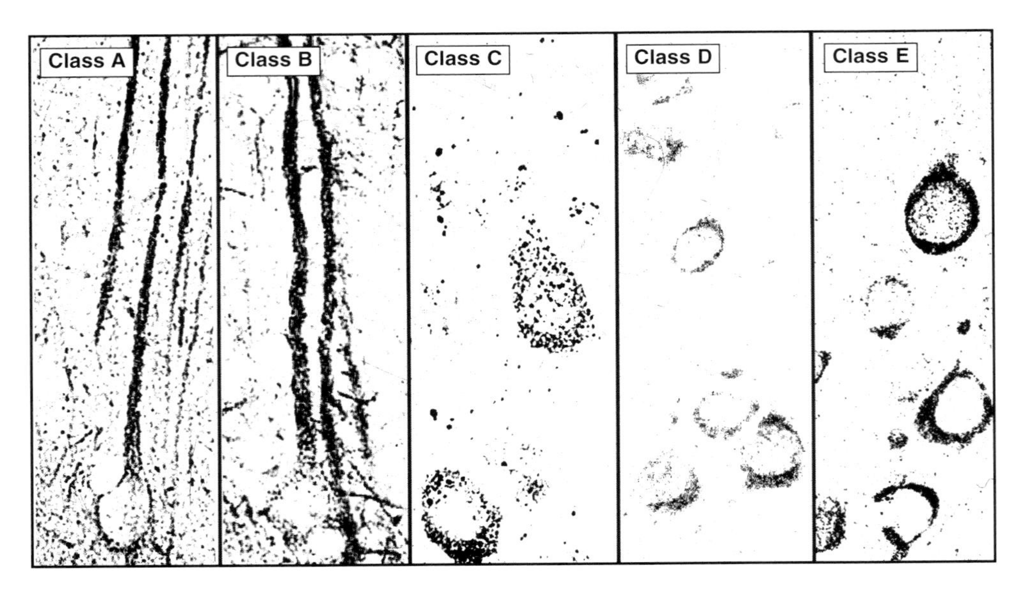

Fig. 2. Differential subcellular localisation of calcium channel subtypes in rat cortical neurons. Saggital sections of dorsal cerebral cortex were incubated with antipeptide antibodies directed against unique amino acid sequences in L_{II-III} of the calcium channel α_1 subunits, and bound antibodies were visualised using immunofluorescence techniques.[13,14]

channels containing α_{1C} subunits. Consistent with this idea, we found that activation of the *N*-methyl-D-aspartate (NMDA)-specific subtype of glutamate receptor could induce proteolytic conversion of full-length α_{1C} to truncated α_{1C} polypeptide through a pathway involving Ca^{2+} entry and activation of the Ca^{2+}-regulated protease calpain.[25]

Calcium channels containing the α_{1E} subunit are the only cloned channel type with several of the functional properties of LVA calcium channels.[9] Therefore, it is of special interest to determine their subcellular distribution. Immunocytochemical analysis using specific antipeptide antibodies reveals that these channels, in common with L-type calcium channels, are primarily located on neuronal cell bodies,[15] as illustrated for cerebral cortical neurons in figure 2. However, calcium channels containing the α_{1E} subunit are also located on the dendrites of certain neurons. Dendritic localisation is particularly striking in the cerebellar Purkinje cells, where the α_{1E} subunit is strongly localised on the fine dendritic branches and bifurcation points but not on the major dendritic trunks, as well as in the olfactory bulb, where the α_{1E} subunit is highly localised in areas of dendro-dendritic synapses between mitral and tufted cells.[15]

N-type and P-/Q-type calcium channels containing α_{1B} and α_{1A} subunits are present in high density on the terminals of central neurons as well as on cell bodies and dendrites.[12,13] Nerve-terminal localisation is revealed by light microscopic immunocytochemistry as an intense punctate staining pattern superimposed on lower-intensity general staining of the dendritic surface and as punctate staining in neuropil areas rich in axons and dendrites. This staining pattern is illustrated for cerebral cortical neurons in figure 2. Antibodies directed against α_{1A} and α_{1B} polypeptides stain the major dendrites of these neurons in an uneven pattern consisting of high-intensity puncta representing nerve terminals and lower-intensity general staining of the dendritic shafts.[12,13] Staining of dendrites is more intense than that of cell bodies, but cell-body staining is detectable above the background staining. Estimates of the fluorescent intensity of bound antibody conjugates indicate that the density of calcium channels on nerve terminals of cerebellar Purkinje cells is at least 8-fold higher than that on the surrounding dendrites,[13] and a similar ratio is observed for other neurons.

The differential localisation of these distinct calcium channel α_1 subunits is an important determinant of their cellular function. Thus, L-type calcium channels are implicated in regulation of neuronal gene expression through Ca^{2+} entry and the transcription factor CREB (cAMP response element binding protein),[26] while N- and P-/Q-type calcium channels are implicated in synaptic transmission at numerous sites within the CNS.[6,27] It appears that a primary reason for the expression of multiple calcium channel types in central neurons lies in the specialised role of the individual channel subtypes in signal transduction. Determination of the molecular features of these channel subtypes that allow them to carry out specific neuronal functions is a subject of great interest. We have focused on two aspects of the presynaptic α_{1A} and α_{1B} subunits which are important determinants of their function in synaptic transmission.

Molecular mechanism of G-protein modulation

N- and P-/Q-type calcium channels are subject to modulation by neurotransmitters acting through G-protein-coupled receptors to inhibit channel activity.[28] This modulatory pathway is thought to have an important influence on neurotransmitter release and synaptic transmission. Inhibition of calcium channel activity by neurotransmitters results from a shift in the voltage-dependence of channel activation toward more positive membrane potentials. The voltage shift can be reversed by strong depolarisation, resulting in voltage-dependent facilitation of channel activity. This inhibitory effect is usually mediated by pertussis toxin-sensitive G proteins of the G_i and G_o families acting through a membrane-delimited pathway, possibly by directly binding to calcium channels.

Since many neurotransmitters require specific G-protein α subunits within the G_o or G_i families to modulate calcium channels, it was thought that the $G\alpha$ subunits are likely to be the final regulators of calcium channel activity. To examine this point directly, we transiently expressed calcium channels containing α_{1A} subunits in the tsA-201 subclone of the HEK293 human embryonic kidney cell line and examined their regulation by endogenous and transfected G proteins.[29] In whole-cell voltage-clamp experiments with the G-protein activator GTPγS in the intracellular solution, activation of transfected calcium channels was shifted to more positive membrane potentials, and this shift could be reversed by positive prepulses resulting in voltage-dependent facilitation (fig. 3 (A)). Transfection of $G\alpha$ subunits had little effect on calcium channel function and did not reproduce the voltage shift and prepulse facilitation observed with GTPγS.[29] However, transfection of $G\beta\gamma$ subunits with the calcium channel subunits resulted in a positive shift in the voltage-dependence of activation which was reversed by depolarising prepulses (see fig. 3 (B)). Similar results were observed when $G\alpha$ and $G\beta\gamma$ subunits were expressed in sympathetic ganglion neurons to modulate endogenous N-type calcium channels.[29,30] Thus, $G\beta\gamma$ subunits are the primary mediators of calcium channel regulation by G-protein-coupled neurotransmitter receptors.

It has been proposed that a consensus sequence of QxxER is required for $G\beta\gamma$ binding and regulation of adenylyl cyclase II, inwardly rectifying potassium channels and phospholipase $C\beta$.[31] This consensus sequence is contained within the amino acid sequence of the intracellular loops connecting domains I and II (L_{I-II}) of α_{1A}, α_{1B} and α_{1E} subunits, but is absent from L_{I-II} of the α_{1C} and α_{1D} subunits of L-type calcium channels, which are not regulated by G proteins. Thus, this consensus sequence may be a component of the $G\beta\gamma$ regulatory site on calcium channels. We have tested the significance of this sequence using peptides containing the QxxER sequence and site-directed mutations of this sequence in α_{1A} subunits. Peptides containing the QxxER sequence from adenylyl cyclase II[32] or the α_{1A} subunit (see fig. 3 (C)) block the modulation of transfected calcium channels by GTPγS. In contrast, the corresponding peptide from adenylyl cyclase II in which the Q, E and R residues have been replaced by Ala has no effect.[32] This suggests that peptides containing the QxxER sequence

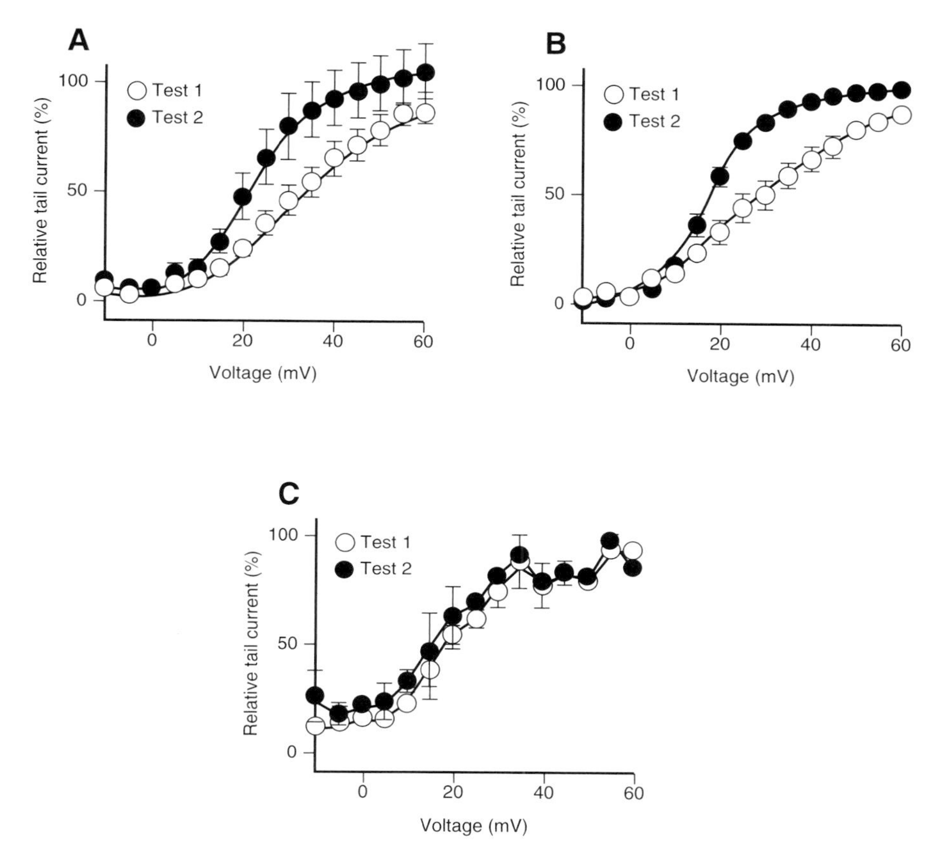

Fig. 3. Modulation of voltage-dependent activation and facilitation of calcium channels by G-protein βγ subunits and site-specific peptide inhibitors. P-/Q-type calcium channels were expressed in tsA-201 cells from cloned α_{1A}, $\alpha_2\delta$ and β_{1b} subunits and analysed by whole-cell voltage clamp.[29] The voltage-dependence of activation and the facilitation of channel activation by positive prepulses were determined by measuring barium tail currents following depolarisation to the indicated membrane potential and repolarisation to the holding potential of –60 mV. The cell was depolarised to the indicated test potential for 4 ms (test 1) and repolarised to –60 mV; after 1 s, a conditioning pulse to +100 mV was applied for 10 ms, the cell was repolarised to –60 mV for 10 ms, and a second 4 ms test pulse to the same indicated membrane potential was applied. Tail currents in test 1 and test 2 are plotted as a function of test pulse potential. Voltage-dependent facilitation is revealed when the tail currents following test 2 are larger than those following test 1. A) Recordings in the presence of GTPγS in the intracellular solution. B) Recordings in the absence of GTPγS in cells transfected with $G\beta_2\gamma_3$ subunits.[29] C) Recordings in the presence of GTPγS and peptide rbA containing a QQIER motif in the intracellular solution.

can competitively inhibit Gβγ modulation of the calcium channel. Consistent with this conclusion, mutations of single amino acid residues within this sequence in the α_{1A} subunit can either enhance or nearly completely inhibit G-protein modulation of calcium channels.[32] Thus, L_{I-II} is likely to be a principal site of modulation of calcium channels by Gβγ, and the QxxER motif is likely to be critically involved in this process. Surprisingly, mutations in this region of L_{I-II} also strongly influence the voltage-dependent inactivation of transfected calcium channels containing α_{1A} subunits.[32] The binding site for calcium channel β subunits is also located in this region, partially overlapping the QxxER sequence.[33] Evidently, this region of L_{I-II} is a site of multiple regulatory influences on calcium channel function.

Interaction with presynaptic SNARE proteins

Presynaptic calcium channels are known to mediate Ca^{2+} influx, thereby initiating neurotransmitter release and synaptic transmission. However, increasing evidence indicates that Ca^{2+} influx is highly localised, and high Ca^{2+} concentrations are required for efficient transmitter release.[34] These results raise the possibility that synaptic vesicles must be positioned near calcium channels for efficient exocytosis and neurotransmitter release. Positioning of synaptic vesicles near calcium channels might be achieved by binding of synaptic vesicles to calcium channels themselves or by binding of calcium channels to the plasma membrane SNARE proteins syntaxin and SNAP-25, which are involved in vesicle docking. Antibodies directed against syntaxin coprecipitate N-type calcium channels in solubilised extracts of brain membranes.[35,36] These results suggest a binding interaction between syntaxin and calcium channels, although the possibility of non-specific interactions of hydrophobic membrane proteins cannot be excluded.

In order to measure directly the binding of calcium channels to SNARE proteins, we expressed each of the large interdomain loops of the α_{1B} subunit as bacterial fusion proteins with hexahistidine epitope tags and measured their binding to syntaxin expressed with a GST epitope tag.[37] These experiments showed that L_{II-III} of the α_{1B} subunit could bind syntaxin, unlike the other intracellular loops and the —NH_2 and —COOH termini. Further deletion of amino acid sequences in L_{II-III} identified an 87-residue synaptic protein interaction (synprint) site that was sufficient for syntaxin binding (fig. 4).[37] This site also binds the other presynaptic SNARE protein SNAP-25, and binding of both syntaxin and SNAP-25 to the synprint site of N-type calcium channels is Ca^{2+}-dependent, with maximum affinity at Ca^{2+} concentrations of 10–30 μM and lower affinity at higher Ca^{2+} concentrations.[38] Interaction between presynaptic calcium channels and syntaxin may also have important consequences for calcium channel function. Coexpression of syntaxin with the α_{1B} subunit produces a

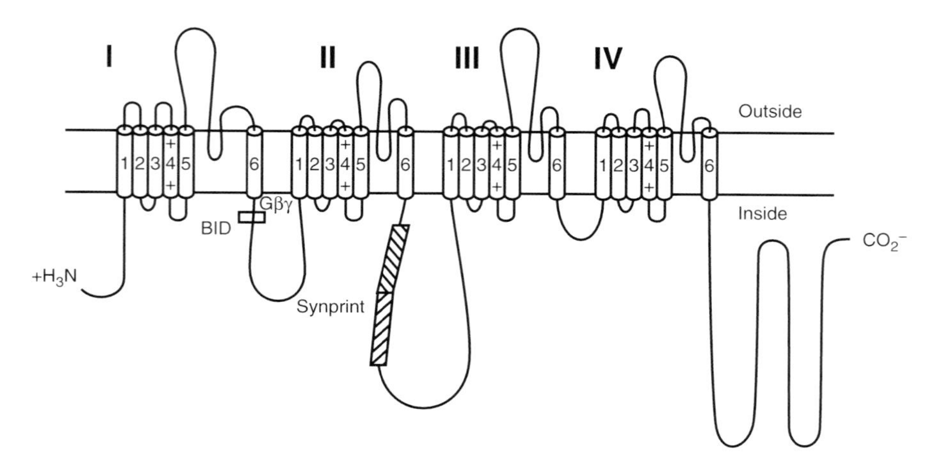

Fig. 4. Sites of interaction of the α_1 subunits of presynaptic calcium channels with G-protein βγ subunits and SNARE proteins. BID = β interaction domain.

negative shift in the voltage-dependence of calcium channel inactivation, suggesting that this interaction may affect the fraction of presynaptic calcium channels that can be activated by a depolarising stimulus.[39]

Presynaptic P-/Q-type calcium channels contain multiple isoforms of the α_{1A} subunit of varying molecular mass and amino acid sequence.[22,23] Two cloned isoforms of α_{1A} that differ in their amino acid sequences in L_{II-III} (BI[40] and rbA[41]) may differ in their interactions with syntaxin and SNAP-25. To examine this point, we prepared bacterial fusion proteins containing the BI and rbA isoforms of α_{1A} and examined their binding to syntaxin and SNAP-25.[42] The BI isoform of L_{II-III} binds to both syntaxin and SNAP-25 *in vitro*, but the binding affinity is lower than that of α_{1B}.[42] In contrast, the rbA isoform of L_{II-III} does not bind syntaxin at a detectable level *in vitro* and shows lower affinity than the BI isoform for SNAP-25.[42] These results demonstrate that the various α_1 subunits of presynaptic calcium channels have different affinities for plasma membrane SNARE proteins, and hence these isoforms may differ in their efficiency in initiating neurotransmitter release.

If the efficiency of transmitter release is dependent upon the interaction between α_1 subunits of calcium channels and presynaptic SNARE proteins, peptides containing the synprint sites of presynaptic calcium channels might be predicted to act as competitive inhibitors of this interaction and thereby inhibit transmitter release and synaptic transmission. To test this hypothesis, peptides containing the synprint site of N-type calcium channels were introduced into the presynaptic partner of pairs of cultured ganglionic neurons, and effects on synaptic transmission were determined by recording excitatory postsynaptic potentials.[43] Synprint peptides from α_{1B} subunits do indeed inhibit synaptic transmission between superior cervical ganglion neurons in cell culture, while corresponding peptides from α_1 subunits of calcium channels in skeletal muscle are without effect.[43] These results suggest that binding of presynaptic calcium channels to plasma membrane SNARE proteins is indeed necessary for efficient neurotransmitter release.

Conclusion

Our experiments on brain calcium channels reveal some elements of the basis for their functional diversity and specialisation (see fig. 4). First, various α_1 subunits are widely expressed in central neurons but are localised in different subcellular compartments where they perform specific functions. Distinct subcellular localisation allows evolution of distinct subtypes of calcium channels to fit specific functional needs. Second, multiple α_1 polypeptides are expressed by each α_1 subunit gene through a combination of alternate mRNA splicing and post-translational proteolytic processing. This latter process may be activated by neurotransmitters and therefore subject to physiological regulation. The multiple polypeptides produced by these processes are differentially phosphorylated by protein kinases, opening the possibility of differential regulation by second-messenger pathways. Third, molecular specialisation in the large, weakly conserved intracellular loops of the α_1 subunits are key determinants of their function and regulation. The synprint site in L_{II-III} of the α_{1A} and α_{1B} subunits is an important determinant of their efficiency in initiating rapid neurotransmitter release. The QxxER motif in L_{I-II} is an important determinant of the modulation of α_{1A} and α_{1B} by G-protein-coupled transduction pathways. Further investigation of the molecular specialisations that allow these calcium channels to perform their individual roles in neuronal signal transduction may lead to new avenues of approach for designing therapeutic agents for CNS disorders.

References

1. Ahlijanian MK, Westenbroek RE, Catterall WA. Subunit structure and localization of dihydropyridine-sensitive calcium channels in mammalian brain, spinal cord, and retina. Neuron 1990; 4: 819–32
2. McEnery MW, Snowman AM, Sharp AH, et al. Purified ω-conotoxin GVIA receptor of rat brain resembles a dihydropyridine-sensitive L-type calcium channel. Proc Natl Acad Sci U S A 1991; 88: 11095–9
3. Witcher DR, De Waard M, Sakamoto J, et al. Subunit identification and reconstitution of the N-type Ca^{2+} channel complex purified from brain. Science 1993; 261: 486–9
4. Leveque C, El Far O, Martin-Moutot N, et al. Purification of the N-type calcium channel associated with syntaxin and synaptotagmin: a complex implicated in synaptic vesicle exocytosis. J Biol Chem 1994; 269: 6306–12
5. Martin-Moutot N, Leveque C, Sato K, et al. Properties of omega conotoxin MVIIC receptors associated with α_{1A} calcium channel subunits in rat brain. FEBS Lett 1995; 366: 21–5
6. Tsien RW, Lipscombe D, Madison DV, et al. Multiple types of neuronal calcium channels and their selective modulation. Trends Neurosci 1988; 11: 431–8
7. Zhang J-F, Randall AD, Ellinor PT, et al. Distinctive pharmacology and kinetics of cloned neuronal Ca^{2+} channels and their possible counterparts in mammalian CNS neurons. Neuropharmacology 1993; 32: 1075–88
8. Hofmann F, Biel M, Flockerzi V. Molecular basis for Ca^{2+} channel diversity. Annu Rev Neurosci 1994; 17: 399–418
9. Stea A, Soong TW, Snutch TP. Voltage-gated calcium channels. In: North RA, editor. Ligand- and voltage-gated ion channels. Boca Raton, Fla.: CRC Press, 1995: 113–51
10. Miljanich GP, Ramachandran J. Antagonists of neuronal calcium channels: structure, function, and therapeutic implications. Annu Rev Pharmacol Toxicol 1995; 35: 707–34
11. Dubel SJ, Starr TVB, Hell J, et al. Molecular cloning of the α-1 subunit of an ω-conotoxin-sensitive calcium channel. Proc Natl Acad Sci U S A 1992; 89: 5058–62
12. Westenbroek RE, Hell JW, Warner C, et al. Biochemical properties and subcellular distribution of an N-type calcium channel α_1 subunit. Neuron 1992; 9: 1099–115
13. Westenbroek RE, Sakurai T, Elliott EM, et al. Immunochemical identification and subcellular distribution of the α_{1A} subunits of brain calcium channels. J Neurosci 1995; 15: 6403–18
14. Hell JW, Westenbroek RE, Warner C, et al. Identification and differential subcellular localization of the neuronal class C and class D L-type calcium channel α_1 subunits. J Cell Biol 1993; 123: 949–62
15. Yokoyama CT, Westenbroek RE, Hell JW, et al. Biochemical properties and subcellular distribution of the neuronal class E calcium channel α_1 subunit. J Neurosci 1995; 15: 6419–32
16. De Jongh KS, Merrick DK, Catterall WA. Subunits of purified calcium channels: a 212-kDa form of alpha 1 and partial amino acid sequence of a phosphorylation site of an independent beta subunit. Proc Natl Acad Sci U S A 1989; 86: 8585–9
17. De Jongh KS, Warner C, Colvin AA, et al. Characterization of the two size forms of the α1 subunit of skeletal muscle L-type calcium channels. Proc Natl Acad Sci U S A 1991; 88: 10778–82
18. Hell JW, Yokoyama CT, Wong ST, et al. Differential phosphorylation of two size forms of the neuronal class C L-type calcium channel α_1 subunit. J Biol Chem 1993; 268: 19451–7
19. De Jongh KS, Murphy BJ, Colvin AA, et al. Specific phosphorylation of a site in the full-length form of the α_1 subunit of the cardiac L-type calcium channel by cAMP-dependent protein kinase. Biochemistry 1996; 35: 10392–402
20. Hell JW, Appleyard SM, Yokoyama CT, et al. Differential phosphorylation of two size forms of the N-type calcium channel α_1 subunit which have different COOH-termini. J Biol Chem 1993; 269: 7390–6
21. Hell JW, Yokoyama CT, Breeze LJ, et al. Phosphorylation of presynaptic and postsynaptic calcium channels by cAMP-dependent protein kinase in hippocampal neurons. EMBO J 1995; 14: 3036–44
22. Sakurai T, Hell JW, Woppmann A, et al. Immunochemical identification and differential phosphorylation of alternatively spliced forms of the α_{1A} subunit of brain calcium channels. J Biol Chem 1995; 270: 21234–42
23. Sakurai T, Westenbroek RE, Rettig J, et al. Biochemical properties and subcellular distribution of the BI and rbA isoforms of α_{1A} subunits of brain calcium channels. J Cell Biol 1996; 134: 511–28

24. Westenbroek RE, Ahlijanian MK, Catterall WA. Clustering of L-type Ca^{2+} channels at the base of major dendrites in hippocampal pyramidal neurons. Nature 1990; 347: 281–4
25. Hell JW, Westenbroek RE, Breeze LJ, et al. N-methyl-D-aspartate receptor-induced proteolytic conversion of postsynaptic class C L-type calcium channels in hippocampal neurons. Proc Natl Acad Sci U S A 1996; 93: 3362–7
26. Deisseroth K, Bito H, Tsien RW. Signaling from synapse to nucleus: postsynaptic CREB phosphorylation during multiple forms of hippocampal synaptic plasticity. Neuron 1996; 16: 89–101
27. Dunlap K, Luebke JI, Turner TJ. Exocytotic Ca^{2+} channels in mammalian central neurons. Trends Neurosci 1995; 18: 89–98
28. Hille B. Modulation of ion-channel function by G-protein-coupled receptors. Trends Neurosci 1994; 17: 531–6
29. Herlitze S, Garcia DE, Mackie K, et al. Modulation of Ca^{2+} channels by G protein $\beta\gamma$ subunits. Nature 1996; 380: 258–2
30. Ikeda SR. Voltage-dependent modulation of N-type calcium channels by G-protein $\beta\gamma$ subunits. Nature 1996; 380: 255–8
31. Chen J, DeVivo M, Dingus J, et al. A region of adenylyl cyclase 2 critical for regulation by G protein $\beta\gamma$ subunits. Science 1995; 268: 1166–9
32. Herlitze S, Hockerman GH, Scheuer T, et al. Molecular determinants of inactivation and G protein modulation in the intracellular loop connecting domains I and II of the calcium channel α_{1A} subunit. Proc Natl Acad Sci U S A 1997; 94: 1512–16
33. Pragnell M, De Waard M, Mori Y, et al. Calcium channel β-subunit binds to a conserved motif in the I–II cytoplasmic linker of the α_1-subunit. Nature 1994; 368: 67–70
34. Augustine GJ, Neher E. Neuronal Ca^{2+} signalling takes the local route. Curr Opin Neurobiol 1992; 2: 302–7
35. Bennett MK, Calakos N, Scheller RH. Syntaxin: a synaptic protein implicated in docking of synaptic vesicles at presynaptic active zones. Science 1992; 257: 255–9
36. Yoshida A, Oho C, Omori A, et al. HPC-1 is associated with synaptotagmin and ω-conotoxin receptor. J Biol Chem 1992; 267: 24925–8
37. Sheng Z-H, Rettig J, Takahashi M, et al. Identification of a syntaxin-binding site on N-type calcium channels. Neuron 1994; 13: 1303–13
38. Sheng Z-H, Rettig J, Cook T, et al. Calcium-dependent interaction of N-type calcium channels with the synaptic core-complex. Nature 1996; 379: 451–4
39. Bezprozvanny I, Scheller RH, Tsien RW. Functional impact of syntaxin on gating of N-type and Q-type calcium channels. Nature 1995; 378: 623–6
40. Mori Y, Friedrich T, Kim M-S, et al. Primary structure and functional expression from complementary DNA of a brain calcium channel. Nature 1991; 350: 398–402
41. Starr TVB, Prystay W, Snutch TP. Primary structure of a calcium channel that is highly expressed in the rat cerebellum. Proc Natl Acad Sci U S A 1991; 88: 5621–5
42. Rettig J, Sheng Z-H, Kim DK, et al. Isoform-specific interaction of the α_{1A} subunits of brain Ca^{2+} channels with the presynaptic proteins syntaxin and SNAP-25. Proc Natl Acad Sci U S A 1996; 93: 7363–8
43. Mochida S, Sheng Z-H, Baker C, et al. Inhibition of neurotransmission by peptides containing the synaptic protein interaction site of N-type Ca^{2+} channels. Neuron 1996; 17: 781–8

Human neuronal voltage-gated calcium channels: splice variants, subunit interactions and subtypes

Michael M. Harpold, Mark E. Williams, Paul F. Brust, Ken Stauderman, Arturo Urrutia, Edwin C. Johnson, Michael Hans

SIBIA Neurosciences Inc., La Jolla, California, USA

Introduction

Ca^{2+} influx through voltage-gated calcium channels mediates an extensive array of neuronal processes, including neurotransmitter release, neuronal excitability, signal transduction via second-messenger systems and gene expression.[1,2] On the basis of their electrophysiological and pharmacological properties, voltage-gated calcium channels have been classified as L, N, P, Q and R type, which are also designated as high-voltage-activated (HVA) calcium channels (half-maximal activation voltage ≥0 mV), and T type, designated as low-voltage-activated (LVA) calcium channels (half-maximal activation voltage less than or equal to –30 mV).[1,3,4] Consistent with this diversity of calcium channel types identified in neurons, molecular cloning has revealed the existence of multiple genes encoding the subunits of neuronal voltage-gated calcium channels. These include 5 genes designated α_{1A}, α_{1B}, α_{1C}, α_{1D} and α_{1E} that encode multiple splice variants of the pore-forming α_1 subunit, a single gene that encodes multiple splice variants of the $\alpha_2\delta$ subunit, and 4 genes designated β_1, β_2, β_3 and β_4 that encode a number of splice variants of the β subunit.[5,6]

The expression of the cloned calcium channel subunit cDNAs, together with biophysical and pharmacological characterisation, has contributed to the correlation of calcium channel molecular subtypes with the functionally defined types expressed in neurons. L-type calcium channels are sensitive to dihydropyridine agonists and antagonists and correspond to the functional properties of α_{1C}- and α_{1D}-containing calcium channels.[7,8] N-type calcium channels are insensitive to dihydropyridines but are completely blocked by ω-CTx-GVIA and correspond to the functional properties of α_{1B}-containing calcium channels.[9] P-type calcium channels are sensitive to low, nanomolar concentrations of ω-Aga-IVA, whereas Q-type channels are blocked by different concentrations of ω-Aga-IVA as well as ω-CTx-MVIIC; both types of channel display characteristics similar, although not identical, to the functional properties of α_{1A}-containing calcium channels.[10–12]

The molecular correlates of R- and T-type calcium channels have not yet been elucidated, although both types share certain properties with α_{1E}-containing calcium channels.[13–17] Whereas some properties, such as deactivation rate and the single-channel conductance exhibited by α_{1E}-containing calcium channels, are characteristic of HVA channels, other properties, including relative Ba^{2+} or Ca^{2+} conductance and sensitivity to Ni^{2+} block, are more characteristic of LVA T-type calcium channels. On the basis of the potential molecular diversity of calcium channel subtypes and the limited studies conducted to date with α_{1E}-containing calcium channels, further investigation of the functional consequences of different combinations of α_{1E}, $\alpha_2\delta$ and β and their splice variants is warranted. Such studies could provide additional insight into the role of specific subunits and their interactions in forming the multiple calcium channel subtypes expressed in the nervous system, including those classified as LVA (or mid-voltage-activated) T-type channels.

We describe here an initial characterisation of the functional properties of calcium channels containing different splice variants of human α_{1E} (α_{1E-1} and α_{1E-3}[15]) and β_1 (β_{1b} and β_{1c}[6]) subunits. These studies demonstrate that each of the calcium channels differs significantly in its inactivation properties and provide new insights into the functional roles and structural interactions of the α_1, $\alpha_2\delta$ and β subunits in different calcium channel subtypes. We also provide preliminary biochemical evidence that an $\alpha_2\delta$ subunit may be a molecular component of LVA T-type calcium channels in human cells.

Materials and methods

The cDNAs encoding the human α_{1E-1} and α_{1E-3}, $\alpha_{2B}\delta$, β_{1b} and β_{1c} calcium channel subunits, their incorporation into mammalian expression vectors and their use for transient transfection and expression in HEK293 cells were as described previously.[6,15] The functional expression of recombinant calcium channels in transfected HEK293 cells was evaluated using the whole-cell patch-clamp technique, essentially as described previously.[15]

An $\alpha_2\delta$-GST fusion protein containing human $\alpha_{2B}\delta$ amino acids 742–859 was generated and used to prepare a monoclonal antibody, designated Ab50-51-72 (unpublished observations, kindly provided by W. Smith, Lilly Research Centre, Windlesham, Surrey, UK). Total membrane protein was isolated as described previously.[18] Deglycosylation of membrane protein by *N*-glycosidase-F (Boehringer Mannheim, Indianapolis, Indiana, USA) was performed according to the manufacturer's instructions. Protein was separated by SDS-PAGE and transferred to nitrocellulose filters (Hybond, Amersham, UK). Blots were blocked for 1–2 hours at room temperature in TBS-T (TRIS 20 mM, NaCl 137 mM, KCl 2.7 mM, pH 7.4, Tween 20 0.1%) with dried milk 5%, followed by incubation with antibody in TBS-T for 1 hour at room temperature. The blots were washed with TBS-T (5 changes), followed by incubation with a 1:2000 dilution of horseradish peroxidase-conjugated sheep anti-mouse Ig (Amersham, UK) in TBS-T for 1 hour. Filters were subsequently washed with TBS-T (8 changes) and developed with the ECL system (Amersham, UK).

Results

α_{1E} and β_1 splice variants produce distinct voltage-gated calcium channels

Multiple cDNAs that encode various splice variants of the mammalian α_{1E} calcium channel subunit have been isolated and described.[13,15,16] We previously characterised the structure of two human α_{1E} subunit splice variants, designated α_{1E-1} and α_{1E-3}.[15]

Relative to the human α_{1E-1} isoform, the human α_{1E-3} splice variant contains a 19-amino acid insert (R^{748}–L^{766}) located near the beginning of the cytoplasmic linker between domains II and III (fig. 1). It is possible that these 19 amino acids arose evolutionarily as a duplication, since they form a conserved repeat with 73.7% homology to the adjacent 19 amino acids. Within this repeat is a single consensus casein kinase II phosphorylation site, S^{757}, lacking in the α_{1E-1} isoform.[15]

To determine whether the relatively modest structural differences between these two α_{1E} subunit isoforms could be responsible for functionally different calcium channels, transient coexpression of the human α_{1E-1} or α_{1E-3} subunits with the human neuronal $\alpha_{2B}\delta$ and β_{1b} subunits in HEK293 was evaluated. Both the $\alpha_{1E-1}\alpha_{2B}\delta\beta_{1b}$ and $\alpha_{1E-3}\alpha_{2B}\delta\beta_{1b}$ calcium channels produced robust voltage-activated barium currents and had similar biophysical properties. The current–voltage relationship for the $\alpha_{1E-1}\alpha_{2B}\delta\beta_{1b}$ and $\alpha_{1E-3}\alpha_{2B}\delta\beta_{1b}$ calcium channels were virtually identical, with maximal inward current between 0 and 10 mV (data not shown).[15] In addition, the voltage-dependence of activation, steady-state inactivation, voltage-dependence for the kinetics of activation and kinetics of deactivation were similar for both channels (data not shown).

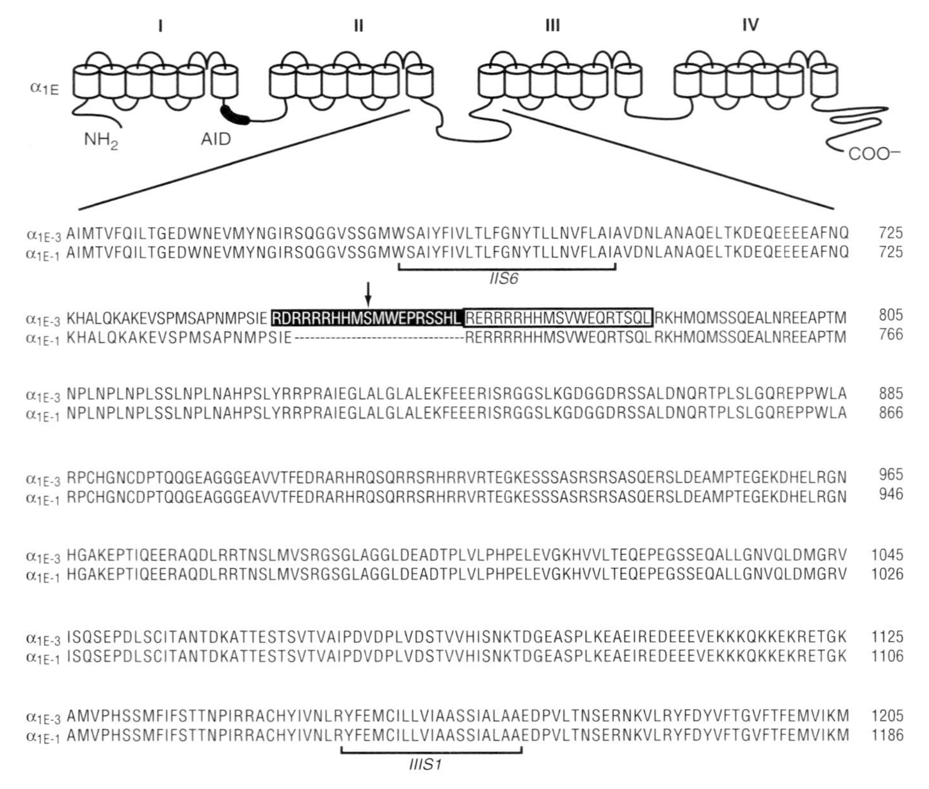

Fig. 1. Human $\alpha_{1E-1}\alpha_{1E-3}$ splice variants. Amino acid sequence of the human α_{1E-1} and α_{1E-3} isoforms in the IIS6 to IIIS1 cytoplasmic loop. An insertion in the α_{1E-3} sequence is shown as white letters on a black background. An indirect repeat of the insert is boxed adjacent to the insert. A potential casein kinase II phosphorylation site within the α_{1E-3}-specific insert is denoted by an arrow. AID = α interaction domain.

In contrast, the voltage-dependent inactivation exhibited by the $\alpha_{1E-1}\alpha_{2B}\delta\beta_{1b}$ and $\alpha_{1E-3}\alpha_{2B}\delta\beta_{1b}$ calcium channels differed significantly. The rate of inactivation was considerably faster for the α_{1E-1}-containing calcium channels relative to those containing the α_{1E-3} subunit, and both calcium channels inactivated with two components (fig. 2 (A)). The α_{1E-1}-containing calcium channels inactivated more quickly mainly because the fast component was more rapid. The time constant of the fast component (τ_1) was approximately two times greater for the α_{1E-3}-containing calcium channels than for the α_{1E-1}-containing channels ($\tau_1 = 71.8 \pm 17.5$ ms *vs* 38.8 ± 13.1 ms at +10 mV; $p<0.005$, Student's t-test for unpaired samples), while the slow component (τ_2) was quite similar for both channels (~400 ms) (see fig. 2 (C & D)). For both calcium channels, the major fraction of the inactivating current was associated with the fast-inactivating component (τ_1), but it was significantly larger for the α_{1E-1}-containing calcium channels ($\alpha_{1E-1}\alpha_{2B}\delta\beta_{1b}$: $83.1 \pm 6.4\%$; $\alpha_{1E-3}\alpha_{2B}\delta\beta_{1b}$: $65.1 \pm 8.7\%$; $p<0.01$) (see fig. 2 (B)).

These results demonstrate that the $\alpha_{1E-1}\alpha_{2B}\delta\beta_{1b}$ and $\alpha_{1E-3}\alpha_{2B}\delta\beta_{1b}$ calcium channels exhibit quite similar biophysical properties except for significant differences in

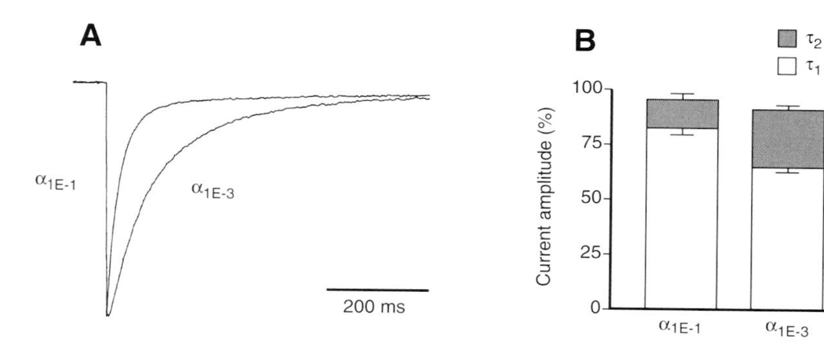

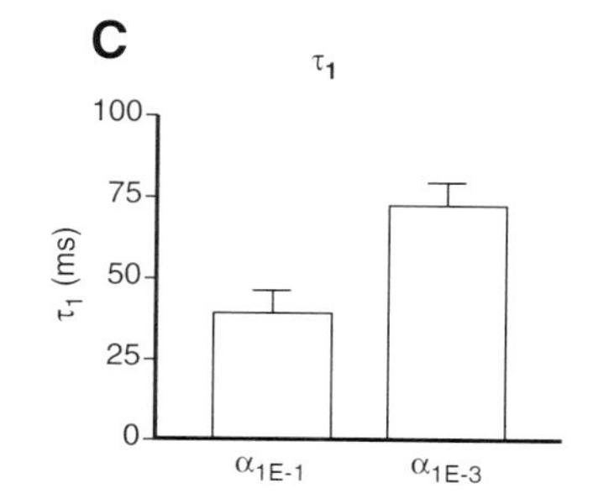

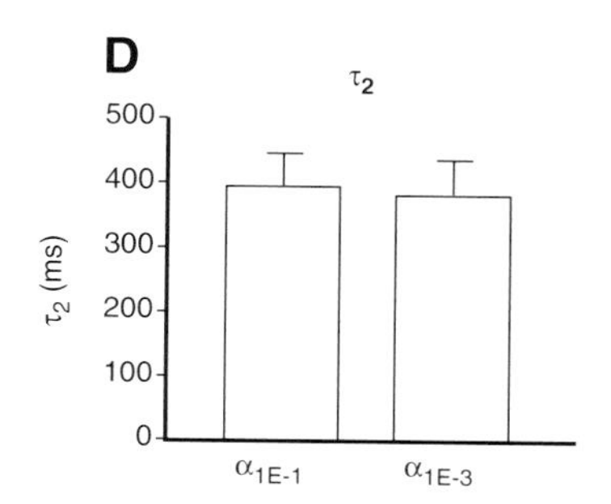

Fig. 2. α_{1E-1}- and α_{1E-3}-containing calcium channels have different inactivation kinetics when coexpressed with $\alpha_{2B}\delta$ and β_{1b} subunits. A) Inactivation kinetics of normalised barium currents from α_{1E-1}- or α_{1E-3}-containing calcium channels elicited by step depolarisations to +10 mV. The inactivation kinetics were best fitted to a biexponential function of the form $I = A_0 + A_1 \exp(-t/\tau_1) + A_2 \exp(-t/\tau_2)$. B) The fraction of the inactivation current (A_1 and A_2) associated with the fast (τ_1) and slow (τ_2) inactivation time constants. Holding potential −90 mV. C & D) Comparison of fast (τ_1) and slow (τ_2) inactivation time constant values.

inactivation kinetics. Since the only structural difference between these two calcium channels resides in the α_{1E} subunits, the results suggest that the functional differences between the channels are related to different intrinsic properties of the pore-forming α_{1E} subunits themselves. However, the functional differences may also be influenced by differences in the structural interactions of the α_{1E-1} and α_{1E-3} subunits with either, or both, of the $\alpha_{2B}\delta$ or β_{1b} subunits. To address these issues, the inactivation kinetics of the α_{1E-1} and α_{1E-3} subunits expressed alone or together with the $\alpha_{2B}\delta$ and/or β_{1b} subunits were evaluated.

Expression of the α_{1E-1} or α_{1E-3} subunits alone in HEK293 cells resulted in functional calcium channels exhibiting similar current–voltage properties (data not shown) and, surprisingly, almost identical inactivation kinetics (τ_{INACT} ~30 ms) (fig. 3 (A)). Interestingly, coexpression of the $\alpha_{2B}\delta$ subunit with either the α_{1E-1} or α_{1E-3} subunit

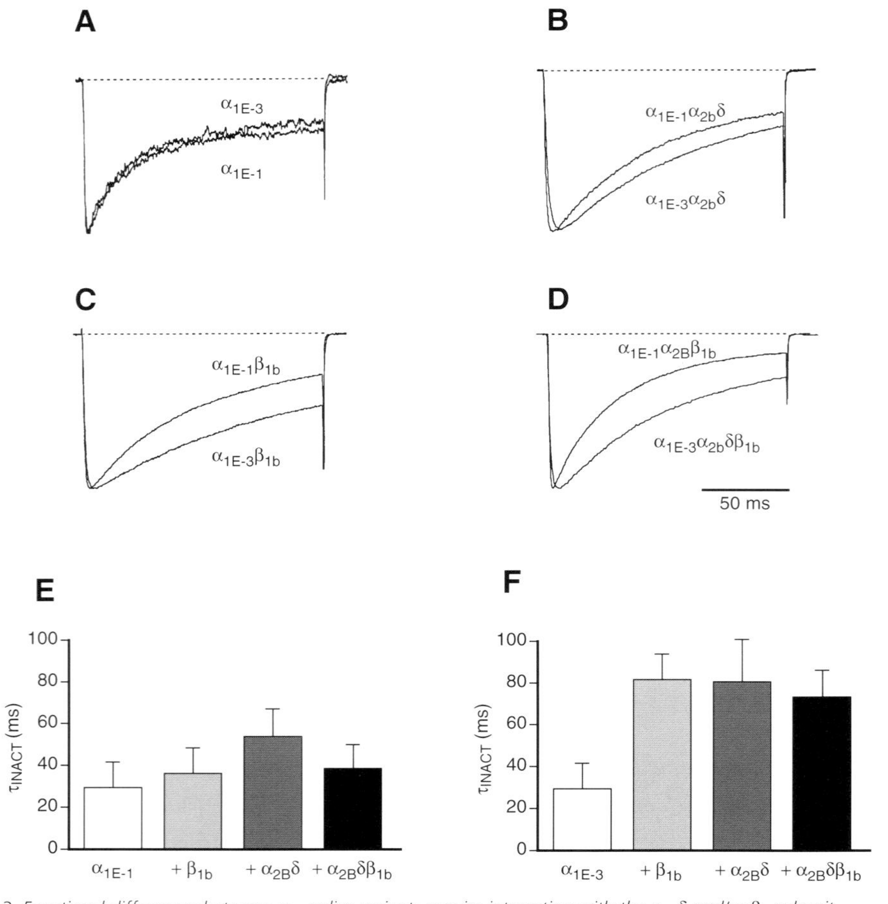

Fig. 3. Functional differences between α_{1E} splice variants require interaction with the $\alpha_{2B}\delta$ and/or β_1 subunit. A–D) Inactivation kinetics of normalised barium currents from calcium channels with the subunit compositions indicated. Currents were elicited by 150 ms step depolarisation to +10 mV. Inactivation kinetics during shorter depolarisations (150 ms) were best fitted to a monoexponential function. E & F) Comparison of inactivation time constants (τ_{INACT}) for calcium channels consisting of the α_{1E-1} or α_{1E-3} subunits, either alone or in combination with the auxiliary subunit(s) $\alpha_{2B}\delta$ and/or β_{1b}.

induced a different extent of slowing in the inactivation kinetics in both channels (see fig. 3 (B)). The time constant for inactivation ($\tau_{INACT,\ 10\ mV}$) was increased by a factor of 1.81 ± 0.4 for $\alpha_{1E\text{-}1}\alpha_{2B}\delta$ and a factor of 2.52 ± 0.8 for $\alpha_{1E\text{-}3}\alpha_{2B}\delta$, compared with $\alpha_{1E\text{-}1}$ and $\alpha_{1E\text{-}3}$, respectively (see fig. 3 (E & F)).

Similar to the results obtained with the $\alpha_{2B}\delta$ subunit, coexpression of the β_{1b} subunit with $\alpha_{1E\text{-}3}$ induced a significant slowing in the inactivation kinetics of the resulting calcium channels compared with those containing the $\alpha_{1E\text{-}3}$ subunit only. However, in contrast to the results with the $\alpha_{2B}\delta$ subunit, coexpression of the β_{1b} subunit had little effect on the inactivation kinetics of $\alpha_{1E\text{-}1}$-containing calcium channels (see fig. 3 (C)). τ_{INACT} was increased by a factor of 2.52 ± 0.8 for $\alpha_{1E\text{-}3}\beta_{1b}$ compared with $\alpha_{1E\text{-}3}$ alone, but there was no significant difference for $\alpha_{1E\text{-}1}\beta_{1b}$ relative to $\alpha_{1E\text{-}1}$ alone (see fig. 3 (E & F)). The differences in τ_{INACT} for the calcium channels comprised of each of the subunit combinations were observed at all membrane potentials tested (data not shown). These results suggest that the observed differences in inactivation kinetics reflect differential interaction of the $\alpha_{2B}\delta$ and β_{1b} subunits with the two α_{1E} subunit splice variants.

It is well established that calcium channel β subunits can influence the functional properties of the channels, including inactivation kinetics (e.g. DeWaard and Campbell[19]). Furthermore, while numerous examples of β subunit splice variants have been described,[5] little information is available on how β subunit splice variants within a single gene class affect the function of calcium channel subtypes. We have previously reported multiple splice variants for the β_1 subunit, two of which (β_{1b} and β_{1c}) are expressed in the human nervous system.[6] The human β_{1b} and β_{1c} subunit isoforms differ only at their carboxyl terminals, with the β_{1b} isoform containing an additional 118 amino acids (fig. 4).

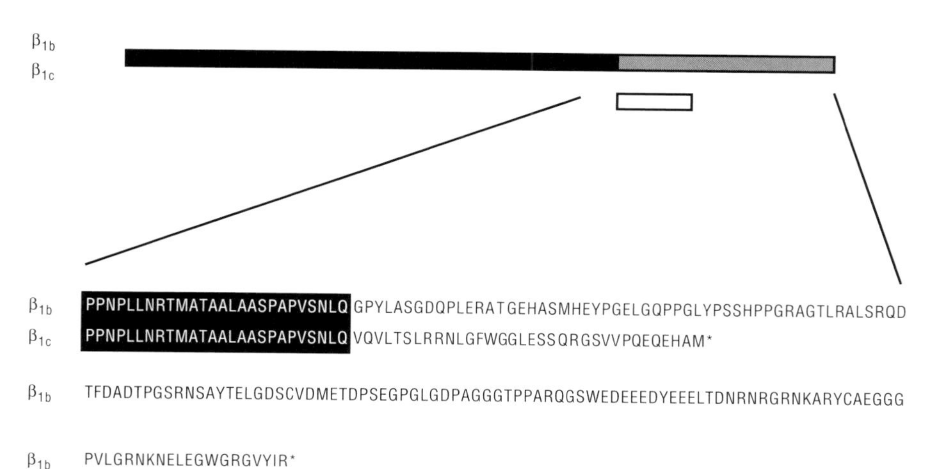

Fig. 4. Human neuronal β_1 splice variants. Sequence of the carboxyl terminal of the β_{1b} and β_{1c} isoforms is shown. Sequence common to both isoforms is shown as white letters on a black background, whereas differences are shown as black letters.

To determine whether the structural differences between the human β_{1b} and β_{1c} subunit splice variants also altered the functional properties of α_{1E}-containing calcium channels, a series of transient coexpression studies were performed. The β_{1b} or β_{1c} subunits were coexpressed with the α_{1E-3} and $\alpha_{2B}\delta$ subunits in HEK293 cells, and both produced calcium channels with substantial voltage-activated barium currents with significant differences in their inactivation kinetics (fig. 5 (A)). The inactivation kinetics of the $\alpha_{1E-3}\alpha_{2B}\delta\beta_{1c}$ calcium channels were approximately 1.5 times faster than those of the $\alpha_{1E-3}\alpha_{2B}\delta\beta_{1b}$ calcium channels. Both channel types inactivated with two components, and again the more rapid inactivation of the $\alpha_{1E-3}\alpha_{2B}\delta\beta_{1c}$ calcium channels was primarily associated with the fast-inactivating component (τ_1), although there was also a slight decrease in the slowly inactivating component (τ_2) (see fig. 5 (B & C)). The results also demonstrate, however, that the inactivation kinetics of the $\alpha_{1E-3}\alpha_{2B}\delta\beta_{1c}$ calcium channels are still slower than those observed for the $\alpha_{1E-1}\alpha_{2B}\delta\beta_{1b}$ calcium channels.

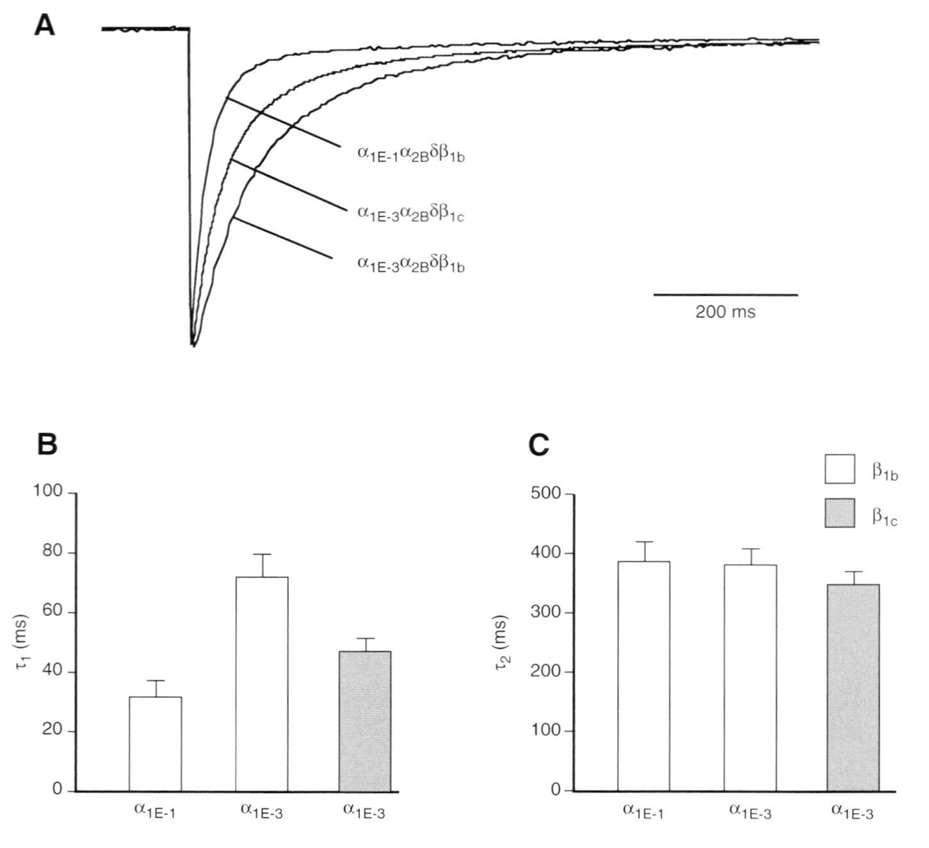

Fig. 5. Splice variants of both α_{1E} and β_1 can influence inactivation kinetics. A) Inactivation kinetics of normalised barium currents from calcium channels (with the subunit combinations indicated) elicited by step depolarisations to +10 mV. Faster calcium channel inactivation kinetics are observed with the α_{1E-1} or β_{1c} subunits compared with α_{1E-3} or β_{1b}, respectively. B & C) The faster inactivation kinetics of either α_{1E-1} or β_{1c} are associated with a decrease in the fast-inactivating component (τ_1) only. τ_2 = slow inactivation time constant.

T-type calcium channels may contain an $\alpha_2\delta$ subunit

Finally, to determine whether any of the known voltage-gated calcium channel subunits are components of LVA T-type calcium channels, we have started using an alternative biochemical approach to elucidate the molecular structure of human T-type calcium channels. Previous studies have shown that the human medullary thyroid carcinoma (TT) cell line expresses only T-type calcium channels.[20–22] Furthermore, since molecular studies to date indicate that voltage-gated calcium channels are multimeric complexes, which include an isoform of the $\alpha_2\delta$ subunit,[23] we investigated the possible expression of an $\alpha_2\delta$ subunit in human TT cells. As shown in figure 6, monoclonal antibody Ab 50-51-72, specific for the human $\alpha_2\delta$ subunit, recognises a protein expressed in TT cell membranes with characteristics virtually indistinguishable from human $\alpha_2\delta$ protein. Under reducing conditions, α_2 (with its apparent molecular weight of ~150 kDa) is separated from the δ subunit.[24] In addition, complete deglycosylation of the α_2 subunit with *N*-glucosidase-F[23] results in

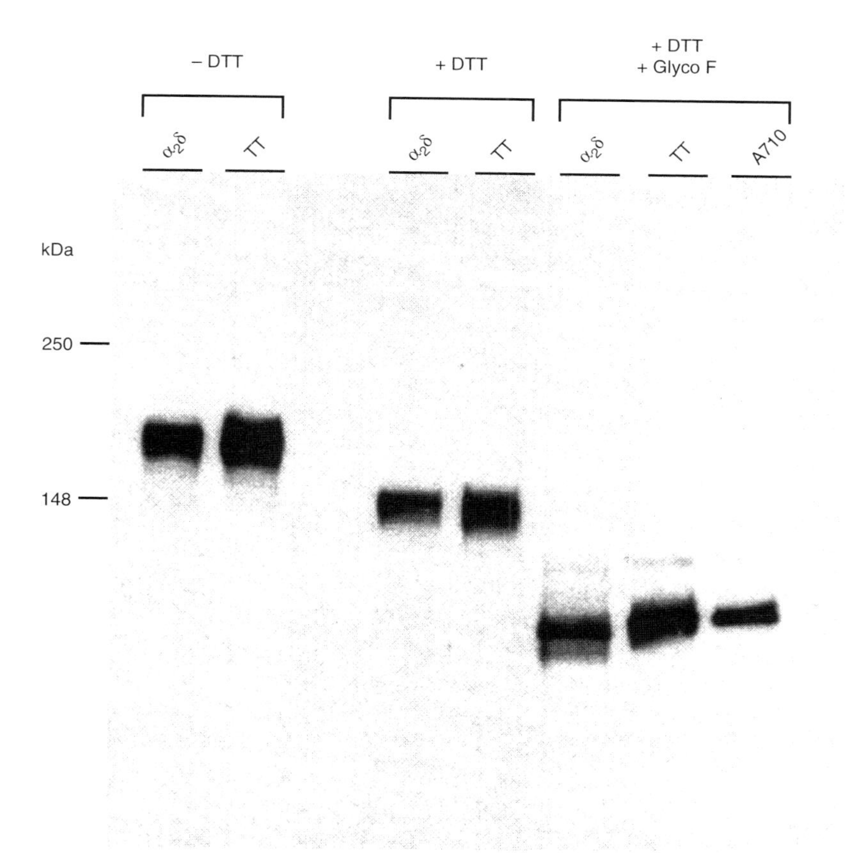

Fig. 6. $\alpha_2\delta$ expression in the human medullary thyroid carcinoma (TT) cell line. Total membrane protein isolation, deglycosylation with N*-glycosidase-F and immunoblotting were performed as described in materials and methods. Protein was separated on a 6% gel in the presence or absence of the reducing agent DTT (dithiothreitol): $\alpha_2\delta$ subunit was detected using monoclonal antibody Ab 50-51-72. The $\alpha_2\delta$ lane contains an authentic $\alpha_2\delta$ subunit expressed in HEK293 cells. The A710 lane represents the deglycosylated $\alpha_2\delta$ subunit expressed in an $\alpha_{1B-1}\alpha_{2B}\delta\beta_{3a}$ stable cell line. The mobility shift in the presence of DTT represents the loss of the δ fragment.*

a further shift in the molecular weight from ~150 kDa to ~105 kDa. These preliminary results indicate that TT cells express an $\alpha_2\delta$ subunit protein (see fig. 6) and that this subunit may be a structural component of human LVA T-type calcium channels.

Discussion

An initial characterisation of the functional properties of calcium channels containing different splice variants of human α_{1E} and β_1 subunits is described here. To date, little information has been available to directly compare the functional properties of voltage-gated calcium channels containing different splice variant isoforms of subunits within the same gene class. This study was focused on splice variants of the α_{1E} subunit partly because previous studies of α_{1E}-containing calcium channels revealed that these channels share some properties with other HVA calcium channels and with LVA T-type calcium channels.[13–17] While this study does not identify any additional characteristics held in common by $\alpha_{1E\text{-}1}\alpha_{2B}\delta\beta_{1b}$, $\alpha_{1E\text{-}3}\alpha_{2B}\delta\beta_{1b}$ and $\alpha_{1E\text{-}3}\alpha_{2B}\delta\beta_{1c}$ human calcium channels and LVA T-type calcium channels, it does provide new insights into the functional roles and structural interactions of α_1, $\alpha_2\delta$ and β subunits in the formation of different calcium channel subtypes.

The characterisation of the properties of the $\alpha_{1E\text{-}1}\alpha_{2B}\delta\beta_{1b}$ and $\alpha_{1E\text{-}3}\alpha_{2B}\delta\beta_{1b}$ calcium channels revealed significant differences in the inactivation kinetics. Since the only structural difference between these two calcium channels is found in the additional amino acids near the beginning of the cytoplasmic linker between domains II and III, it seemed most likely that the functional differences between the two calcium channel types are intrinsic properties of the specific α_{1E} subunit splice variant. However, expression of the $\alpha_{1E\text{-}1}$ or $\alpha_{1E\text{-}3}$ subunits alone produced calcium channels with almost identical inactivation kinetics. Previous studies have shown that the coexpression of β subunits can influence the voltage-dependence, inactivation kinetics and current magnitude of calcium channels (see, for example, DeWaard and Campbell[19]). It has also been shown that a 30-amino acid N-terminal sequence of β subunits (designated 'β interaction domain'; BID) binds to an 18-amino acid sequence (designated 'α interaction domain'; AID) present in the cytoplasmic linker between domains I and II of α_1 subunits.[25,26] Interestingly, the coexpression of the $\alpha_{1E\text{-}3}$ and β_{1b} subunits induced a significant slowing of inactivation kinetics relative to those in channels containing the $\alpha_{1E\text{-}3}$ subunit alone, whereas the β_{1b} subunit had little effect on the inactivation kinetics of $\alpha_{1E\text{-}1}$-containing calcium channels. Furthermore, the coexpression of the β_{1c} subunit splice variant with the $\alpha_{1E\text{-}3}\alpha_{2B}\delta$ subunits produced calcium channels with significantly more rapid inactivation kinetics than those comprising $\alpha_{1E\text{-}3}\alpha_{2B}\delta\beta_{1b}$. The only structural differences between these two $\alpha_{1E\text{-}3}$-containing calcium channels are found in the C-terminal regions of the β_{1b} and β_{1c} subunits. All these results considered together suggest that additional structural interactions may occur between the C terminals of β subunits and sequences near the beginning of the cytoplasmic linker between domains II and III of the α_{1E} subunit, and that these play a role in calcium channel inactivation kinetics.

The most surprising finding was that the coexpression of the $\alpha_{2B}\delta$ subunit with either the α_{1E-1} or α_{1E-3} subunits had dramatic effects on the inactivation kinetics of the resulting calcium channels. Although the stimulation of current amplitude by the $\alpha_2\delta$ subunit[6,9,10] and increased binding affinity of calcium channels for ligands such as ω-CTx-GVIA[6] have been shown previously, this is the first indication that the $\alpha_2\delta$ subunit can influence the kinetic properties of calcium channels. While the earlier studies suggested that $\alpha_2\delta$ subunit coassembly may conformationally alter calcium channel structure,[6] a recent study has demonstrated that the transmembrane domain is necessary for subunit interaction and that the extracellular glycosylated domain plays a role in the enhancement of current amplitude.[23] However, that study was unable to identify the sites of interaction for the $\alpha_2\delta$ subunit transmembrane domain and the α_1 subunit.[23] The results reported here describing the functional effects of the coexpression of $\alpha_{2B}\delta$ with α_{1E-1} or α_{1E-3} suggest there may be structural interactions between the $\alpha_{2B}\delta$ transmembrane domain and the IIS6 and/or IIIS1 transmembrane domains of α_{1E}, and that these interactions influence calcium channel inactivation kinetics.

As an alternative approach to determining the molecular structure of LVA T-type calcium channels, we also performed preliminary biochemical studies with the human medullary thyroid carcinoma TT cell line. This cell line has previously been shown to express only T-type calcium channels.[20–22] The results presented here indicate that an $\alpha_2\delta$ protein is expressed in TT cell membranes and provide the first evidence that human LVA T-type calcium channels may contain an $\alpha_2\delta$ subunit. Further studies, including immunoprecipitation experiments with antibodies specific for the $\alpha_2\delta$ subunit, will be necessary to establish conclusively that the $\alpha_2\delta$ subunit is a component of T-type calcium channels and may be useful in elucidating the nature of other subunits contained in LVA T-type calcium channels.

In conclusion, the expression of cloned cDNAs encoding calcium channel subunits, in conjunction with their biophysical and pharmacological characterisation, has contributed significantly to the correlation of defined molecular subtypes with previously identified functional calcium channel subtypes expressed in the nervous system and other tissues. However, the molecular nature of certain functionally identified calcium channels, including the LVA T-type calcium channels, remains to be elucidated. To date, multiple genes and splice variants that encode the three primary subunits of voltage-gated calcium channels have been identified, and it is probable that others remain to be identified. The molecular and functional diversity that can result from the combinatorial association of these structurally distinct α_1, $\alpha_2\delta$ and β subunits may provide a basis for additional correlations of molecular subtypes with previously identified native calcium channel activities. Furthermore, since this molecular diversity greatly exceeds the number of known functional voltage-gated calcium channel subtypes, coexpression studies with different combinations of recombinant α_1, $\alpha_2\delta$ and β subunits allows identification of new functional properties that may lead to the discovery of novel voltage-gated calcium channel subtypes expressed in the nervous system.

References

1. Miller RJ. Voltage-sensitive Ca^{2+} channels. J Biol Chem 1992; 267: 1403–6
2. Hille B. Ionic channels of excitable membranes. Sunderland, Mass.: Sinauer Associates, 1992
3. Miller RJ. A tale of two toxins. New peptide toxins from spiders and molluscs hold the key to understanding calcium channel diversity. Curr Biol 1993; 3: 481–3
4. Huguenard JR. Low-threshold calcium currents in central nervous system neurons. Annu Rev Physiol 1996; 58: 329–48
5. Birnbaumer L, Campbell KP, Catterall WA, et al. The naming of voltage-gated channels. Neuron 1994; 13: 505–6
6. Brust PF, Simerson S, McCue AF, et al. Human neuronal voltage-dependent calcium channels: studies on subunit structure and role in channel assembly. Neuropharmacology 1993; 32: 1089–102
7. Williams ME, Feldman DH, McCue AF, et al. Structure and functional expression of α_1, α_2, and β subunits of a novel human neuronal calcium channel subtype. Neuron 1992; 8: 71–84
8. Tomlinson JW, Stea A, Bourinet E, et al. Functional properties of a neuronal class C L-type calcium channel. Neuropharmacology 1993; 32: 1117–26
9. Williams ME, Brust PF, Feldman DH, et al. Structure and functional expression of an ω-conotoxin-sensitive human N-type calcium channel. Science 1992; 257: 389–95
10. Mori Y, Friedrich T, Kim MS, et al. Primary structure and functional expression from complementary DNA of a brain calcium channel. Nature 1991; 350: 398–402
11. Sather WA, Tanabe T, Zhang JF, et al. Distinctive biophysical and pharmacological properties of class A (BI) calcium channel α_1 subunits. Neuron 1993; 11: 291–303
12. Stea A, Tomlinson WJ, Soong TW, et al. Localization and functional properties of a rat brain α_{1A} calcium channel reflect similarities to neuronal Q- and P-type channels. Proc Natl Acad Sci U S A 1994; 91: 10576–80
13. Soong TW, Stea A, Hodson CD, et al. Structure and functional expression of a member of the low voltage-activated calcium channel family. Science 1993; 260: 1133–6
14. Ellinor PT, Zhang JF, Randall AD, et al. Functional expression of a rapidly inactivating neuronal calcium channel. Nature 1993; 363: 455–8
15. Williams ME, Marubio LM, Deal CR, et al. Structure and functional characterization of neuronal α_{1E} calcium channel subtypes. J Biol Chem 1994; 269: 22347–57
16. Schneider T, Wei X, Olcese R, et al. Molecular analysis and functional expression of the human type E neuronal Ca^{2+} channel α_1 subunit. Receptors Channels 1994; 2: 255–70
17. Bourinet E, Zamponi GW, Stea A, et al. The α_{1E} calcium channel exhibits permeation properties similar to low-voltage-activated calcium channels. J Neurosci 1996; 16: 4983–93
18. Perez-Reyes E, Kim HS, Lacerda AE, et al. Induction of calcium currents by the expression of the α_1-subunit of the dihydropyridine receptor from skeletal muscle. Nature 1989; 340: 233–6
19. De Waard M, Campbell KP. Subunit regulation of the neuronal α_{1A} Ca^{2+} channel expressed in *Xenopus* oocytes. J Physiol (Lond) 1995; 485: 619–34
20. Biagi BA, Mlinar B, Enyeart JJ. Membrane currents in a calcitonin-secreting human C cell line. Am J Physiol 1992; 263: C986–94
21. Mlinar B, Enyeart JJ, et al. Block of current through T-type calcium channels by trivalent metal cations and nickel in neural rat and human cells. J Physiol (Lond) 1993; 469: 639–52
22. Mehrke G, Zong XG, Flockerzi V, et al. The Ca^{++}-channel blocker Ro 40-5967 blocks differently T-type and L-type Ca^{++} channels. J Pharmacol Exp Ther 1994; 271: 1483–8
23. Gurnett CA, De Waard M, Campbell KP. Dual function of the voltage-dependent Ca^{2+} channel $\alpha_2\delta$ subunit in current stimulation and subunit interaction. Neuron 1996; 16: 431–40
24. Jay SD, Sharp AH, Kahl SD, et al. Structural characterization of the dihydropyridine-sensitive calcium channel α_2-subunit and the associated δ peptides. J Biol Chem 1991; 266: 3287–93
25. Pragnell M, De Waard M, Mori Y, et al. Calcium channel β-subunit binds to a conserved motif in the I–II cytoplasmic linker of the α_1-subunit. Nature 1994; 368: 67–70
26. De Waard M, Pragnell M, Campbell KP. Ca^{2+} channel regulation by a conserved β subunit domain. Neuron 1994; 13: 495–503

Structural determinants of calcium channel β subunit function

Hongyan Liu, Kevin P. Campbell

Howard Hughes Medical Institute, Department of Physiology and Biophysics and Program in Neuroscience, University of Iowa College of Medicine, Iowa City, Iowa, USA

Summary

L-, N- and P-/Q-type voltage-dependent calcium channels share a common structure, and are composed of at least one primary α_1 subunit and auxiliary β and $\alpha_2\delta$ subunits. Expression of the α_1 subunit alone in mammalian cells usually results in small calcium currents, and these are increased many times in amplitude by coexpression of auxiliary β and $\alpha_2\delta$ subunits. The β subunit, a cytoplasmically located protein, clearly regulates the calcium current through its interaction with the α_1 subunit, altering the latter's conformation and promoting its transportation to the plasma membrane. In the presence of β subunits in heterologous expression systems, calcium current amplitude is comparable to that of native channels; the kinetic properties and voltage-dependence of the channels also resemble those of native calcium channels.

Molecular properties of voltage-dependent calcium channels

Although calcium channels are expressed at very low densities in most tissues, in skeletal muscle they are enriched in the T-tubule system and serve as voltage sensors to trigger excitation–contraction coupling.[1,2] The skeletal muscle calcium channel (L-type channel) is sensitive to dihydropyridines and binds this class of drugs with high affinity. The abundance of calcium channels in skeletal muscle and their high affinity for dihydropyridine binding were essential for the purification of voltage-dependent calcium channels.[3–6] Data derived from the L-type calcium channels in the skeletal muscle have greatly facilitated our understanding of other types of calcium channels in cardiac and brain tissues.

The purified calcium channel from skeletal muscle is a complex containing five subunits (α_1, α_2, β, γ and δ) (fig. 1). The α_1 subunit is a 170 kDa protein which binds dihydropyridine drugs that either inhibit or stimulate calcium channel activity.[7–12] The protein contains extracellular, intracellular and hydrophobic domains but has not been reported to be glycosylated. The α_1 subunit is a substrate for protein kinase A, protein kinase G, protein kinase C, casein kinase II and calmodulin (CaM)-dependent protein kinase II.[13–15] The 140 kDa α_2 subunit is heavily glycosylated and is exclusively present in the extracellular space.[16] It is linked by disulphide bonds to the δ subunit, which contains a hydrophobic transmembrane domain. The β subunit, which is approximately 52 kDa in size and largely hydrophilic,[5,6] is a substrate for many kinases, including protein kinase A, protein kinase C and a protein kinase intrinsic to

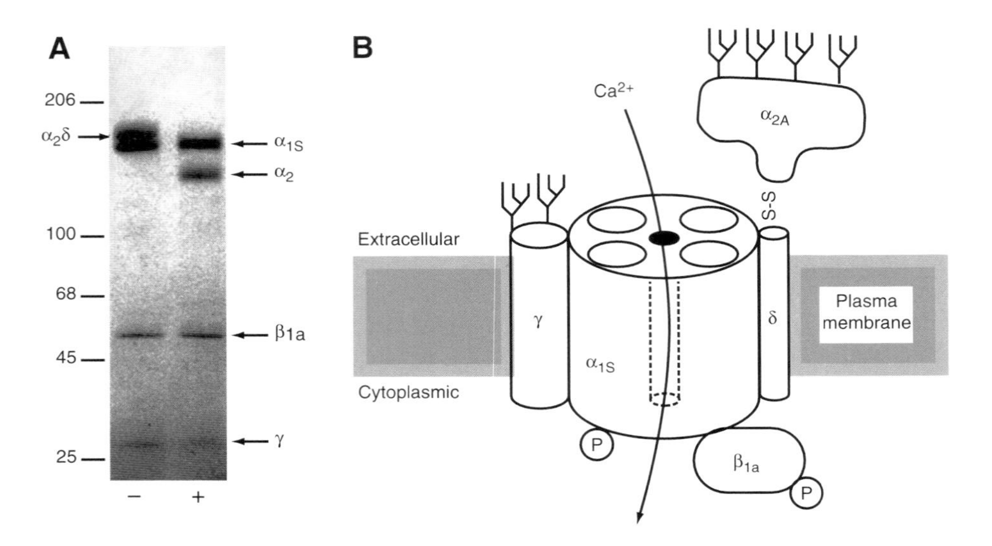

Fig. 1. A) Subunits of the purified skeletal muscle L-type calcium channel are shown separated on an SDS-polyacrylamide gel stained with Coomassie blue under non-reducing (–) and reducing (+) conditions.[13] *The α_{2A} and δ subunits, which are linked by disulphide bonds under non-reducing conditions, separate into two proteins under reducing conditions. Molecular weight standards are shown on the left. B) Model of the skeletal muscle L-type calcium channel. The α_{1S}, γ and δ subunits are transmembrane proteins; the $\alpha_{2A}\delta$ and γ subunits are glycosylated; the β_{1a} subunit lies within the cytoplasm. P = phosphorylation sites.*

skeletal muscle triads.[13–15] The γ subunit is uniquely expressed in skeletal muscle and also contains hydrophobic transmembrane domains.[17] All five subunits are tightly associated and copurify during the various stages of channel purification.

cDNAs coding for all five subunits have now been isolated. The amino acid sequence deduced from cDNA for the α_1 subunit predicts a protein with 24 transmembrane domains which group into four similar repeats.[18] The fourth hydrophobic domain of each repeat contains an orderly pattern of positive charges which could be the voltage sensor for the calcium channel. The structure of the α_1 subunit is comparable to that of the voltage-dependent sodium channel and, to a certain extent, that of the potassium channel.

The α_2 and δ subunits (referred to as the $\alpha_2\delta$ subunit) are encoded by one gene and are post-translationally cleaved to give rise to two proteins.[19] The δ subunit contains one presumed transmembrane domain, leaving only five amino acids in the C terminus which can be located intracellularly. Although the α_2 subunit contains two hydrophobic regions, it has recently been shown to be entirely extracellular.[20] The cDNA sequence for the γ subunit indicates that this subunit has four apparent membrane-spanning domains and a few possible glycosylation sites.[21] As for the β subunit, its cDNA sequence predicts a hydrophilic protein with no hydrophobic domains.[22] After identification of the genes coding for the subunits of the skeletal muscle L-type channel, homologous cDNA sequences to the α_1, $\alpha_2\delta$ and β subunits have been isolated from other tissues. Overall, six α_1 genes (α_{1S}, α_{1A}, α_{1B}, α_{1C}, α_{1D}

and α_{1E}), four β genes (β_1, β_2, β_3 and β_4) and one $\alpha_2\delta$ gene have been identified.[23–26] Several splice variants for each α_1, $\alpha_2\delta$ and β gene have been reported.[27–31]

Based on the electrophysiological, pharmacological and molecular properties of the calcium channels studied so far, calcium channels can be grouped into six types (T, L, N, P, Q and R type) (table I). The T-type channel is distinguished from the other types by its activation at relatively negative potentials, and for this reason it is also known as the low-voltage-activated (LVA) channel.[32–34] It is responsible for the rhythmic electrical activity in cardiac muscle and endocrine cells. All the other types of calcium channels are high voltage activated (HVA) (see table I). The L-type channel is uniquely sensitive to dihydropyridine drugs. Three α_1 subunits (α_{1S}, α_{1C} and α_{1D}) can independently form L-type channels and therefore they are grouped together as the L-type subfamily (see table I).[27,35–38] The α_{1C} subunit is expressed in cardiac muscle and brain, while the α_{1D} subunit is present in neurons and endocrine cells (table II). L-type calcium channels are involved in excitation–contraction coupling, excitation–secretion coupling and control of gene expression.

The N-type channel is specifically blocked by two peptide toxins found in fish-hunting snails: ω-CTx-GVIA and ω-CTx-MVIIA (see table I).[39] The α_{1B} subunit binds these toxins and confers basic properties such as voltage-dependent activation and ionic permeability. The P- and Q-type channels are sensitive to the peptide toxins ω-Aga-IVA and ω-CTx-MVIIC (see table I).[40–41] These two channels are probably formed by α_{1A} subunits,[42] which have several isoforms (see table II) and appear to be expressed in several different sizes in neurons.[43,44] The R-type channel is blocked by ω-Aga-IIIA and,[45] in common with N-type and P-/Q-type channels, is expressed in neuronal tissues (see table I). N-type and P-/Q-type channels are principally involved

Table I. Properties of different types of calcium channel

	Channel type					
	T	L	N	P	Q	R
Activation threshold	>–70 mV LVA	>–30 mV HVA	>–30 mV HVA	>–40 mV HVA	>–40 mV HVA	>–40 mV HVA
Inactivation time-course	Fast	Slow	Moderate	Very slow	Moderate	Fast
Primary tissue location	Cardiac Neuronal Endocrine	Skeletal Cardiac Neuronal Endocrine	Neuronal	Neuronal	Neuronal	Neuronal
Pharmacology		DHPs (agonists/ antagonists)	ω-CTx-GVIA ω-CTx-MVIIA ω-CTx-MVIIC ω-Aga-IIIA	ω-Aga-IVA ω-CTx-MVIIC ω-Aga-IIIA	ω-Aga-IVA ω-CTx-MVIIC ω-Aga-IIIA?	ω-Aga-IIIA
Function	Membrane excitability	E–C coupling E–S coupling	E–S coupling	E–S coupling	E–S coupling	E–S coupling
Pore-forming subunit		α_{1S} α_{1C} α_{1D}	α_{1B}	α_{1A}?	α_{1A}?	α_{1E}?

Abbreviations: DHPs = dihydropyridines; E–C = excitation–contraction; E–S = excitation–secretion; HVA = high-voltage-activated; LVA = low-voltage-activated.

Table II. Properties of cloned α_1 subunits

Gene	Splice products	Chromosomal localisation (human)	Channel type	Distribution	Drug sensitivity
α_{1S}	a,b	1q31–q32	L	Skeletal muscle	Dihydropyridines
α_{1C}	a,b,c,d	12p13.3	L	Cardiac muscle, brain, smooth muscle	Dihydropyridines
α_{1D}	a,b,c,d	3p14.3	L	Endocrine tissue, brain	Dihydropyridines ω-CTx-GVIA
α_{1A}	a,b,c,d	19p13.1–13.2	P/Q	Brain, heart	ω-CTx-MVIIC ω-Aga-IVA FTX
α_{1B}	a,b	9q34	N	Brain	ω-CTx-GVIA
α_{1E}	a,b,c	1q25–q31	R?	Brain	Ni^{2+}

Abbreviations: FTX = funnel web spider toxin.

in neurotransmitter release, and the R-type channel may have a similar function also.[46,47]

Biochemical characterisation of cardiac L-type, brain N-type and brain P-/Q-type channels suggest that most voltage-dependent calcium channels may have similar subunit composition: an α_1, $\alpha_2\delta$ and β subunit (see table II; table III).[10,48–52] The heterogeneity of calcium channels forms the molecular basis for their diversity of function and this heterogeneity is primarily related to the existence of distinct α_1 subunits (see table II).[24,27] The α_1 subunits contain within themselves the functions of voltage-sensing, voltage-dependent activation and inactivation, drug sensitivity and ion permeability. However, cellular expression of the α_1 subunit alone usually provides insignificant calcium current. Furthermore, the β and $\alpha_2\delta$ subunits, in addition to increasing greatly the amplitude of calcium currents, profoundly alter many properties of calcium channels when coexpressed with α_1 subunits (see table III).[24,53–55] It is clear now that different β subunits also contribute to the functional diversity of calcium channels.[52,56–58]

Table III. Properties of cloned auxiliary subunits

Gene	Splice products	Chromosomal localisation (human)	Channel type	Distribution	Phosphorylation sites
β_1	a,b,c,d	17q21–22	Isoform a: L Rest: N, P/Q, other	a: skeletal muscle Rest: brain, heart, skeletal muscle	PKA, PKC, CK2
β_2	a,b,c,d	ND	P/Q, N, other	Cardiac muscle, brain	PKA, PKC, CK2
β_3	a,b,c	12q13	N, P/Q, other	Brain, cardiac muscle	PKC, CK2
β_4	a,b	ND	P/Q, N, other	Brain	PKC, CK2
$\alpha_2\delta$	a,b,c,d,e	7q21–q22	L, N, P/Q, other	Brain, heart, skeletal muscle	
γ		17q24	Skeletal muscle L	Skeletal muscle	

Abbreviations: CK2 = casein kinase II; ND = not determined; PKA = protein kinase A; PKC = protein kinase C.

Regulation of calcium channel function by the β subunit

Various β subunit cDNAs have been identified in humans, rat, rabbit, mouse, *Xenopus* and *Drosophila*.[59] These cDNAs are all similar in two regions (fig. 2 (A)), suggesting largely conserved structure for all the β subunits. Four different genes have been found in rat, and these are probably present in other species as well.[22,31,54,55,60] In addition, multiple splice variants have also been identified for human β_1, human β_2, rabbit β_2 and human β_3 genes, and it is likely that they exist for other β genes.[23]

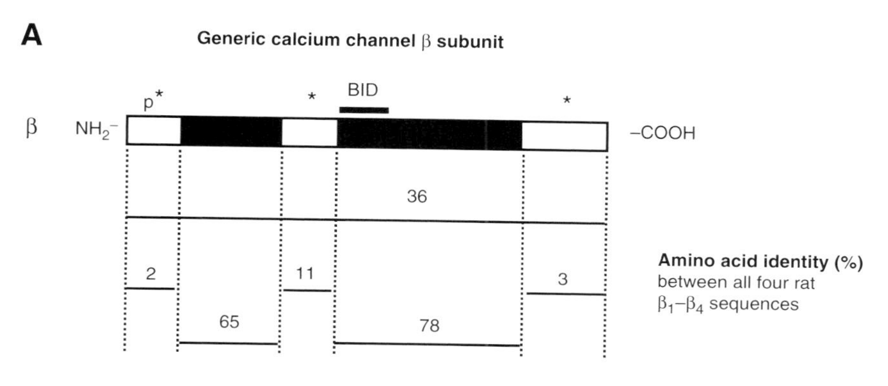

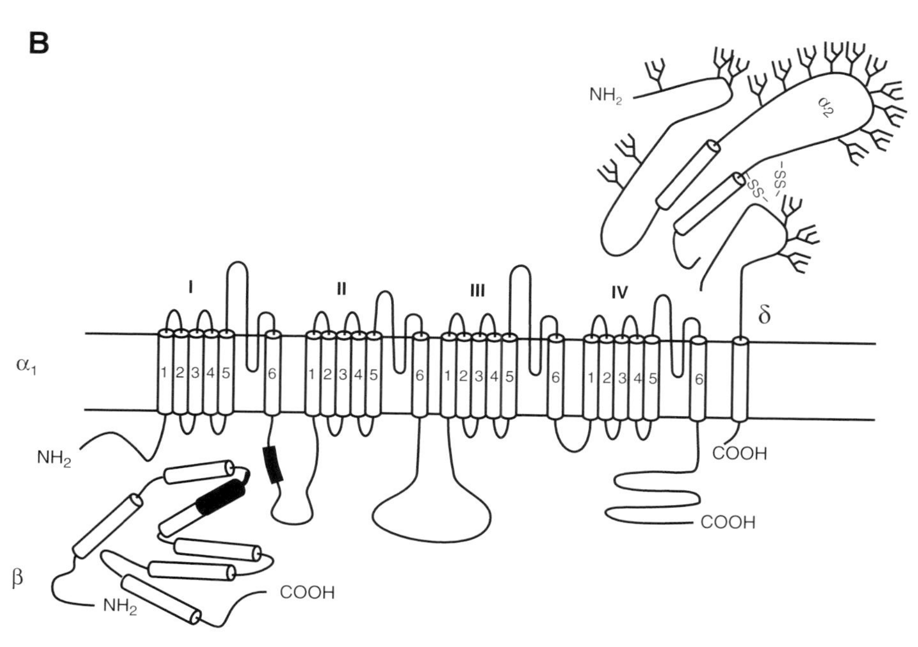

*Fig. 2. A) The generic β subunit of the calcium channel. Shaded regions represent highly homologous domains common to all four β subunits. The amino acid identities of different regions of the β subunits are obtained from a comparison of four rat β subunit sequences; * = involved in inactivation kinetics; BID (β interaction domain) = involved in binding to α_1 subunit, voltage-dependence, open probability, etc.; p = palmitoylation sites in β_{2a}. B) Schematic representation of the association between α_1 and β subunits of the calcium channel. Highlighted regions represent the α_1 interaction domain (AID; α_1 subunit) and β interaction domain (BID; β subunit). The α_1 subunit contains 24 transmembrane α-helical domains which can be grouped into four repeats.*

Notably, analysis of all β subunit sequences predicts many putative phosphorylation sites, including sites for protein kinase A, protein kinase C and casein kinase II, suggesting that the β subunit is a regulatory target for these protein kinases. Indeed, the β_{1a} subunit is phosphorylated *in vitro* by protein kinase A, CaM-dependent protein kinase II and protein kinase C.[13,15] Furthermore, β subunits contain an Src-homology-3 domain (SH3), based on sequence similarity to the known SH3 domains, suggesting a role for the β subunit in Ca^{2+}-mediated signalling and signal transduction.

Many combinations of α_1 and β subunits have been coexpressed in mammalian cell lines (COS-7, HEK293, L cell, etc.) and *Xenopus* oocytes. In all cases, β subunit coexpression increased the amplitude of the calcium current in comparison to α_1 subunit expression alone.[30,54,55,61] In most cases a 3- to 20-fold enhancement was recorded. In some studies, specific binding of calcium channel blockers was measured to determine whether β subunit coexpression increased the total number of calcium channels. β_1 subunit coexpression with the human α_{1B} subunit in HEK293 cells increased the number of binding sites for ω-CTx-GVIA without significantly affecting binding affinity,[62] and β_1 subunit coexpression with the rabbit α_{1C} subunit in Chinese hamster ovary (CHO) and COS-7 cells also increased the number of dihydropyridine binding sites.[63,64] However, α_1 protein level was not significantly altered by the presence of the β subunit in α_{1C} cotransfection experiments,[63] suggesting that the increase in current amplitude and channel binding sites may be related to cell surface localisation and a conformational change in the α_1 subunit in response to the β subunit, rather than to a change in α_1 protein synthesis. Indeed, β subunit coexpression altered the affinity of dihydropyridine binding to the α_1 subunit.[64]

The presence of the β subunit also modifies the channel kinetics of the α_1 subunit. The β subunit facilitates the activation kinetics of the α_{1S}, α_{1B} and α_{1C} subunits,[65,66] and slows the activation kinetics of the α_{1E} channel,[61] but has no effect on the activation kinetics of the α_{1A} subunit.[24] Interestingly, the most obvious difference among the various coexpressed β subunits is in their effects on the inactivation kinetics of the α_1 subunit.[56,57] In the case of the α_{1A} subunit, coexpression of the β_3 subunit induced the fastest inactivation kinetics, followed by the β_4 and β_{1b} subunits, whereas $\alpha_{1A}\beta_2$ channels showed rather slow inactivation. The inactivation time constants for the coexpressed $\alpha_{1A}\beta_2$ and $\alpha_{1A}\beta_3$ subunits can vary almost 10-fold. These results strongly suggest that the various β subunits can further broaden the functional phenotypes of calcium channels, enabling them to carry out diverse cellular activities.

β subunit coexpression has been shown to shift the voltage-dependence of activation of α_{1A}, α_{1C} and α_{1E} subunits to hyperpolarising potentials and to alter the voltage-dependence of inactivation of α_{1A}, α_{1B}, α_{1C} and α_{1E} subunits.[25,56,67] These functional modifications produced by the β subunit endow the expressed channel with properties resembling those of native calcium channels. In summary, the β subunit regulates the activity of the α_1 subunit in many ways, modifying the current amplitude, current kinetics and voltage-dependence of calcium channels.

Association of α_1 and β subunits of calcium channels

Given that the β subunit is an important regulator of α_1 subunit function, there are several important questions concerning the association of calcium channel α_1 and β subunits.

1. Are α_1 and β subunits associated in a 1:1 ratio?
2. Is there a specific assembly of one type of α_1 subunit with one type of β subunit in the cell?
3. Are there factors which can facilitate or disrupt α_1–β subunit interaction?

Several studies have addressed these questions. For the purified skeletal muscle L-type calcium channel, the stoichiometry of α_1, $\alpha_2\delta$, β and γ subunits was determined to be approximately 1:1:1:1.[68] The stoichiometry for the subunits in other types of calcium channels remains to be fully investigated. In addition, immunoprecipitation data suggest that virtually all skeletal muscle α_1 subunits, brain N-type channel α_1 subunits and P-/Q-type α_{1A} subunits are associated with β subunits.[52,58] However, it remains possible that some types of α_1 subunit may function *in vivo* in the absence of the β subunit. Six different α_1 genes and four distinct β genes have been identified, and the specificity of the α_1–β association has been investigated. It seems that most neurons express multiple types of calcium channels and several α_1 and β subunits.[69–72] In the rabbit brain, the α_{1B} subunit can be associated with any one of the β_{1b}, β_3 and β_4 subunits, and the α_{1A} subunit forms a complex with any one of the four brain β subunits (β_{1b}, β_2, β_3 and β_4).[52,58] In PC12 cells, the α_{1B} subunit of the N-type channel is associated with either the β_3 or β_2 subunit.[72] This association is mostly dependent upon the level of β subunit expression and, possibly, the affinity of the α_1–β subunit interaction. *In vitro* biochemical studies indicate that the α_1 and β subunits show high mutual affinity and that this interaction is not disrupted by high salt concentrations, small variations in physiological pH or the presence of detergents.[73] It remains to be seen if there are physiological factors which can affect this association.

Identification of a β subunit interaction site on the α_1 subunit

Several lines of evidence point to a direct interaction between the α_1 and β subunits of the calcium channel. First, calcium channel subunits are tightly associated in cells and remain associated during the purification process. Second, antibodies against α_1 or β subunits can co-immunoprecipitate the other subunit from native tissues. Third, the β subunit can regulate α_1 function when these two subunits alone are expressed. Finally, the *in vitro* synthesised β subunit has been shown to bind the purified α_{1S} subunit. Pragnell and colleagues have used a novel library screening method to identify the domains on the α_1 subunit responsible for β subunit interaction.[74] Radiolabelled β subunits synthesised *in vitro* were used to detect interactions with small fragments of α_1 subunit expressed from an α_1 epitope library. All positive clones thus identified contained a sequence of 18 amino acids localised at the cytoplasmic linker connecting repeats I and II of the calcium channel α_1 subunit. No other interaction domains on the α_1 subunit have been identified by this method. The 18-amino acid binding region is termed the 'α_1 interaction domain' (AID), and mutations in this domain abolish the regulatory effects (current stimulation, shift of voltage-dependence of activation and changes in inactivation kinetics) produced by β subunit coexpression on the α_{1A} channel in *Xenopus* oocytes, demonstrating that the AID is necessary for β subunit attachment and regulation. This finding provides a molecular basis for β subunit function and suggests several possible ways in which the β subunit can modify the α_1 current. First, β subunit binding to the α_1 subunit via the I–II cytoplasmic linker may introduce conformation change in the α_1 subunit and thus alter some properties (voltage-dependence and open probability) of the calcium channel. Second, conformational change or β subunit association may protect the α_1 subunit from degradation. Third, while this interaction site anchors the β subunit to the α_1 subunit, additional interactions between these subunits may alter calcium channel function. Fourth, the β subunit may be required for the correct transport of the α_1 subunit to the surface membrane.

Conformational change in the α_1 subunit may account for some biophysical properties of the $\alpha_1\beta$ channel. In *Xenopus* oocytes, coexpression of the β subunit has been shown to increase the maximum conductance (g_{max}) and to shift the g_{max}–voltage curve towards a more hyperpolarising potential without affecting charge movement.[75] This suggests that β subunit association lowered the energy barrier required for the opening of the channel pore and increased the open probability of the channel. Results from transfection experiments with HEK293 cells differ from those obtained with oocytes in that the former show an increase in charge movement with β coexpression, albeit coupled with an increase in channel open probability.[76,77] In addition, binding studies with α_{1C} L-type channels expressed in CHO cells show increased dihydropyridine binding in the presence of the β subunit with no change in α_1 subunit expression.[63] Despite some discrepancies among these studies, overall this work suggests that the β subunit induces a conformational change in the α_1 subunit for ligand binding and channel gating.

Primary and secondary interactions between α_1 and β subunits

Shortly after the identification of the AID site, a β subunit region that interacts with the α_1 subunit was identified by expressing truncated β subunits with α_1 subunits in oocytes.[78] A 34-amino acid sequence of the β subunit, localised on the N terminal of the second conserved domain, maintained the ability to increase the current amplitude of the α_1 subunit. This sequence was later referred to as the 'β interaction domain' (BID) (see fig. 2 (A)), and mutations in the BID altered the ability of the β subunit to enhance the α_{1A} channel current. One mutation in the β_{1b} subunit (P221R) increased the α_{1A} current amplitude more effectively than did the wild-type β_{1b} subunit, while other mutations decreased the ability of the β_{1b} subunit to stimulate current through the α_{1A} channel. Although these mutations showed differences in their stimulation of the α_{1A} channel current, the α_1-interacting β mutations were similar in their abilities to shift the voltage-dependence of activation and inactivation. These results suggest that the shift in voltage-dependence of activation and inactivation may result solely from the conformational change in the α_1 subunit after association with the β subunit, regardless of the nature of the β subunit. On the other hand, the kinetic properties of the calcium channel seem to depend on other regions of the β subunit besides the BID, because coexpression with the different truncations of the β subunit resulted in dramatic and irregular changes in current kinetics. Therefore it is possible that secondary interaction occurs between the β and α_1 subunits, with the BID acting as the primary interaction site with the AID (see fig. 2 (B)). Mutations disrupting the AID–BID association completely abolished β subunit regulation, suggesting that the primary interaction between these two molecules is a prerequisite for secondary interaction.

The N terminus of the β subunit has been demonstrated to control the inactivation kinetics of the α_{1E} subunit.[79] Thus, the β_1 subunit increased the inactivation of the α_{1E} subunit, while the β_2 subunit slowed α_{1E} inactivation. Chimeras produced from transposition of the N terminus of β_1 and β_2 subunits had opposite effects on α_{1E} subunit inactivation. This clearly indicates that the α_1 subunit interacts with the β subunit at a site outside the BID. Recently, the linker region between the two highly homologous domains of the β subunit has also been shown to regulate the rate of α_{1E} subunit inactivation.[80] In addition, the effect of the N terminus prevails over that of the linker region, which suggests that some modulation of the β subunit is required to unmask the effect of the linker domain. Thus, these results suggest that the β subunit interacts with the α_1 subunit at multiple sites in addition to the primary AID–BID binding site and that the inactivation kinetics may be determined by secondary interaction between α_1 and β subunits.

Localisation of the α_1 subunit and chaperone-like effects of the β subunit

Current stimulation, the most obvious effect of β subunit coexpression, may be partly attributable to the correct transport of the α_1 subunit to the plasma membrane.[81] Many proteins, including heterotrimeric G-protein α and γ subunits, are localised to the plasma membrane because of post-translational modification by the addition of lipid moieties such as myristoylation. The β subunit has such putative lipid modification sites. Although the β subunit is believed to be hydrophilic and cytoplasmic, the β_{2a} subunit has been shown to localise to the surface membrane when expressed alone in HEK (tsA201) cells. The β_{2a} subunit is post-translationally modified in HEK cells, and this modification results from palmitoylation (see fig. 2 (A)).[82] The protein level of the α_{1C} subunit remained similar with or without coexpression of the β_{2a} subunit. However, most of the α_{1C} subunit localised to the plasma membrane in the presence of the β_{2a} subunit, while immunostaining of the α_{1C} subunit transfected alone was largely perinuclear. Therefore, the β subunit is important for correct transposition of the α_{1C} subunit to the plasma membrane, through lipid modification and membrane localisation of the β subunit.

When mutations in the N-terminal cysteines of the β_{2a} subunit resulted in a palmitoylation-deficient β_{2a} mutant, this mutant β_{2a} subunit remained able to target the α_1 channel to the plasma membrane but failed to increase the macroscopic current.[82] This interesting observation suggests that targeting the channel alone may not account for the stimulation of channel current by the β subunit. Moreover, some unknown cytoskeletal interactions may play a role in targeting the β subunit to the plasma membrane.

Although it is unclear whether the calcium channel β subunit promotes the correct folding and modification of the α_1 subunit during its biosynthesis, this might be one of the mechanisms by which the β subunit increases cell surface expression of the α_1 subunit. Voltage-gated calcium channels are quite comparable to voltage-gated potassium channels: the calcium channel α_1 subunit is similar in structure to the potassium channel pore-forming α subunit, and the potassium channel α subunit is associated with a cytoplasmic protein, Kvβ1-3, which shares functional (but not structural) similarity with the calcium channel β subunit. Notably, Kvβ2 associates with the Kv1.2 potassium channel α subunit during an early stage of channel biosynthesis, and this association promotes cotranslational N-linked glycosylation of the Kv1.2 polypeptide and increases the stability of Kv1.2 protein.[83] Therefore it is possible that the calcium channel β subunit also plays a similar role to that of the potassium channel in stabilising the α_1 subunit and promoting the surface expression of the mature channel complex.

Interactions between calcium channel subunits and non-channel proteins

In vivo, α_1, β and other subunits of the neuronal calcium channel form a tightly associated complex which interacts with the synaptic vesicle docking proteins syntaxin, SNAP-25 and, possibly, other unidentified proteins.[84–86] Calcium channel activity is dynamically modified by protein kinases, heterotrimeric G proteins, ryanodine receptors, SNAP-25 and syntaxin.[87–94] The modulation of α_1 subunit function by β subunits may be altered by the presence of these other proteins. In fact, it is now recognised that modulation of calcium channels by G proteins is mediated by the Gβγ subunit rather than the Gα subunit, and that Gβγ subunits may interact with the calcium channel α_1 subunit at the site where the calcium channel β subunit is anchored.[95–98] This raises the possibility that G-protein-mediated inhibition of the calcium channel may allosterically modify the α_1–β subunit interaction. The close proximity of the Gβγ subunits and calcium channel α_1 and β subunits suggests a complex interaction between these proteins.

Conclusions

Calcium channels are involved in the pathogenesis of several human diseases, and calcium channels blockers are widely used to treat cardiovascular and neurological disorders.[99,100] To date, hypokalaemic periodic paralysis has been linked to the mutations in the calcium channel α_{1S} subunit, and a number of diseases have been linked to the α_{1A} subunit gene, including familial hemiplegic migraine, episodic ataxia type 2 and spinocerebellar ataxia type 6.[101–104] In mouse models, tottering and leaner mice have been found to carry mutations in the α_{1A} subunit.[105] The diseases resulting from the α_{1A} subunit dysfunction, such as cerebellar abnormalities, all share similar phenotypes. More recently, the β_4 subunit gene has been linked to neurological disorders in lethargic mice,[106] which display ataxia and lethargic behaviour as well as seizures. These features are somewhat similar to the defects caused by α_{1A} subunit mutations. Notably, both α_{1A} and β_4 subunits are highly expressed in cerebellar Purkinje and granule cells.[24,57] The β_4 subunit has also been shown to be a dominant form of β subunit in α_{1A}-containing channels in brain tissue.[52] In addition, while the β_4 subunit is very important in α_{1A}-containing channels, it is also present in N-type and perhaps other types of calcium channels,[58] and is expressed in other brain regions. Therefore, absence of a functional β_4 subunit may impair several different types of calcium channel function. In skeletal muscle, β_1 subunit deficiency in the transgenic mouse is associated with a reduced calcium current and impaired excitation–contraction coupling.[107] Future research will probably identify more human disorders caused by calcium channel dysfunction. Since auxiliary subunits play an essential part in calcium channel function, a better understanding of the regulatory role of the auxiliary β subunit will be essential in understanding calcium channel dysfunction in disease.

Acknowledgements

Kevin P. Campbell is an investigator at the Howard Hughes Medical Institute. We thank Drs Christina Gurnett, Ricardo Felix, Gloria Biddlecome, Klaus Bielefeldt and Michel De Waard for their helpful comments on this manuscript.

References

1. Tanabe T, Beam KG, Adams BA, et al. Regions of the skeletal muscle dihydropyridine receptor critical for excitation–contraction coupling. Nature 1990; 346: 567–79
2. Beam KG, Adams BA, Niidome T, et al. Function of a truncated dihydropyridine receptor as both voltage sensor and calcium channel. Nature 1992; 360: 169–71
3. Curtis BM, Catterall WA. Reconstitution of the voltage-sensitive calcium channel purified from skeletal muscle transverse tubules. Biochemistry 1986; 25: 3077–83
4. Flockerzi V, Oeken H-J, Hofmann F, et al. Purified dihydropyridine-binding site from skeletal muscle t-tubules is a functional calcium channel. Nature 1986; 323: 66–8
5. Leung AT, Imagawa T, Campbell KP. Structural characterization of the 1,2-dihydropyridine receptor of the voltage-dependent calcium channel from rabbit skeletal muscle. J Biol Chem 1987; 262: 7943–6
6. Takahashi M, Seagar MJ, Jones JF, et al. Subunit structure of dihydropyridine-sensitive calcium channels from skeletal muscle. Proc Natl Acad Sci U S A 1987; 84: 5478–82
7. Sharp AH, Imagawa T, Leung AT, et al. Identification and characterization of the dihydropyridine-binding subunit of the skeletal muscle dihydropyridine receptor. J Biol Chem 1987; 262: 12309–15
8. Striessnig J, Glossmann H, Catterall WA. Identification of a phenylalkylamine binding region within the α_1 subunit of skeletal muscle calcium channels. Proc Natl Acad Sci U S A 1990; 87: 9108–12
9. Striessnig J, Murphy BJ, Catterall WA. Dihydropyridine receptor of L-type calcium channels: identification of binding domains for [^{3}H](+)-PN200-110 and [^{3}H]azidopine within the α_1 subunit. Proc Natl Acad Sci U S A 1991; 88: 10769–73
10. De Jongh KS, Merrick DK, Catterall WA. Subunits of purified calcium channels: a 212-kDa form of α_1 and partial amino-acid sequence of a phosphorylation site of an independent β subunit. Proc Natl Acad Sci U S A 1989; 86: 8585–9

11. Regulla S, Schneider T, Nastainczyk W, et al. Identification of the site of interaction of the dihydropyridine channel blockers nitrendipine and azidopine with calcium-channel α_1 subunit. EMBO J 1991; 10: 45–9
12. Mitterdorfer J, Wang Z, Sinnegger MJ, et al. Two amino acid residues in the IIIS5 segment of L-type calcium channels differentially contribute to 1,4-dihydropyridine sensitivity. J Biol Chem 1996; 271: 30330–5
13. Imagawa T, Leung AT, Campbell KP. Phosphorylation of the 1,4-dihydropyridine receptor of the voltage-dependent calcium channel by an intrinsic protein kinase in isolated triads from rabbit skeletal muscle. J Biol Chem 1987; 262: 8333–9
14. Nastainczyk W, Rohrkasten A, Sieber M, et al. Phosphorylation of the purified receptor for calcium channel blockers by cAMP kinase and protein kinase C. Eur J Biochem 1987; 169: 137–42
15. Jahn H, Nastainczyk W, Rohrkasten A, et al. Site specific phosphorylation of the purified receptor for calcium channel blockers by cAMP- and cGMP-dependent protein kinases, protein kinase C, calmodulin-dependent protein kinase II and casein kinase II. Eur J Biochem 1988; 178: 535–42
16. Jay SD, Sharp AH, Kahl SD, et al. Structural characterization of the dihydropyridine-sensitive calcium channel α_2-subunit and the associated δ peptides. J Biol Chem 1991; 266: 3287–93
17. Sharp AH, Campbell KP. Characterization of the 1,4-dihydropyridine receptor using subunit-specific polyclonal antibodies. Evidence for a 32,000 Dalton subunit. J Biol Chem 1989; 264: 2816–25
18. Tanabe T, Takeshima H, Mikami A, et al. Primary structure of the receptor for calcium channel blockers from skeletal muscle. Nature 1987; 328: 313–18
19. Ellis SB, Williams ME, Ways NR, et al. Sequence and expression of mRNAs encoding the α_1 and α_2 subunits of a DHP-sensitive calcium channel. Science 1988; 241: 1661–4
20. Gurnett CA, De Waard M, Campbell KP. Dual function of the voltage-dependent calcium channel $\alpha_2\delta$ subunit in current stimulation and subunit interaction. Neuron 1996; 16: 431–40
21. Jay SD, Ellis SB, McCue AF, et al. Primary structure of the γ subunit of the DHP-sensitive calcium channel from skeletal muscle. Science 1990; 248: 490–2
22. Ruth P, Rohrkasten A, Biel M, et al. Primary structure of the β subunit of the DHP-sensitive calcium channel from skeletal muscle. Science 1989; 245: 1115–18
23. Birnbaumer L, Campbell KP, Catterall WA, et al. The naming of voltage-gated calcium channels. Neuron 1994; 13: 505–6
24. Mori Y, Friedrich T, Kim M-S, et al. Primary structure and functional expression from complementary DNA of a brain calcium channel. Nature 1991; 350: 398–402
25. Soong TW, Stea A, Hodson CD, et al. Structure and functional expression of a member of the low voltage-activated calcium channel family. Science 1993; 260: 1113–36
26. Williams ME, Feldman DH, McCue AF, et al. Structure and functional expression of α_1, α_2, and β subunits of a novel human neuronal calcium channel subtype. Neuron 1992; 8: 71–84
27. Snutch TP, Tomlinson WJ, Leonard JP, et al. Distinct calcium channels are generated by alternative splicing and are differentially expressed in the mammalian CNS. Neuron 1991; 7: 45–57
28. Diebold RJ, Koch WJ, Ellinor PT, et al. Mutually exclusive exon splicing of the cardiac calcium channel α_1 subunit gene generates developmentally regulated isoforms in the heart. Proc Natl Acad Sci U S A 1992; 89: 1497–501
29. Powers PA, Liu S, Hogan K, et al. Skeletal muscle and brain isoforms of a β-subunit of human voltage-dependent calcium channels are encoded by a single gene. J Biol Chem 1992; 267: 22967–72
30. Collin T, Wang J-J, Nargeot J, et al. Molecular cloning of three isoforms of the L-type voltage-dependent calcium channel β subunit from normal human heart. Circ Res 1993; 72: 1337–44
31. Hullin R, Singer-Lahat D, Freichel M, et al. Calcium channel β subunit heterogeneity: functional expression of cloned cDNA from heart, aorta and brain. EMBO J 1992; 11: 885–90
32. Carbone E, Lux HD. Kinetics and selectivity of a low-voltage-activated calcium current in chick and rat sensory neurons. J Physiol 1987; 386: 547–70
33. Hagiwara N, Trisawa H, Kameyama M. Contribution of two types of calcium currents to the pacemaker potentials of rabbit sino-atrial node cells. J Physiol 1988; 395: 233–53
34. Zhang J-F, Randall AD, Ellinor PT, et al. Distinctive pharmacology and kinetics of cloned neuronal calcium channels and their possible counterparts in mammalian CNS neurons. Neuropharmacology 1993; 32: 1075–88
35. Mikami A, Imoto K, Tanabe T, et al. Primary structure and functional expression of the cardiac dihydropyridine-sensitive calcium channel. Nature 1989; 340: 230–3
36. Koch WJ, Ellinor PT, Schwartz A. cDNA cloning of a dihydropyridine-sensitive calcium channel from rat aorta. J Biol Chem 1990; 265: 17786–91
37. Hui A, Ellinor PT, Krizanova O, et al. Molecular cloning of multiple subtypes of a novel rat brain isoform of the α_1 subunit of the voltage-dependent calcium channel. Neuron 1991; 7: 35–44
38. Condignola A, Tarroni P, Clementi F, et al. Calcium channel subtypes controlling serotonin release from human small cell lung carcinoma cell lines. J Biol Chem 1993; 268: 26240–7
39. Kristipati R, Nadasdi L, Tarczy-Hornoch K, et al. Characterization of the binding of omega-conopeptides to different classes of non-L-type neuronal calcium channels. Mol Cell Neurosci 1994; 5: 219–28
40. Hillyard DR, Monje VD, Mintz IM, et al. A new conus peptide ligand for mammalian presynaptic calcium channels. Neuron 1992; 9: 69–77

41. Mintz IM, Venema VJ, Swiderek K, et al. P-type calcium channels blocked by the spider toxin ω-Aga-IVA. Nature 1992; 355: 827–9
42. Gillard SE, Volsen SG, Smith W, et al. Identification of pore-forming subunit of P-type calcium channels: an antisense study on rat cerebellar Purkinje cells in culture. Neuropharmacology 1997; 36: 405–9
43. Martin-Moutot N, Leveque C, Sato K, et al. Properties of ω–conotoxin MVIIC receptors associated with α_{1A} calcium channel subunits in rat brain. FEBS Lett 1995; 366: 21–5
44. Sakurai T, Hell JW, Woppmann A, et al. Immunochemical identification and differential phosphorylation of alternatively spliced forms of the α_{1A} subunit of brain calcium channels. J Biol Chem 1995; 270: 21234–42
45. Randall A, Tsien RW. Pharmacological dissection of multiple types of Ca^{2+} channel currents in rat cerebellar granule neurons. J Neurosci 1995; 15: 2995–3012
46. Robitaille R, Adler EM, Charlton MP. Strategic location of calcium channels at transmitter release sites of frog neuromuscular synapses. Neuron 1990; 5: 773–9
47. Wheeler DB, Randall A, Tsien RW. Roles of N-type and Q-type calcium channels in supporting hippocampal synaptic transmission. Science 1994; 264: 107–11
48. Cooper CL, Vandaele S, Barhanin J, et al. Purification and characterization of the dihydropyridine-sensitive voltage-dependent calcium channel from cardiac tissue. J Biol Chem 1987; 262: 509–12
49. Haase H, Streissnig J, Holtzhauser M, et al. A rapid procedure for the purification of cardiac 1,4-dihydropyridine receptors from porcine heart. Eur J Pharmacol 1991; 207: 51–5
50. Kuniyasu A, Oka K, Ide-Yamada T, et al. Structural characterization of the dihydropyridine receptor-linked calcium channel from porcine heart. J Biochem 1992; 112: 235–42
51. Witcher DR, De Waard M, Sakamoto J. Subunit identification and reconstitution of the N-type calcium channel complex purified from brain. Science 1993; 261: 486–9
52. Liu H, De Waard M, Scott VES, et al. Identification of three subunits of the high affinity ω-conotoxin MVIIC sensitive calcium channels. J Biol Chem 1996; 271: 13804–10
53. Itagaki K, Koch WJ, Bodi I, et al. Native-type DHP-sensitive calcium channel currents are produced by cloned rat aortic smooth muscle and cardiac α_1 subunits expressed in *Xenopus laevis* oocytes and are regulated by α_2- and β-subunits. FEBS Lett 1992; 297: 221–5
54. Castellano A, Wei X, Birnbaumer L, et al. Cloning and expression of a third calcium channel β subunit. J Biol Chem 1993; 268: 3450–5
55. Castellano A, Wei X, Birnbaumer L, et al. Cloning and expression of a neuronal calcium channel β subunit. J Biol Chem 1993; 268: 12359–66
56. De Waard M, Campbell KP. Subunit regulation of the neuronal α_{1A} calcium channel expressed in *Xenopus* oocytes. J Physiol (Lond) 1995; 485: 619–34
57. Stea A, Tomlinson J, Soong TW, et al. Localization and functional properties of a rat brain α_1 calcium channel reflect similarities to neuronal Q- and P-type channels. Proc Natl Acad Sci U S A 1994; 91: 10576–80
58. Scott VES, De Waard M, Liu H, et al. β subunit heterogeneity in N-type calcium channels. J Biol Chem 1996; 271: 3207–12
59. De Waard M, Gurnett CA, Campbell KP. Structural and functional diversity of voltage-activated calcium channels. Ion Channels 1996; 4: 41–87
60. Pragnell M, Sakamoto J, Jay SD, et al. Cloning and tissue-specific expression of the brain calcium channel β-subunit. FEBS Lett 1991; 291: 253–8
61. Wakamori M, Niidome T, Furutama D, et al. Distinctive functional properties of the neuronal BII (class E) calcium channel. Receptors Channels 1994; 2: 303–14
62. Williams ME, Brust PF, Feldman DH, et al. Structure and functional expression of an ω-conotoxin-sensitive human N-type calcium channel. Science 1992; 257: 389–95
63. Nishimura S, Takeshima H, Hofmann F, et al. Requirement of the calcium channel β subunit for functional conformation. FEBS Lett 1993; 324: 283–6
64. Mitterdorfer J, Froschmayr M, Grabner M, et al. Calcium channels: the β subunit increases the affinity of dihydropyridine and calcium binding sites of the α_1 subunit. FEBS Lett 1994; 352: 141–5
65. Varadi G, Lory P, Schultz D, et al. Acceleration of activation and inactivation by the β subunit of the skeletal muscle calcium channel. Nature 1991; 352: 159–62
66. Lacerda AE, Kim HS, Ruth P, et al. Normalization of current kinetics by interaction between the α_1 and β subunits of the skeletal muscle dihydropyridine-sensitive calcium channel. Nature 1991; 352: 527–30
67. Stea A, Dubel SJ, Pragnell M, et al. A β-subunit normalizes the electrophysiological properties of a cloned N-type calcium channel α_1-subunit. Neuropharmacology 1993; 32: 1103–16
68. Leung AT, Imagawa T, Block B, et al. Biochemical and ultrastructural characterization of the 1,4-dihydropyridine receptor from rabbit skeletal muscle. Evidence for a 52,000 Da subunit. J Biol Chem 1988; 263: 994–1001
69. Mintz IM, Bean B. Block of calcium channels in rat neurons by synthetic ω-Aga-IVA. Neuropharmacology 1993; 32: 1161–9
70. Pearson HA, Sutton KG, Scott RH, et al. Characterization of calcium channel currents in cultured rat cerebellar granule neurons. J Physiol 1995; 482: 493–509
71. Liévano A, Bolden A, Horn R. Calcium channels in excitable cells: divergent genotypic and phenotypic expression of α_1-subunits. Am J Physiol 1994; 267: C411–24

72. Liu H, Felix R, Gurnett CA, et al. Expression and subunit interaction of voltage-dependent calcium channels in PC12 cells. J Neurosci 1996; 16: 7557–65
73. De Waard M, Witcher DR, Pragnell M, et al. Properties of the α_1–β anchoring site in voltage-dependent calcium channels. J Biol Chem 1995; 270: 12056–64
74. Pragnell M, De Waard M, Mori Y, et al. Calcium channel β-subunit binds to a conserved motif in the I–II cytoplasmic linker of the α_1-subunit. Nature 1994; 368: 67–70
75. Neely A, Wei X, Olcese R, et al. Potentiation by the β subunit of the ratio of the ionic current to the charge movement in the cardiac calcium channel. Science 1993; 262: 575–8
76. Kamp TJ, Perez-Garcia MT, Marban E. Enhancement of ionic current and charge movement by coexpression of calcium channel β_{1A} subunit with α_{1C} subunit in a human embryonic kidney cell line. J Physiol 1996; 492.1: 89–96
77. Josephson IR, Varadi G. The β subunit increases calcium currents and gating charge movements of human cardiac L-type calcium channels. Biophysical J 1996; 70: 1285–93
78. De Waard M, Pragnell M, Campbell KP. Calcium channel regulation by a conserved β subunit domain. Neuron 1994; 13: 495–503
79. Olcese R, Qin N, Schneider T, et al. The amino terminus of a calcium channel β subunit sets rates of channel inactivation independently of the subunit's effect on activation. Neuron 1994; 13: 1433–8
80. Qin N, Olcese R, Zhou J, et al. Identification of a second region of the beta-subunit involved in regulation of calcium channel inactivation. Am J Physiol 1996; 271: C1539–45
81. Chien AJ, Zhao X, Shirokov RE, et al. Roles of a membrane-localized β subunit in the formation and targeting of functional L-type calcium channels. J Biol Chem 1995; 270: 30036–44
82. Chien AJ, Carr KM, Shirokov RE, et al. Identification of palmitoylation sites within the L-type calcium channel β_{2a} subunit and effects on channel function. J Biol Chem 1996; 271: 26465–8
83. Shi G, Nakahira K, Hammond S, et al. β subunits promote K^+ channel surface expression through effects early in biosynthesis. Neuron 1996; 16: 843–52
84. Sheng Z-H, Rettig J, Takahashi M, et al. Identification of a syntaxin-binding site on N-type calcium channels. Neuron 1994; 13: 1303–13
85. Sheng Z-H, Retting J, Cook T, et al. Calcium dependent interaction of N-type calcium channels with the synaptic core complex. Nature 1996; 379: 451–4
86. Martin-Moutot N, Charvin N, Leveque C, et al. Interaction of SNARE complexes with P/Q-type calcium channels in rat cerebellar synaptosomes. J Biol Chem 1996; 271: 6567–70
87. Yatani A, Imoto Y, Codina J, et al. The stimulatory G protein of adenylyl cyclase, G_S, also stimulates dihydropyridine-sensitive calcium channels. J Biol Chem 1988; 263: 9887–95
88. Delcour AH, Tsien RW. Altered prevalence of gating modes in neurotransmitter inhibition of N-type calcium channels. Science 1993; 259: 980–4
89. Swartz KJ. Modulation of calcium channels by protein kinase C in rat central and peripheral neurons: disruption of G protein-mediated inhibition. Neuron 1993; 11: 305–20
90. Boland LM, Bean BP. Modulation of N-type calcium channels in bullfrog sympathetic neurons by luteinizing hormone-releasing hormone: kinetics and voltage dependence. J Neurosci 1993; 13: 516–33
91. Diversé-Pierluissi M, Goldsmith PK, Dunlap K. Transmitter-mediated inhibition of N-type calcium channels in sensory neurons involves multiple GTP-binding proteins and subunits. Neuron 1995; 14: 191–200
92. Nakai J, Dirksen R, Nguyen HT, et al. Enhanced dihydropyridine receptor channel activity in the presence of ryanodine receptor. Nature 1996; 380: 72–5
93. Bezprozvanny I, Scheller RH, Tsien RW. Functional impact of syntaxin on gating of N-type and Q-type calcium channels. Nature 1995; 378: 623–6
94. Wiser O, Bennett MK, Atlas D. Functional interaction of syntaxin and SNAP-25 with voltage-sensitive L- and N-type calcium channels. EMBO J 1996; 15: 4100–10
95. Ikeda SR. Voltage-dependent modulation of N-type calcium channels by G protein $\beta\gamma$ subunits. Nature 1996; 380: 255–8
96. Herlitze S, Garcia DE, Mackie K, et al. Modulation of calcium channels by G-protein $\beta\gamma$ subunits. Nature 1996; 380: 258–62
97. Zamponi GW, Bourinet E, Nelson D, et al. The domain I–II linker of the calcium channel α_1 subunit mediates crosstalk between G-protein inhibition and protein kinase C up-regulation. Nature 1997; 385: 442–6
98. De Waard M, Liu H, Walker D, et al. Direct binding of G protein $\beta\gamma$ complex to voltage-dependent calcium channels. Nature 1997; 385: 446–50
99. Rosenfeld MR, Wong E, Dalmau J, et al. Cloning and characterization of a Lambert–Eaton myasthenic syndrome antigen. Ann Neurol 1993; 33: 113–20
100. Lennon VA, Kryzer TJ, Griesmann GE. Calcium-channel antibodies in the Lambert–Eaton syndrome and other paraneoplastic syndromes. N Engl J Med 1995; 332: 1467–74
101. Jurkat-Rott K, Lehmann-Horn F, Elbaz A, et al. A calcium channel mutation causing hypokalemic periodic paralysis. Hum Mol Genet 1994; 3: 1415–19
102. Ptacek LJ, Tawil R, Griggs RC, et al. Dihydropyridine receptor mutations cause hypokalemic periodic paralysis. Cell 1994; 77: 863–8
103. Ophoff RA, Terwindt GM, Vergouwe MN, et al. Familial hemiplegic migraine and episodic ataxia type-2 are caused by mutations in the calcium channel gene CACNL1A4. Cell 1996; 87: 543–52

104. Zhuchenko O, Bailey J, Bonnen P, et al. Autosomal dominant cerebellar ataxia (SCA6) associated with small polyglutamine expansions in the α_{1A}-voltage-dependent calcium channel. Nature Genetics 1997; 15: 62–9
105. Fletcher CF, Lutz CM, O'Sullivan TN, et al. Absence epilepsy in tottering mutant mice is associated with calcium channel defects. Cell 1996; 87: 607–17
106. Burgess DL, Jones JM, Meisler MH, et al. Mutation of the Ca^{2+} channels β subunit gene Ccb4 is associated with ataxia and seizures in the lethargic (lh) mouse. Cell 1997; 88: 1–20
107. Strube C, Beurg M, Powers PA, et al. Reduced calcium current, charge movement, and absence of calcium transients in skeletal muscle deficient in dihydropyridine receptor β_1 subunit. Biophysical J 1996; 71: 2531–43

Two splice variants of human L-type calcium channels with different inactivation properties

R.D. Zühlke,[1] N.M. Soldatov,[2]* A. Bouron[1], H. Reuter[1]*

[1] *Pharmakologisches Institut, Berne, Switzerland;* [2] *Department of Pharmacology, Georgetown Medical Center, Washington, District of Columbia, USA*

**R.D. Zühlke and N.M. Soldatov have contributed equally to this study*

Summary

We have compared the inactivation properties of two human calcium channel α_{1C} subunits derived from alternative splicing. The difference between the constructs consisted of 80/81 amino acids in the carboxyl-terminal tails. The channel with $\alpha_{1C,77}$ showed slow and incomplete voltage-dependent inactivation, while this type of inactivation was fast and complete with $\alpha_{1C,86}$. In contrast, Ca^{2+}-dependent inactivation was prominent with $\alpha_{1C,77}$ but absent with $\alpha_{1C,86}$.

Introduction

Voltage-gated calcium channels are heteromeric protein complexes composed of the voltage-sensitive, pore-forming α_1 subunit and of the auxiliary $\alpha_2\delta$ and β subunits.[1,2] The α_{1C} subunit of the human L-type calcium channel is encoded by a gene of 50 exons, and its expression is regulated through extensive alternative splicing.[3,4] For example, this has been demonstrated for exons 40–43, encoding the second quarter of the carboxyl-terminal cytoplasmic tail, through identification of partial transcripts of α_{1C} in a cDNA library from human hippocampus.[3,5] We have compared the inactivation properties of an α_{1C} channel subunit ($\alpha_{1C,77}$) derived from a human fibroblast cDNA library[3] with those of a chimeric construct ($\alpha_{1C,86}$) prepared by incorporation of a partial clone found in the cDNA library of human hippocampus[3] into the recombinant plasmid coding for the $\alpha_{1C,77}$ subunit.[5] As a result, 80 amino acids in the cytoplasmic tail of $\alpha_{1C,77}$ were replaced by 81 non-identical amino acids in $\alpha_{1C,86}$. The rest of the sequences, including the putative Ca^{2+}-binding EF hand motif in the first quarter of the cytoplasmic tail near transmembrane segment IVS6,[6,7] were the same in both constructs. A full description of the molecular and electrophysiological properties of $\alpha_{1C,77}$, $\alpha_{1C,86}$ and another chimeric α_{1C} subunit ($\alpha_{1C,72}$) has recently been published.[5]

Methods

Details of the preparation of cDNAs encoding the subunit splice variants $\alpha_{1C,77}$ and $\alpha_{1C,86}$ and of the electrophysiological techniques have been extensively described.[5,8] Briefly, cRNAs for $\alpha_{1C,77}$ or $\alpha_{1C,86}$ were mixed with those for $\alpha_2\delta$ and β_1 subunits in equimolar ratios. About 50 nl of these mixtures were injected into defolliculated *Xenopus laevis* oocytes. The oocytes were stored at 18 °C for 5–8 days before beginning electrophysiological recording. Whole-cell barium currents or calcium currents were measured by a conventional two-electrode voltage-clamp method. The glass electrodes were filled with CsCl 3 M and had resistances between 0.2 and 1 MΩ. During barium current recordings, the oocyte was constantly superfused with a solution containing $Ba(OH)_2$ 40 mM, NaOH 50 mM, KOH 1 mM and HEPES 10 mM (adjusted to pH 7.4 with methanesulphonic acid). When calcium current was measured, oocytes were initially injected with 50 nl of a BAPTA 40 mM solution and $Ba(OH)_2$ in the superfusion solution was replaced by $Ca(NO_3)_2$.

Voltage-clamp protocols, current recordings and leak-subtractions were performed using EPC software (Cambridge Electronic Design, Cambridge, UK). For the construction of inactivation curves, 2 s prepulses to different voltages, from a holding potential of –90 mV, were followed by a test pulse to +20 mV. Although the 2 s prepulses were not long enough to achieve the presumptive steady-state inactivation observed with 20 s prepulses, these longer prepulses were poorly tolerated by the oocytes. Therefore, inactivation curves with 2 s prepulses are referred to as being 'isochronic' rather than 'steady state'. All data are presented as mean ± SEM.

Results

Co-injection of cRNAs for $\alpha_{1C,77}$ or $\alpha_{1C,86}$ together with those for the auxiliary subunits $\alpha_2\delta$ and β_1 into *Xenopus* oocytes led to the expression of functional calcium channels. However, the currents through $\alpha_{1C,77}$ and $\alpha_{1C,86}$ showed very different electrophysiological properties. Panel A of figure 1 shows typical current traces, with Ba^{2+} as the charge

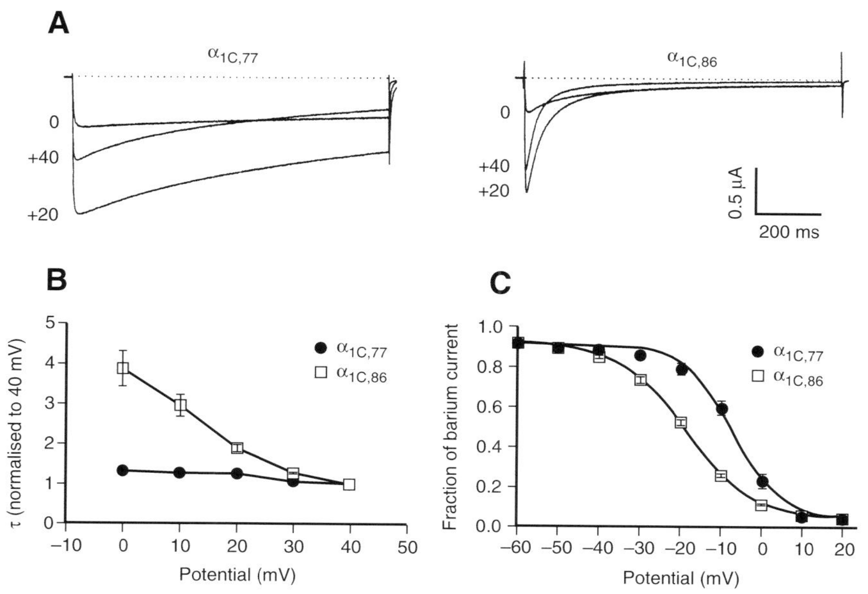

Fig. 1. Barium current inactivation properties of $\alpha_{1C,77}$ and $\alpha_{1C,86}$. A) Traces of barium current recorded at 0, +20 and +40 mV. Test pulses of 1 s duration were applied every 30 s from a holding potential of –90 mV. B) Voltage-dependence of the inactivation time constant (τ) was determined by fitting current traces of barium current in the range of 0 to +40 mV with exponential functions. Values of τ, normalised with respect to τ at +40 mV, were determined by monoexponential ($\alpha_{1C,77}$, n=15) or biexponential ($\alpha_{1C,86}$, n=10–14) fittings. For $\alpha_{1C,86}$ only the fast component has been plotted. C) Mean isochronic inactivation curves for $\alpha_{1C,77}$ and $\alpha_{1C,86}$ were obtained with 2 s conditioning prepulses (n=12–16).

carrier for both constructs. While barium current through $\alpha_{1C,77}$ had slow kinetics with incomplete inactivation, that through $\alpha_{1C,86}$ was rapid and during a 1 s test pulse inactivation was about 85% complete. The time-course of inactivation of $\alpha_{1C,77}$ was monoexponential (τ = 484 ± 22 ms at +20 mV). In contrast, a biexponential fit was required for the inactivation kinetics of $\alpha_{1C,86}$ (τ_{fast} = 47.5 ± 2.6 ms, τ_{slow} = 210.5 ± 10.2 ms at +20 mV). The time constants of inactivation of barium current through $\alpha_{1C,77}$ were voltage-independent, while those of $\alpha_{1C,86}$ exhibited a strong voltage-dependence (see fig. 1 (B)). The isochronic inactivation curves (see fig. 1 (C)) were also different for the two calcium channel homologues. Thus, the slope of the inactivation curve for $\alpha_{1C,77}$ was steeper (slope factor k = –5.7 ± 0.3) than that for $\alpha_{1C,86}$ (k = –7.8 ± 0.2) and the potential for half-maximal inactivation for $\alpha_{1C,77}$ (–8.4 ± 1.1 mV) was less than half that for $\alpha_{1C,86}$ (–19.9 ± 0.5 mV). The differences between all parameters for the two constructs are statistically significant (n=12–16).

The most important difference in the inactivation properties between $\alpha_{1C,77}$ and $\alpha_{1C,86}$ became apparent when Ca^{2+} rather than Ba^{2+} was used as the charge carrier through the channels. Figure 2 shows current traces activated by voltage steps to +30 mV from a holding potential of –90 mV. When Ba^{2+} in the external medium was replaced by Ca^{2+} at equimolar concentrations (40 mM), the currents through both channels became smaller because of the higher permeability of Ba^{2+} compared with Ca^{2+}

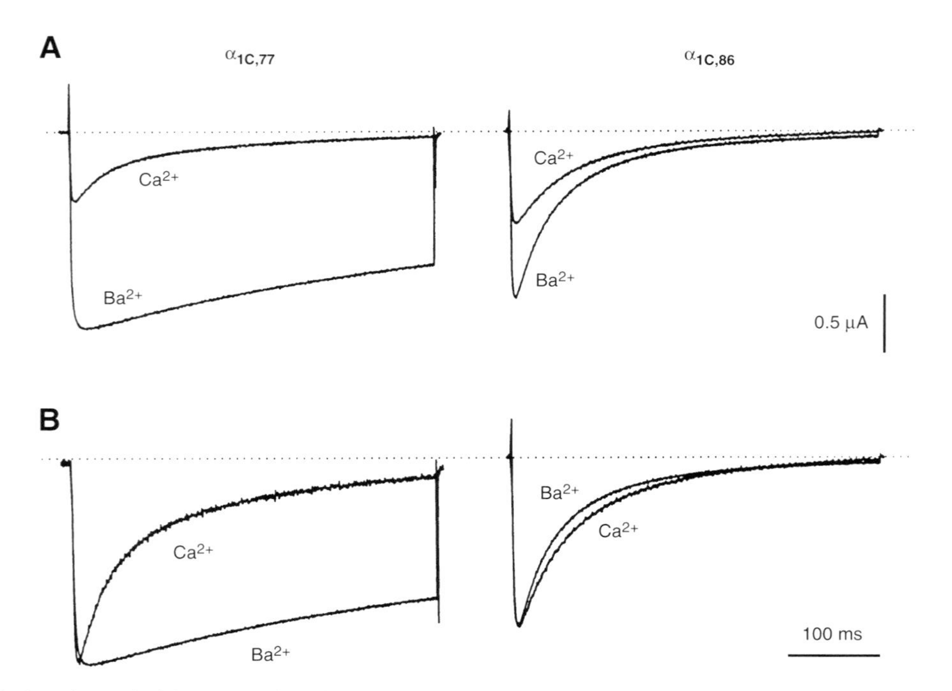

Fig. 2. Barium and calcium current through $\alpha_{1C,77}$ and $\alpha_{1C,86}$ were recorded in Xenopus oocytes after injection of BAPTA 40 mM (50 nl). Current traces were evoked by 400 ms depolarising steps from a holding potential of –90 mV to +30 mV. The oocytes were superfused with a bath solution containing Ba^{2+} 40 mM or Ca^{2+} 40 mM. A) Barium and calcium current recorded from the same oocyte expressing either $\alpha_{1C,77}$ or $\alpha_{1C,86}$. B) Calcium current traces from panel A normalised to peak barium current show that Ca^{2+}-dependent inactivation is present in $\alpha_{1C,77}$ but absent in $\alpha_{1C,86}$.

through calcium channels.[9] The replacement also induced much faster inactivation in $\alpha_{1C,77}$, but not in $\alpha_{1C,86}$. This is best seen in panel B of figure 2, in which peak calcium current has been scaled up to peak barium current. The much more rapid inactivation of calcium current compared with that of barium current in the natural splice variant $\alpha_{1C,77}$ is typical for L-type calcium channels under physiological conditions[10] and in heterologously expressed channels.[11,12] Surprisingly, the substitution of 81 amino acids in the carboxyl-terminal tail of $\alpha_{1C,77}$ confers inactivation properties that are completely different from those of $\alpha_{1C,86}$. The kinetics are not only much faster but are also independent of Ca^{2+} or Ba^{2+} as charge carriers. The slight prolongation in the time-course of calcium current as opposed to barium current (see fig. 2 (B; right) can be accounted for by different surface potentials for both ions.[13]

A crucial test for Ca^{2+}-dependent inactivation is the demonstration that it depends on the size of preceding calcium current.[10] This was demonstrated using a standard two-pulse protocol (fig. 3 (A)). The first pulse potential was stepped to different voltages to obtain a current–voltage relationship for calcium current (see fig. 3 (B)). Then, after a 50 ms interval at a holding potential of –90 mV, a test potential was applied to reactivate calcium current. If the current at the test potential is smallest when calcium current at the pulse potential is largest, Ca^{2+}-dependent inactivation is important (see fig. 3 (C)). Oocytes were usually subjected to two runs, one in Ba^{2+} solution and another in Ca^{2+} solution. Then, after each pulse potential, the peak currents at the test potential (–20 mV) were normalised to that current after a pulse potential to –40 mV. Subtraction of the normalised barium current at the test potential from the normalised calcium current at this potential showed that for $\alpha_{1C,77}$ the difference current matched the voltage-dependence of calcium current at the pulse potential. This indicates that inactivation of calcium current through $\alpha_{1C,77}$ at a test potential of +20 mV depends largely on the influx of Ca^{2+} during the preceding pulse potential at different voltages. In contrast, such a relationship could not be established for calcium current through $\alpha_{1C,86}$, indicating that inactivation of this channel is Ca^{2+}-independent (see fig. 3 (C)).

Since L-type calcium channels are highly sensitive to block by 1,4-dihydropyridines, we tested the sensitivity of $\alpha_{1C,77}$ and $\alpha_{1C,86}$ to (+)-isradipine. Barium current through both channels was potently inhibited by this drug, with IC_{50} values for $\alpha_{1C,77}$ and $\alpha_{1C,86}$ of 146 ± 12 nM (n=34) and 38 ± 5 nM (n=9), respectively. This shows that the isradipine-sensitivity of the two constructs was not related to the Ca^{2+}-sensitivity of inactivation.

Discussion

In this study we have shown that the replacement of 80 amino acids of $\alpha_{1C,77}$ in position 1572-1651 by 81 non-identical amino acids in $\alpha_{1C,86}$ resulted in completely different inactivation properties of the channels. These sequences constitute parts of the carboxyl-terminal regions and, hence, of the cytoplasmic tails of the α_{1C} subunits. The rapid voltage-dependent inactivation properties of the $\alpha_{1C,86}$ channel contrast

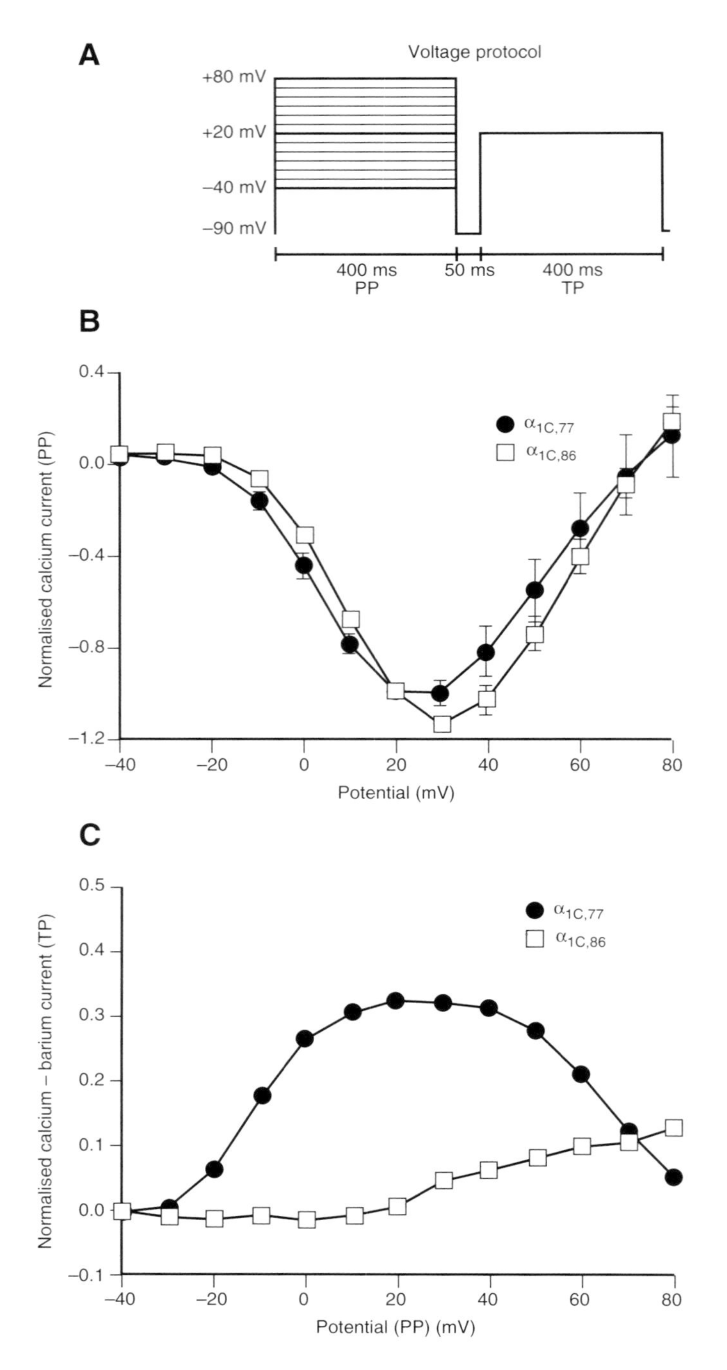

Fig. 3. A) Barium and calcium current in BAPTA-injected oocytes were elicited by a double-pulse protocol. 400 ms depolarising prepulses (PP), applied in 10 mV increments from –90 mV to voltages ranging from –40 mV to +80 mV, were followed by a 400 ms test pulse (TP) to +20 mV after a 50 ms pulse interval at –90 mV. B) Peak current amplitudes at PP were normalised to the PP peak current at +20 mV. C) Peak barium current amplitudes at TP were normalised to the current after a PP to –40 mV and were subtracted from similarly normalised calcium currents. Subtracted peak currents are plotted against the PP potential. Data points are means of 4 oocytes expressing $\alpha_{1C,77}$ and 7 expressing $\alpha_{1C,86}$.

with the much slower ones of $\alpha_{1C,77}$ in Ba^{2+} solution. Voltage-dependent inactivation of calcium channels has been attributed in part to sequences near or in the S6 segments of domains I, III and IV of α_1 subunits.[14,15] These structures were identical in our channels. However, recent studies have also implicated carboxyl-terminal segments as being involved in voltage-dependent inactivation.[16,17] Our results suggest that a stretch of 80/81 amino acids in the second quarter of the cytoplasmic tail is important for the large variability in the inactivation behaviour of class C calcium channels. Furthermore, this segment regulates not only the rate of voltage-dependent inactivation, but also the Ca^{2+}-dependent inactivation properties. The channel containing the $\alpha_{1C,86}$ subunit completely lacked Ca^{2+}-dependent inactivation, which, however, was very prominent with the $\alpha_{1C,77}$ subunit. These results are surprising, because the putative Ca^{2+}-binding EF hand motif in the carboxyl-terminal region near segment IVS6 of α_{1C}[6] has been shown to be essential for Ca^{2+}-dependent inactivation.[7] This motif, however, is located upstream of the variable 80/81-amino acid sequences in our constructs and is therefore identical in $\alpha_{1C,77}$ and $\alpha_{1C,86}$. At present we have no indication as to which of the 80/81 amino acids encoded by the alternative splice variants of exons 40–43 are responsible for the different inactivation properties of our α_{1C} subunits. However, it is interesting to note that $\alpha_{1C,86}$ has certain features in common with T-type calcium channels.

Acknowledgements

We thank H. van Hees for excellent technical assistance, and F. Hofmann (Munich) and V. Flockerzi (Heidelberg) for gifts of clones of β_1 and $\alpha_2\delta$ subunits. Financial support of grants from the Swiss National Science Foundation (31-45093.5) and by the Sandoz Foundation is gratefully acknowledged.

References

1. Hofmann F, Biel M, Flockerzi V. Molecular basis for Ca^{2+} channel diversity. Annu Rev Neurosci 1994; 17: 399–418
2. Catterall WA. Structure and function of voltage-gated ion channels. Annu Rev Biochem 1995; 64: 493–531
3. Soldatov NM. Genomic structure of human L-type Ca^{2+} channel. Genomics 1994; 22: 77–87
4. Perez-Reyes E, Wei X, Castellano A, et al. Molecular diversity of L-type calcium channels. J Biol Chem 1990; 265: 20430–6
5. Soldatov NM, Zühlke RD, Bouron A, et al. Molecular structures involved in L-type calcium channel inactivation. Role of the carboxyl-terminal region encoded by exons 40–42 in α_{1C} subunit in the kinetics and Ca^{2+}-dependence of inactivation. J Biol Chem 1997; 272: 3560–6
6. Babitch J. Channel hands. Nature 1990; 346: 321–2
7. De Leon M, Wang Y, Jones L, et al. Essential Ca^{2+}-binding motif for Ca^{2+}–sensitive inactivation of L-type Ca^{2+} channels. Science 1995; 270: 1502–6
8. Soldatov NM, Bouron A, Reuter H. Different voltage-dependent inhibition by dihydropyridines of human Ca^{2+} channel splice variants. J Biol Chem 1995; 270: 10540–3
9. Tsien RW, Hess P, McCleskey EW, et al. Calcium channels: mechanisms of selectivity, permeation, and block. Annu Rev Biophys Biophys Chem 1987; 16: 265–90
10. Eckert R, Chad JE. Inactivation of Ca channels. Prog Biophys Mol Biol 1984; 44: 215–67
11. Neely A, Olcese R, Wei X, et al. Ca^{2+}-dependent inactivation of a cloned cardiac Ca^{2+} channel α_1 subunit (α_{1C}) expressed in *Xenopus* oocytes. Biophys J 1994; 66: 1895–903
12. Zong XG, Hofmann F. Ca^{2+}-dependent inactivation of the class C L-type Ca^{2+} channel is a property of the alpha(1) subunit. FEBS Lett 1996; 378: 121–5

13. Hille B. Ionic channels of excitable membranes. Sunderland, Mass.: Sinauer Associates, 1992
14. Zhang J, Ellinor PT, Aldrich RW, et al. Molecular determinants of voltage-dependent inactivation in calcium channels. Nature 1994; 372: 97–100
15. Yatani A, Bahinski A, Wakamori M, et al. Alteration of channel characteristics by exchange of pore-forming regions between two structurally related Ca^{2+} channels. Mol Cell Biochem 1994; 140: 93–102
16. Klöckner U, Mikala G, Varadi M, et al. Involvement of the carboxyl-terminal region of the alpha(1) subunit in voltage-dependent inactivation of cardiac calcium channels. J Biol Chem 1995; 270: 17306–10
17. Schmid R, Seydl K, Baumgartner W, et al. Trypsin increases availability and open probability of cardiac L-type Ca^{2+} channels without affecting inactivation induced by Ca^{2+}. Biophys J 1995; 69: 1847–57

α_{1E}: an orphan calcium channel?

Emmanuel Bourinet,[1] Gerald Zamponi,[2] Joël Nargeot,[1] Terry P. Snutch[2]

[1] *Centre de Recherches de Biochimie Macromoléculaire, Centre National de la Recherche Scientifique, Montpellier, France;* [2] *Biotechnology Laboratory, University of British Columbia, Vancouver, British Columbia, Canada*

Ca^{2+} ions serve as crucial intracellular signals, mediating a diverse spectrum of Ca^{2+}-dependent physiological processes. The rapid entry of Ca^{2+} into excitable cells is mediated by a pharmacologically and physiologically heterogeneous family of voltage-activated calcium channels. A goal of many laboratories is to correlate the functional properties of particular subtypes of calcium channel with the regulation of specific Ca^{2+}-dependent physiological processes. Typically, in order to characterise calcium channel subtypes, a number of criteria are used. One functional distinction between calcium channel subtypes is based upon the magnitude of the depolarisation required to open the channel. Low-voltage-activated (LVA; T-type) calcium channels activate at relatively negative membrane potentials (in the range of –60 to –40 mV), while high-voltage-activated (HVA) calcium channels activate at more positive membrane potentials (usually –20 mV or higher). Sensitivity to various classes of pharmacological agents and peptide toxins further defines the various calcium channel subtypes. According to pharmacological criteria, at least three types of HVA calcium channel have been identified (L, N and P/Q types).[1]

Subunit composition of calcium channels

Biochemical and molecular cloning studies have shown that calcium channels are multimeric complexes consisting of a pore-forming α_1 subunit and two or three ancillary subunits, namely $\alpha_2\beta$ subunits in neuronal membranes and an additional γ subunit in skeletal muscle.[2] To date, six distinct α_1 subunit genes (α_{1A}, α_{1B}, α_{1C}, α_{1D}, α_{1E} and α_{1S}) and four β subunit genes (β_1, β_2, β_3 and β_4) have been identified. Based on a comparison of their amino acid sequences, α_1 subunits can be divided into two groups (fig. 1). Functional expression and immunoprecipitation studies have shown that the α_{1C}, α_{1D} and α_{1S} subunits are present in those calcium channels that are sensitive to blockade by dihydropyridines (L-type channels).[2–4] In contrast, the α_{1A}, α_{1B} and α_{1E} subunits are associated with three distinct types of calcium channel: the α_{1A} subunit occurs in a channel that displays similar properties to both P- and Q-type channels,[5–7] and the α_{1B} subunit is associated with an ω-CTx-sensitive N-type channel,[8–10] whereas the α_{1E} subunit is not linked to any of the functionally described native calcium channel subtypes.

The physiological and pharmacological properties of the rat α_{1E} subunit expressed in *Xenopus* oocytes are not identical to those of T-type channels expressed in cardiac and endocrine cells, although they display several properties shared by a subset of neuronal mid- to low-threshold calcium channels. These include: relatively negative potentials for half-activation and -inactivation; apparently high sensitivity to blockade

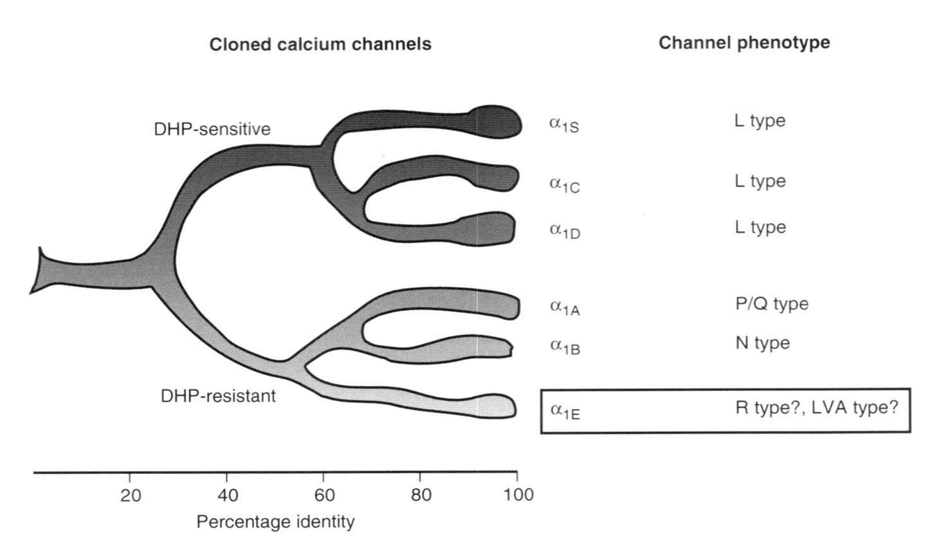

Fig. 1. Comparison of the amino acid sequences of cloned calcium channel α_1 subunits shows two distinct groups. One group is formed by α_{1S}, α_{1C} and α_{1D} and corresponds to the different subtypes of L-type channel. The second group consists of α_{1A} and α_{1B} (P-/Q- and N-type channels, respectively) and α_{1E}, for which the native counterpart remains to be conclusively established. DHP = dihydropyridine.

by Ni^{2+}; and insensitivity to low concentrations of dihydropyridines, ω-CTx-GVIA and ω-Aga-IVA.[11,12] On this basis, and in conjunction with *in situ* data indicating a high level of α_{1E} expression in certain neurons that generate low-threshold, Ca^{2+}-dependent spikes, Soong and co-workers[11] suggested that α_{1E} constitutes a novel type of LVA calcium channel. However, this notion is controversial and, based on the differences between the kinetic and voltage-dependent properties of human α_{1E} and classical T-type channels, Williams and colleagues have proposed that α_{1E} more closely resembles an HVA rather than LVA calcium channel.[13] Moreover, based on the apparent similarities between the recombinant α_{1E} current and that of a native channel resistant to dihydropyridines and peptide toxins (ω-CTx-GVIA, ω-CTx-MVIIC, ω-Aga-IVA), Tsien and co-workers have suggested that the α_{1E} channel mediates a residual HVA 'R-type' current of the type found in rat cerebellar granule cells.[14,15]

Pore properties as a tool in the classification of cloned calcium channels

Many of the parameters used to define cloned and native calcium channels (e.g. kinetics, voltage-dependence) are subject to modulation by various intracellular constituents, including G proteins, protein kinases and divalent ion species. In order to characterise the α_{1E} channel in a more rigorous manner, we compared the ionic selectivity of the inner pore of the α_{1E} channel with that of other cloned neuronal calcium channels.[16] Native HVA and LVA calcium channels exhibit distinct permeability characteristics with respect to Ca^{2+}, Ba^{2+} and Sr^{2+} ions (table I). In general, HVA channels are more permeable to Ba^{2+} than to Ca^{2+}, while LVA (T-type) channels are at least as permeable to Ca^{2+} as to Ba^{2+}.[17]

Table 1. Relative conductance of Ca^{2+}, Ba^{2+} and Sr^{2+} through native calcium channels[16]

	Native channel type (gene)					
	T (unknown)	L ($\alpha_{1C}\alpha_{1D}\alpha_{1S}$)	N (α_{1B})	P (α_{1A})	Q (α_{1A})	R (unknown)
Current ratios						
$I_{Ca} : I_{Ba}$	1–1.8[18–24]	0.2–0.6[19,20,22,23,25–27]	0.6–0.8[20,28]	0.5[29]	Unknown	0.8[15]
$I_{Sr} : I_{Ba}$	1.5–1.9[18,21,30]	0.6–0.8[28,31]	0.7[28]	Unknown	Unknown	Unknown
Relative conductance	$Sr^{2+} > Ca^{2+} \geq Ba^{2+}$	$Ba^{2+} > Sr^{2+} > Ca^{2+}$	$Ba^{2+} > Sr^{2+} > Ca^{2+}$	$Ba^{2+} > Ca^{2+}$	Unknown	$Ba^{2+} > Ca^{2+}$

Abbreviations: I_{Ba} = barium current; I_{Ca} = calcium current; I_{Sr} = strontium current.

Prior to this study, there had been no direct comparisons of the conductance characteristics of cloned neuronal calcium channels. In agreement with previous studies indicating that native HVA calcium channels carry larger currents with Ba^{2+} than with Ca^{2+} or Sr^{2+} (see table I), we found that peak whole-cell currents for HVA α_{1A}, α_{1B} and α_{1C} channels were greatest with Ba^{2+} (fig. 2 (A)). The absolute current

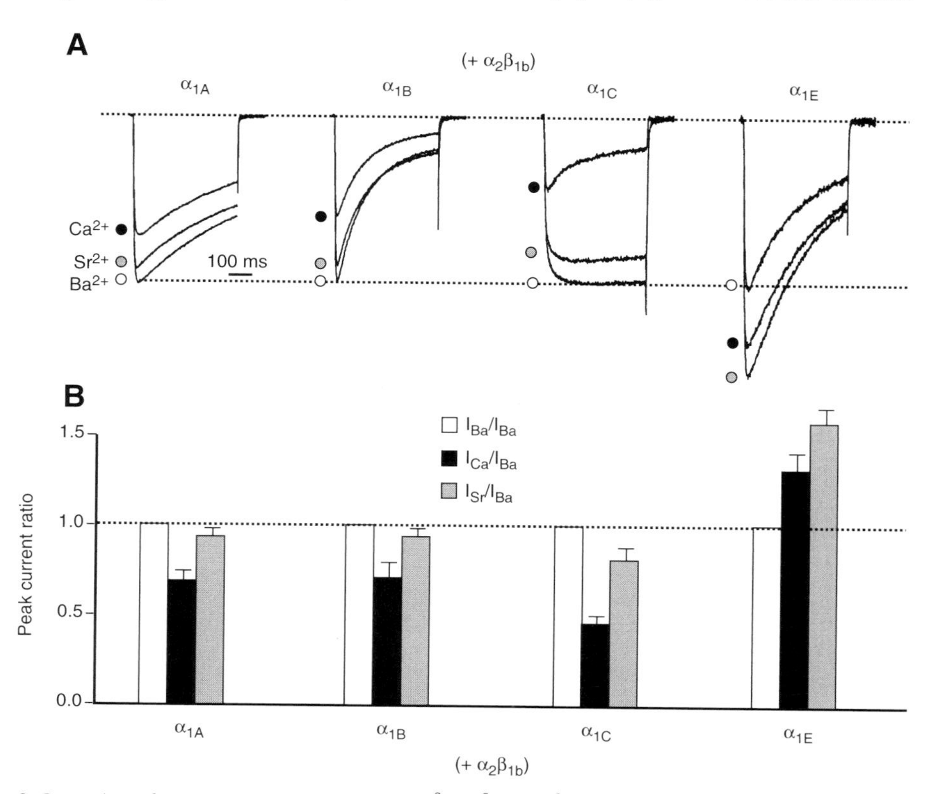

Fig. 2. Comparison of macroscopic currents carried by Ba^{2+}, Ca^{2+} and Sr^{2+} 5 mM. A) Current traces obtained at the peak of the current–voltage relationship for α_{1A}, α_{1B}, α_{1C} and α_{1E} transiently expressed in Xenopus oocytes (with α_2 and β_{1b} subunits). Ba^{2+} produces the largest whole-cell currents for α_{1A}, α_{1B} and α_{1C} but the smallest whole-cell currents for α_{1E} channels. Note the pronounced Ca^{2+}-dependent inactivation of α_{1C}. B) Peak current values for different ionic species, normalised to that for Ba^{2+} (I_{max} ion/I_{max} Ba^{2+}). Note the different conductivity profile of the α_{1E} channel. Standard errors are based on 5–12 determinations. Data were obtained in the two-electrode voltage-clamp mode. BAPTA was injected into the oocytes to suppress the endogenous Ca^{2+}-activated chloride current. (Reproduced with permission.[16])

ratios obtained with these three recombinant HVA calcium channels (see fig. 2 (B)) were virtually identical to those reported for their respective native counterparts (P-/Q-, N- and L-type channels; see table I). Also consistent with native cardiac and neuronal L-type channel behaviour, substitution of Ca^{2+} for Ba^{2+} selectively increased the rate of inactivation of α_{1C} currents.[32] Overall, the results indicate that recombinant HVA Ca^{2+} channels resemble their native counterparts in their ionic selectivity and conductance characteristics.

In contrast to the established HVA channels, Sr^{2+} and Ca^{2+} current through the α_{1E} channel exceeded that of Ba^{2+} (see fig. 2 (A)). As summarised in table I, this pattern of ionic selectivity is characteristic of LVA calcium channels and is seen in a variety of tissues, including atrial and ventricular myocytes,[20,24] skeletal and smooth muscle cells,[19,27] pancreatic β cells,[23] and both peripheral and central neurons.[18,21,22,30] One exception to this general trend is an unusual T-type channel in the thalamic reticular nucleus which exhibits greater Ba^{2+} than Ca^{2+} conductance.[33]

Overall, our results with the α_{1E} channel are consistent with those reported for the majority of LVA calcium channels. In contrast, the R-type channel in cerebellar granule cells[14,15] exhibits a larger Ba^{2+} conductance than Ca^{2+} conductance. However, it is possible that this resistant current comprises multiple components, one of which may well exhibit the properties observed for α_{1E}.[34,35]

Coexpressed α_2 and β subunits have been shown to modulate the biophysical properties of several α_1 subunits.[2] We therefore examined the conductance properties of the isolated α_{1E} subunit to rule out possible confounding effects of auxiliary subunits. Exclusion of the α_2 and β subunits did not significantly affect the barium:calcium current conductance ratio for either the α_{1A} or α_{1E} subunits,[16] suggesting that the basic conductance properties are intrinsic features of the α_1 subunit of the calcium channel.

While it is possible that some of the cellular effects are related to altered channel kinetics,[36] single-channel recordings further support the notion that the dependence of cell conductance on the ionic species is an intrinsic pathway property. Figure 3 compares the single-channel properties of α_{1C} and α_{1E} subunits: while the α_{1E} unitary current was similar for Ba^{2+} and Ca^{2+}, the α_{1C} unitary current was approximately 55% smaller for Ca^{2+} than for Ba^{2+}. For the α_{1E} channel the magnitude of the cellular current was as follows: $Sr^{2+} > Ca^{2+} > Ba^{2+}$. In contrast, single-channel conductances were virtually identical with respect to Ba^{2+}, Ca^{2+} and Sr^{2+}. From a preliminary analysis of the open probability at the plateau of the activation curve, we suggest that the higher conductances obtained with Sr^{2+} and Ca^{2+} ions are attributable to an increase in the open probability of the channel and a reduction in the number of blank sweeps.[16] A similar dependence of open probability on cation type has previously been described for native low-threshold channels.[36,37]

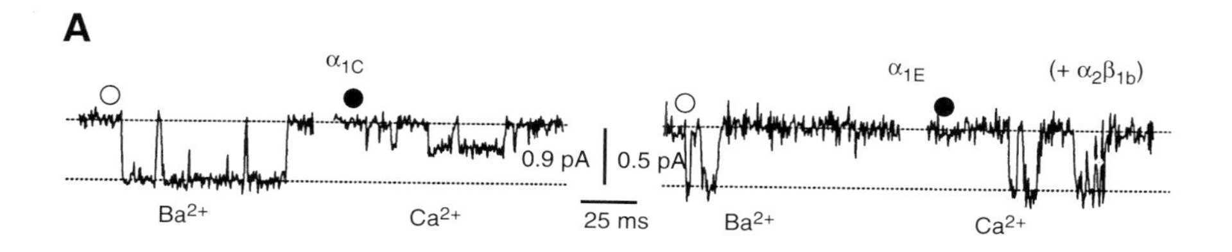

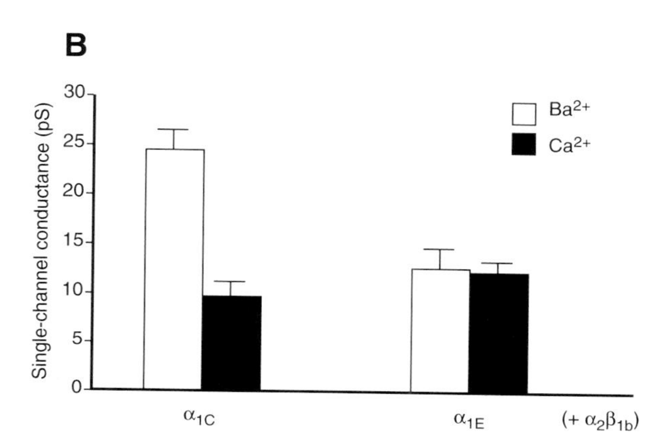

Fig. 3. Dependence of single-channel conductance on the ionic species. A) Current traces for α_{1C} and α_{1E} were evoked by stepped depolarisation from −100 to 0 mV in the cell-attached patch mode. Barium currents were normalised to the same level to facilitate comparison. NB: the unitary current for α_{1C} is of lower amplitude with Ca^{2+} than with Ba^{2+}, whereas the amplitude for α_{1E} is not significantly affected by the permeant ion. B) Summarised results (± standard deviations) obtained for α_{1C} and α_{1E} channels. Membrane potential was reduced towards 0 mV by placing oocytes in a high K^+ concentration. The sampling frequency for acquisition was 10 kHz and records were filtered at 1 kHz. For α_{1C} recordings, BayK8644 5 mM was included in the pipette solution. (Reproduced with permission.[16])

Conclusion

With regard to the debate concerning the nature of the α_{1E} subunit, a picture emerges of conductance characteristics which qualitatively resemble those of most LVA (T-type) calcium channels. Thus, the α_{1E} subunit appears to represent a new member of this family.[11] What is the native neuronal calcium current mediated by the α_{1E} channel? How can we characterise the native current without specific pharmacological tools? At present, these questions remain to be answered. If the residual cerebellar granular cell R-type channel represents a homogenous population of channels,[14] then on the basis of its conductance properties we can conclude that the α_{1E} channel is unlikely to belong to this type of calcium channel. However, a heterogeneous population of calcium channels may contribute to the resistant R-type current in cerebellar granular cells.[34] One of these components, the G2 channel, appears similar in many respects to the recombinant α_{1E} subunit. For example, they both exhibit unitary currents of approximately 0.5 pA at 0 mV (in Ba^{2+} 90 mM and 100 mM solutions), have similar slope conductances (13–15 pS) and have activation thresholds at relatively negative potentials (Bourinet and Snutch, unpublished observations).[34,38] Unfortunately, at this point no information is available regarding the relative Ba^{2+}:Ca^{2+}:Sr^{2+} conductances of the G2 channel and we cannot compare it to the α_{1E} channel. Further evidence for the existence of multiple types of currents resistant to the actions of dihydropyrines and peptide blockers has also recently been reported in dorsal root ganglion (DRG) cells.[39] Interestingly, the conductance properties of the DRG cell channels more closely resemble those of the α_{1E} channel than the cerebellar granular cell R-type channel. Overall, there are likely to be a number of calcium channels that are distinct from the classical T-, L-, N-, and P-/Q-types, and these have yet to be described fully, either molecularly or in their native environments. It is also likely that in the future it will be necessary to revise the notion that calcium channels can be functionally divided into LVA and HVA subtypes; rather, further investigation is likely to reveal a continuum of voltage-dependent properties.

References

1. Zamponi GW, Bourinet E, Snutch TP. Limitations of Ni^{2+} ions as a tool for discrimination between high- and low-threshold calcium channels. In: Tsien RW, Clozel J-P, Nargeot J, editors. Low-Voltage-Activated T-type Calcium Channels. Proceedings from the International Electrophysiology Meeting: 1996 Oct 21–22; Montpellier, France. Chester, UK: Adis International Ltd, 1998: 92–8
2. Stea A, Soong TW, Snutch TP. Voltage-gated calcium channels. Ligand- and voltage-gated ion channels. In: North RA, editor. Handbook of receptors and channels. Boca Raton, Fla.: CRC Press, 1995: 113–52
3. Tomlinson JW, Stea A, Bourinet E, et al. Functional properties of a neuronal class C L-type calcium channel. Neuropharmacology 1993; 32: 1117–26
4. Williams ME, Feldman DH, McCue AF, et al. Structure and functional expression of α_1, α_2, and β subunits of a novel human neuronal calcium channel subtype. Neuron 1992; 8: 71–84
5. Mori Y, Friedrich T, Kim M-S, et al. Primary structure and functional expression from complementary DNA of a brain calcium channel. Nature 1991; 350: 398–402
6. Sather WA, Tanabe T, Zhang J-F, et al. Distinctive biophysical and pharmacological properties of class A (BI) calcium channel α_1 subunits. Neuron 1993; 11: 291–303
7. Stea A, Tomlinson JW, Soong TW, et al. The localization and functional properties of a rat brain α_{1A} calcium channel reflect similarities to neuronal Q- and P-type channels. Proc Natl Acad Sci U S A 1993; 91: 10576–80
8. Dubel SJ, Starr TV, Hell J, et al. Molecular cloning of the α_1 subunit of an ω-conotoxin-sensitive calcium channel. Proc Natl Acad Sci U S A 1992; 89: 5058–62
9. Fujita Y, Mynlieff M, Dirksen RT, et al. Primary structure and functional expression of the ω-conotoxin-sensitive N-type calcium channel from rabbit brain. Neuron 1993; 10: 585–98
10. Williams ME, Brust PF, Feldman DH, et al. Structure and functional expression of an ω-conotoxin-sensitive human N-type calcium channel. Science 1992; 257: 389–95
11. Soong TW, Stea A, Hodson CD, et al. Structure and functional expression of a member of the low voltage-activated calcium channel family. Science 1993; 260: 1133–6
12. Zamponi GW, Bourinet E, Snutch TP. Nickel block of a family of neuronal calcium channels. Subtype- and subunit-dependent action at multiple sites. J Membrane Biol 1996; 151: 77–90
13. Williams ME, Marubio LM, Deal CR, et al. Structure and functional characterization of neuronal α_{1E} Ca^{2+} channel subtype. J Biol Chem 1994; 269: 22347–57
14. Randall A, Tsien RW. Pharmacological dissection of multiple types of Ca^{2+} channel currents in rat cerebellar granule neurons. J Neurosci 1995; 15: 2995–3012
15. Zhang J-F, Randall AD, Ellinor PT, et al. Distinctive pharmacology and kinetics of cloned neuronal Ca^{2+} channels and their possible counterparts in mammalian CNS neurons. Neuropharmacology 1993; 32: 1075–80
16. Bourinet E, Zamponi GW, Stea A, et al. The α_{1E} calcium channel exhibits permeation properties similar to low-voltage-activated calcium channels. J Neurosci 1996; 16: 4983–93
17. Hille B. Ionic channels of excitable membrane. Sunderland, Mass.: Sinauer Associates, 1992
18. Akaike N, Kostyuk PG, Osipchuk YV. Dihydropyridine-sensitive low-threshold calcium channels in isolated rat hypothalamic neurons. J Physiol 1989; 412: 181–95
19. Beam KG, Knudson CM. Calcium current in embryonic and neonatal mammalian skeletal muscle. J Gen Physiol 1986; 91: 781–98
20. Bean BP. Two kinds of calcium channels in canine atrial cells. Differences in kinetics, selectivity, and pharmacology. J Gen Physiol 1984; 86: 1–30
21. Carbone E, Lux HD. Kinetics and selectivity of a low-voltage-activated calcium current in chick and rat sensory neurons. J Physiol 1987; 386: 547–70

22. Fox AP, Nowycky MC, Tsien RW. Kinetic and pharmacological properties distinguishing three types of calcium currents in chick sensory neurons. J Physiol 1986; 394: 149–72
23. Hiriat M, Matteson DR. Na channels and two types of Ca^{2+} channels in rat pancreatic B cells identified with the reverse hemolytic plaque assay. J Gen Physiol 1988; 91: 617–39
24. Nilius B, Hess P, Lansman JB, et al. A novel type of cardiac calcium channel in ventricular cells. Nature 1986; 316: 443–6
25. Almers W, McCleskey EW. Non-selective conductance in calcium channels of frog muscle: calcium selectivity in a single-file pore. J Physiol 1994; 353: 585–608
26. Hess P, Tsien RW. Mechanism of ion permeation through calcium channels. Nature 1984; 309: 453–6
27. Neveu D, Quignard J-F, Fernandez A, et al. Differential β-adrenergic regulation and phenotypic modulation of voltage-activated calcium currents in rat aortic myocytes. J Physiol 1994; 479: 171–82
28. Kasai H, Neher E. Dihydropyridine-sensitive and ω-conotoxin-sensitive calcium channels in a mammalian neuroblastoma-glioma cell line. J Physiol 1992; 448: 161–88
29. Regan LJ. Voltage-dependent calcium currents in Purkinje cells from rat cerebellar vermis. J Neurosci 1991; 11: 2259–69
30. Takahashi K, Ueno S, Akaike N. Kinetic properties of T-type Ca^{2+} currents in isolated rat hippocampal CA1 pyramidal neurons. J Neurophysiol 1991; 65: 148–55
31. Hagiwara S, Ohmori H. Studies of calcium channels in rat clonal pituitary cells with patch electrode voltage clamp. J Physiol 1982; 49: 807–18
32. Imredy JP, Yue DT. Mechanism of Ca^{2+}-sensitive inactivation of L-type Ca^{2+} channels. Neuron 1994; 12: 1301–18
33. Huguenard JR, Prince DA. A novel T-type current underlies prolonged Ca^{2+}-dependent burst firing in GABAergic neurons of rat thalamic reticular nucleus. J Neurosci 1992; 12: 3804–17
34. Tottene A, Moretti A, Pietrobon D. Functional diversity of P-type and R-type calcium channels in rat cerebellar neurons. J Neurosci 1996; 16: 6353–63
35. Tottene A, Forti L, Moretti A, et al. G2 and G3: two different R-type (toxin-resistant) calcium channels coexpressed in rat cerebellar granule cells. In: Tsien RW, Clozel J-P, Nargeot J, editors. Low-Voltage-Activated T-type Calcium Channels. Proceedings from the International Electrophysiology Meeting: 1996 Oct 21–22; Montpellier, France. Chester, UK: Adis International Ltd, 1998: 72–9
36. McDonald TF, Pelzer S, Trautwein W, et al. Regulation and modulation of calcium channels in cardiac, skeletal, and smooth muscle cells. Physiol Rev 1994; 74: 365–507
37. Shuba YM, Teslenko VI, Savchenko AN, et al. The effect of permeant ions on single calcium channel activation in mouse neuroblastoma cells: ion–channel interaction. J Physiol 1991; 443: 25–44
38. Forti L, Tottene A, Moretti A, et al. Three novel types of voltage-dependent calcium channels in rat cerebellar neurons. J Neurosci 1994; 14: 5243–56
39. Hilaire C, Diochot S, Desmadryl G, et al. Toxin-resistant calcium currents in embryonic mouse sensory neurons. Neuroscience 80: 267–76

Studies on the regulation of the human neuronal α_{1E} *calcium channel by* β *and* $\alpha_2\delta$ *subunits*

Lutz Birnbaumer,[1,2,4,5] Ning Qin,[1] Riccardo Olcese,[1] Erwin Tareilus,[1] Enrico Stefani[1,3,4]

[1] Department of Anesthesiology, [2] Department of Biological Chemistry and [3] Department of Physiology, UCLA School of Medicine, and [4] Brain Research Institute and [5] Molecular Biology Institute, University of California, Los Angeles, California, USA

Summary

β subunits regulate activation and inactivation of and interact with more than one site on α_{1E}, and are essential for expression on the surface of Xenopus laevis *oocytes. Like β subunits, $\alpha_2\delta$ also modulates activation and inactivation of α_{1E}, and does so in parallel with that of β subunits. A minimum structural model is proposed, in which $\alpha_{1E}\beta$ is the minimum channel structure that is regulated by $\alpha_2\delta$ and, most likely, by a second β subunit.*

Introduction

Analysis of the subunit composition of voltage-gated calcium channels has shown that they are invariably formed from four subunits: α_1, β, α_2 and δ, of which the last two are a proteolytically processed disulphide-linked dimer that originates from a single precursor mRNA. Six non-allelic α_1 genes, four non-allelic β genes and one $\alpha_2\delta$ gene have thus far been discovered (reviewed by Perez-Reyes and Schneider[1]), and the transcripts of most (if not all) genes are subject to alternative splicing. This gives rise to a large degree of molecular diversity, based on the genes responsible for the components that make up the functional channel and the processing to which the individual subunit pre-RNA molecules are subjected. Pore formation, voltage sensing and drug/toxin binding are properties conferred by the α_1 subunits.[2] Correlative studies based on functional properties of cloned α_1 subunits expressed in conjunction with β and $\alpha_2\delta$ subunits in eukaryotic cells, and determination of the sites of expression of the cloned α_1 subunits, have indicated that: α_{1S} forms the skeletal muscle calcium channel; α_{1C} forms the cardiac, smooth muscle calcium channel and a dihydropyridine-sensitive type of neuronal calcium channel; α_{1D} is responsible primarily for the dihydropyridine-sensitive receptor/$G_{i/o}$-regulated calcium channel found in endocrine cells; and α_{1B} forms the dihydropyridine-insensitive receptor/$G_{i/o}$-regulated calcium channel found in neurons (although α_{1A}- and α_{1E}-based channels may also be regulated by $G_{i/o}$). Investigation of subcellular distribution places both α_{1B} and α_{1A} subunits in presynaptic terminals, and functional studies indicate that N-type channels are formed by α_{1B} subunits and Q-type channels by α_{1A} subunits. Although subcellular distribution suggests α_{1A} to be also responsible for P-type channels in cerebellar Purkinje cells, the pharmacological properties of expressed α_{1A} subunits have not mimicked those of P-type channels closely enough to date for this to be unequivocally demonstrated. This could be because the exact α_1 subunit that forms P-type channels has not yet been cloned, because P-type channels are formed by specific splice variants of α_{1A} that have not yet been properly assembled or because the pharmacological behaviour of these channels depends not only on the identity of the α_{1A} subunit, but also on its association with particular β and $\alpha_2\delta$ subunits.

The most elusive molecular identity is that of the T-type calcium channel. Of the α_1 subunits cloned, the one that comes closest to exhibiting T-type properties is α_{1E}. It has permeation properties expected for T-type calcium channels[3] and activates at lower voltages than all other α_1 subunits. However, the voltages at which it begins to activate and the kinetic profile of its blockade by Ni^{2+}[4] differ from the kinetic profiles of and Ni^{2+} blockade observed in T-type calcium channels. Whether or not α_{1E} subunits are responsible for a subclass of T-type current remains controversial. As shown elsewhere in this book (see Armstrong pp. 5–15), T-type currents are not generated by a homogeneous set of channels.

Here follows a summary of the effects of β and $\alpha_2\delta$ subunits on α_{1E}, as seen after their expression in *Xenopus* oocytes and upon analysis of direct protein–protein interactions. The implications of our discovery that oocytes express an endogenous β subunit that is essential for the functional and structural maturation of any α_1 subunit will also be discussed.

Effects of β subunits on activation and inactivation

Activation

α_1 subunits are the pore-forming, voltage-sensing and drug-binding components of functional calcium channel complexes. Their gating behaviour is profoundly affected by the so-called regulatory or auxiliary β and $\alpha_2\delta$ subunits. A regulatory role for a β subunit was first demonstrated by the transfection and expression in stable form of β_{1a} in L cells expressing α_{1S}, the skeletal muscle α_1 subunit.[5] Studies in which α_{1C} was expressed in oocytes in the presence and absence of a β subunit (β_{2a}) showed that this regulatory effect is complex and is best summarised as an improvement of the coupling between voltage sensing (charge movement) and pore opening.[6] While this effect is very marked with α_{1C}, often giving the impression that the β subunit may be increasing expression when perhaps most of the action is on coupling, it is also observed with α_{1E}. Coupling of charge movement to pore opening is much tighter in α_{1E} than in α_{1C}.[7] The primary effect of β subunits is thus not one of left-shifting the overall voltage–conductance relationship, but rather one of switching gating modes so that the proportion of channels that activate with half-activation potentials of around 0 mV is increased from approximately 50 to 75–80%. This is accompanied by a reduction in the proportion of channels that are activated by half-activation potentials of around 50 mV. Depending on the β subunit, this is also accompanied by an increase in the absolute $P_{o,max}$ through a reduction in the number of channels trapped in a non-opening gating mode (nulls[8]).[9] Importantly, all β subunits had the same qualitative effect on α_{1E} activation, regardless of the gene of origin or the type of splice variant (fig. 1).

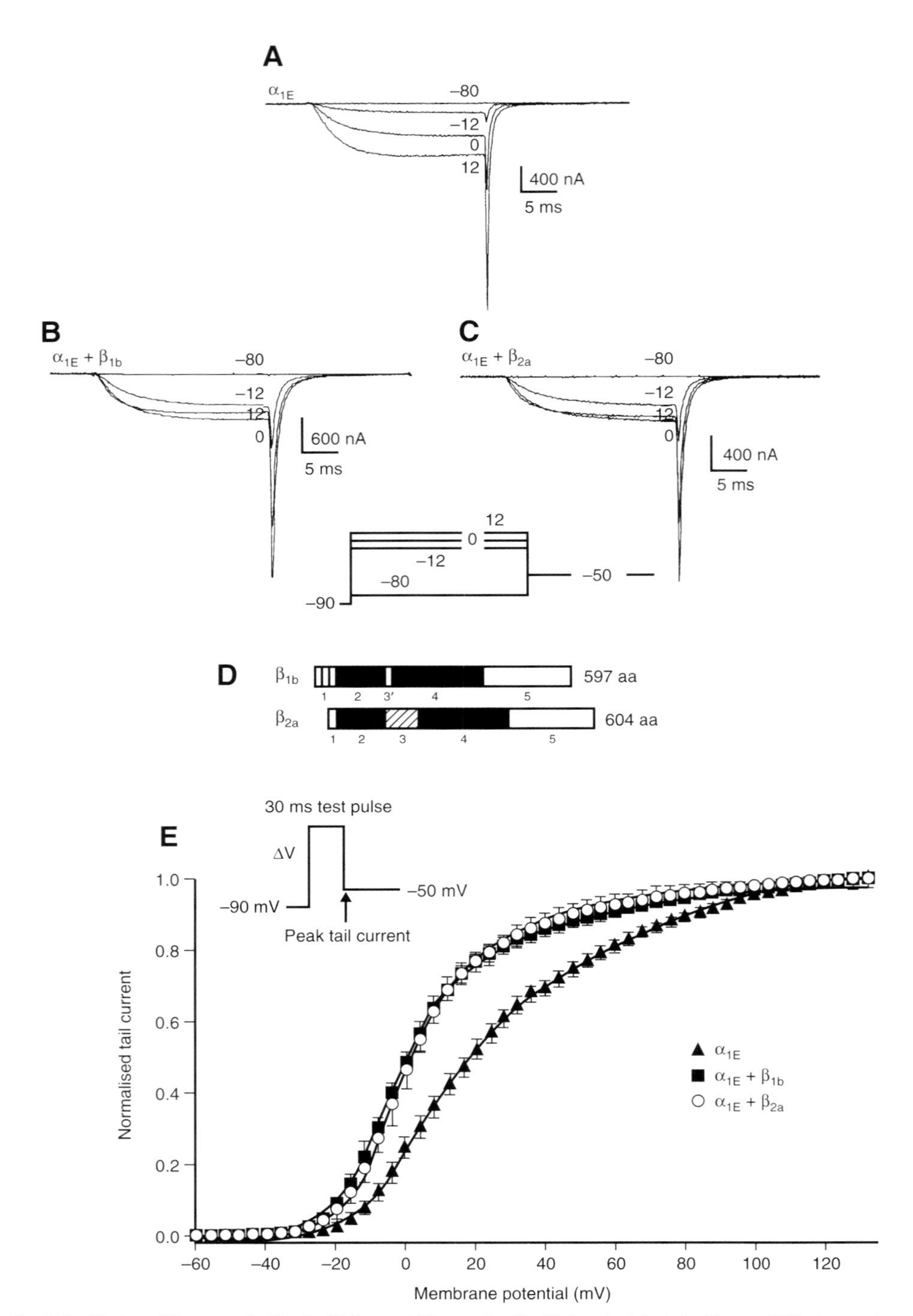

Fig. 1. Facilitation of (A) α_{1E} activation by (B) β_{1b} and (C) β_{2a} subunits. D) Oocytes injected with α_{1E} cRNA alone or in combination with cRNA of β_{1b} or the β_{2a} subunits were analysed for calcium channel currents using the cut-open vaseline-gap technique and Ba^{2+} as the charge carrier. E) Note that β subunits accelerate activation and promote a left shift in the conductance–voltage curve. Curves fitted using two Boltzmann distributions showed the effect to be related mainly to an increase in the amplitude of a component that is activated between 0 and 5 mV. NB: the effects of the two β subunits are indistinguishable.[10]

Inactivation

In contrast to α_{1C}, α_{1E} channels undergo rapid voltage-induced inactivation; this is strongly modulated by β subunits in a type-specific manner. The first report on the abilities of different β subunits to confer differential inactivation properties on an α_1 subunit was in a study of inactivation of Doe-1.[11] This was subsequently extended to other α_1 subunits (e.g. relative to other β subunits, the slowest inactivation of α_{1A} channels was reported in the presence of β_{2a}[12]). The use of α_{1E}, which in contrast to Doe-1 and α_{1A} expresses well in *Xenopus* oocytes without the need for simultaneous coexpression of an exogenous β subunit,[4] showed that the effects of β_{2a} and β_{1b} differed not in the extent to which they accelerated inactivation but in that the two β subunits had opposing effects. β_{1b} accelerated inactivation and left-shifted the potential at which a given protocol promotes 50% inactivation, whereas β_{2a} had the opposite effect: inactivation was established more slowly and 50% inactivation occurred at higher potentials (fig. 2). The β region responsible for the opposing effects on α_{1E} inactivation was localised in the N terminal.[10] A variable region in the 'middle' of the β_1 and β_2 molecules, inserted between two highly conserved domains, was subsequently found to be a second region with the ability to affect α_{1E} inactivation. This region is encoded in two alternative exons,[13] one of which encodes only 7 amino acids, of which only one varies from one β subunit to another; the other encodes 45 (β_2) or 52 (β_1) amino acids.[14] Compared with their short counterparts, β subunits with long middle sections slow inactivation and cause a right shift in the voltage-dependence for steady-state inactivation. In contrast to the N termini, the effect of the long/short middle domain is cryptic (i.e. only seen when the inactivation-setting N-terminal domains are mutationally removed). Further studies are therefore necessary to determine the importance, if any, of this middle domain in the regulation of α_{1E} inactivation.[15]

Effect of $\alpha_2\delta$ on α_{1E} and $\alpha_{1E}\beta$ channels

Expression of exogenous $\alpha_2\delta$ in *Xenopus* oocytes has profound effects on the kinetics of activation, deactivation and inactivation of α_{1E}. The accelerating effect of $\alpha_2\delta$ on α_{1E} activation and deactivation are illustrated in figure 3. The coexpression of neither β_{1b} nor β_{2a} altered these effects of $\alpha_2\delta$. The effect on deactivation was more pronounced than that on activation, so that the resulting conductance–voltage relationships were right-shifted relative to those obtained without $\alpha_2\delta$. Likewise, $\alpha_2\delta$ accelerated inactivation, the effect being additive to that of β_{1b} and opposed to that of β_{2a}. As a result, the fastest-inactivating α_{1E} was obtained by expression of the $\alpha_{1E}\beta_{1b}\alpha_2\delta$ complex. The slowest α_{1E} channels were given by $\alpha_{1E}\beta_{2a}$. Figure 4 illustrates representative traces obtained at 10 mV from rapidly and slowly inactivating α_{1E} calcium channels. It can be seen that adjustment of the subunit composition can vary the rate of inactivation of α_{1E} within the same cellular environment (in this case the *Xenopus* oocyte) by as much as a factor of 10.

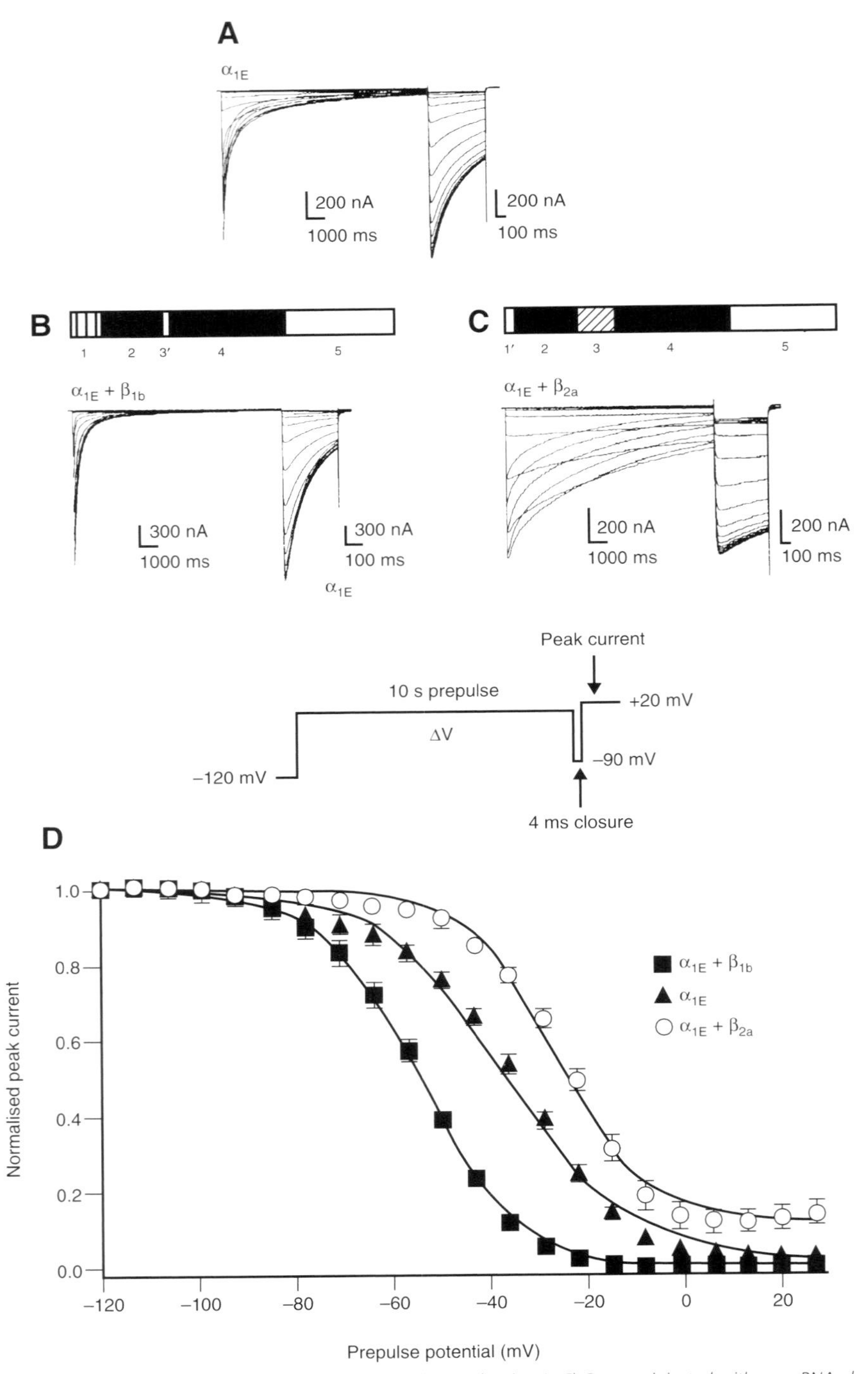

Fig. 2. Differential modulation of α_{1E} inactivation by β_{1b} and β_{2a} subunits. A–C) Oocytes injected with α_{1E} cRNA alone or in combination with cRNA of β_{1b} or the β_{2a} subunits were analysed for voltage-induced inactivation following the pulse protocols shown on the figure. D) Steady state inactivation of α_{1E}, $\alpha_{1E}\beta_{1b}$ and $\alpha_{1E}\beta_{2a}$ channels. NB: in contrast to activation, the two β subunits have opposing effects on inactivation. Other experiments showed that the opposing effect is conferred on the β subunit by the N terminal and that in the absence of an N terminal the long form of the middle section of β_{2a} can also confer the ability to delay channel inactivation on a β subunit.

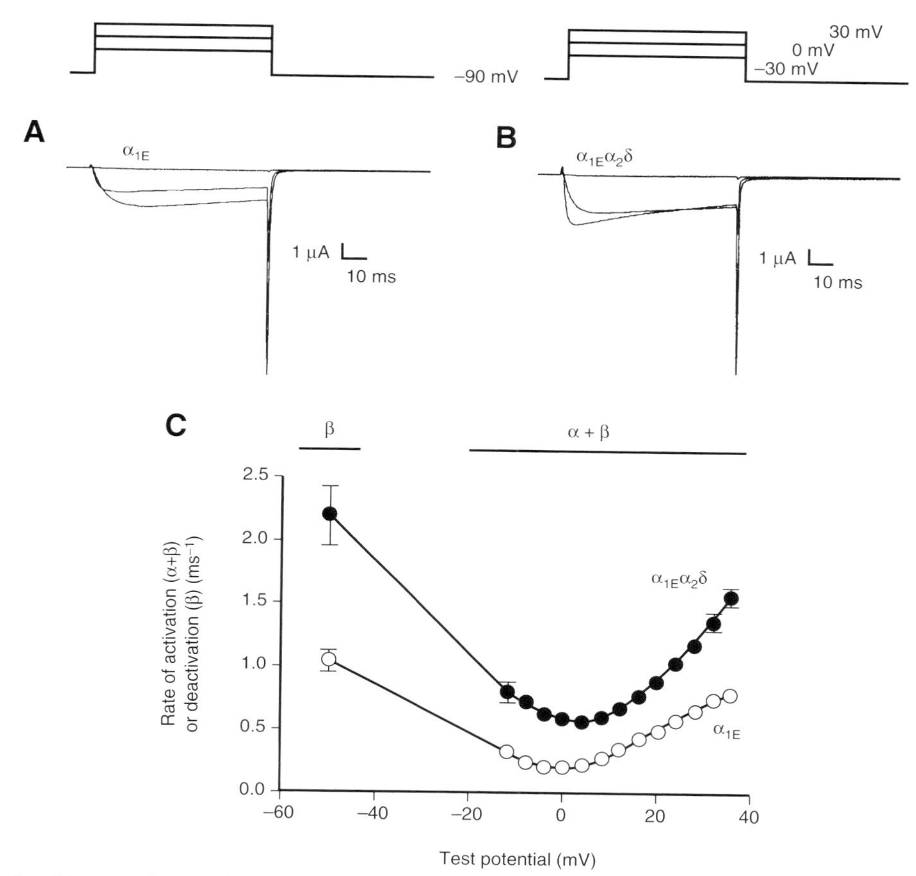

Fig 3. $\alpha_2\delta$ increases the rate of activation (A vs B) and deactivation (C) of α_{1E}. Other experiments showed that $\alpha_2\delta$ affects $\alpha_{1E}\beta_{1b}$ and $\alpha_{1E}\beta_{2a}$ channels in the same way and that conductance–voltage relationships for α_{1E}, $\alpha_{1E}\beta_{1b}$ and $\alpha_{1E}\beta_{2a}$ channels are all slightly right-shifted by $\alpha_2\delta$. Curves fitted using two Boltzmann distributions show that $\alpha_2\delta$ affects both relative amplitudes, decreasing the component with the lower half-activation potential and right-shifting the half-activation values by 5–10 mV but leaving the zδ values unchanged.

A β subunit in *Xenopus* oocytes

Lacerda and colleagues reported the occurrence of *Xenopus* oocytes expressing endogenous calcium channel currents that could be up-regulated by injection of exogenous β cRNA alone. We also encountered batches of oocytes with endogenous calcium channel currents, but less frequently (once every 2–3 months). Whether these were α_1- or $\alpha_1\beta$-type channels was investigated by searching for mRNA encoding a β subunit in the oocytes. We found two such sequences. Using a RACE-PCR (rapid amplification of cDNA ends by polymerase chain reaction) approach we cloned two cDNAs in full-length form. These differ in their coding regions in only 74 randomly distributed nucleotides and encode two β subunits of 484 amino acids that differ in only 22 amino acids. *Xenopus laevis* is a tetraploid species, and the two subunits are likely to be two alleles of a single relatively polymorphic gene. Comparison of the amino acid sequences of the *Xenopus* β subunits to those of the four known mammalian β subunits places them into the type 3 category.

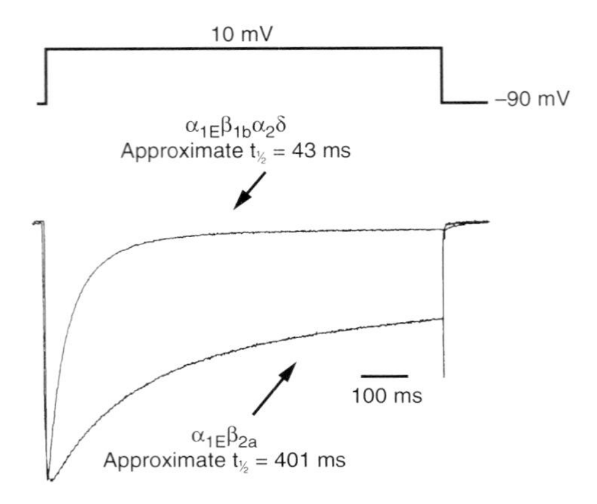

Fig. 4. Selection of subunits coexpressed with α_{1E} leads to formation of channels that are relatively long lasting ($\alpha_{1E}\beta_{2a}$ channels) or relatively transient ($\alpha_{1E}\beta_{1b}\alpha_2\delta$ channels). Intermediate behaviour is observed with other α_{1E}, β and $\alpha_2\delta$ combinations. Note that under the conditions used, and in Xenopus *oocytes, the most transient of the α_{1E} channels has a half-life ($t_{½}$) of inactivation of ~40 ms.*

These β_3Xo subunits play an essential role in the expression of endogenous and exogenous α_1 subunits, as deduced from the following observations:

- co-injection of α_{1E} or α_{1C} cRNA with β_3Xo cRNA resulted in calcium channel currents that resembled those obtained by coexpression of these α_1 subunits with rat β_3
- injection of antisense oligonucleotides to β_3Xo resulted in suppression of ionic calcium channel currents and the gating currents associated with the expression of α_1 subunits
- injection of oocytes with mammalian β_{1a} cRNA together with concentrations of anti-β_3Xo oligonucleotides that resulted in the loss of approximately 95% of calcium channel current activity 'rescued' expression of α_1.

This last experiment (fig. 5), together with other experiments in which sense oligonucleotides had no effect on expression of 'α_{1E} alone' currents, and β_3Xo antisense oligonucleotides that suppressed calcium channel currents had no effect on the expression of Shaker potassium channels, indicated that the effect of antisense was not a non-specific inhibition of the translation machinery of the oocyte. We conclude that the so-called 'α_1 alone' currents recorded by us and others from oocytes that had been injected with only α_1 cRNA must be currents that at some point required the interaction of the exogenous α_1 subunit with the endogenous *Xenopus* β_3 subunit (β_3Xo). The most plausible explanation for these observations is that association of α_1 with β is required for correct channel-folding and membrane insertion.

Thus arises the question of what might constitute the molecular nature of the so-called 'α_1 alone' channels in *Xenopus* oocytes. We offer two possibilities.

1. Once delivered fully assembled to the surface of the oocyte, the $\alpha_1\beta$Xo complex is in equilibrium with α_1 + βXo and, because of low expression of βXo, the equilibrium of this reaction favours the predominance of free α_1 channels over $\alpha_1\beta$Xo channels.

2. The βXo subunit, instead of dissociating from the channel it helped to assemble, remains attached to it. In this case 'α_1 alone' would in reality be '$\alpha_1\beta$Xo' channels.

To account for effects of an exogenous β subunit, we postulate formation of $[\alpha_1\beta]/\beta$ complexes with a mixed population of βXo and exogenous β_i, in which the exogenous β is likely to be in large excess. A possible corollary of this is that α_1 subunits have not one but two (or more) sites that are able to interact with β subunits.

Two sites on α_{1E} for interaction with β subunits

On the basis of the data showing differential effects of β subunits on α_{1E} inactivation but identical effects on activation, we hypothesised that α_{1E} might interact with more than one β subunit or that β subunits should contact α_{1E} at more than one point. The pioneering work of Campbell and collaborators had shown that loop 1, the segment

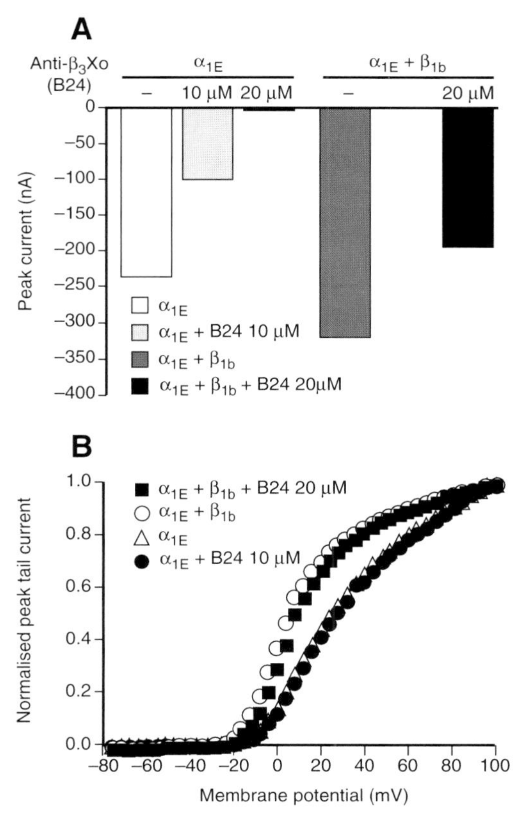

Fig. 5. Inhibition of expression of α_{1E} calcium channel currents by a Xenopus *oocyte calcium channel β subunit antisense oligonucleotide (anti-β_3Xo or B24: 5'-TGAACCCACTTCTGAGTCTTCAAA) and rescue by rat β_{1b} cRNA. A) Dose-dependent inhibition of α_{1E} by B24 and rescue by co-injected β_{1b} cRNA. B) Conductance–voltage relationships of α_{1E} channels expressed in oocytes injected with the indicated cRNAs and B24 10 μM. NB: the α_{1E} current of an oocyte in which α_{1E} expression was 60% inhibited by anti-β_3Xo (10 μM) did not differ from that recorded in oocytes that had received α_{1E} cRNA alone. This infers that the dual-gating mode implied by the two-Boltzmann fit is not related to expression of a mixture of α_{1E} alone plus $\alpha_{1E}\beta$ channels. Furthermore, the inhibition of expression by >95% with anti-β_3Xo 20 μM is not related to a non-specific or toxic effect of the oligonucleotide, as it can be overcome to a significant extent by injection of β_{1b} cRNA.*

connecting repeat domain I to repeat domain II of α_1 subunits, binds β subunits with high affinity.[16,17] However, while a single high-affinity site coupled to additional lower-affinity contacts may fit a scenario in which β dissociates from α_1 after channel assembly, permanent association of the β subunit that acts as a 'chaperone' with the assembled channel requires a second site on α_1 with affinity for β if the effects of exogenously expressed β subunits on channel gating are to be accounted for. We therefore searched for the existence of an additional region on α_{1E} that is able to interact with β subunits. Two approaches were used – the yeast two-hybrid system, and *in vitro* binding of recombinant β subunits prepared by *in vitro* translation[16] to GST fusion proteins formed from GST fused to the following segments of α_1: N terminal, loop 1 (between repeats I and II); loop 2 (between repeats II and III); loop 3 (between repeats III and IV); and C terminal. We confirmed the finding of Campbell and collaborators that loop 1 interacts with β. In addition, with both types of assay we found that β interacts with another region of α_{1E}, namely its C terminal (fig. 6).

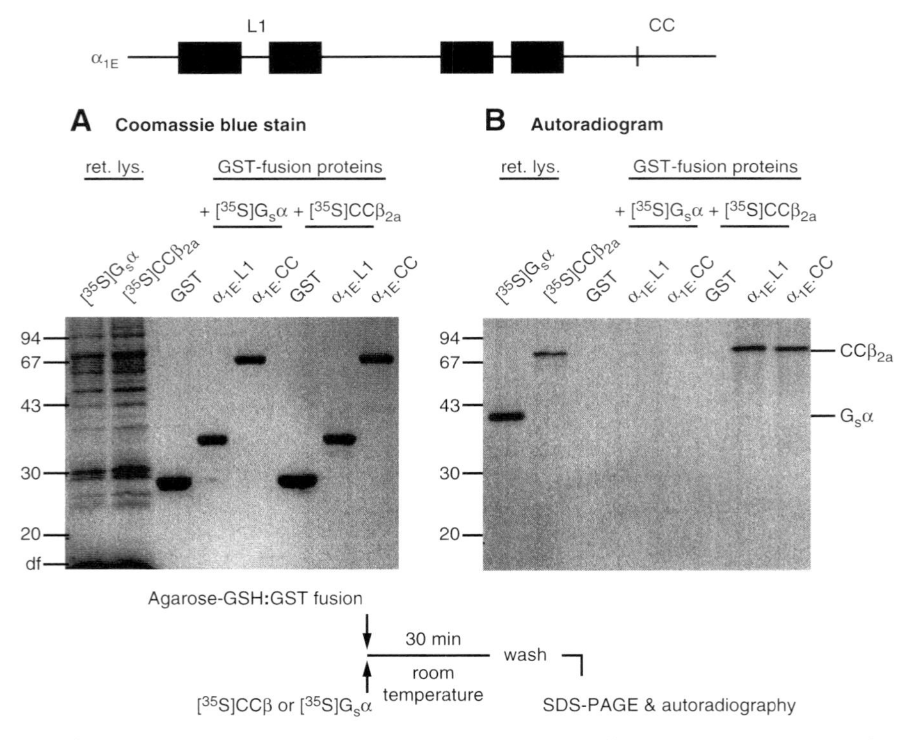

Fig. 6. Identification of two sites on α_{1E} that interact with β subunits. Binding of β_{2a} to the L1 and CC regions of α_{1E} is shown. The loop connecting α_{1E} repeat domains I and II (L1), previously identified by Campbell and collaborators[16] to interact with β subunits, and the carboxyl half of the C-terminal tail of α_{1E} (last 277 amino acids of the 2312-amino acid α_{1E}) were expressed in Escherichia coli *fused to the C terminal of GST and purified from bacterial lysates by affinity adsorption onto glutathione agarose beads. The beads with the adsorbed GST:α_{1E} fusion proteins were incubated with ^{35}S-labelled calcium channel β_{2a} (CCβ_{2a}) or G$_s\alpha$ (control) made by* in vitro *translation in the presence of [^{35}S]methionine. After 30 min at room temperature, the beads were collected by centrifugation, washed several times and resuspended in Laemmli's sample buffer with SDS 1%. The mixtures were placed into sample wells of polyacrylamide gel slabs and subjected to electrophoresis (SDS-PAGE). Gels were stained with Coomassie blue (A) and dried and autoradiographed (B) to determine whether [^{35}S]G$_s\alpha$ or [^{35}S]CCβ_{2a} had bound to GST or any of the GST fusion proteins. NB: both α_{1E} L1 and α_{1E}CC bound [^{35}S]CCβ_{2a}, but not an unrelated protein, [^{35}S]G$_s\alpha$. The G$_s\alpha$ used was the human 379-amino acid [Q/L]G$_s\alpha$, a constitutively activated form of G$_s\alpha$.*

In summary, we found that α_{1E} has two regions that can independently interact with a β subunit (in this case β_{2a}). This finding is consistent with the minimum model of a calcium channel shown in figure 7. According to this model, the channel is formed as follows:

- the pore-forming α_1 subunit
- the regulatory $\alpha_2\delta$ subunit, now known to be present in calcium channel complexes from skeletal muscle, cardiac muscle and central nervous tissue, and thus likely to be a constitutive subunit of all naturally expressed calcium channels
- a tightly associated β subunit interacting with loop 1 between repeats I and II
- a second, less tightly associated β subunit.

The existence of this last member of the complex is postulated on the basis of the biochemical binding data presented here and functional data showing at least three distinct roles for β subunits that are difficult to reconcile without invoking two separate β binding sites. These roles are structural and functional. The structural role is apparent from the fact that without a β subunit, voltage-gated calcium channels cannot assemble and/or transfer to the plasma membrane (see fig. 5). There are two functional roles.

1. The facilitation of activation,[6] common to all types of β subunit.[10]
2. The modulation of inactivation,[10] which varies between β subunits, both in the extent and in the nature of the change.

In spite of the fact that two sites able to bind β subunits have now been identified, it is not clear which site is responsible for which role of the β subunits. Indeed, it is possible that α_1 subunits have more β subunit interaction sites than the two found thus far. The challenge for the immediate future will be to determine the role of each of the β subunit binding sites and the mechanism by which β subunits function.

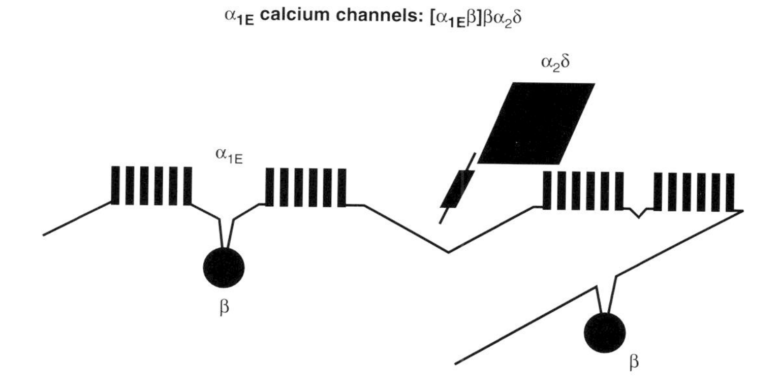

Fig. 7. Minimal model of subunit composition of an α_{1E} calcium channel under the regulation of β and $\alpha_2\delta$ subunits.

Acknowledgements

Research reported herein was supported in part by grants from the National Institutes of Health (AR-43411 to L.B. and AR-38970 to E.S.), by NRSA GM-17120 to N.Q., by a fellowship from the Deutsche Forschungsgemeinschaft to E.T. and by Grant-in-Aid 1113-GI1 from the American Heart Association (Los Angeles Affiliate) to R.O.

References

1. Perez-Reyes E, Schneider T. Molecular biology of calcium channels. Kidney Int 1995; 48: 1111–24
2. Perez-Reyes E, Kim HS, Lacerda AE, et al. Induction of calcium currents by the expression of the α_1-subunit of the dihydropyridine receptor from skeletal muscle. Nature 1989; 340: 233–6
3. Bourinet E, Zamponi GW, Stea A, et al. The α_{1E} calcium channel exhibits permeation properties similar to low voltage-activated calcium channels. J Neurosci 1996; 16: 4983–93
4. Schneider T, Wei X, Olcese R, et al. Molecular analysis and functional expression of the human type E neuronal Ca^{2+} channel α_1 subunit. Receptors Channels 1994; 2: 255–70
5. Lacerda AE, Kim H, Ruth P, et al. Normalization of current kinetics by interaction between the α_1 and β subunits of the skeletal muscle dihydropyridine-sensitive Ca^{2+} channel. Nature 1991; 352: 527–30
6. Neely A, Wei X, Olcese R, et al. Potentiation by the β subunit of the ratio of the ionic current to the charge movement in the cardiac calcium channel. Science 1993; 262: 575–8
7. Olcese R, Neely A, Qin N, et al. Coupling between charge movement and pore opening in vertebrate neuronal α_{1E} calcium channels. J Physiol (Lond.) 1996; 497: 675–86
8. Noceti F, Baldelli P, Wei X, et al. Effective gating charges per channel in voltage-dependent K^+ and Ca^{2+} channels. J Gen Physiol 1996; 108: 143–56
9. Noceti F, Olcese R, Baldelli P, et al. Charges per channel in calcium channels: effect of regulatory β subunit coexpression on α_1 pore-forming subunit currents. In: Tsien RW, Clozel J-P, Nargeot J, editors. Low-Voltage-Activated T-type Calcium Channels. Proceedings from the International Electrophysiology Meeting: 1996 Oct 21–22 Montpellier, France. Chester, UK: Adis International Ltd 1998; 311–23.
10. Olcese R, Qin N, Neely A, et al. The amino terminus of calcium channel β subunit sets rates of channel inactivation independently of the subunit's effects on activation. Neuron 1994; 13: 1433–8
11. Ellinor PT, Zhang JF, Randall AD, et al. Functional expression of a rapidly inactivating neuronal calcium channel. Nature 1993; 363: 455–8
12. Stea A, Tomlinson WJ, Soong TW, et al. Localization and functional expression of a rat brain α_{1A} calcium channel reflects similarities to neuronal Q- and P-type channels. Proc Natl Acad Sci U S A 1994; 91: 10576–80
13. Murakami M, Wissenbach U, Flockerzi V. Gene structure of the murine calcium channel beta-3 subunit, cDNA and characterization of alternative splicing and transcription products. Eur J Biochem 1996; 236: 138–43
14. Castellano A, Wei X, Birnbaumer L, et al. cloning and expression of a neuronal calcium channel β subunit. J Biol Chem 1993; 268: 12359–66
15. Qin N, Olcese R, Zhou J, et al. Identification of a second region of the β subunit involved in regulation of calcium channel inactivation. Am J Physiol 1996; 271: 1539–45
16. Pragnell M, De Waard M, Mori Y, et al. Calcium channel β-subunit binds to a conserved motif of the I–II cytoplasmic linker of the α_1-subunit. Nature 1994; 368: 67–70
17. Witcher DR, De Waard M, Liu H, et al. Association of native Ca^{2+} channel β subunits with the α_1 subunit interaction domain. J Biol Chem 1995; 270: 18088–93

Properties and modulation of T-type currents in dorsal root ganglia and ND7-23 cells: comparison with α_{1E} currents expressed in COS-7 cells

Annette C. Dolphin

Department of Pharmacology, University College London, London, UK

Summary

This article describes two studies conducted on T-type calcium currents: one with dorsal root ganglion (DRG) neurons in culture, and one with a DRG–neuroblastoma hybrid cell line (ND7-23). The biophysical and pharmacological properties are both described, showing significant differences between the two cell types. Finally, the biophysical and pharmacological properties of the rat α_{1E} calcium channel clone, transiently expressed in COS-7 cells, and the similarities and differences between these and native T-type channels, are discussed.

Introduction

We have investigated the properties of neuronal T-type voltage-dependent calcium channels, particularly in two cell types: dorsal root ganglion neurons (DRGs) and a DRG-neuroblastoma hybrid cell line (ND7-23). The pharmacological properties and modulation of the low-voltage-activated (LVA) currents differ in the two cell types. This work has been described in detail by Kobrinsky et al. and Scott et al.[1,2] A recent review provides a more detailed comparison between the properties of high-voltage-activated (HVA) and LVA calcium currents.[3]

In these studies, cultured neonatal rat DRGs, of which about 40% showed LVA currents, were observed from a holding potential of –90 mV. The production and properties of the ND7-23 cell line have been described previously.[4,5] This line showed only LVA calcium currents in all undifferentiated cells, whereas a proportion of differentiated cells, increasing with time of differentiation, also contained HVA currents.[1] We have also examined the properties of α_{1E} channels coexpressed with β_{1b} and $\alpha_2\delta$ in a mammalian cell line for comparison with T-type channels.

Pharmacological properties of T-type current in DRGs and ND7-23 cells

The biophysical properties and pharmacology of T-type currents in DRGs have been described by several groups.[6,7,8] The currents are fairly rapidly inactivating, with a time constant of inactivation of about 30–40 ms at –20 mV. These currents have been found by our group to be sensitive to Ni^{2+} 100 μM and octanol 1 μM, but they were not inhibited by ω-CTx-GVIA 1 μM.[2] We have also observed that T-type currents in DRGs are inhibited by synthetic FTX (funnel web spider toxin, also called arginine polyamine) at concentrations lower than those required to block HVA currents.[9] The maximal effect was observed with synthetic FTX 100 nM and represented about 60% inhibition of the T-type current, whereas block of HVA currents was greatest with FTX 100 µM.

In ND7-23 cells, two types of LVA current were observed: slow- and fast-inactivating (fig. 1).[1] The time constant of inactivation was voltage-dependent for both current

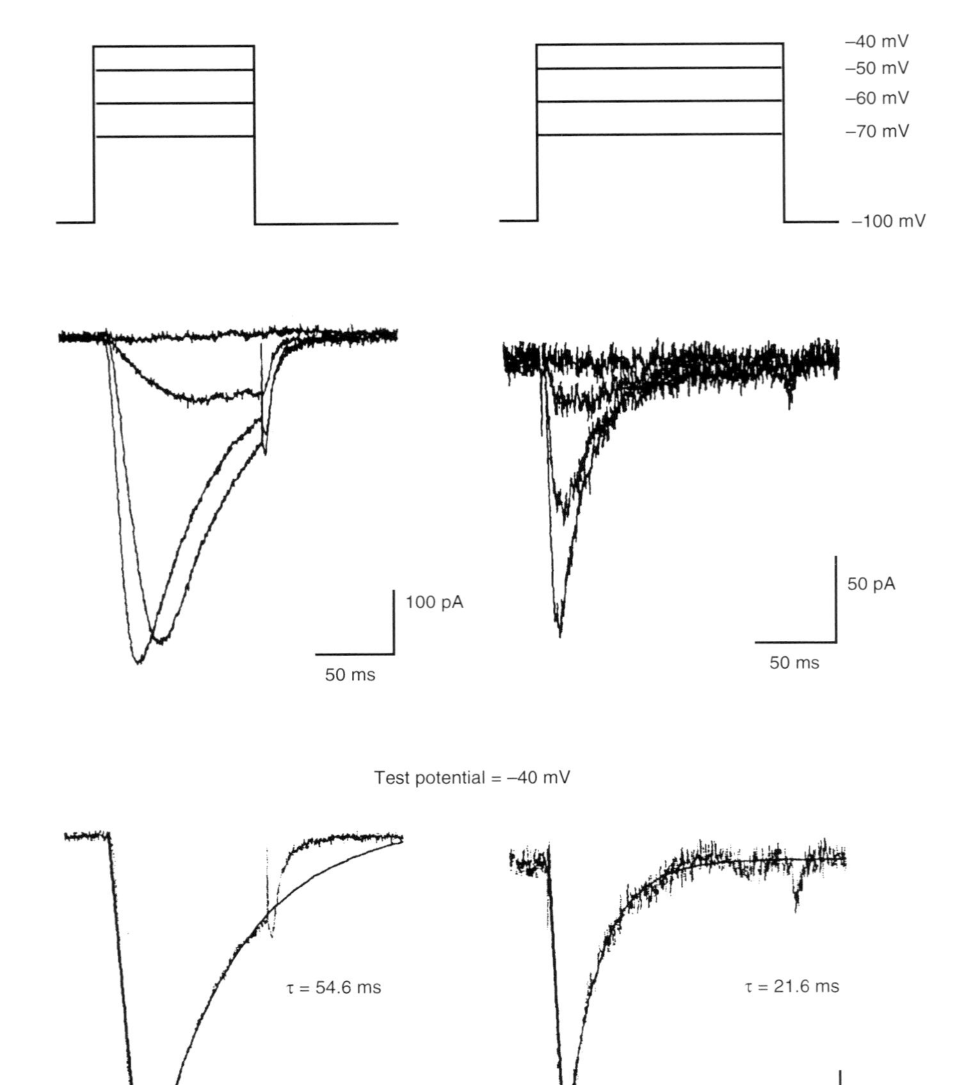

Fig. 1. Two types of T-type current in ND7-23 cells. Families of T-type currents are shown in two different cells, activated at –70 to –40 mV, from a holding potential of –100 mV (left = slowly inactivating type of low-voltage-activated current; right = rapidly inactivating current). Bottom: a single exponential fit to the steps to –40 mV, giving a time constant of inactivation (τ) of 54.6 ms for the slowly inactivating current and 21.6 ms for the rapidly inactivating current. Details of electrophysiological methods are given in Kobrinsky et al.[1]

types, being about 55 and 21 ms, respectively, at –40 mV.[1] The slowly inactivating currents also usually showed a prolonged non-inactivating pedestal current. The time to peak activation was also voltage-dependent, with the slowly inactivating currents also being more slowly activating. The recovery from inactivation at –100 mV showed two time constants (89 and 845 ms) that accounted for recovery of approximately equal proportions of the current. The slowly inactivating currents predominated in most preparations; for this reason the pharmacology of the slowly inactivating LVA currents was investigated most extensively.

Complete block was observed with Ni^{2+} (100 μM), and almost complete (84%) but rapidly reversible block was observed with ω-CTx-GVIA (1 μM).[1] Surprisingly, another peptide toxin, ω-Aga-IVA, previously thought to be selective for P-/Q-type calcium currents,[10] also partially inhibited T-type currents in these cells at a concentration of 100 nM.[11] In contrast to studies on T-type currents in some central neurons,[12] we observed no effect with the 1,4-dihydropyridine antagonists (–)-202-791 and isradipine.[1] However, the effects of these drugs on rapidly inactivating T-type currents (the subtype of LVA current selectively inhibited by dihydropyridines in central neurons[12]) were not assessed.

Phenytoin (10 μM) inhibited approximately 30% of the T-type current in ND7-23 cells, with no effect at this concentration on HVA current. HVA and LVA currents were also differentiated by intracellular alkalinisation with NH_4Cl, which increased HVA currents (as previously described[13]) but had no effect on LVA currents. Inhibition of T-type current by the drugs mentioned above was accompanied by little effect on the kinetics of activation or inactivation of the current, which suggests that these drugs have no time- or voltage-dependent effects.

It would appear from a comparison of our own and other pharmacological studies that T-type currents represent a far from homogeneous entity.[14] Many drugs that inhibit components of HVA currents in a selective manner also inhibit T-type currents in a rapidly reversible manner (e.g. the block by ω-CTx-GVIA of T-type currents is rapidly reversible, whereas that of N-type currents is not). In certain cell types, inhibition of both T-type and HVA currents by dihydropyridine antagonists has been observed.[15] In contrast, in the ND7-23 cell line studied here, dihydropyridine antagonists had no effect on T-type currents.

Single T-type calcium channels were observed in ND7-23 cells. From a holding potential of –100 mV, a channel with a slope conductance of about 8 pS in Ba^{2+} 110 mM was observed. Openings were brief and often clustered towards the beginning of the sweep, although openings were also observed near the end of a 200 ms step. The late openings may correspond to the sustained phase of the slowly inactivating T-type current. This sustained T-type current component seen in whole-cell recordings is unlikely to result from contamination with L- or N-type current, as it was not affected by dihydropyridine agonists or antagonists and was not irreversibly inhibited by ω-CTx-GVIA.[1]

Modulation of low-threshold calcium currents in DRGs and ND7-23 cells

Modulation of T-type calcium currents by G-protein activation in DRGs was examined by photorelease of a photolabile precursor of GTPγS.[2] We observed that photorelease of a low concentration of GTPγS (2 μM) enhanced T-type currents in DRGs, whereas photorelease of a higher concentration (20 μM) by exposure to further flashes inhibited the current. There was no effect of G-protein activation on the kinetics of activation or inactivation of the LVA current, whereas flash release of caged GTPγS clearly slowed the activation and reduced the amplitude of the HVA current.[16] The effect of GTPγS was subsequently examined in the presence of pertussis toxin (PTX), which prevents receptor-mediated effects via inhibitory G proteins G_i and G_o. Enhancement of the T-type current only was observed under these conditions.[1] This indicates that the inhibition is caused by activation of a G protein of the PTX-sensitive subgroup. Since PTX usually prevents receptor-mediated effects, but not those related to direct G-protein activation, this suggests that the exchange of GTPγS for GDP on these G proteins was made possible by receptor activation (e.g. endogenous adenosine or other compounds released in an autocrine manner). In contrast, the enhancement of T-type current may be mediated by a PTX-insensitive G protein of the G_q/G_{11} class. The GABA-B agonist (–)-baclofen inhibited both HVA and LVA currents in DRGs, although the inhibitory effect on LVA currents was small.[2] However, low concentrations of (–)-baclofen enhanced LVA currents, in corroboration of the effects of low concentrations of GTPγS. Clearly, several G-protein-linked processes are involved in both inhibitory and stimulatory modulation of T-type currents in DRGs.

In ND7-23 cells, only inhibitory modulation of T-type calcium current by (–)-baclofen was observed at both a low concentration (2 μM) and (to a greater extent) at a high concentration (100 μM) (fig. 2). This inhibition was only observed in differentiated cells, which suggests that the receptors or the signal-transduction mechanism were not present in undifferentiated cells, since T-type currents were always present in the ND7-23 cells, whether differentiated or not. The inhibitory modulation by (–)-baclofen was not prevented by pretreatment of the cells with PTX, although inhibition of the HVA current by (–)-baclofen was PTX-sensitive.[1] Bradykinin, which has been shown to have receptors on ND7-23 cells,[4] also inhibited T-type currents.[1] Nor was this effect prevented by PTX. It is therefore possible that $G_{q/11}$ or one of its downstream products (e.g. activated protein kinase C) is responsible for this inhibition. Inclusion of GTPγS in the patch pipette produced a gradual, small inhibition of the current, with no clear change in activation kinetics relative to control currents. It is possible that exchange of GTPγS for GDP on the G protein involved is extremely slow when no receptor agonist is present, and GTPγS does not, therefore, produce inhibition to the same extent as an agonist.

Modulation of HVA current by GTP analogues and G-protein-linked receptors has been studied in numerous cell types, and it is very often found that the modulation

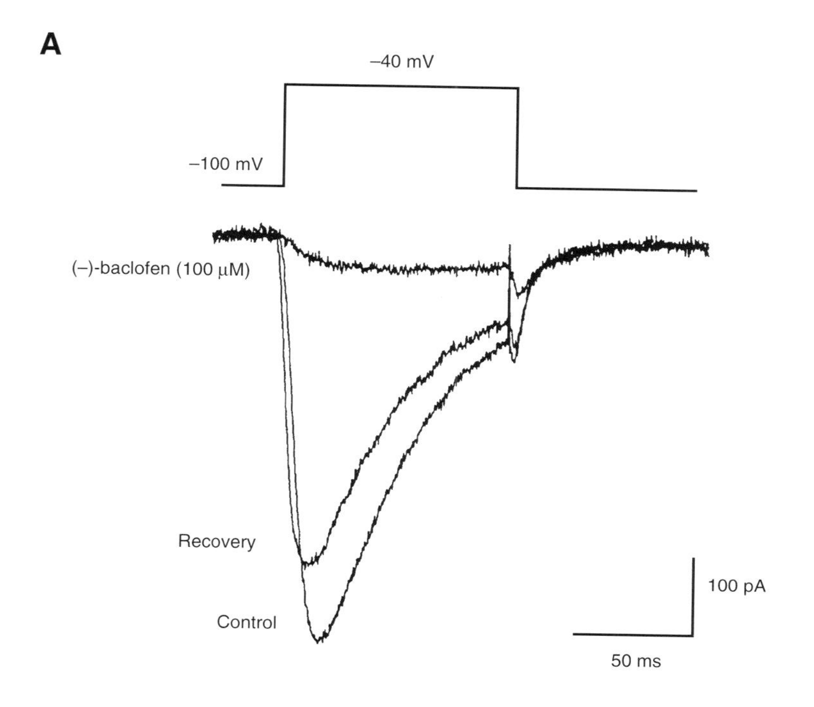

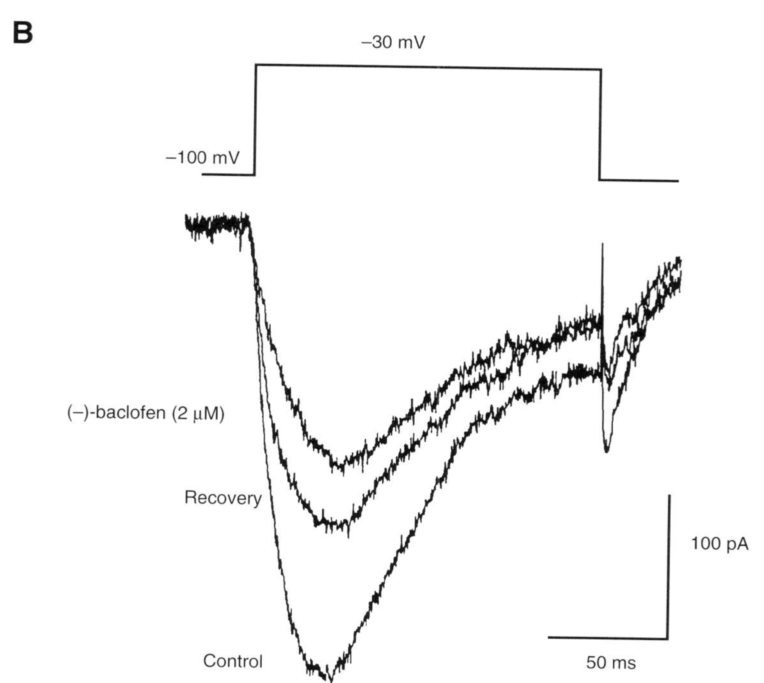

Fig. 2. Effect of the GABA-B agonist (–)-baclofen on T-type currents in the ND7-23 cell line. The inhibitory effect of (–)-baclofen 100 μM (A) and 2 μM (B) on slowly inactivating T-type currents activated at –40 mV from a holding potential of –100 mV. The inhibitory effect was readily reversible upon washing. Details of electrophysiological methods are given in Kobrinsky et al.[1]

involves kinetic slowing that can be reversed by a depolarising prepulse (for a review, see Dolphin[17]). It is thought that the mechanism of this modulation involves a direct interaction of activated G-protein $\beta\gamma$ subunits with the calcium channels.[18,19] The inhibition of T-type currents does not appear to involve the same mechanism, as no element of kinetic slowing is normally observed. Instead, there is a scaled reduction in current amplitude. This suggests that the mechanism of inhibitory modulation of HVA and LVA currents may not be identical.

Comparison of the properties of T-type current and cloned α_{1E} channels

We have examined the properties of rat brain α_{1E} channels transiently transfected in COS-7 cells and coexpressed with the brain $\alpha_2\delta$ splice variant and β_{1b}.[20] The current inactivation kinetics were slower than those of the slowly inactivating T-type current (e.g. the time constant of inactivation at 0 mV was about 150 ms). Furthermore, the activation and steady-state inactivation occurred at more positive potentials than would be consistent with T-type current. The voltage for 50% inactivation was –59 mV, and the voltage for 50% activation was –13 mV (in Ba^{2+} 10 mM), as determined using Boltzmann functions (fig. 3). In panel B of figure 3, for the inactivation curve, cells were held at the conditioning potential for 5 s before stepping to –10 mV to activate the current. The activation curve was taken from the amplitude of the tail current following 20 ms depolarisations to the potentials shown and repolarisation to –80 mV, where the tail current duration was sufficiently long for the amplitude to be measured accurately.

For α_{1E} expression in oocytes it has consistently been found that the biophysical properties of α_{1E} currents do not match those of T-type currents.[21–23] The time constant of tail current deactivation for T-type currents has been shown to be slower than that for HVA currents by approximately 1 order of magnitude,[24,25] and has been shown to be dependent on repolarisation voltage between –120 and –60 mV.[24] We therefore examined the rate of deactivation and its voltage-dependence for α_{1E} currents (fig. 3 (C)). A single exponential was fitted to the tail current decay, and the time constant was plotted on a log scale against repolarisation potential. A single exponential was fitted to the curve and showed that the open/closed transition is dominated by a single voltage-dependent transition. The deactivation time constant increased e-fold for a 34.1 mV depolarisation of the repolarisation voltage (see fig. 3 (C)). The time constant of deactivation reached a voltage-independent minimum of 0.43 ms (n=2) at a repolarisation potential of –120 mV, reflecting a voltage-independent initial open/closed transition of 2.3 ms^{-1}. The time constant of deactivation was more rapid than that determined for native T-type currents in GH3 cells,[24] where the equivalent time constant at –120 mV was about 2 ms. However, a similar voltage-dependence was observed. Thus, it is possible either that α_{1E} does not carry a T-type current or that there are other α_{1E}-like channels or splice variants that have properties more representative of T-type channels.

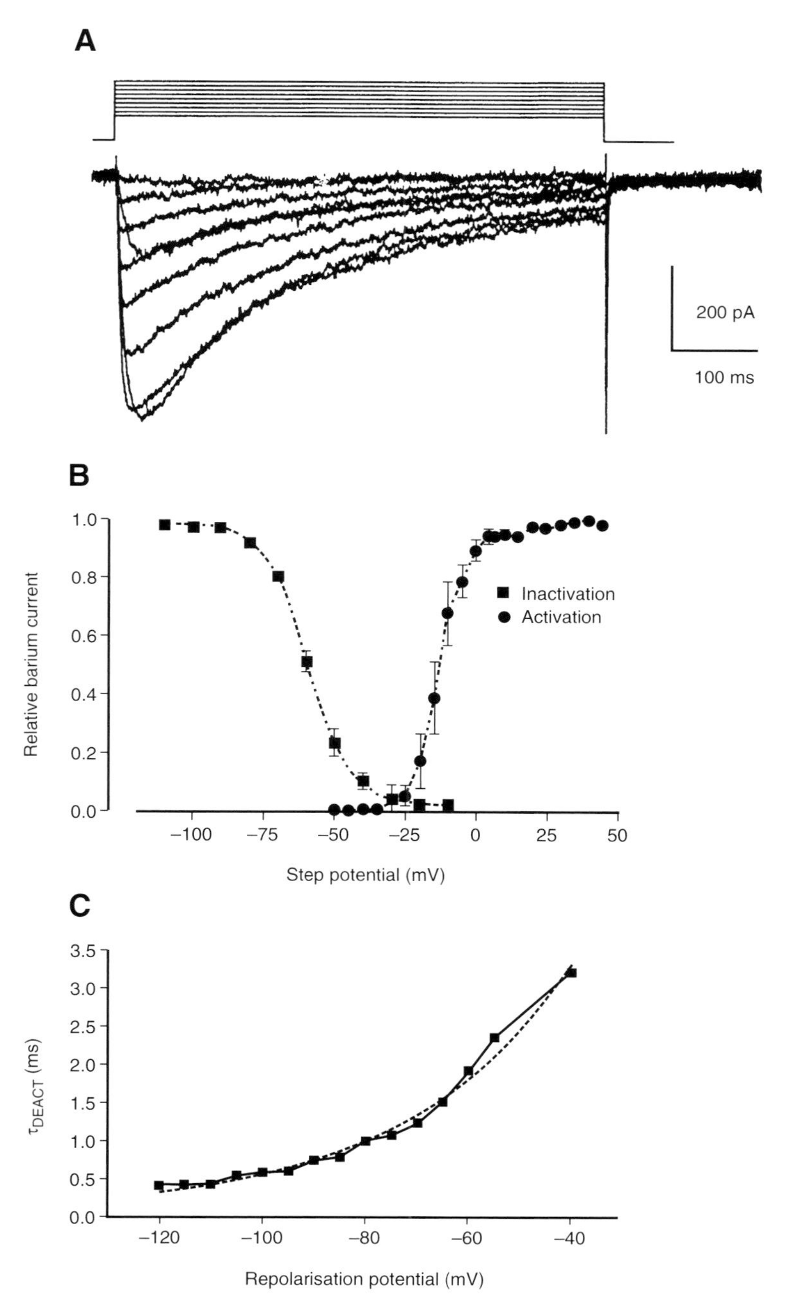

Fig. 3. Activation, steady-state inactivation and deactivation for α_{1E} coexpressed with $\alpha_2\delta$ and β_{1b} transiently in COS-7 cells. A) Examples of a family of $\alpha_{1E}\alpha_2\delta\beta_{1b}$ currents activated from a holding potential of −100 mV. The charge carrier was Ba^{2+} 10 mM. Voltage steps were increased in 10 mV steps from −45 mV to +35 mV. B) Steady-state inactivation curve for 3 cells, and activation curve for 4 cells. C) Voltage-dependence of tail current deactivation kinetics. Currents were activated at −10 mV for 20 ms, and the cell was repolarised to potentials between −120 and −40 mV. The data represent the mean results from 2 cells. Transient transfection by electroporation was used, with the inclusion of cDNA for green fluorescent protein as a reporter. Details of transfection procedures and electrophysiological methods are given in Stephens et al.,[20] except that the tail currents were filtered at 10 kHz and sampled at 20 kHz. τ_{DEACT} = deactivation time constant.

The one biophysical finding that consistently links α_{1E} channels with T-type currents is the relatively high permeability to Ca^{2+} (relative to Ba^{2+}), which we also observed in our expression system.[20]

In terms of pharmacology, we observed reversible 50% inhibition of α_{1E} currents by nicardipine 1 μM and no effect of BayK8644.[20] Block of α_{1E} currents by other organic calcium channel blockers has been observed previously.[22] This is similar to the observation that certain T-type currents are dihydropyridine sensitive.[12,26] The α_{1E} currents were also partially blocked by ω-Aga-IVA (fig. 4),[20] as has been observed previously.[21] This correlates with our finding that T-type currents in ND7-23 cells are inhibited by ω-Aga-IVA.

It should be noted that we observed no inhibition of α_{1E} currents by ω-CTx-MVIIC. This latter finding makes the identification of Q- and R-type current, defined as components of current in native cells that are inhibited by high concentrations of ω-Aga-IVA and by ω-CTx-MVIIC (Q type), or are inhibited by neither toxin (R type),[10] rather difficult as α_{1E} currents are incompletely inhibited by ω-Aga-IVA with low affinity, but not by ω-CTx-MVIIC. Therefore, according to the first criterion, α_{1E} currents would be counted as a component of Q-type current, although the incomplete block would cause a proportion of E-type current to be classed as residual or R-type current. According to the second criterion, the entire E-type current would be counted as a component of R-type current.

Conclusions

T-type calcium currents have a wide variety of different pharmacologies, suggesting that they do not derive from a single molecular entity. The DRG–neuroblastoma hybrid cell line ND7-23 showed two types of LVA current: rapidly or slowly inactivating, with the slowly inactivating current predominating. In two different systems (DRGs and ND7-23 cells), LVA currents have been shown to be inhibited by activation of a G-protein-coupled receptor (the GABA-B receptor). The mechanism of this inhibition remains to be determined.

Neither the biophysical properties nor the pharmacology of expressed α_{1E} currents that have been studied to date correlate exactly with any known T-type currents. However, some properties of α_{1E} currents show intriguing similarities to T-type currents, suggesting that the molecular correlate(s) of T-type currents may bear more resemblance to α_{1E} than to other calcium channels cloned to date.

Acknowledgements

The work described here was performed together with Drs E. Kobrinsky, K. Sutton, H. Pearson, G.J. Stephens and R.H. Scott. We collaborated with Prof. J. Wootton, Cornell University, USA, in the studies using caged GTPγS. The work was supported by the Medical Research Council and the Wellcome Trust. We thank Dr T. Snutch

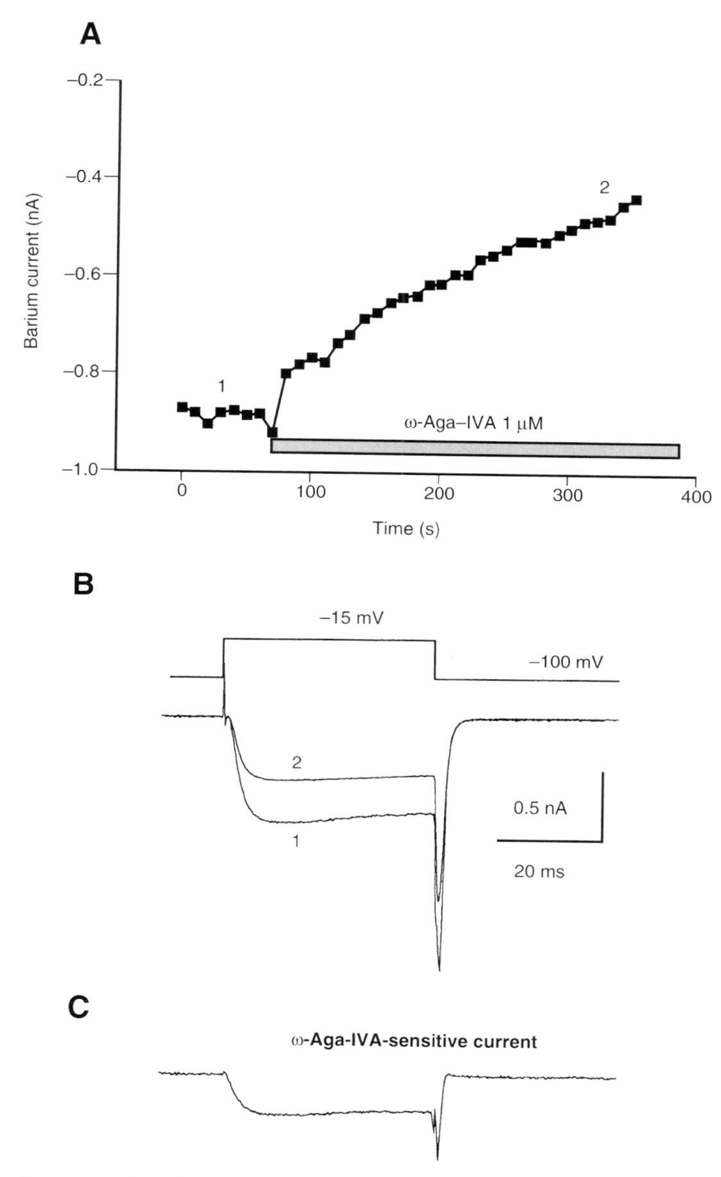

Fig. 4. Inhibition of α_{1E} current by ω-Aga-IVA. α_{1E} was cotransfected with $\alpha_2\delta$ and β_{1b} in COS-7 cells. Details of transfection procedures and electrophysiological methods are given in Stephens et al.[20] A) Time-course of inhibition of the α_{1E} barium current by ω-Aga-IVA 1 μM. B) Examples of currents before and during application of ω-Aga-IVA, at the times shown in panel A. C) ω-Aga-IVA current obtained by subtraction of the currents 1 and 2 shown in panel B.

(Vancouver) for α_{1E}, Dr H. Chin (National Institutes of Health) for $\alpha_2\delta$ and Dr E. Perez-Reyes (Chicago) for β_{1b}.

References

1. Kobrinsky EM, Pearson HA, Dolphin AC. Low- and high-voltage-activated calcium channel currents and their modulation in the dorsal root ganglion cell line ND7-23. Neuroscience 1994; 58: 539–52

2. Scott RH, Wootton JF, Dolphin AC. Modulation of neuronal T-type calcium channel currents by photoactivation of intracellular guanosine 5'-*0* (3-thio)triphosphate. Neuroscience 1990; 38: 285–94
3. Dolphin AC. Voltage-dependent calcium channels and their modulation by neurotransmitters and G proteins: GL Brown prize lecture. Exp Physiol 1995; 80: 1–36
4. Dunn PM, Coote PR, Wood JN, et al. Bradykinin evoked depolarization of a novel neuroblastoma × DRG neurone hybrid cell line (ND7-23). Brain Res 1991; 549: 80–6
5. Wood JN, Bevan SJ, Coote PR, et al. Novel cell lines display properties of nociceptive sensory neurons. Proc R Soc Lond B Biol Sci 1990; 241: 187–94
6. Carbone E, Lux HD. A low voltage-activated fully inactivating Ca channel in vertebrate sensory neurones. Nature 1984; 310: 501–2
7. Fedulova SA, Kostyuk PG, Veselovsky NS, et al. Two types of calcium channels in the somatic membrane of new-born rat dorsal root ganglion neurones. J Physiol 1985 359: 431–46
8. Fox AP, Nowycky MC, Tsien RW. Kinetic and pharmacological properties distinguishing three types of calcium currents in chick sensory neurones. J Physiol 1987; 394: 149–72
9. Scott RH, Sweeney MI, Kobrinsky EM, et al. Actions of arginine polyamine on voltage and ligand-activated whole cell currents recorded from cultured neurones. Br J Pharmacol 1992; 106: 199–207
10. Randall A, Tsien RW. Pharmacological dissection of multiple types of Ca^{2+} channel currents in rat cerebellar granule neurons. J Neurosci 1995; 15: 2995–3012
11. Pearson HA, Sutton KG, Scott RH, et al. Characterization of Ca^{2+} channel currents in cultured rat cerebellar granule neurones. J Physiol 1995; 482: 493–509
12. Akaike N, Kostyuk PG, Osipchuk YV. Dihydropyridine-sensitive low-threshold calcium channels in isolated rat hypothalamic neurones. J Physiol 1989; 412: 181–95
13. Mironov SL, Lux HD. Cytoplasmic alkalinization increases high-threshold calcium current in chick dorsal root ganglion neurones. Pflugers Arch 1991; 419: 138–43
14. Huguenard JR. Low-threshold calcium currents in central nervous system neurons. Annu Rev Physiol 1996; 58: 329–48
15. Allen TGJ, Sim JA, Brown DA. The whole-cell calcium current in acutely dissociated magnocellular cholinergic basal forebrain neurones of the rat. J Physiol 1993; 460: 91–116
16. Dolphin AC, Wootton JF, Scott RH, et al. Photoactivation of intracellular guanosine triphosphate analogues reduces the amplitude and slows the kinetics of voltage-activated calcium channel currents in sensory neurones. Pflugers Arch 1988; 411: 628–36
17. Dolphin AC. Facilitation of Ca^{2+} current in excitable cells. Trends Neurosci 1996; 19: 35–43
18. Ikeda SR. Voltage-dependent modulation of N-type calcium channels by G protein $\beta\gamma$ subunits. Nature 1996; 380: 255–8
19. Herlitze S, Garcia DE, Mackie K, et al. Modulation of Ca^{2+} channels by G-protein $\beta\gamma$ subunits. Nature 1996; 380: 258–62
20. Stephens GJ, Page K, Burley JR, et al. Functional expression of rat brain cloned α_{1E} calcium channels in COS-7 cells. Pflugers Arch 1997; 433: 523–32
21. Soong TW, Stea A, Hodson CD, et al. Structure and functional expression of a member of the low voltage-activated calcium channel family. Science 1993; 260: 1133–6
22. Schneider T, Wei X, Olcese R, et al. Molecular analysis and functional expression of the human type E neuronal Ca^{2+} channel α_1 subunit. Receptors Channels 1994; 2: 255–70
23. Williams ME, Marubio LM, Deal CR, et al. Structure and functional characterization of neuronal α_{1E} calcium channel subtypes. J Biol Chem 1994; 269: 22347–57
24. Herrington J, Lingle CJ. Kinetic and pharmacological properties of low voltage activated Ca^{2+} current in rat clonal GH_3 pituitary cells. J Neurophysiol 1992; 68: 213–31
25. Armstrong CM, Matteson DR. Two distinct populations of calcium channels in a clonal line of pituitary cells. Science 1985; 227: 65–7
26. Berjukow S, Doring S, Froschmayr M, et al. Endogenous calcium channels in human embryonic kidney (HEK293) cells. Br J Pharmacol 1996; 118: 748–54

Does α_{1E} code for T-type calcium channels? A comparison of recombinant α_{1E} calcium channels with GH3 pituitary T-type and recombinant α_{1B} calcium channels

David M. Rock,[1] William A. Horne,[2] Sally J. Stoehr,[1] Chica Hashimoto,[2] Mei Zhou,[2] Ruth Cong,[2] Andrew Palma,[2] Debra Hidayetoglu,[3] James Offord[3]

[1] Neuroscience Therapeutics, Parke-Davis Pharmaceutical Research Division, Warner-Lambert Company, Ann Arbor, Michigan, USA; [2] Neurex Corporation, Menlo Park, California, USA; [3] Molecular Biology, Parke-Davis Pharmaceutical Research Division, Warner-Lambert Company, Ann Arbor, Michigan, USA

Summary

Expression of α_{1E} (E class) subunits in Xenopus *oocytes or in mammalian cell lines produces calcium channels that show rapid inactivation. It was originally proposed that α_{1E} was the α_1 subunit for low-voltage-activated (LVA) calcium channels. Under identical recording conditions, we compared biophysical and pharmacological properties of α_{1E} expressed in HEK293 cells with α_{1B} (B class) expressed in the same cell line and LVA calcium channel currents in a rat pituitary cell line (GH3). α_{1E} calcium channels showed biophysical properties that were similar to those of α_{1B} channels, activation voltages that were depolarised relative to GH3 T-type current and potent block by Cd^{2+} and the non-selective calcium channel toxin ω-Aga-IIIA. These features of α_{1E} calcium channels are similar to those of R-type calcium channels described in cerebellar granule neurons, and not to GH3 T-type or other LVA calcium channels.*

Introduction

The voltage-activated calcium channels of vertebrates are involved in a variety of physiological processes, including electrical signalling, muscle contraction, hormone secretion and neurotransmitter release.[1–4] Various calcium channel isoforms or subtypes that mediate these processes have been classified according to their electrophysiological and pharmacological properties into T, L, N, Q, P and R types.[3,5–7] T-type calcium channels can be differentiated from the other calcium channel subtypes according to both biophysical and pharmacological criteria. T-type calcium channels are activated at relatively hyperpolarised membrane potentials and inactivate rapidly, while the other calcium channel subtypes are activated at more depolarised membrane potentials and show varied patterns of inactivation. Anticonvulsants have been shown to selectively block T-type calcium channel currents,[8,9] while high-voltage-activated (HVA) calcium channels are sensitive to dihydropyridines (L type), the ω-conopeptides GVIA, MVIIA and MVIIC derived from cone snails (N type and Q type) and the funnel web spider toxin ω-Aga-IVA (P type).[3,10–14] The R-type calcium channel, described in cerebellar granule cells, is insensitive to ω-Aga-IVA, ω-CTx-MVIIA, ω-CTx-GVIA and ω-CTx-MVIIC, as well as to dihydropyridines.[15–17]

Molecular experiments have shown that calcium channels contain a number of different subunits. The α_1 subunit has been identified as the pore-forming subunit through which Ca^{2+} ions flow and is the primary determinant of the biophysical and pharmacological characteristics of each channel subtype. The level of conservation between the various α_1 subunits is quite high. The accessory subunits $\alpha_2\delta$ and β affect expression levels, voltage-dependence of activation and inactivation and, to a lesser extent, the pharmacology of recombinant calcium channels.[18–23] Several isoforms of $\alpha_2\delta$ and β subunits have also been isolated from both neuronal and muscle tissue.

Several distinct classes of α_1 subunits have been described and have been aligned with subtypes of calcium channels based mainly on pharmacological criteria,[3,5,7,15] with the exception of α_{1E}. Expression of α_{1E} (E class) calcium channels in *Xenopus* oocytes or in mammalian cell lines results in rapidly inactivating currents that can be blocked in a voltage-dependent manner by Ni^{2+}[24–27]and have permeation properties similar to those of T-type calcium channels.[28] However, some of the biophysical and pharmacological properties of α_{1E} calcium channels are dissimilar to those of T-type calcium channels.[25]

In order to compare the biophysical and pharmacological properties of ion channels, it is desirable to perform the experiments under conditions that are as comparable as possible. Differences in the concentrations of divalent cation charge carrier can affect biophysical and pharmacological properties, making results hard to interpret. In the experiments described here, under identical recording conditions we compared the biophysical and pharmacological properties of cell lines expressing recombinant α_{1E} and α_{1B} with those of a clonal rat pituitary cell line (GH3) that expresses T-type calcium channels.[29]

Materials and methods

Cell lines

The GH3 rat pituitary cell line was obtained from the American Type Culture Collection (ATCC). GH3 cells were maintained in Ham's F10 medium with horse serum 15%, foetal calf serum 2.5% and glutamine 2 mM in poly-L-lysine-coated T75 flasks.

α_{1E} and α_{1B} subunits

cDNA for α_{1E} was isolated from a human hippocampal cDNA library and α_{1B} cDNA was cloned as described in Ellinor et al.[30] The α_{1B} clone has a short sequence from an α_{1A} at the 5′ end to enhance expression in *Xenopus* oocytes. The channels expressed in oocytes with this clone have electrophysiological and pharmacological properties similar to those of N-type calcium channels.[30]

HEK293 human embryonic kidney cells were obtained from the ATCC and maintained in RPMI 1640 medium supplemented with glutamine 2 mM and foetal bovine serum 10%. The HEK cells were transfected using lipofectamine-mediated transfection with the cDNA for the rabbit skeletal muscle $\alpha_2\delta$ subunit and a cDNA for the human neuronal β_2 subunit, both of which were cloned into the plasmid pcDNA-III (Invitrogen, Carlsbad, California, USA). Stable cell lines containing the transfected plasmids were selected using the antibiotic G418. Clonal cell lines that were resistant to G418 were analysed for the expression of $\alpha_2\delta$ and β_2 mRNA by northern blot analysis, and a cell line (2L) expressing high levels of both $\alpha_2\delta$ and β_2 mRNA was chosen. The 2L cells were expanded and then retransfected with the cDNAs for the α_{1E} or α_{1B} cloned into pcDNA-III. The plasmid pREP4 (Invitrogen) containing the gene for hygromycin resistance was cotransfected with the α_1 clones, and cell lines were selected in the presence of G418 and hygromycin B sulphate. Stable cell lines were analysed by biochemical and whole-cell voltage-clamp techniques for the presence of functional calcium channels.

Lipofectamine, RPMI 1640 medium, optimem-1 medium, foetal bovine serum and the antibiotic G418 were obtained from Life Technologies Inc. (Gaithersburg, Maryland, USA). The antibiotic hygromycin B sulphate was obtained from Boehringer Mannheim (Indianapolis, Indiana, USA).

Electrophysiological recording

Calcium channel currents were measured using single-electrode whole-cell voltage-clamp techniques[31] with low-resistance (2–5 MΩ) glass micropipettes. Recordings were performed with an Axopatch 200 A amplifier (Axon Instruments, Foster City, California, USA) and a TL-1 interface for computer generation of test protocols and data analysis using pCLAMP 6.0 (Axon Instruments, Foster City, California, USA). All records were leak-subtracted using a P/4 protocol. Voltage-clamp potentials were not corrected for junction potential. The external solution contained TEAC 100 mM, choline Cl 52 mM, NaCl 15 mM, HEPES 10 mM, glucose 5.6 mM, $CaCl_2$ 2 mM and $MgCl_2$ 0.8 mM, and the pH was adjusted to 7.35 with KOH. The internal solution contained Cs methanesulphonate 140 mM, EGTA 10 mM and HEPES 10 mM and was supplemented with Mg^{2+}-ATP 5 mM on the day of the experiment, and the pH was adjusted to 7.4 with CsOH. All reagents were obtained from Sigma Chemical Company, St Louis, Missouri, USA.

The current–voltage relationship for calcium channels was evaluated by stepping to test potentials between –80 and +50 mV for 120 ms from the holding potential of –110 mV. For evaluation of peptide and divalent cation blockers, calcium channel currents were evoked by stepping from a holding potential of –90 mV to either +20 mV (α_{1E} and α_{1B}) or –20 mV (GH3) for 150 ms every 40 s. Peptide or divalent cation blockers were diluted from concentrated stock solutions into the external solution and applied from a modified U-tube apparatus by gravity feed. Peak inward currents were measured; reductions in currents are expressed as percentage inhibition from control amplitudes. Data are expressed as mean ± SEM. IC_{50} values were calculated by fitting concentration-dependent inhibitions with the logistic equation.[32]

Results

Activation properties

In GH3 cells, depolarisation to potentials above –50 mV resulted in a rapidly inactivating inward current (fig. 1). The threshold for activation of inward currents in GH3 cells was between –50 and –40 mV, with half-activation at –25 mV and peak activation at –20 mV (fig. 2). At potentials greater than –20 mV, a slowly inactivating current component was elicited (see fig. 1 (trace d)) which could be blocked by the addition of the dihydropyridine nitrendipine (data not shown[29]). To evaluate the effects of peptide and divalent cation blockers on the rapidly inactivating component of GH3 cell currents, a step to –20 mV was used which maximally activated the rapidly inactivating T-type current component.

The voltage-dependence of activation for α_{1E} and α_{1B} calcium channels was significantly shifted to more depolarised potentials. In the cells expressing α_{1E} calcium channels, the threshold for activation of inward current was around –15 mV (see fig. 1; fig. 2), with half-activation at +5 mV and peak between +15 mV and +20 mV (see fig. 2). Results were similar for the cells expressing α_{1B} calcium channels, with the threshold for activation at –5 mV, half-activation at +10 mV and peak at +25 mV (see fig. 2).

Pharmacology of peptide calcium channel blockers

ω-CTx-MVIIA selectively blocks N-type calcium channels, while ω-CTx-MVIIC blocks N-, Q- and P-type calcium channels.[11,13,14] Neither of these peptides had any effect on GH3 T-type current, with ω-CTx-MVIIA (1 μM) producing –1 ± 1.9% inhibition (n=3) and ω-CTx-MVIIC (1 μM) producing –1 ± 3.8% inhibition (n=3) (fig. 3). Neither peptide blocked α_{1E} calcium channel current (ω-CTx-MVIIA (100 nM) 2 ± 0.9% inhibition (n=3), ω-CTx-MVIIC (1 μM) 0.3 ± 0.3% inhibition (n=3)) (see fig. 3). In contrast, α_{1B} calcium

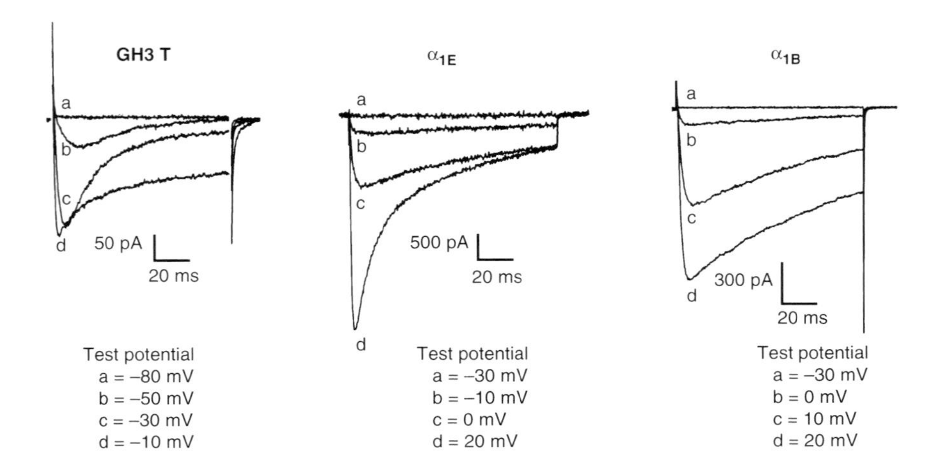

Figure 1. Representative raw data traces of depolarisation of GH3 and α_{1E}- and α_{1B}-expressing cells. Depolarisation resulted in inward whole-cell calcium channel currents in all three cell lines.

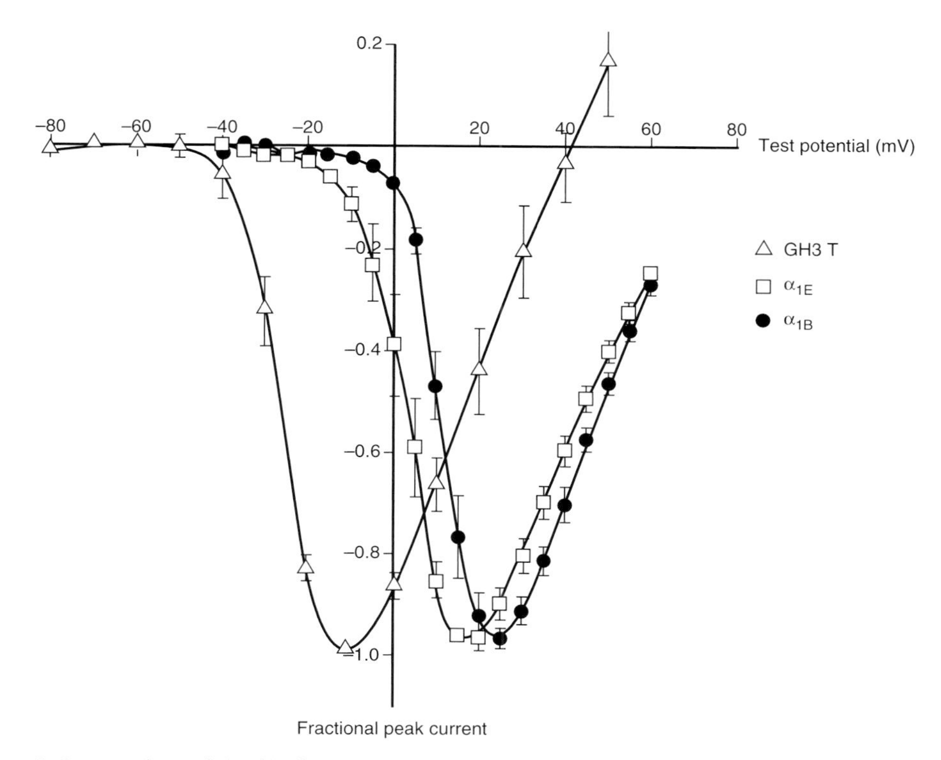

Figure 2. Current–voltage relationships for GH3 and α_{1E}- and α_{1B}-expressing cells. Data were normalised to the maximal peak inward current in each cell. Data are means ± SEM (n=5–9 observations).

channel currents were blocked by both ω-CTx-MVIIA and ω-CTx-MVIIC. ω-CTx-MVIIA inhibited α_{1B} calcium channels by 62 ± 5.8% at a concentration of 100 nM (n=5) (see fig. 3), with an IC_{50} of 61 nM (data not shown). ω-CTx-MVIIC blocked α_{1B} calcium channels by 93 ± 2.0% at 1 μM (n=3) (see fig. 3), with an IC_{50} of 42 nM (data not shown).

ω-Aga-IIIA, a non-selective peptide blocker purified from funnel web spider venom,[33,34] also had differential effects on calcium channel currents. ω-Aga-IIIA potently blocked α_{1E} calcium channels, with 52 ± 4.9% (n=6) inhibition at 20 nM and an IC_{50} of 7 nM (n=2), while α_{1B} calcium channels were inhibited by only 23 ± 9.8% (n=3) at 20 nM (fig. 4). GH3 T-type calcium channels were only partially sensitive to ω-Aga-IIIA, with 18 ± 5.2% (n=7) inhibition at 200 nM and 3 ± 2.1% inhibition at 20 nM (see fig. 4).

Divalent cation blockers

Heightened sensitivity to block by Ni^{2+} has been used to differentiate between HVA and low-voltage-activated (LVA) calcium channel subtypes.[35] Calcium channel currents in T-type, α_{1E} and α_{1B} cells were blocked by Ni^{2+}, with IC_{50} concentrations of about 200 μM (figs 5 and 6). While Ni^{2+} sensitivity was essentially the same over most of the concentration range, at concentrations below 100 μM α_{1E} calcium channels were blocked slightly more than T-type and α_{1B} channels (see fig. 6). For example,

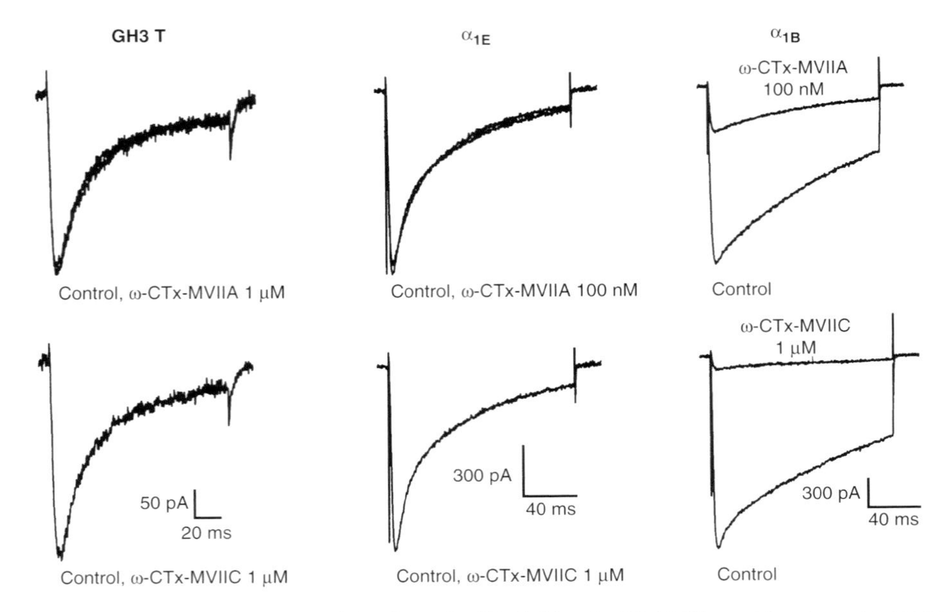

Figure 3. Representative raw data traces of the effects of ω-CTx-MVIIA and ω-CTx-MVIIC on calcium channel currents in GH3 and α_{1E}- and α_{1B}-expressing cells. ω-CTx-MVIIA and ω-CTx-MVIIC only blocked α_{1B} calcium channels and had no effect on GH3 or α_{1E} calcium channel currents.

Ni^{2+} 30 μM blocked 8 ± 2.1% (n=6) of GH3 T-type current but blocked 26 ± 2.6% (n=4) of α_{1E} calcium channels. Ni^{2+} also produced a slowing in the activation of α_{1E} channels (see fig. 5), similar to that described by Zamponi.[27]

There was a distinct difference in the potency of Cd^{2+} block of the different types of calcium channels. Cd^{2+} blocked α_{1E} calcium channel current, with an IC_{50} of 1.6 μM (see fig. 6) and 81 ± 3.8% (n=9) inhibition at 10 μM (see fig. 4). α_{1B} calcium channels were blocked with a similar potency, 86 ± 2.4% (n=6) at 10 μM (see fig. 4). GH3 T-type calcium channels were not blocked with the same potency. The IC_{50} for Cd^{2+} block of T-type current was 144 μM (see fig. 6), with 100 μM inhibiting 46 ± 1.6% (n=5) (see fig. 4).

Discussion

While other groups have successfully produced stable cell lines by transfecting all three calcium channel subunits simultaneously,[22,36] our approach to generating mammalian cell lines that express calcium channels involved an intermediate step in which the $\alpha_2\delta$ and β subunits were expressed before the α_1 subunit was introduced. While this approach was somewhat slower than transfecting all three subunits at once, it has distinct advantages. This method makes it easier to generate cell lines that each express different calcium channel subtypes. Rather than having three subunits to introduce each time a different channel type is needed, only the requisite α_1 subunit can be transfected into the cell line that already contains the $\alpha_2\delta$ and β subunits. More importantly, the approach allows a more direct comparison of the

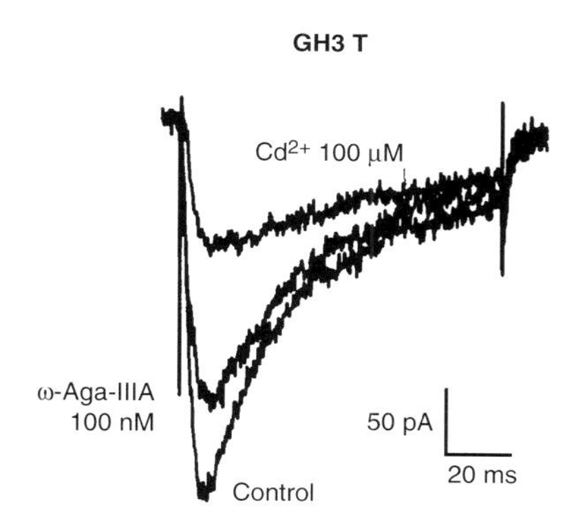

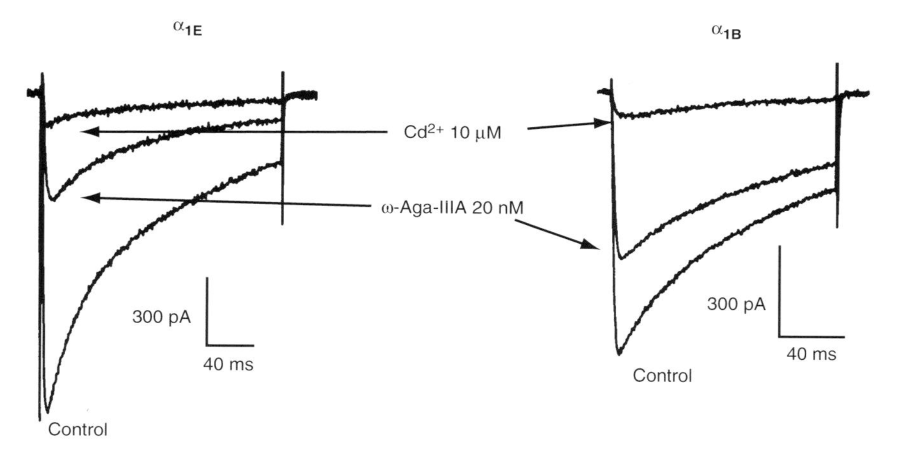

Figure 4. Representative raw data traces of the effects of ω-Aga-IIIA and Cd^{2+} on calcium channel currents in GH3 and α_{1E}- and α_{1B}-expressing cells. ω-Aga-IIIA potently blocked α_{1E} calcium channels, but only partially inhibited α_{1B} and GH3 calcium channels. Cd^{2+} potently blocked α_{1E} and α_{1B} calcium channels, but had a weaker effect on GH3 calcium channel currents.

properties of different α_1 subunits. Because the background into which α_1 subunits were introduced was identical with respect to the type and expression level of accessory subunits, any differences in pharmacology or biophysical properties of expressed calcium channel subtypes must be related to the differences in α_1 subunits. This is a significant advantage, since it is clear that the properties of calcium channels are dependent not only on the particular α_1 subunit present, but also on the interactions between the α_1 and accessory subunits $\alpha_2\delta$ and β.[18–20]

Comparison of the pharmacological and biophysical properties of α_{1E} and α_{1B} calcium channels expressed in mammalian HEK293 cells suggested that there were significant similarities between these two subtypes of calcium channels. Both were HVA channels and showed inactivation with relatively rapid kinetics. The α_{1E} calcium channel, however, inactivated slightly more rapidly than the α_{1B}, which was further evidence suggesting that the α_1 subunit plays an important role in determining voltage-dependent inactivation properties. Both channels were sensitive to divalent

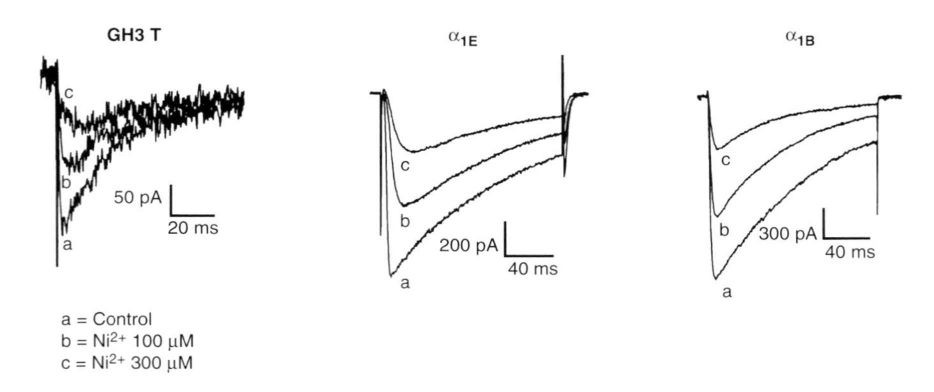

Figure 5. Representative raw data traces of the effects of Ni^{2+} on calcium channel currents in GH3 and α_{1E}- and α_{1B}- expressing cells.

cation blockers (Ni^{2+} and Cd^{2+}), as well as to the peptide blocker ω-Aga-IIIA, which non-selectively blocks HVA calcium channels.[33,34]

α_{1B} channels had a profile similar to that of neuronal N-type calcium channels. ω-CTx-MVIIA selectively blocks N-type calcium channels and ω-CTx-MVIIC blocks both the N- and P-/Q-type channels with high potency.[11] Expressed α_{1B} channels were blocked by both ω-CTx-MVIIA and ω-CTx-MVIIC and also had electrophysiological properties similar to those of N-type calcium channels. While biophysical properties may change depending upon the accessory subunits expressed,[18,20] the conopeptide sensitivity indicated that α_{1B} calcium channels most closely resemble neuronal N-type calcium channels.

Classification of expressed α_{1E} calcium channels was difficult. α_{1E} channels were not blocked by either ω-CTx-MVIIA or ω-CTx-MVIIC, eliminating a classification of N- and P-/Q-type channels because ω-CTx-MVIIA and ω-CTx-MVIIC do block these calcium channel subtypes.[11,14] Early experiments with α_{1E} channels expressed in *Xenopus* oocytes suggested that α_{1E} channels may in fact be low-threshold or T-type calcium channels because activation and inactivation properties were similar in the recombinant channels and T-type calcium channels.[24] However, results from our experiments using identical recording conditions and techniques indicated that α_{1E} channels had threshold and peak activation at voltages significantly more depolarised than T-type current in GH3 cells (see fig. 2)[29] or those reported for T-type current in dorsal root ganglion (DRG) cells or smooth muscle cells.[33–35,37] In fact, the activation properties of α_{1E} calcium channels were much more like those of α_{1B} (HVA) calcium channels.

Importantly, α_{1E} channels were also blocked by low concentrations of ω-Aga-IIIA, while GH3 cell T-type current was only partially blocked by high concentrations of ω-Aga-IIIA. Since GH3 cells express both T- and L-type calcium channels,[29] it is possible that the partial inhibition by ω-Aga-IIIA could be accounted for by blockade of L-type calcium channels activated under the conditions of the experiment. Neuronal T-type calcium channels in DRG cells were unaffected by ω-Aga-IIIA.[33,34]

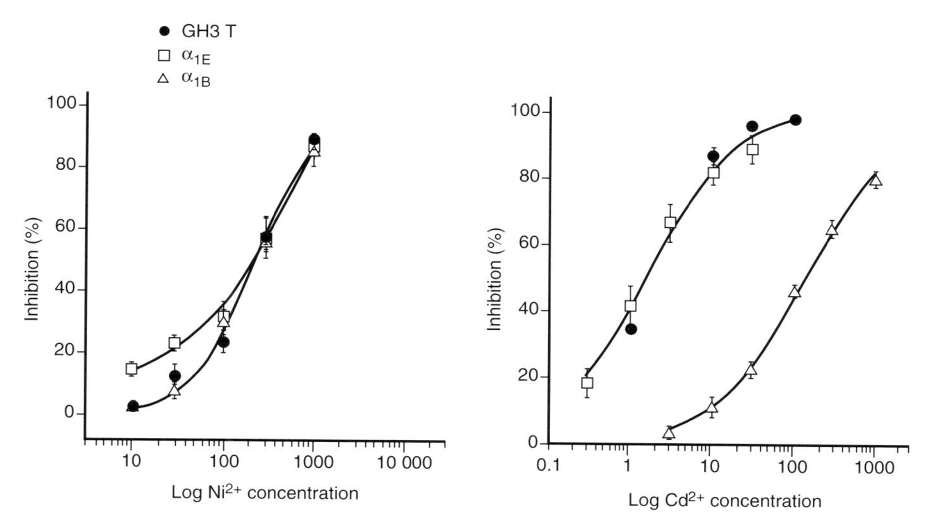

Figure 6. Concentration dependency of the Ni^{2+} and Cd^{2+} blockade of GH3 and α_{1E} and α_{1B} calcium channels. Data are means ± SEM (n=4–7 observations).

There were also differences in divalent cation sensitivity between α_{1E} calcium channels and GH3 T-type channels. A distinct property of T-type calcium channels is higher sensitivity to the divalent cation blocker Ni^{2+}.[35] While the block of GH3 and α_{1E} and α_{1B} channels by Ni^{2+} was similar, low concentrations of Ni^{2+} were more effective in blocking α_{1E} calcium channels, suggesting some similarity with conventional T-type calcium channels. These data, along with the data from Bourinet et al. on permeation properties of α_{1E} calcium channels,[28] suggest that α_{1E} and an analogous component of the T-type calcium channel may share some homology. However, Cd^{2+} blocked α_{1E} and α_{1B} channels more potently than GH3 T-type channels. The difference in potency for Cd^{2+} was similar to that described for rat aorta smooth muscle cell T-type current (IC_{50} = 400 μM) and HVA calcium channel currents (IC_{50} = 6 μM),[37] suggesting a profile for α_{1E} more like that of HVA channels.

Taken together, these data suggest that α_{1E} calcium channels share many features with HVA calcium channels, depolarised activation voltages and a potent block by ω-Aga-IIIA and Cd^{2+}. Recently, a calcium channel subtype found in cerebellar granule cells has been described that has a biophysical and toxin-sensitivity profile similar to that of α_{1E} calcium channels.[15,16,38] However, without knowing which accessory subunits associate with α_{1E} in cells to form functional calcium channels and without identification of a selective antagonist for α_{1E} such as ω-CTx-MVIIA for α_{1B} and N-type calcium channels, it is difficult to make a definitive alignment between α_{1E} and a subtype of neuronal calcium channels.

Acknowledgements

The authors would like to thank Greg Campbell for technical assistance in preparing cultures, Dr L. Nadasni (Neurex Corporation) for supplying ω-CTx-MVIIA and ω-CTx-MVIIC, and Dr M. Adams (U.C. Riverside) for supplying ω-Aga-IIIA. The authors would also like to thank George Miljanich (Neurex Corporation) for comments on the manuscript.

References

1. Catterall WA. Structure and function of voltage-gated ion channels. Trends Neurosci 1993; 16: 500–6
2. Catterall WA, Epstein PN. Ion channels. Diabetologia 1992; 35: S22–33
3. Birnbaumer L, Campbell KP, Catterall WA, et al. The naming of voltage-gated calcium channels. Neuron 1994; 13: 505–6
4. Rorsman P, Bokvist K, Ammala C, et al. Ion channels, electrical activity and insulin secretion. Diabete Metab 1994; 20: 138–45
5. Tsien RW, Ellinor PT, Horne WA. Molecular diversity of voltage-dependent Ca^{2+} channels. Trends Pharmacol Sci 1991; 12: 349–54
6. Miller RJ. Voltage-sensitive Ca^{2+} channels. J Biol Chem 1992; 267: 1403–6
7. Perez-Reyes E, Schneider T. Molecular biology of calcium channels. Kidney Int 1995; 48: 1111–24
8. Coulter DA, Huguenard JR, Prince DA. Characterization of ethosuximide reduction of low-threshold calcium current in thalamic neurons. Ann Neurol 1989; 25: 582–99
9. Kelly KM, Gross RA, Macdonald RL. Valproic acid selectively reduces the low-threshold (T) calcium current in rat nodose neurons. Neurosci Lett 1990; 116: 233–8
10. Mintz IM, Venema VJ, Swiderek KM, et al. P-type calcium channels blocked by the spider toxin ω-Aga-IVA. Nature 1992; 355: 827–9
11. Hillyard DR, Monje VD, Mintz IM, et al. A new conus peptide ligand for mammalian presynaptic Ca^{2+} channels. Neuron 1992; 9: 69–77
12. Boland LM, Morrill JA, Bean BP. ω-conotoxin block of N-type calcium channels in frog and rat sympathetic neurons. J Neurosci 1994; 14: 5011–27
13. Regan LJ, Sah DWY, Bean BP. Ca^{2+} channels in rat central and peripheral neurons: High-threshold current resistant to dihydropyridine blockers and ω-conotoxin. Neuron 1991; 6: 269–80
14. Olivera BM, Miljanich G, Ramachandran J, et al. Calcium channel diversity and neurotransmitter release: the ω-conotoxins and ω-agatoxins. Ann Rev Biochem 1994; 63: 823–67
15. Zhang J-F, Randall AD, Ellinor PT, et al. Distinctive pharmacology and kinetics of cloned neuronal Ca^{2+} channels and their possible counterparts in mammalian CNS neurons. Neuropharm 1993; 32: 1075–88
16. Randall AD, Tsien RW. Pharmacological dissection of multiple types of Ca^{2+} channel currents in rat cerebellar granule cells. J Neurosci 1995; 15: 2995–3012
17. Pearson HA, Sutton KG, Scott RH, et al. Characterization of Ca^{2+} channel currents in rat cerebellar granule neurones. J Physiol (Lond) 1995; 482: 493–509
18. Neely A, Wei X, Olcese R, et al. Potentiation by the β subunit of the ratio of the ionic current to the charge movement in the cardiac calcium channel. Science 1993; 262: 575–8
19. Wei X, Pan S, Lang W, et al. Molecular determinants of cardiac Ca^{2+} channel pharmacology. J Biol Chem 1995; 270: 27106–11
20. Varadi G, Lory P, Schultz D, et al. Acceleration of activation and inactivation by the β subunit of the skeletal muscle calcium channel. Nature 1991; 352: 159–62
21. Zamponi GW, Soong TW, Bourinet E, et al. β subunit coexpression and the α_1 subunit domain I–II linker affect piperidine block of neuronal calcium channels. J Neurosci 1996; 6: 2430–43
22. Welling A, Bosse E, Cavalie A, et al. Stable co-expression of calcium channel α_1, β and α_2/δ subunits in a somatic cell line. J Physiol (Lond) 1993; 471: 749–65
23. Perez-Garcia MT, Kamp TJ, Marban E. Functional properties of cardiac L-type calcium channels transiently expressed in HEK293 cells: roles of α_1 and β subunits. J Gen Physiol 1995; 105: 289–306
24. Soong TW, Stea A, Hodson CD, et al. Structure and functional expression of a member of the low voltage-activated calcium channel family. Science 1993; 260: 1133–6
25. Williams ME, Marubio LM, Deal CR, et al. Structure and functional characterization of neuronal α_{1E} calcium channel subtypes. J Biol Chem 1994; 269: 22347–57
26. Bezprozvanny I, Tsien RW. Voltage-dependent blockade of diverse types of voltage-gated Ca^{2+} channels expressed in *Xenopus* oocytes by the Ca^{2+} channel antagonist mibefradil (Ro 40-5967). Mol Pharmacol 1995; 48: 540–9
27. Zamponi GW, Bourinet E, Snutch TP. Nickel block of a family of neuronal calcium channels: subtype- and subunit-dependent action at multiple sites. J Membr Biol 1996; 77–90
28. Bourinet E, Zamponi GW, Stea A, et al. The α_{1E} calcium channel exhibits permeation properties similar to low-voltage-activated calcium channels. J Neurosci 1996; 16: 4983–93
29. Simasko SM, Weiland GA, Oswald RE. Pharmacological characterization of two calcium currents in GH3 cells. Am J Physiol 1988; 2543: E328–36
30. Ellinor PT, Zhang J, Horne WA, et al. Structural determinants of the blockade of N-type calcium channels by a peptide neurotoxin. Nature 1994; 372: 272–5

31. Hammil OP, Marty A, Neher E, et al. Improved patch clamp techniques for high-resolution current recording from cells and cell-free membrane patches. Pflugers Arch 1981; 391: 85–100
32. Barlow R, Blake JF. Hill coefficients and the logistic equation. Trends Pharmacol Sci 1989; 10: 440–1
33. Mintz IM, Venema VJ, Adams ME, et al. Inhibition of N- and L-type Ca^{2+} channels by the spider venom toxin ω-Aga-IIIA. Proc Natl Acad Sci U S A 1991; 88: 6628–31
34. Mintz IM. Block of Ca channels in rat central neurons by the spider toxin ω-Aga-IIIA. J Neurosci 1994; 14: 2844–53
35. Nowycky MC, Fox AP, Tsien RW. Three types of neuronal calcium channel with different calcium agonist sensitivity. Nature 1985; 316: 440–3
36. Bleakman D, Bowman D, Bath CP, et al. Characterization of a human N-type calcium channel expressed in HEK293 cells. Neuropharmacology 1995; 34: 753–65
37. Akaike N, Kanaide H, Kuga T, et al. Low-voltage activated calcium current in rat aorta smooth muscle cells in primary culture. J Physiol (Lond) 1989; 416: 141–60
38. Randall A, Tsien RW. Distinctive biophysical and pharmacological features of T-type calcium channels. In: Tsien RW, Closel J-P, Nargeot J, editors. Low-Voltage-Activated T-type Calcium Channels. Proceedings from the International Electrophysiology Meeting: 1996 Oct 21–22; Montpellier, France. Chester, UK: Adis International Ltd, 1998: 29–43

Molecular characterisation of T-type calcium channels

Edward Perez-Reyes,[1,2] Leanne L. Cribbs,[1,2] Asif Daud,[1] Jie Yang,[1] Antonio E. Lacerda,[3] Jane Barclay,[4] Magali P. Williamson,[4] Margaret Fox,[5] Michele Rees,[4] Jung-Ha Lee[1]

[1] Department of Physiology and [2] Cardiovascular Institute, Loyola University Medical Center, Maywood, Illinois, USA; [3] Rammelkamp Center for Research & Education, MetroHealth Medical System, and Department of Physiology and Biophysics, Case Western Reserve University, Cleveland, Ohio, USA; [4] Department of Paediatrics, The Rayne Institute, University College London Medical School, London, UK; [5] Medical Research Council Human Biochemical Genetics Unit, The Galton Laboratory, London, UK

Summary

Low-voltage-activated, T-type calcium channels are thought to be involved in pacemaker activity, low-threshold calcium spikes, neuronal oscillations and resonance, and postanodal exaltation. Mutations in T-type channel genes may be a contributing factor to neurological and cardiovascular disorders, such as epilepsy, arrhythmia and hypertension. Since there is a lack of selective blockers, little is known about their structure or molecular biology. This paper reports the cloning, distribution, chromosomal localisation and functional expression of the first T-type calcium channel.

Introduction

Molecular diversity of voltage-activated calcium channels was established by studies showing that channels could be distinguished by their voltage-dependence, kinetics and single-channel conductance.[1–3] Low-voltage-activated (LVA) calcium channels open after small depolarisations of the membrane potential, while high-voltage-activated (HVA) channels require larger depolarisations (30 mV). LVA channels are also called 'T' type because their currents are both **t**ransient (because of their fast inactivation) and **t**iny (because of their small conductance).[2] T-type channels also inactivate near the resting membrane potential, but they recover quickly after small hyperpolarisations.[4] These properties allow the channel to gate in a manner distinct from conventional voltage-activated channels: inhibitory postsynaptic potentials (IPSP) allow the channel to recover from inactivation, followed by channel opening as the membrane potential returns to its resting value. This property has been called 'postanodal exaltation',[5] or 'rebound burst-firing'. The involvement of T-type channels in generating low-threshold spikes and rebound burst-firing has been demonstrated in neurons from the inferior olive, thalamus, hippocampus and neocortex.[6] Their localisation on dorsal root ganglion neurons suggests they may be involved in transmission of pain.[1] Physiological roles for T-type channels have been proposed in many tissues: pacing of the heart,[7] smooth muscle contraction,[8] adrenal hormone secretion[9,10] and fertilisation.[11] Genetic abnormalities in T-type channel genes have been proposed in absence epilepsy[12] and cardiomyopathy.[13]

Our cloning strategy began with an analysis of all the cDNA clones of the Genbank (Bethesda, Maryland, USA) that were defined as having homology to calcium channels. We sequenced a human brain clone, H06096, then used it to clone a full-length cDNA from rat brain. Northern analysis indicates that this gene is expressed predominantly in brain, in particular the amygdala, cerebellum and thalamus. Using both radiation hybrid mapping and fluorescent *in situ* hybridisation, we mapped the human gene to chromosome 17q22 and the mouse gene to chromosome 11. Functional expression of the channel was measured in *Xenopus* oocytes. Based on the channel's distinctive voltage-dependence, kinetics and 7.5 pS single-channel conductance, we identify this channel as an LVA T-type calcium channel.

Materials and methods

cDNA library screening

All cDNA probes were released from the vector by restriction digestion, then separated on agarose gels and purified using the QIAquick gel extraction kit (QIAGEN Inc., Chatsworth, California, USA). Probes were labelled using ^{32}P-α-dCTP and the RadPrime DNA Labeling System (Life Technologies Inc., Gaithersburg, Maryland, USA). A rat brain cDNA library was obtained from Clontech (Palo Alto, California, USA). All library screening was performed using conventional filter hybridisation according to the manufacturer's protocol. The original probe was H06096, an LLNL (Lawrence Livermore National Laboratory, Livermore, California, USA) cDNA obtained from Genome Systems Inc. (St Louis, Missouri, USA). Successive screening of the same cDNA library resulted in multiple overlapping clones, of which five were chosen to construct the full-length cDNA. The 5' terminus was synthesised by polymerase chain reaction (PCR; Hoffmann-La Roche Inc.) using clone D3 as the template, beginning near the initial methionine (nt 379-825). This PCR fragment was joined to a *Bam*H1-*Spe* I fragment from clone AH3 (nt 825-2299), *Spe*I-*Eag*I from cDNA clone 5 (nt 2299-3982), *Eag*I-*Bgl*II from cDNA clone 2 (nt 3982-5316) and *Bgl*II-*Eco*RI (nt 5316-7540) from clone Un7. This full-length sequence (nt 379-7540) was assembled in the vector pSP72 (Promega Corporation, Madison, Wisconsin, USA). The sequence of α_{1G} was determined on both strands of the plasmid using oligonucleotide primers, Sequenase 2.0 (Amersham, UK), a digitiser and WDNASIS software (Hitachi).

Northern analysis

Northern blots of mRNA 2 µg were obtained from Clontech. The blots were hybridised at 42 °C for 16–20 hours in standard solutions containing formamide 50%. Blots were washed at up to 60 °C in a final buffer of SSC 0.1× (NaCl 15 mM, sodium citrate 1.5 mM), SDS 0.1%, and exposed to X-ray film at –80 °C for the times indicated in the results.

Chromosomal localisation

The human chromosomal location was determined using the Genbridge 4 radiation hybrid panel obtained from the UK HGMP (Human Genome Mapping Project)

Resource Centre (Cambridge, UK). PCR primers were GACCTGAAGAAGTGCTACAG and GAGAGACTCAGCACATCTTT. The hybrids were scored as directed and the results entered into the database at HGMP (www.hgmp.mrc.ac.uk/cgi-bin/contig/rhmapper.pl). Fluorescent *in situ* hybridisation of the *CACNA1G* cDNA clone R19524 to normal male human metaphase spreads was carried out as described previously.[14] The mouse chromosomal location was determined using the EUCIB back-cross panel,[15] obtained from the UK HGMP Resource Centre. A PCR product was amplified from C57BL/6 and *Mus spretus* mouse genomic DNA using the following primers: CTCCGCCTCCTGGGCAGTC and ATATACATAGAGATTCTGCAC. Fifty random N_2 mice were typed as directed using a polymorphic *Sfa*NI restriction site by digestion of the amplified product. The results are coded as 97/MW/001 at www.hgmp.mrc.ac.uk/MBx/MBxHomepage.html.

Oocyte expression

Capped cRNA was synthesised from plasmid linearised with *Bsa*AI using the T7 cRNA synthesis kit (Ambion, Austin, Texas, USA). The concentration of cRNA was measured spectrophotometrically. Oocytes were prepared from *Xenopus laevis* (Nasco, Fort Atkinson, Wisconsin, USA) using standard techniques.[16] Each oocyte was injected with 10 or 30 ng of cRNA in a volume of 50 nl. For the single-channel experiments, the amount of the cRNA was increased to 100 ng per oocyte and the eggs were incubated for at least 1 week prior to recording. To compare currents of similar size, we had to decrease the amount of α_{1E} injected 1000-fold (0.1 ng). The results were obtained from seven batches of oocytes derived from five frogs.

Electrophysiological analysis of injected oocytes

Oocytes were voltage-clamped using a two-microelectrode voltage-clamp amplifier (OC-725B; Warner Instrument Corp; Hamden, Connecticut, USA) as described previously.[16] The standard bath solution contained the following: $Ba(OH)_2$ 40 mM, NaOH 50 mM, KOH 1 mM, EDTA 0.1 mM and HEPES 5 mM, adjusted to pH 7.4 with methanesulphonate. The osmolarity of the Ba^{2+} 2 mM and 10 mM solutions were balanced by increasing the NaOH concentration as described by Lory et al.[17] Similar results were obtained in the absence of Na^+ using $BaCl_2$ solutions described by Bourinet et al.[18] Unless otherwise stated, the holding potential was –90 mV. Voltage and current electrodes (1.5–1.8 MΩ tip resistance) were filled with KCl 3 M. Except where noted, data were acquired at 4 kHz using the pCLAMP 6.0 system (Digidata 1200 and pCLAMP 6.0; Axon Instruments, Foster City, California, USA) and filtered at 1 kHz. Data were analysed using pCLAMP 6.0 software. Boltzmann fits and linear regression were calculated using Prism (GraphPad, San Diego, California, USA). Single channels were measured with standard depolarising bath and pipette ($BaCl_2$ 115 mM, EGTA 1 mM and HEPES 10 mM; pH 7.4) solutions.[19] The data were analysed using TRANSIT.[20] Single-channel amplitudes were measured by averaging the values obtained from Gaussian fits to all-points histograms of traces with openings, selected openings and amplitude histograms of idealised openings. In a previous study we reported that exceptional batches of oocytes contain a 9 pS channel.[19] These endogenous channels can be distinguished by their 2-fold-larger current amplitudes at the potentials we tested: at –20 mV, current amplitude was 0.8 pA for endogenous channels *vs* 0.4 pA for α_{1G}. Endogenous calcium channels were not detected at either the whole-cell or single-channel level.

Results

Molecular biology of α_{1G} subunits

Our alternative cloning strategy was to use a text-based search of the Genbank to find novel sequences that had homology to cloned calcium channels. Our first search using the terms 'calcium' and 'channel' returned 347 entries. Twenty-eight of these entries were labelled as being 'similar to' a calcium channel. These cDNA fragments were cloned by the IMAGE Consortium (Livermore, California, USA) and partially sequenced by the Washington University-Merck EST (**e**xpressed **s**equence **t**agged) project.[21] The clones were compared to identified genes, then deposited in the Genbank along with a comment on which gene they matched. Based on its 45% identity with domain III S1 of the carp α_{1S} (Genbank #P22316), we decided to sequence H06096. Although the deduced amino acid sequence of this clone was only 30% identical to cloned calcium channels, it contained readily identifiable motifs, including an S4 region and a pore loop. Using H06096 as the probe, we screened a rat brain λgt10 cDNA library. A full-length cDNA, referred to as 'α_{1G}' (Genbank #AF027984) or '$Ca_vT.1$', was assembled from five overlapping clones. Search of the non-redundant division of the Genbank revealed that α_{1G} was similar to other calcium channel α_1 subunits, but most similar to C54D2.5 (Genbank #U37548), a putative protein found in the genomic DNA of *Caenorhabditis elegans*.[22] Homologous human (H19230, R19524) and mouse (AA386626) EST clones were also identified and sequenced. Sequence identity among the calcium channel α_1 subunits is highest in the putative membrane-spanning regions, with most changes being conservative with respect to structure (fig. 1). Charged residues are particularly conserved, with many charges being conserved across all domains and in voltage-gated sodium and potassium channels.[23] The charged residues of the S4 regions are also conserved, consistent with their role as voltage sensors.[26] The cation selectivity of calcium channels requires a ring of negative charge provided by glutamate residues found at similar locations in each domain.[24] In α_{1G}, two of these glutamates are replaced by aspartate, suggesting an altered selectivity. In contrast, there is little conservation of the sequences that link these regions within a domain, and even less between the intracellular loops that connect the domains. Notably absent are the motifs involved in binding the β subunit,[27,28] and Ca^{2+}.[29]

Northern blot analysis of human and rat tissues indicates there are two α_{1G} mRNA transcripts, with a predominant band of 8.5 kb and another of 9.7 kb (fig. 2). The detected signals were strongest in brain and less abundant in heart. Longer exposure reveals expression in placenta, kidney and lung. Transcripts were detected in all human brain regions studied, with strong signals from (in relative order of

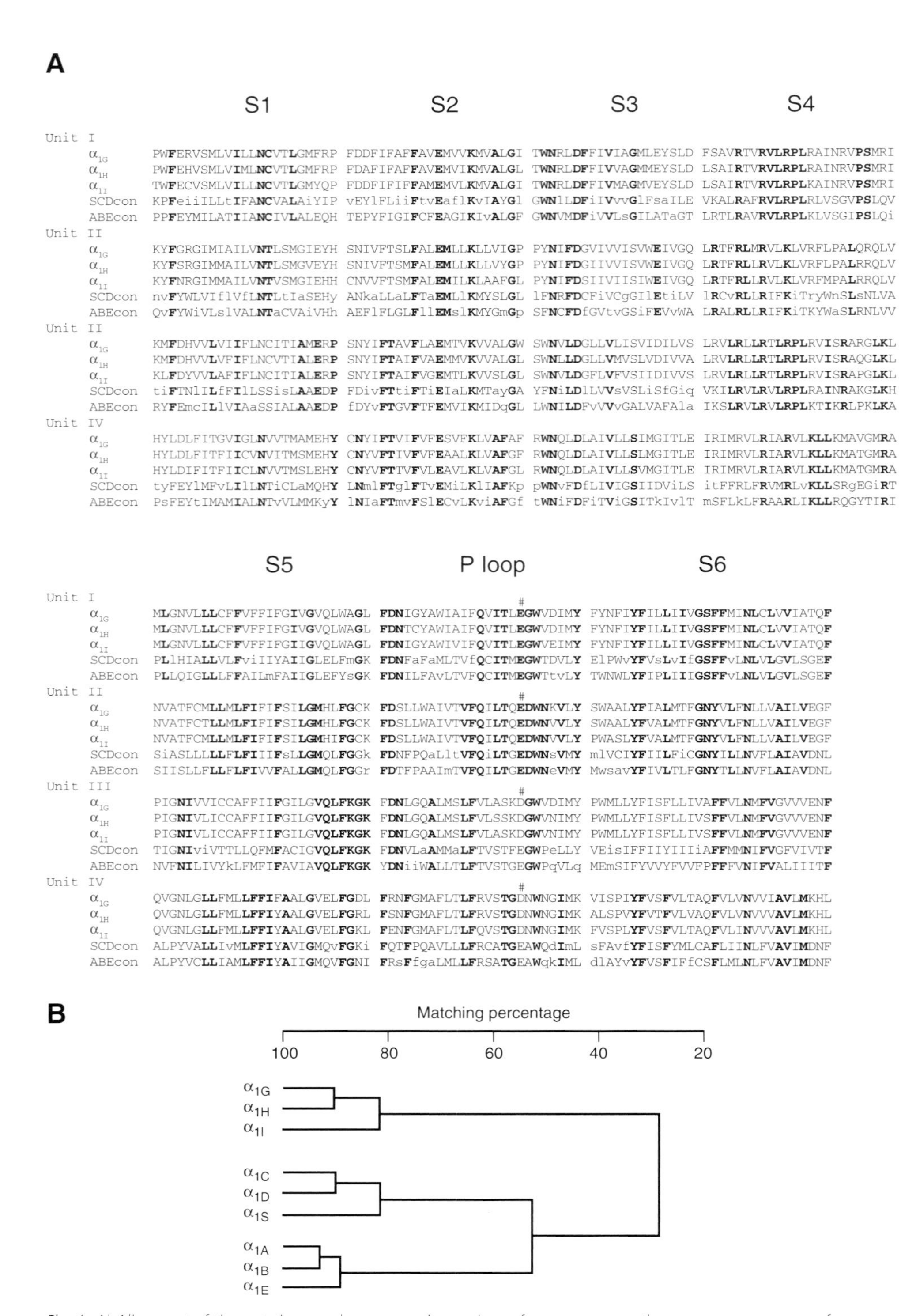

Fig. 1. A) Alignment of the putative membrane-spanning regions of α_{1G}, α_{1H}, α_{1I}, the consensus sequence of α_{1S}, α_{1C} and α_{1D} (SCDcon), and the consensus sequence of α_{1A}, α_{1B} and α_{1E} (ABEcon). The regions were first selected using

(continued opposite)

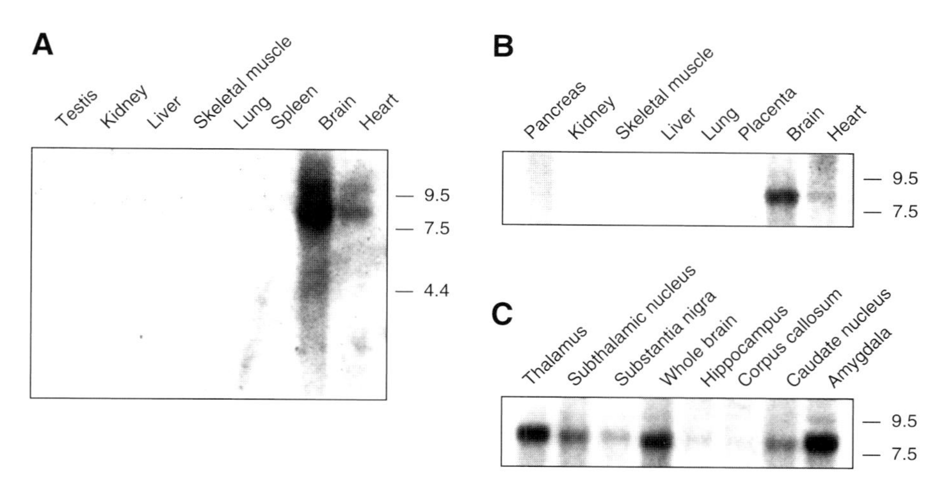

Fig. 2. Distribution of α_{1G} mRNA in rats and humans. A) A rat multiple-tissue Northern blot was probed with α_{1G}, nt 6166-7533, then exposed for 24 hours to X-ray film. B) A human multiple-tissue Northern blot was probed with human H06096, which is homologous with α_{1G} nt 3973-4929, then exposed for 1 week to X-ray film. C) Human brain region Northern blot was probed and exposed as in panel B. Molecular-weight markers are indicated on the right in kilobases. At least two independent blots were hybridised with probes from both transmembrane and 3′ untranslated regions of each probe, giving similar results, thereby minimising the possibility that the signals are a result of cross-reactivity with another mRNA.

abundance) amygdala, thalamus, subthalamic nuclei (see fig. 2 (C)) and cerebellum (data not shown). To confirm the Northern analysis, we performed PCR, followed by subcloning and sequencing.

Genetic mutations of either the calcium channel α_{1A} subunit or β_4 subunits result in ataxic and epileptic phenotypes.[30–32] A similar link between T-type channels and absence epilepsy was suggested by Tsakiridou et al.[12] As a first step in exploring such a link we mapped the human and murine α_{1G} genes. The human chromosomal location of the α_{1G} gene, *CACNA1G*, was determined using the Genbridge 4 radiation hybrid panel. PCR products were analysed by Southern hybridisation with a 360 bp human genomic DNA PCR product. *CACNA1G* was mapped to human chromosome 17 between the markers AFMA126YD5 and D17S798 with an LOD (logarithm for the likelihood of linkage) score of >3.0. Fluorescent *in situ* hybridisation to normal male human metaphase spreads was carried out using the α_{1G} cDNA clone R19524. Analysis of 22 metaphases confirmed the localisation of *CACNA1G* to chromosome 17 (fig. 3 (A)) and 59% of these could be assigned to the 17q22 band (see fig. 3 (B)). The mouse chromosomal location of α_{1G} was determined using radiation hybrid mapping, fluorescent *in situ* hybridisation and a mouse interspecific back-cross.[15] A 260 bp product was amplified from C57BL/6 and *Mus spretus* mouse genomic DNA using

(Fig. 1 continued)
published alignments,[23] but were then extended to include highly conserved residues. Amino acids that are conserved in all nine mammalian α_1 subunits within a domain are marked in bold. The highly conserved amino acids in the pore (P) loop that determine Ca^{2+} selectivity in high-voltage-activated calcium channels[24] are marked with a # sign.
B) Evolutionary-tree analysis based on alignment of the membrane-spanning regions as shown in panel A. Matching percentage was calculated using CLUSTAL (WONASIS, Hitachi, San Bruno, California, USA).[25] Sequences used for the alignment and their respective Genbank accession numbers were: α_{1G}, AF027984; α_{1I}, AL008716; α_{1C}, L04569; α_{1E}, L27745; α_{1S}, L33798; α_{1D}, M76558; α_{1A}, X99897; and α_{1B}, M94172.

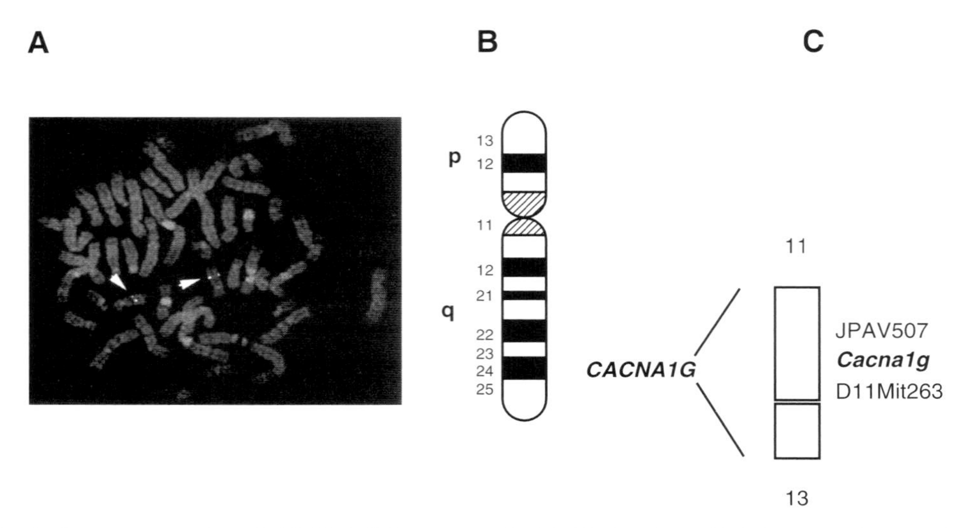

Fig. 3. Chromosomal locations of CACNA1G. *A) Fluorescent* in situ *hybridisation of α_{1G} cDNA clone R19524 on normal male metaphase chromosomes showing hybridisation to 17q22. Chromosomes were counterstained with 4,6-diamidino-2-phenylindole and the signal detected with fluoroscein-5-isothiocyanate. Images were captured by a cooled charge-coupled device (CCD; Photometrics, Tucson, Arizona, USA) from a Zeiss Axiophot fluorescence microscope using Smartcapture software (Digital Scientific, Cambridge, UK). B) Idiogram of human chromosome 17 illustrating the position of* CACNA1G *in band 17q22. C) Regions of mouse chromosomes 11 and 13 display synteny homology with human 17q22. Analysis of* Cacna1g *in the EUCIB panel positioned it between JPAV507 and D11Mit263, indicating that it maps to mouse chromosome 11.*

primers designed from the mouse α_{1G} cDNA sequence (AA049807). The *Cacna1g* locus was assigned to mouse chromosome 11 between the markers JPAV507 and D11Mit263 at approximately 55 cM from the centromere with an LOD score of 8.0.

The mapping of the human *CACNA1G* to human chromosome 17q22, and the mouse locus to distal mouse chromosome 11, is consistent with conserved linkage groups. A spontaneous recessive mouse neurological mutant, teetering *(tn)*, maps to mouse chromosome 11, approximately 59 cM from the centromere. Teetering homozygous mutants show dysgenesis of the brain stem and spinal cord, progressive Purkinje cell loss, ataxia, growth retardation and unusual stiff postures.[33] The involvement of calcium channels in normal brain function has been demonstrated by the discovery of mutations in the *Cacna1a* gene in the mouse tottering leaner (tg^{la}) mutant, in which degeneration of differentiated granule, Golgi and Purkinje cells occur, in addition to absence seizures.[30] No obvious human candidate phenotypes map to the 17q22 region. *Cacna1g* is currently being investigated as a candidate for the teetering mutation.

Electrophysiological characterisation of α_{1G} currents

Functional expression of α_{1G} was measured in *Xenopus* oocytes. Figure 4 (A) shows a representative family of current traces elicited by depolarising pulses of the oocyte.

Inward barium currents activated slowly near threshold potentials (–60 mV in Ba^{2+} 2 mM), while stronger depolarisations produced a current that activated and inactivated quickly (fig. 5). Randall and Tsien have called such crossing of successive

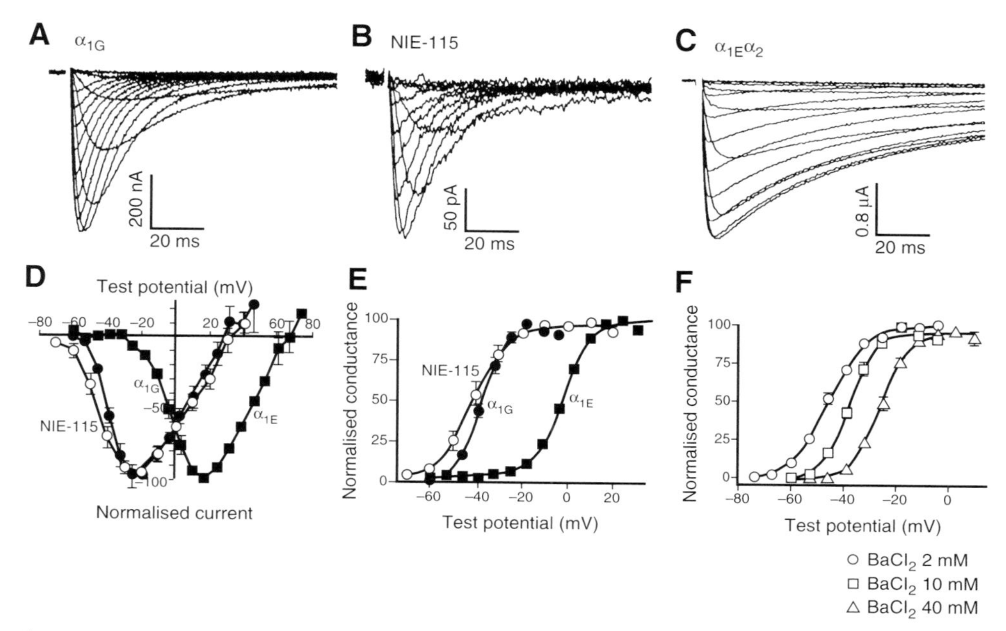

Fig. 4. Current–voltage relationships of cloned α_{1G} compared to native T-type currents in NIE-115 cells and cloned α_{1E} channels. Cloned channels were expressed in Xenopus *oocytes. A) Cloned α_{1G} currents recorded using Ba^{2+} 40 mM as charge carrier. B) Currents from an undifferentiated mouse neuroblastoma cell recorded using the nystatin-perforated patch method (Ba^{2+} 10 mM). C) Cloned α_{1E} plus α_2 currents recorded from an oocyte injected with 50 nl of BAPTA 25 mM (Ba^{2+} 2 mM). D) Average current–voltage curves recorded in Ba^{2+} 10 mM. Peak currents for each cell were normalised to the maximum current observed, then averaged. Error bars represent the SEM from NIE-115 cells, or oocytes injected with either α_{1G} or α_{1E}. E) Conductance was calculated ($I_{test}/(V_{rev} - V_{test})$) using the apparent reversal potentials, normalised to the peak conductance observed, averaged, then plotted versus the test potential. Curves represent Boltzmann fits to the data. F) Normalised conductance of α_{1G} in solutions containing Ba^{2+} 2 mM (n=6), Ba^{2+} 10 mM (same data as in panels D and E) or Ba^{2+} 40 mM. Similar results were obtained when conductance was calculated from peak currents, from the amplitude of an exponential fit to the currents or from tail currents recorded at –50 mV after a 10 ms test pulse.*

currents a signature pattern of classical T-type channels.[34] To illustrate this pattern (see fig. 4 (B)) we recorded bona fide T-type currents from undifferentiated NIE-115 mouse neuroblastoma cells.[35] In contrast, currents from oocytes injected with α_{1E} have a distinct pattern, since activation is uniformly fast. Uninjected oocytes had no detectable (>10 nA) inward barium currents (for example, see panel A of fig. 5). Panel D of figure 4 shows the current–voltage curves for α_{1G} and α_{1E} and the T-type currents from NIE-115 cells (Ba^{2+} 10 mM). These data were transformed into conductance (see fig. 4 (E)), then fit with the Boltzmann equation to calculate the mid-point of activation. Both α_{1G} and NIE-115 currents gated at low voltages (α_{1G}: –38 ± 1 mV, n=8; NIE-115: –41 mV, n=10), while α_{1E} required less negative potentials (–2.6 mV, n=3). To facilitate comparison of these results with published values,[6] we recorded α_{1G} currents using varying concentrations of charge carrier (see fig. 4 (F)). In solutions containing Ba^{2+} 2 mM, the mid-point of activation was –46.5 mV and the slope factor (k) was 6.6 (n=7). We routinely used solutions containing Ba^{2+} 40 mM since the current recorded from most α_{1G}-injected oocytes was <0.5 A/F. As a result of the effect of Ba^{2+} on surface charge screening,[36] the mid-point of activation was shifted to –21 mV in Ba^{2+} 40 mM. These results demonstrate that rat brain α_{1G} is the

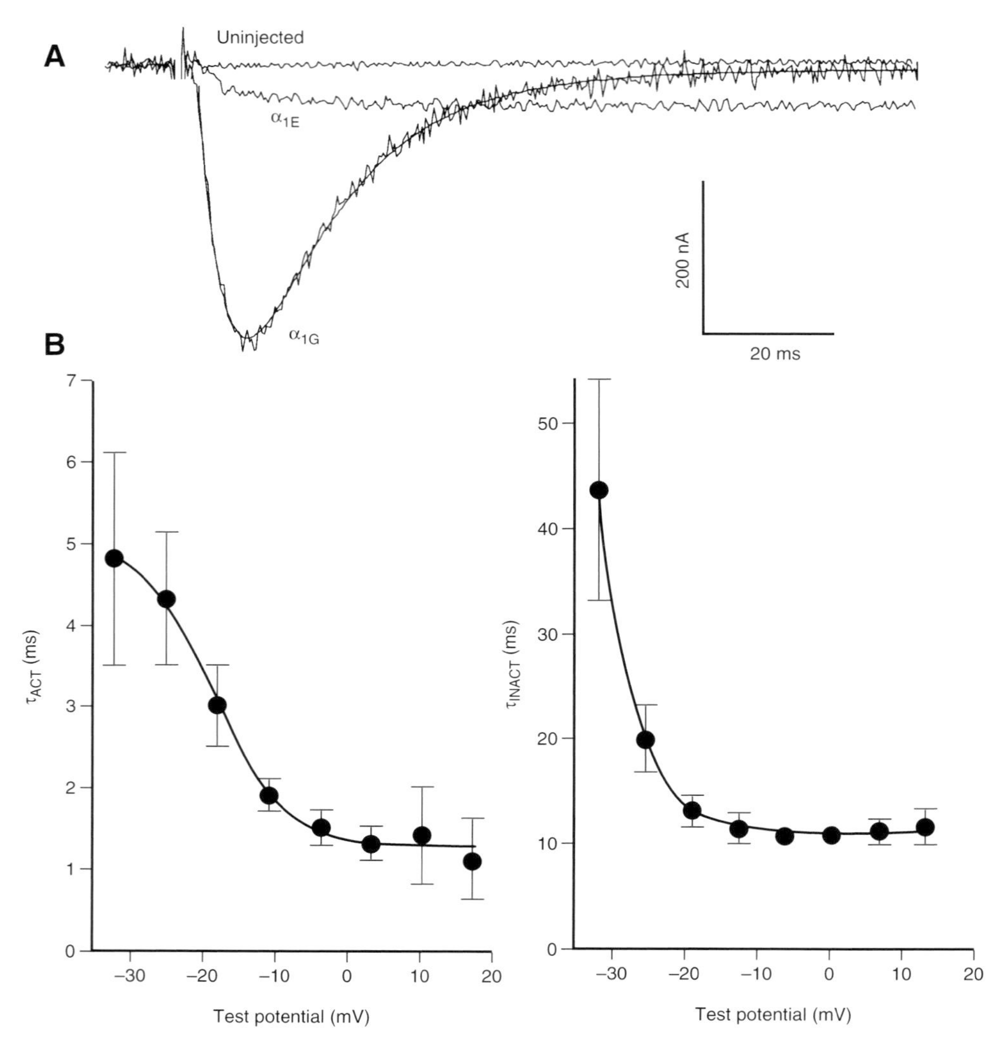

Fig. 5. Kinetic analysis of α_{1G} currents. A) Typical currents recorded during pulses to –20 mV in oocytes that were not injected, or were injected with either α_{1E} or α_{1G}. Each trace represents the average of 5 sweeps recorded at 2 kHz and filtered at 1 kHz. The charge carrier was Ba^{2+} 40 mM. The currents from the α_{1E}-injected oocyte were greater than 500 nA at +20 mV. The smooth line superimposed on the α_{1G} current trace is the biexponential fit to the data. B) Voltage-dependence of α_{1G} activation (left) and inactivation (right) time constants. Data represent the mean ± SD from 13 oocytes.

first LVA channel to be cloned. In addition, α_{1G} currents activate and inactivate with kinetics similar to those observed for T-type channels (reviewed by Huguenard[6] and Chen and Hess[4]). The fact that these results were obtained after injection of α_{1G} alone suggests that other subunits are not required,[28] or that they are supplied by the oocyte.[19]

One of the defining features of LVA calcium channels is their slow deactivation (tail current) after a test pulse.[37] Figure 6 illustrates the time- and voltage-dependence of deactivation. Tail envelopes (see fig. 6 (A)) show that the current elicited at –50 mV

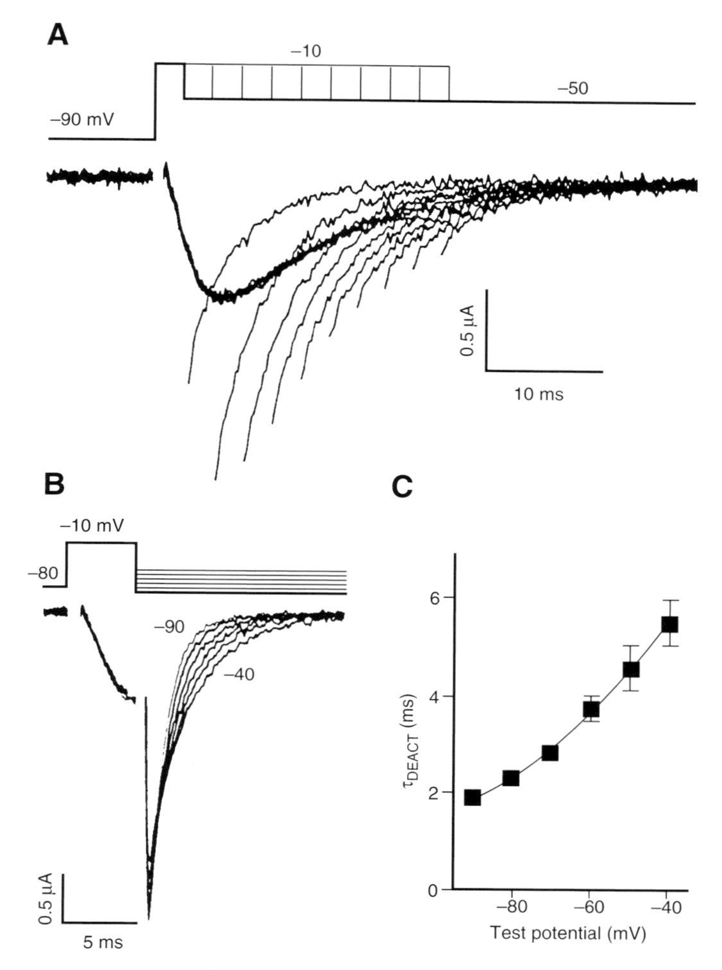

Fig. 6. Deactivation of α_{1G} currents. A) Tail current amplitudes follow the time-course of current activation and inactivation. The tail envelope voltage protocol is shown above the currents. B & C) Voltage-dependence of deactivation. Voltage protocol and currents are shown in panel B. The data were fit with a single exponential, then plotted as a function of the repolarisation potential (C). Data are the mean ± SD from 3 oocytes. Tail currents were acquired at 10 kHz and were not filtered.

(10 mV below threshold) follows the time-course of the current measured at −10 mV. This result confirms that the tail currents are related to α_{1G} and that the decline of the current is related to inactivation, rather than activation of a contaminating outward current. Deactivation kinetics were voltage-dependent, as demonstrated for native T-type tail currents.[4,34,38]

The classic studies of Jahnsen and Llinás established the ionic and voltage-dependent properties of thalamic low-threshold spikes.[39,40] They concluded that the switch from burst-firing to repetitive firing of neurons was related to inactivation of low-threshold calcium currents and that recovery from inactivation allowed for rebound burst-firing.[41] Since it is abundantly expressed in human thalamus, we tested whether α_{1G} could mimic these properties. Figure 7 shows that α_{1G} currents inactivate

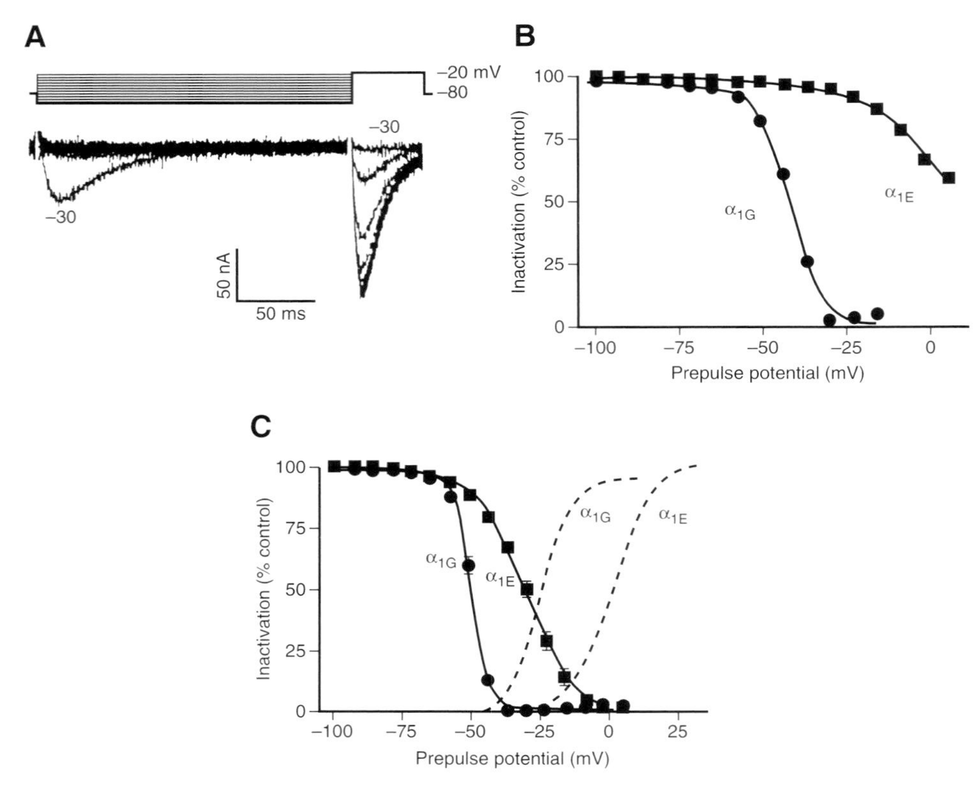

Fig. 7. Voltage-dependence of α_{1G} inactivation. A) Inactivation was induced by 200 ms prepulse to various potentials, followed by a test pulse to –20 mV. Typical currents are shown below the voltage protocol. B) Average results obtained using a 200 ms prepulse. Control was defined as the current measured after a prepulse to –100 mV. Data represent the mean from 4 (α_{1G}) or 2 (α_{1E}) oocytes. C) Voltage-dependence of inactivation induced by 10 s prepulses. Data represent the mean ± SEM from 5 (α_{1G}) or 6 (α_{1E}) oocytes. Curves are from Boltzmann fits to the data. Dotted lines are activation curves measured under the same ionic conditions. The α_{1G} data are shown in figure 4. Activation of α_{1E} currents was measured from peak currents (average peak current –610 nA; n=6).

totally during prepulses of 200 ms duration, while α_{1E} currents do not. To approximate steady-state conditions, we also measured inactivation following 10 s prepulses (see fig. 7 (C)). Inactivation of α_{1G} occurred at subthreshold potentials and displayed a steep voltage-dependence (mid-point of inactivation –50.0 ± 0.2 mV; k = –3.2 ± 0.2; n=5). Inactivation of α_{1E} occurred at more positive potentials and displayed a weaker voltage-dependence (mid-point –30.0 mV; k = –9.4; n=6). However, coexpression of α_{1E} with β_{1b} can shift the voltage-dependence of inactivation 15–20 mV towards more negative potentials.[42,43] Therefore, steady-state inactivation cannot be used to classify either cloned channels or native currents.[34]

We next tested whether α_{1G} currents could recover from inactivation over the same time-course as an IPSP. Figure 8 shows that most of the control current could recover quickly ($t_{½}$ = 160 ms) from complete inactivation (holding potential –40 mV). Recovery of T-type currents is usually measured after inducing inactivation with short depolarising pulses. Using a 200 ms prepulse to –20 mV and an interpulse (and holding) potential of –90 mV, we found that recovery was faster ($t_{½}$ = 66 ms) and

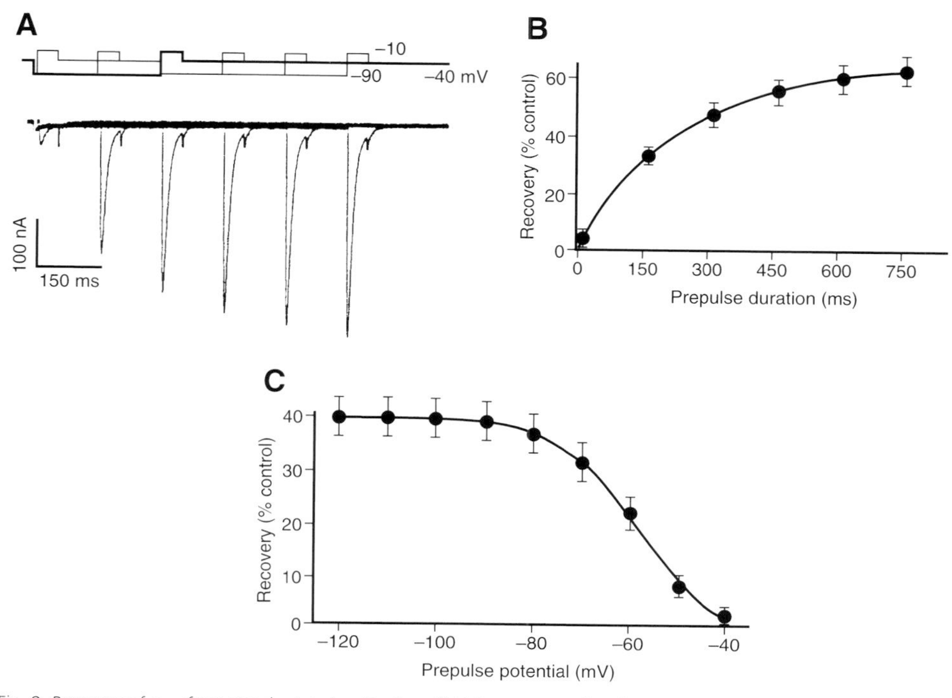

Fig. 8. Recovery of α_{1G} from steady-state inactivation. A) Voltage protocol and typical currents used to calculate the time-course of recovery from inactivation. Steady-state inactivation was induced by holding the oocyte membrane potential at –40 mV. B) Average recovery following repolarisation to –90 mV. Control current was measured before the experiment using a holding potential of –90 mV. Data represent the mean ± SEM from 7 oocytes. Curve represents a single exponential fit to the data. C) Voltage-dependence of recovery measured with 300 ms hyperpolarising steps. Data represent the mean ± SEM from 6 oocytes. The curve is from a Boltzmann fit to the data.

complete (100% recovery in 10 s). Since an IPSP can last up to 300 ms, we applied 300 ms prepulses and varied their potential. The voltage-dependence of recovery displayed a mid-point at –58 mV and a slope factor of –8 (n=7; see fig. 8 (C)). Recovery of thalamic low-threshold spikes occurs over the same voltage range and with a similar time-course.[39]

A final defining characteristic of T-type calcium channels is that their unitary conductance is tiny.[1,2] Measurement of this conductance is complicated by the low probability of channel opening at negative potentials where the driving force is stronger. Therefore, we used tail current protocols as shown in panel B of figure 6 to enhance channel opening at negative potentials. Figure 9 (A) shows representative channel openings from a single patch. Opening and closing to a half-amplitude subconductance state was also observed. A subconductance state of the cardiac T-type channel was reported by Droogmans and Nilius.[44] An ensemble current from 100 sweeps (–40 mV) is shown in panel B of figure 9. The ensemble current decayed with the same kinetics as observed in the macroscopic current (see fig. 6). The average single-channel conductance was 7.5 ± 1.5 pS (n=7 patches). An average of the values reported in the literature for neuronal T-type channels was 7.7 ± 1.1 pS (10 studies, as reviewed by Huguenard[6]).

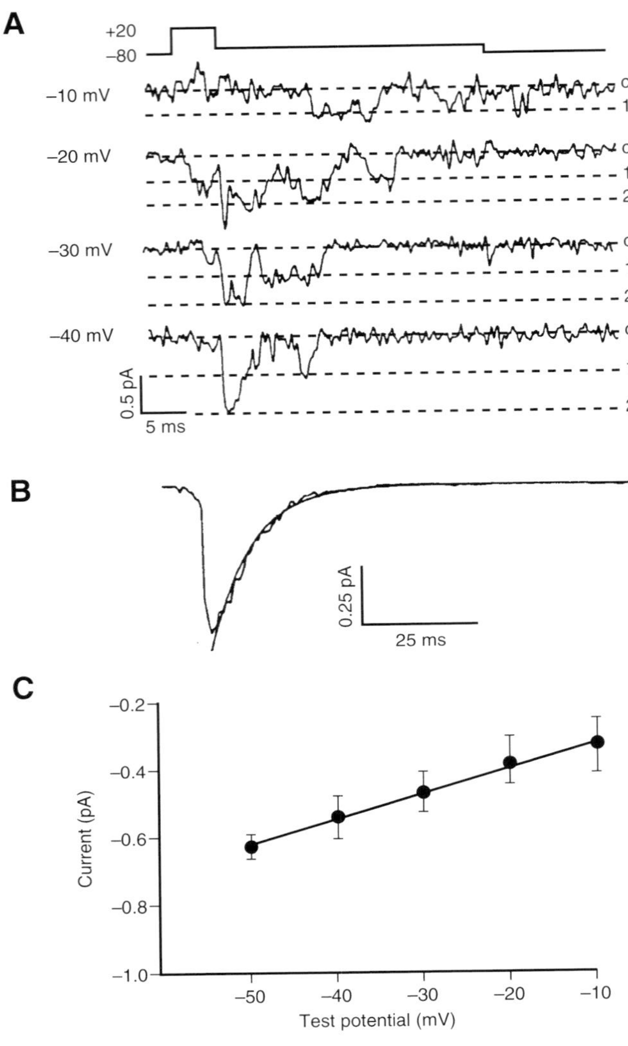

Fig. 9. Single-channel conductance of α_{1G}. A) Single channels were measured in oocytes expressing large α_{1G} currents (>500 nA). The voltage protocol included a 5 ms step to +20 mV followed by repolarisation to the indicated potentials. This patch contained at least four α_{1G} channels. Data were acquired at 10 kHz, filtered on line at 2 kHz and filtered again off line at 1 kHz. The numbers on the right indicate the number of channels open at any particular time. B) The ensemble current recorded from 100 sweeps. This patch contained at least two α_{1G} channels. The ensemble current was calculated from the idealised data, then fit with a single exponential (τ = 5.8 ms). C) The current through the main open state of the channel was measured at each potential, then plotted versus the test potential (mean ± SD). The slope of the line was calculated by linear regression.

Discussion

Our results demonstrate that we have cloned the first member of the LVA T-type calcium channel family. Although we concentrated on rat brain cDNA, we have also identified human and mouse homologues. Furthermore, we localised the human and mouse genes to chromosomes 17 and 11, respectively. The mouse locus lies close to the teetering mutation, suggesting that mutations of the mouse *Cacna1g* gene may lead to neurological disorders, as has been demonstrated for α_{1A}.[30,31] We show that α_{1G} mRNA has a wide distribution in brain, with a relatively high expression in thalamic regions. Functional expression of α_{1G} in oocytes allowed us to measure its biophysical properties. Based on the following criteria we unambiguously demonstrate that α_{1G} is a T-type calcium channel: its activation at negative test potentials, slow activation kinetics at threshold potentials, slow deactivation, fast inactivation, steep voltage-dependence of inactivation near the resting membrane potential, fast recovery from inactivation, and its small unitary conductance. We conclude that the biophysical properties of α_{1G} are consistent with a physiological role in neuronal low-threshold spiking, oscillations and rebound burst-firing.[5,41]

We have also cloned and expressed a second member of the T-type family, 'α_{1H}' or '$Ca_vT.2$'. This cDNA was cloned from both rat brain and human heart. Expression of the human heart channel in HEK293 cells demonstrated that its functional properties are very similar to those of α_{1G} in terms of its voltage-dependence and kinetics. We have mapped the location of the human α_{1H} gene, *CACNA1H*, to chromosome 16p13.3, and the mouse gene to the syntenic region on chromosome 17 (between markers D17Mit55 and D17Mit100). A third gene that is highly related to α_{1G} and α_{1H}, which we call 'α_{1I}', was sequenced as part of a study on chromosome 22.[45] The membrane-spanning regions of α_{1G}, α_{1H} and α_{1I} are very similar (see fig. 1), while the intracellular loops are more divergent. Definitive evidence that α_{1I} encodes a T-type channel will require its functional expression. Although sequence analysis can be used to show that genes are related, it cannot be used to predict physiological function, as evidenced by α_{1S}, which functions primarily as a voltage sensor for skeletal muscle contraction.[46] Finally, the identification of multiple genes encoding T-type calcium channels may provide a molecular basis for the diverse properties of T-type currents observed in different preparations and provide a tool for the discovery of T-type selective drugs.

Acknowledgements

The figures in this chapter are adapted from the following paper: Perez-Reyes E, Cribbs LL, Daud A, et al. Molecular characterisation of a neuronal low-voltage-activated T-type calcium channel. Nature 1998; 391. In press.

We thank the UK HGMP Resource Centre for the Genbridge 4 radiation hybrid mapping panel and the EUCIB mouse panel. This work was supported by grants from the National Institutes of Health, the Potts Foundation and the Medical Research Council. E.P.-R. is an Established Investigator of the American Heart Association.

References

1. Carbone E, Lux HD. A low voltage-activated, fully inactivating Ca channel in vertebrate sensory neurones. Nature 1984; 310: 501–2
2. Nilius B, Hess P, Lansman JB, et al. A novel type of cardiac calcium channel in ventricular cells. Nature 1985; 316: 443–6

3. Nowycky MC, Fox AP, Tsien RW. Three types of neuronal calcium channel with different calcium agonist sensitivity. Nature 1985; 316: 440–3
4. Chen CF, Hess P. Mechanism of gating of T-type calcium channels. J Gen Physiol 1990; 96: 603–30
5. Andersen P, Eccles JC, Sears TA. The ventro-basal complex of the thalamus: types of cells, their responses and functional organization. J Physiol 1964; 174: 370–99
6. Huguenard JR. Low threshold calcium currents in central nervous system neurons. Annu Rev Physiol 1996; 58: 329–48
7. Hagiwara N, Irisawa H, Kameyama M. Contribution of two types of calcium currents to the pacemaker potentials of rabbit sino-atrial node cells. J Physiol 1988; 395: 233–53
8. Akaike N, Kanaide H, Kuga T, et al. Low-voltage-activated calcium current in rat aorta smooth muscle cells in primary culture. J Physiol 1989; 416: 141–60
9. Cohen CJ, McCarthy RT, Barrett PQ, et al. Ca channels in adrenal glomerulosa cells: K^+ and angiotensin II increase T-type Ca channel current. Proc Natl Acad Sci U S A 1988; 85: 2412–16
10. Enyeart JJ, Mlinar B, Enyeart JA. T-type Ca^{2+} channels are required for adrenocorticotropin-stimulated cortisol production by bovine adrenal zona fasciculata cells. Mol Endocrinol 1993; 7: 1031–40
11. Arnoult C, Cardullo RA, Lemos JR, et al. Activation of mouse sperm T-type Ca^{2+} channels by adhesion of the egg zona pellucida. Proc Natl Acad Sci U S A 1996; 93: 13004–9
12. Tsakiridou E, Bertollini L, de Curtis M, et al. Selective increase in T-type calcium conductance of reticular thalamic neurons in a rat model of absence epilepsy. J Neurosci 1995; 15: 3110–17
13. Sen L, Smith TW. T-type Ca^{2+} channels are abnormal in genetically determined cardiomyopathic hamster hearts. Circ Res 1994; 75: 149–55
14. Banfi S, Borsani G, Rossi E, et al. Identification and mapping of human cDNAs homologous to *Drosophila* mutant genes through EST database searches. Nat Genet 1996; 13: 167–74
15. Breen M, Deakin L, MacDonald D, et al. Towards high resolution maps of the mouse and human genomes – a facility for ordering markers to 0.1cM resolution. Hum Mol Genet 1994; 3: 621–7
16. Bernal J, Lee J-H, Cribbs LL, et al. Full reversal of Pb^{++} block of L-type Ca^{++} channels requires treatment with heavy metal antidotes. J Pharmacol Exp Ther 1997; 282: 172–80
17. Lory P, Rassendren FA, Richard S, et al. Characterization of voltage-dependent calcium channels expressed in *Xenopus* oocytes injected with mRNA from rat heart. J Physiol 1990; 429: 95–112
18. Bourinet E, Zamponi GW, Stea A, et al. The α_{1E} calcium channel exhibits permeation properties similar to low-voltage-activated calcium channels. J Neurosci 1996; 16: 4983–93
19. Lacerda AE, Perez-Reyes E, Wei X, et al. T-type and N-type calcium channels of *Xenopus* oocytes: evidence for specific interactions with beta subunits. Biophys J 1994; 66: 1833–43
20. VanDongen AMJ. A new algorithm for idealizing single ion channel data containing multiple unknown conductance levels. Biophys J 1996; 70: 1303–15
21. Lennon G, Auffray C, Polymeropoulus M, et al. The IMAGE Consortium: an integrated molecular analysis of genomes and their expression. Genomics 1996; 33: 151–2
22. Wilson R, Ainscough R, Anderson K, et al. 2.2 Mb of contiguous nucleotide sequence from chromosome III of *C. elegans*. Nature 1994; 368: 32–8
23. Jan LY, Jan YN. A superfamily of ion channels. Nature 1990; 345: 672
24. Yang J, Ellinor PT, Sather WA, et al. Molecular determinants of Ca^{2+} selectivity and ion permeation in L-type Ca^{2+} channels. Nature 1993; 366: 158–61
25. Higgins DG, Sharp PM. CLUSTAL: a package for performing multiple sequence alignments on a microcomputer. Gene 1988; 73: 237–44
26. Stuhmer W, Conti F, Suzuki H, et al. Structural parts involved in activation and inactivation of the sodium channel. Nature 1989; 339: 597–603
27. Pragnell M, De Waard M, Mori Y, et al. Calcium channel beta-subunit binds to a conserved motif in the I–II cytoplasmic linker of the alpha 1-subunit. Nature 1994; 368: 67–70
28. Lambert RC, Maulet Y, Mouton J, et al. T-type Ca^{2+} current properties are not modified by Ca^{2+} channel β subunit depletion in nodosus ganglion neurons. J Neurosci 1997; 17: 6621–8
29. de Leon M, Wang Y, Jones L, et al. Essential Ca^{2+}-binding motif for Ca^{2+}-sensitive inactivation of L-type Ca^{2+} channels. Science 1995; 270: 1502–6
30. Fletcher CF, Lutz CM, O'Sullivan TN, et al. Absence epilepsy in tottering mutant mice is associated with calcium channel defects. Cell 1996; 87: 607–17
31. Ophoff RA, Terwindt GM, Vergouwe MN, et al. Familial hemiplegic migraine and episodic ataxia type-2 are caused by mutations in the Ca^{2+} channel gene CACNL1A4. Cell 1996; 87: 543–52
32. Burgess DL, Jones JM, Meisler MH, et al. Mutation of the Ca^{2+} channel subunit gene *Cchb4* is associated with ataxia and seizures in the lethargic (*lh*) mouse. Cell 1997; 88: 385–92
33. Meier M. The neuropathy of teetering, a neurological mutation in the mouse. Arch Neurol 1967; 16: 59–66
34. Randall AD, Tsien RW. Contrasting biophysical and pharmacological properties of T-type and R-type calcium channels. Neuropharmacol 1997; 36: 879–93
35. Shuba YM, Teslenko VI, Savchenko AN, et al. The effect of permeant ions on single calcium channel activation in mouse neuroblastoma cells: ion–channel interactions. J Physiol 1991; 443: 25–44
36. Wilson DL, Morimoto K, Tsuda Y, et al. Interaction between calcium ions and surface charge as it relates to calcium currents. J Membr Biol 1983; 72: 117–30

37. Matteson DR, Armstrong CM. Properties of two types of calcium channels in clonal pituitary cells. J Gen Physiol 1986; 87: 161–82
38. Santi CM, Darszon A, Hernandez-Cruz A. A dihydropyridine-sensitive T-type Ca^{2+} current is the main Ca^{2+} current carrier in mouse primary spermatocytes. Am J Physiol 1996; 271: C1583–93
39. Jahnsen H, Llinas R. Electrophysiological properties of guinea-pig thalamic neurones: an *in vitro* study. J Physiol 1984; 349: 227–47
40. Jahnsen H, Llinas R. Ionic basis for the electroresponsiveness and oscillatory properties of guinea-pig thalamic neurones *in vitro*. J Physiol 1984; 349: 227–47
41. Llinas R, Jahnsen H. Electrophysiology of mammalian thalamic neurons *in vitro*. Nature 1982; 297: 406–8
42. Soong TW, Stea A, Hodson CD, et al. Structure and functional expression of a member of the low voltage-activated calcium channel family. Science 1993; 260: 1133–6
43. Olcese R, Qin N, Schneider T, et al. The amino terminus of a calcium channel beta subunit sets rates of channel inactivation independently of the subunit's effect on activation. Neuron 1994; 13: 1433–8
44. Droogmans G, Nilius B. Kinetic properties of the cardiac T-type calcium channel in the guinea-pig. J Physiol 1989; 419: 627–50
45. Trofatter JA, Long KR, Murrel JR, et al. An expression-independent catalogue of genes from human chromosome 22. Genome Res 1995; 5: 214–24
46. Stern MD, Pizarro G, Rios E. Local control model of excitation–contraction coupling in skeletal muscle. J Gen Physiol 1997; 110: 414–40

Section 4

Regulation, modulation and novel pharmacology

Introduction

The topics covered in this set of chapters fall together easily. The regulation of calcium channel function by β subunits has direct bearing on the channels' voltage-dependent gating and their modulation by G proteins. Likewise, the pharmacological effectiveness of cardiovascular drugs depends critically upon detailed molecular differences between various calcium channel subunits and, in some cases, on voltage-dependent activation and inactivation. **Noceti et al.** present an elegant analysis of the relationship between ionic currents carried by calcium channels and the underlying rearrangement of the charged groups that confer voltage-dependence, monitored as 'gating current'. They develop the idea that coupling between gating current and channel opening varies in efficiency among specific α_1 subunits, being much more efficient for α_{1E} than for α_{1C}. For either α_1 subunit, coexpression with a particular form of β subunit (β_{2a}) can make the coupling more efficient. It is suggested that the increase in efficiency may be associated with a decreased likelihood of 'nulls', trials where channel openings cannot be detected. **Vassort and Alvarez** describe T-type current in bullfrog atrial cells and suggest that some of the controversy about the existence of this current may have arisen from different enzyme treatments used to isolate these cells. They found that isoproterenol enhances T-type current, but not by the same well-described cAMP-dependent mechanism found for the L-type channels. Interestingly, the enhancement remains very much the same when cells are dialysed with GTPγS but is greatly enhanced with internal ATPγS. **Shekter et al.** summarise experiments in nucleus tractus solitarius neurons, showing modulation by G proteins of both N- and P-/Q-type calcium channels. Further experiments in HEK293 cells stably transfected with cloned α_1 subunits demonstrate that susceptibility to G-protein modulation also extends to currents supported by α_{1E} subunits (presumed R type), albeit to a far lesser extent than for other channel types. **Best et al.** tackle the question of why expression of T-type calcium current often appears correlated with cellular growth or hypertrophy. They show that T-type current in atrial cells greatly increases in response to growth hormone and insulin-like growth factor 1, both in adult rats harbouring a growth hormone-secreting tumour and in rats undergoing normal postnatal development. The regulation involves increased density of T-type channels rather than a change in their single-channel properties.

The next group of chapter focuses on present understanding of the actions of agents with real or potential cardiovascular benefit. **Mitterdorfer et al.** review their extensive efforts to understand the actions of three major families of calcium channel blocking drugs, 1,4-dihydropyridines, phenylalkylamines and benzothiazepines. The general strategy involves transfer of antagonist susceptibility to a non-responding subunit (α_{1A}). Critical residues are concentrated in transmembrane segments IIIS5, IIIS6 and IVS6, close to structural motifs that govern ion permeation and inactivation. There is greater overlap between the molecular determinants for the various calcium channel antagonists than might have been expected from earlier binding studies. **Hermsmeyer** reviews his experiments on the blocking effects of mibefradil (Posicor®).

Working in vascular smooth muscle, the primary target of the clinical actions of this new drug, the author separated T- and L-type currents by appropriate membrane voltage protocols or by pharmacologically inhibiting L-type currents. Mibefradil was found to inhibit T-type currents at concentrations 30- to 100-fold lower than those needed to block L-type currents. **Klugbauer et al.** compare mibefradil's effects on T-type channels in human medullary thyroid carcinoma (hMTC) cells and on L-type channels supported by α_{1C} in Chinese hamster ovary (CHO) cells. Mibefradil block of L-type channels was strongly potentiated at depolarised potentials, displaying a voltage-dependence similar to that found for classical calcium channel antagonists; this voltage-dependence was dependent on the splice variant of α_{1C}. In contrast, block of T-type channels was much less affected by depolarisation, appearing to be highly potent even at negative membrane potentials. Interestingly, calcium currents through T-type channels were much more sensitive to mibefradil block than barium currents.

Finally, **Benardeau and Ertel** present a detailed comparison of the effects of mibefradil and the 1,4-dihydropyridine compound amlodipine. In myocardial cells, just as in smooth muscle, mibefradil blocked T-type channels much more potently than L-type channels. The opposite was true for amlodipine. The inhibitory action of mibefradil on either T- or L-type channels was potentiated by steady depolarisations favouring inactivation or by trains of depolarising pulses that open the channels repeatedly. Thus, mibefradil block shows voltage- and use-dependence similar to those found for classical calcium channel blockers.

Charges per channel in calcium channels: effect of regulatory β subunit coexpression on α_1 pore-forming subunit currents

Francesca Noceti,[1] *Riccardo Olcese,*[1] *Pietro Baldelli,*[6] *Ning Qin,*[1]
Lutz Birnbaumer,[1–4] *Enrico Stefani*[1,4,5,7]

[1] *Department of Anesthesiology,* [2] *Department of Biological Chemistry,* [3] *Molecular Biology Institute,* [4] *Brain Research Institute and* [5] *Department of Physiology, UCLA School of Medicine, Los Angeles, California, USA;* [6] *Department of Neuroscience, Università degli Studi, Turin, Italy;* [7] *Conicet, Buenos Aires, Argentina*

Summary

In voltage-dependent ion channels, gating is determined by the movement of the voltage sensor. This movement can be thought of as a net displacement of elementary charges (e_0) through the membrane (z: effective number of elementary charges). In this chapter, we measured z in neuronal α_{1E} and α_{1A} and cardiac α_{1C} calcium channels by: (a) limiting slope analysis of the conductance–voltage relationship; and (b) variance analysis, to evaluate the number of active channels and measure charge movement in a given patch.

The limiting slope method gave consistent results regardless of the presence or type of β subunit tested (z = 9.6). However, as seen with α_{1E}, the variance analysis gave different results depending on the β subunit used. α_{1E} and $\alpha_{1E}\beta_{1a}$ gave higher z values than $\alpha_{1E}\beta_{2a}$. Both the β_{1a} and β_{2a} subunits, coexpressed with α_{1E} calcium channels, facilitated channel opening by shifting the activation curve to more negative potentials, but only the β_{2a} subunit increased the maximum open probability. Coexpression of α_{1E} with the β_{2a} subunit did not modify the voltage-dependence of charge movement.

The coupling efficiency between the charge movement and pore opening was estimated by the ratio between limiting conductance (g_{max}) and maximum charge movement (Q_{max}). Coexpression of the β_{2a} subunit together with the α_{1E} subunit increased the g_{max}:Q_{max} ratio. Using variance analysis, the higher z obtained for α_{1E} and $\alpha_{1E}\beta_{1a}$ compared with $\alpha_{1E}\beta_{2a}$ can be explained by a set of charges not coupled to pore opening. This set of charges moves in transitions leading to 'nulls', thus not contributing to the ionic current fluctuations but eliciting gating currents. Coexpression of the β_{2a} subunit would minimise the fraction of 'nulls', leading to the more accurate estimation of the number of channels and z. The different ratio between ionic and gating currents for α_{1E} and α_{1C} suggests that pore opening in α_{1E} is more efficiently coupled to the movement of the voltage sensor than in α_{1C}.

Hodgkin and Huxley were the first to propose that 'changes in ionic permeability depend on the movement of some component of the membrane, which behaves as though it has a large charge or dipole moment. Movement of any charged particle should contribute to the total current.'[1] This was the first proposition that the voltage sensor, a specific part of voltage-dependent channels, should rearrange itself with changes in the transmembrane electric field.

Gating currents are the electrical manifestation of the voltage-sensor rearrangement. The charge movement could either consist of a net displacement of unitary charges or could result from local polarisation of a cloud of charges or dipoles. Alternatively, charge movement could arise from an asymmetric change in the electric field in relation to the voltage sensor, which encompasses changes in the overall structure of the protein and affects the exposure of the charged residues to the external and internal sides of the membrane.[2–6]

The primary structure of channel proteins was still unknown when Hodgkin and Huxley set the foundations for the theory of excitability,[1] but once channel proteins were cloned the region for the voltage sensor was soon identified in the positively charged S4 transmembrane segment.[7–10] Mutations of charged amino acids in the S4 segment of voltage-dependent channels affect the voltage sensitivity of channel opening.[11–14] Moreover, neutralisation of S4-charged residues alters both charge movement and the number of charges per channel.[15–16] Concordant with the view that gating currents are the electrical manifestation of voltage-dependent conformational changes, it has been shown that some S4 residues have differential exposure to the cytoplasmic and extracellular environments, depending on the membrane potential. Furthermore, voltage-dependent fluorescence changes have been shown to correlate with the charge movement of S4 fluorophore-labelled residues.[5,6,17,18]

A critical quantity to evaluate in voltage-dependent channels is the size of the total charge movement per channel, detected as the number of effective charges per channel (z); z is given by the number of elementary charges, z_0, multiplied by the fraction of the field, x, that the charge traverses across the membrane ($z = z_0x$), and can be derived from the conductance–voltage (g(V)) relationship by its limiting slope value at a very low probability of opening.[3,19–21] Alternatively, z can be obtained from the ratio between the limiting charge (Q_{max}) and the number of channels, which may be evaluated by the variance method in the same patch[22] or by channel particle measurement in freeze-fractured membranes.[23]

Together with measurement of the effective number of charges per channel, it is important to characterise the efficiency of the movement of the voltage sensor in driving the rest of the molecule toward the open conformation. This efficiency will reflect on the biophysical properties of the channels, such as the position of the g(V) curve relative to the charge movement–voltage (Q(V)) curve along the voltage axis. The fact that Q(V) and g(V) curves are separated on the voltage axis can be explained by a sequential model with several closed states (C) and a final open state (O). Each transition between the conformational closed states along the activation pathway involves a discrete charge movement. Under these conditions, the voltage position of the Q(V) curve is more negative than the g(V) curve, which represents the equilibrium between the open and closed states. Thus, a theoretical voltage-dependent ion channel that is able to swing between only two states (closed and open) would show superimposed Q(V) and g(V) curves. The physical manifestation of this is a channel protein in which a small movement of the voltage sensor produces a large change in the probability of the pore being open.

Number of charges per channel: two methods of observation

Given the above observations, measurement of the number of effective charges per channel together with measurement of the efficiency of opening can help in the drawing of a comprehensive picture of the behaviour of voltage-dependent channels. This work is an extension of two previous papers by Noceti[24] and Olcese.[25] z has been measured in voltage-dependent calcium channels expressed in *Xenopus laevis* oocytes. The neuronal α_{1A} and α_{1E}[26,27] and the cardiac α_{1C}[28] subunits have been expressed either alone or together with regulatory β subunits.[29–32]

Limiting slope analysis

The ionic current recorded during a voltage ramp is subtracted off line from linear leakage and is subsequently converted to conductance by dividing the ionic current by its driving force. The leakage subtraction is performed by fitting the leak current to a straight line before detection of the inward ionic current, and by then subtracting this linear component from the total current. Current data points recorded at potentials more negative than the voltage-detectable threshold for activation are fitted for linear leakage ($\alpha_{1C}\beta_{2a}$ calcium channel) (fig. 1). Under these experimental conditions, the large inward calcium currents are easily distinguishable from the linear leak current. The conductance versus potential (g(V)) plot is fitted to the monoexponential approximation of the Boltzmann function in the limit for very negative potentials:

$$g(V) = Ae^{z\frac{e_0 V}{kT}} \tag{1}$$

where g(V) is the conductance (S), z the number of effective charges per channel, e_0 the electronic charge (1.602×10^{-19} °C), k the Boltzmann constant (1.38×10^{-23} J/K), T the absolute temperature (K), V the membrane potential (V) and A the amplitude of the exponential (S). This approximation was resolved for a linear sequential model with one open state.[19,20]

The z value evaluated from the fit to equation 1 has then to be compared with the slope of ln g versus conductance:

$$z(V) = \frac{kT}{e_0}\frac{d}{dV}\ln g(V) \tag{2}$$

Figure 1 illustrates a limiting slope experiment in $\alpha_{1C}\beta_{2a}$. The experiment shown is performed with the cut-open Vaseline gap (COVG) technique[33] with external BaMES 10 mM. A slow voltage ramp from –90 to –20 mV (3.5 mV/s) is used to elicit the ionic

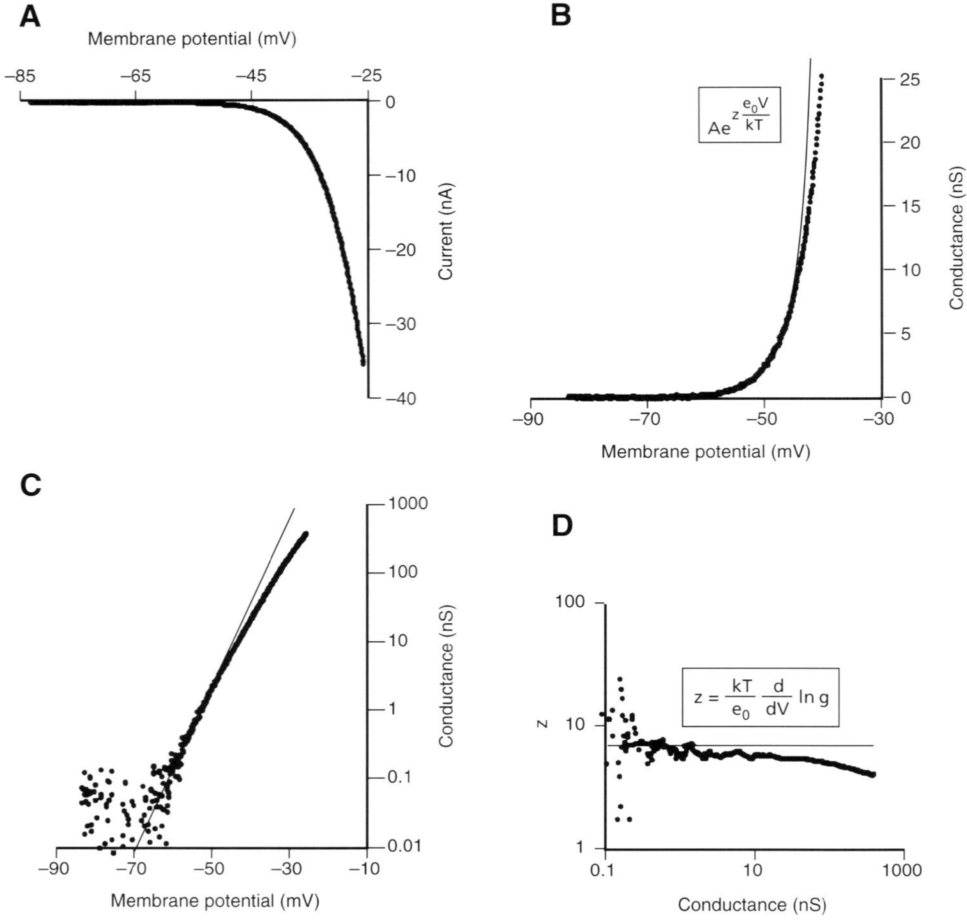

Fig. 1. Limiting slope analysis in $\alpha_{1C}\beta_{2a}$ calcium channel. A) Ionic current recorded with the cut-open oocyte technique from an oocyte expressing the $\alpha_{1C}\beta_{2a}$ calcium channel. External solution = BaMES 10 mM. Holding potential –90 mV. Slow depolarisation (0.0035 mV/ms), with voltage ramp to –20 mV. Linear leakage-correction was performed off line with a linear fit to the points at potentials more negative than –65 mV. Data points were decimated (average of 3 points). B) Conductance–voltage relationship in a linear plot, at potentials near detection of current activation. Data points between –80 and –50 mV were fitted to the function in the inset (solid line); A (amplitude of the exponential) = 3.63×10^6 nS and z (number of effective charges/channel) = 7.20. C) Conductance–voltage curve and fitted limiting slope (solid line) on semi-log scale. D) Relationship between calculated z at different potentials and the corresponding conductance (g). z values were calculated according to the equation in the inset. The voltage derivative of ln g was obtained from an average running slope of 20 data points. The straight line shows the fitted value of z. External solution was BaMES 10 mM at room temperature. (Reproduced from the Journal of General Physiology by copyright permission of The Rockefeller University Press .[24])

current in panel A, which is then converted into conductance (panels B & C). The monoexponential fit to the initial part of the g(V) curve (–80 to –50 mV) gives A = 3.63×10^6 nS and z = 7.20.

Variance analysis

Series of identical current traces are recorded by pulsing to a positive potential from the holding potential. Pairs of M subsequent records $X_i(t)$, $X_{i+1}(t)$ are subtracted in order to compute the experimental non-stationary variance as:

$$\sigma^2(t) = \frac{2}{M-1}\sum_{i=1}^{M-1}(Y_i(t) - \mu_i)^2 \qquad (3)$$

where $Y_i(t)$ is:

$$Y_i(t) = \tfrac{1}{2}\left(X_i(t) - X_{i+1}(t)\right) \qquad (4)$$

and μ_i is the mean value of $Y_i(t)$. The average basal variance at the holding potential is subtracted from the variance during the pulse stimulation. The difference variance is plotted against the mean current I(t) (mean of the records) and fitted to the theoretical variance function with the assumption that the single-channel current has only one non-zero value:[34–36]

$$\sigma^2(t) = I(t)i - \frac{I(t)^2}{N} \qquad (5)$$

where i is the single-channel current amplitude and N is the number of channels. i is obtained from the initial slope of the variance (I = 0), and N is determined by the abscissa of the maximum of the parabolic function (corresponding to open probability $P_o = 0.5$), according to the first derivative of the variance:

$$\frac{\delta\sigma^2(t)}{\delta I(t)} = i - \frac{2}{N} I(t) \qquad (6)$$

The maximum open probability, $P_{o,max}$, can be extrapolated from the maximum mean current, I_{max}:

$$P_{o,max} = \frac{I_{max}}{iN} \qquad (7)$$

and the effective charge per channel, z, can be extrapolated from the maximum charge Q_{max} (time integral of the gating current at saturating potential):

$$z = \frac{Q_{max}}{e_0 N} \qquad (8)$$

Figure 2 illustrates the procedures used to obtain N and the $P_{o,max}$ for the neuronal calcium channel α_{1E}, both alone and coexpressed with β subunits (β_{1a} and β_{2a}). The typical ionic current response to a +150 mV voltage step (from a holding potential of −80 mV) followed by a repolarisation to −30 mV is shown in panel A. The experimental variance, obtained from the records according to equations 3 and 4, is shown together with the mean current in panel B. Panels D–F show plots and fits of the variance against mean current for α_{1E}, $\alpha_{1E}\beta_{1a}$ and $\alpha_{1E}\beta_{2a}$. The $P_{o,max}$ values reached by both α_{1E} and $\alpha_{1E}\beta_{1a}$ are low (0.55 and 0.61, respectively), whereas $P_{o,max}$ for $\alpha_{1E}\beta_{2a}$ is 0.84.

Gating currents might induce errors in the estimation of the ionic current at the beginning of a voltage jump. However, since noise fluctuations of gating currents are several orders of magnitude smaller than noise fluctuations of ionic currents, they should not affect the calculation.[4] Nevertheless, the mean current after the pulse jump could be overestimated because of the associated gating currents. Because of the relative size of gating and ionic currents, this overestimation should not be of

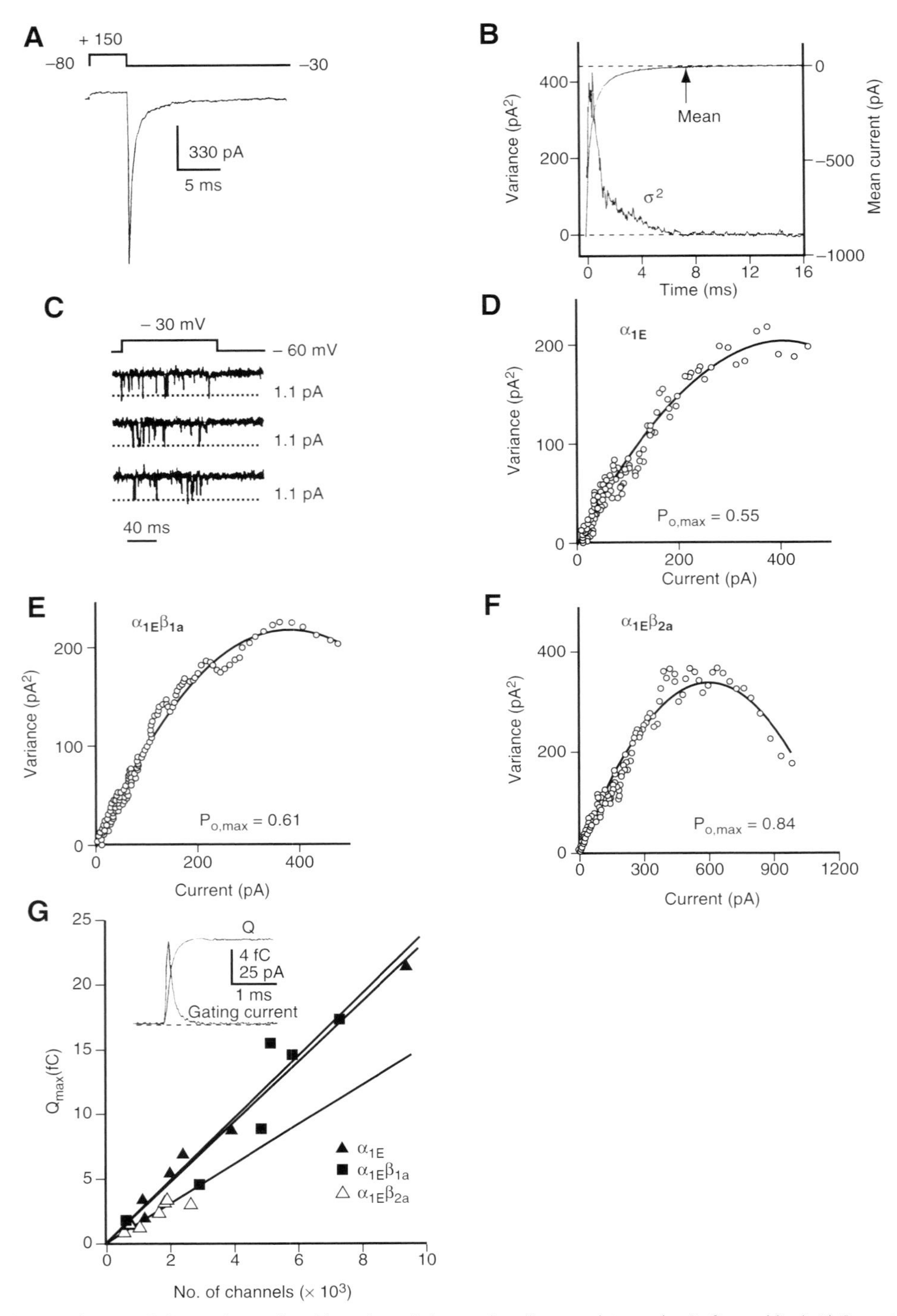

Fig. 2. Variance analysis experiments in calcium channels (α_{1E} and auxiliary regulatory subunits β_{1a} and β_{2a}). A) Current recorded in an oocyte coexpressing the neuronal α_{1E} calcium channel and the β_{2a} subunit. Cell-attached configuration of the patch technique used at 30 °C. Holding potential –80 mV, pulse to 150 mV followed by a return potential to –30 mV. B) Mean tail current and corresponding non-stationary variance. C) Single channels recorded at –30 mV under

(continued opposite)

great significance. Gating current contamination should be negligible for P_o values smaller than 0.5 for the OFF, which is the critical region for the fitting of the parabolic function (equation 6). The measurements are validated by the relationship between single-channel amplitude recorded with a small pipette at –30 mV (~1 pA; see fig. 2 (C)) and the calculated values from the initial slope of the variance–mean current curves ($i_{\alpha 1E}$ = 1.0 pA, $i_{\alpha 1E\beta 1a}$ = 1.13 pA, $i_{\alpha 1E\beta 2a}$ = 1.14 pA). The traces in panel C of figure 2 were recorded at 2 kHz and sampled at 100 μs/point, which is sufficient to resolve the single-channel openings. For the variance analysis, traces are collected at 10 kHz and sampled at 20 μs/point. Thus, the variance analysis should provide a band width adequate to resolve the amplitude of the unitary events. This is confirmed by performing variance analysis with filtering up to 2 kHz, which gives similar results.

The total charge Q_{max} is measured in the α_{1E} calcium channel by the following procedure: gating currents are recorded at a voltage close to the reversal potential in the same patch as that used for the variance analysis. The maximum values of the integrals of the gating currents (the inset in panel G of figure 2 shows a record from an $\alpha_{1E}\beta_{1a}$ experiment) are then plotted against the number of channels. Panel G of figure 2 shows the results for α_{1E}, $\alpha_{1E}\beta_{1a}$ and $\alpha_{1E}\beta_{2a}$. The slope of the regression lines for α_{1E} and $\alpha_{1E}\beta_{1a}$ data points are: 0.00237 pA × ms and 0.00242 pA × ms, corresponding to $z_{\alpha 1E} = 14.77 \pm 0.29$ and $z_{\alpha 1E\beta 1a} = 15.13 \pm 0.71$. These values are not significantly different (p=0.63). In the case of $\alpha_{1E}\beta_{2a}$, the slope of the regression line to the data points is 0.00152 pA × ms, corresponding to $z_{\alpha 1E\beta 2a} = 9.50 \pm 0.14$. This z value is significantly different from those for α_{1E} and $\alpha_{1E}\beta_{1a}$ ($p<0.01$ in both cases).

Coupling between charge movement and channel opening: effect of the β subunit

With simultaneous measurement of gating and ionic currents of α_{1E} with and without the β_{2a} subunit it is possible to detect a shift of the activation curve to more negative potentials for the channels coexpressed with the β subunit. In contrast, the β_{2a} subunit does not change the voltage-dependence of the charge movement.

Figure 3 shows this observed shift. The g(V) and Q(V) curves are fitted to the sum of two Boltzmann distributions. Q(V) for α_{1C} is fitted by a single Boltzmann distribution. The parameters fitting the experimental data are shown in table I: z_1 and z_2 are the effective valencies; $V_{1,½}$ and $V_{2,½}$ are half-activation potentials; g_1 and g_2 and Q_1 and Q_2 are the relative amplitudes of the g(V) or Q(V) curves. The main difference between α_{1E} and α_{1C} is the voltage separation of their Q(V) and g(V) curves.

(Fig. 2 continued)
the same ionic conditions in the same oocyte. D–F) Variance–mean current data and corresponding fitted curves to the theoretical function in α_{1E}, $\alpha_{1E}\beta_{1a}$ and $\alpha_{1E}\beta_{2a}$. i (single-channel current amplitude) = 1.00 pA, N (number of channels) = 801, $P_{o,max}$ (maximum open probability) = 0.55 in α_{1E} expressed alone; i = 1.13 pA, N = 674, $P_{o,max}$ = 0.61 in $\alpha_{1E}\beta_{1a}$; and i = 1.14 pA, N = 1033, $P_{o,max}$ = 0.84 in $\alpha_{1E}\beta_{2a}$. G) Q_{max} (maximum charge) versus number of channels in α_{1E}, $\alpha_{1E}\beta_{1a}$ and $\alpha_{1E}\beta_{2a}$. Fitted slopes of the three straight lines give z (number of effective charges/channel) = 14.77 ± 0.29 in α_{1E} (n=7 oocytes); z = 15.13 ± 0.71 in $\alpha_{1E}\beta_{1a}$ (n=7 oocytes); z = 9.50 ± 0.14 in $\alpha_{1E}\beta_{2a}$ (n=8 oocytes). Values are the slope ± SEM. External solution KMES; pipette solution BaMES 75 mM. Temperature 30 °C. Inset = ON gating current in $\alpha_{1E}\beta_{1a}$ and its time integral. (Reproduced from the Journal of General Physiology by copyright permission of The Rockefeller University Press.[24])

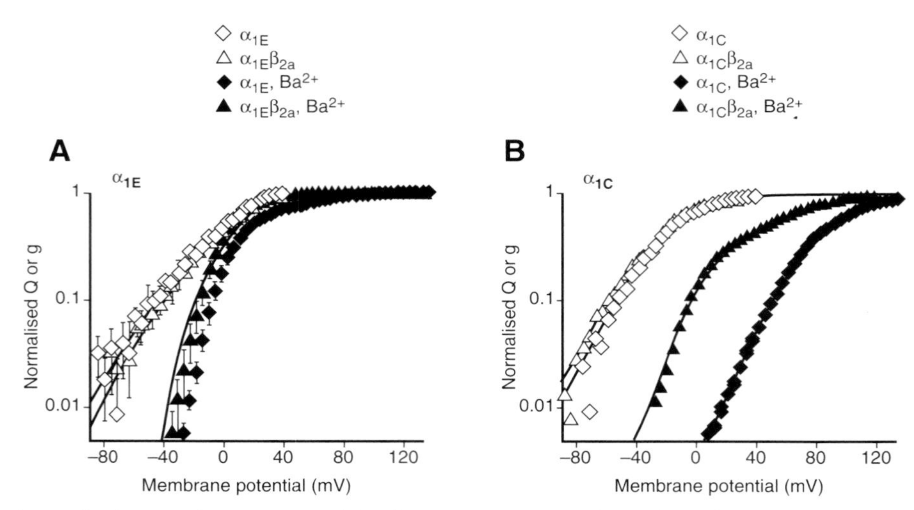

Fig. 3. Coupling between charge movement (Q) and pore opening in α_{1E} and α_{1C} calcium channels. A) Averaged voltage-dependence of the charge movement for α_{1E} and $\alpha_{1E}\beta_{2a}$, and the Ba^{2+} conductance for both of these. B) Analogous semi-log plot for cardiac α_{1C} and $\alpha_{1C}\beta_{2a}$. Error bars are SEM (n=3). (Reproduced with permission.[25])

When these experimental results are combined, it is reasonable to conclude that the overall effect of the β_{2a} subunit coexpression on α_{1E} currents is the creation of a channel in which, for the same charge displacement, a higher P_o is reached.

Among the huge variety of voltage-dependent calcium channels, it is possible to characterise channels according to their different coupling efficiencies. Figure 4 shows traces of α_{1E} (panel A) and α_{1C} (panel B) currents in the presence of external Ba^{2+} 10 mM for pulses to –30 mV, 0 mV and +30 mV from a holding potential of –90 mV. The recordings illustrate small transient upward deflections at the beginning of the voltage pulses that correspond to the gating currents (ON gating current). This initial ON current is followed by inward barium currents for pulses to 0 and +30 mV. At the end of the pulses, the barium current jumps to a large negative value as a result of the abrupt increase in the barium driving force. This so-called tail current decays as the channels close at the return potential. A noteworthy difference

Table I. Parameters for voltage-dependence of charge movement and activation

	Q(V)						g(V)					
	Q_1	z_1	$V_{1,½}$ (mV)	Q_2	z_2	$V_{2,½}$ (mV)	g_1	z_1	$V_{1,½}$ (mV)	g_2	z_2	$V_{2,½}$ (mV)
α_{1E}	0.58	1.42	–18	0.42	3.33	13	0.59	3.47	5	0.41	1.53	59
$\alpha_{1E}\beta_{2a}$	0.72	1.50	–11	0.28	3.90	16	0.78	3.47	–3	0.22	1.62	48
α_{1C}	1.00	1.52	–17	–	–	–	0.54	1.89	69	0.46	1.52	100
$\alpha_{1C}\beta_{2a}$	1.00	1.44	–20	–	–	–	0.30	2.77	–3.9	0.70	1.38	58

Abbreviations: g_1, g_2 = relative amplitudes of the g(V) curve; g(V) = conductance–voltage; Q_1, Q_2 = relative amplitudes of the Q(V) curve; Q(V) = charge movement–voltage; $V_{1,½}$, $V_{2,½}$ = half-activation potentials; z_1, z_2 = effective valencies.

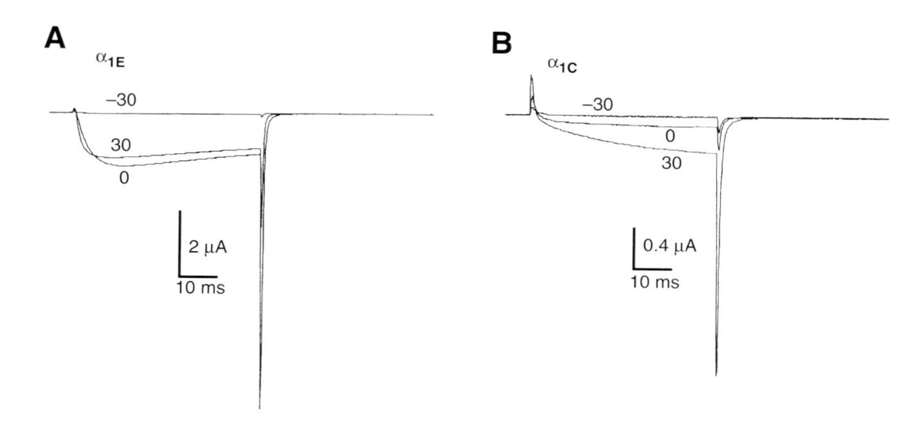

Fig. 4. Ionic and gating current in α_{1E} (A) and α_{1C} (B) calcium channels. Time-courses of ionic and gating currents. Barium currents (BaMES 10 mM) were elicited by voltage steps to –30, 0 and +30 mV from a holding potential of –90 mV. All external solutions contained ouabain 0.1 mM to block endogenous Na^+/K^+-ATPase, which produces non-linear charge movement under conditions of voltage stepping. (Reproduced with permission.[25])

between the α_{1E} and α_{1C} clones is that during depolarising steps the ON gating current is much smaller in neuronal α_{1E} than in cardiac α_{1C} subunits for similarly sized inward currents. The much smaller ratio between gating and ionic currents in α_{1E} than in α_{1C} subunits suggests that pore opening in α_{1E} is more efficiently coupled to the movement of the voltage sensor than that in α_{1C}. Thus, for an equivalent amount of charge moved, a larger proportion of channels will open in α_{1E} than in α_{1C}.

Panel A of figure 5 illustrates α_{1E} calcium currents recorded with macropatches. The bar chart in panel B represents a summary of the $P_{o,max}$ results for the α_{1E} calcium channel with or without β subunits. $P_{o,max}$ for $\alpha_{1E}\beta_{2a}$ is significantly different from both α_{1E} and $\alpha_{1E}\beta_{1a}$ ($p<0.001$ and $p<0.005$, respectively). Panel C of figure 5 summarises the number of charges obtained with the two methods for different calcium channels and β subunits. Although both methods agree for the $\alpha_{1E}\beta_{2a}$ combination, the variance method gives larger z values for α_{1E} and $\alpha_{1E}\beta_1$. This discrepancy may be explained by the correlation between low values of $P_{o,max}$ in α_{1E} and $\alpha_{1E}\beta_{1a}$ and higher numbers of traces in the absence of channel opening ('nulls'). Null traces have charge movement but do not contribute to the variance, which causes an underestimation of N. The limiting slope method gave similar results, of approximately 9 e_0, for all calcium channel combinations tested.

Conclusions

Both methods used to determine z have inherent limitations, and their validity is strictly dependent on the model of channel function. The variance analysis is valid only if all channels open at least once during the pulse and thereby contribute to the noise fluctuations. Thus, by using large depolarising pulses, one can maximise the probability of the final open state O in:

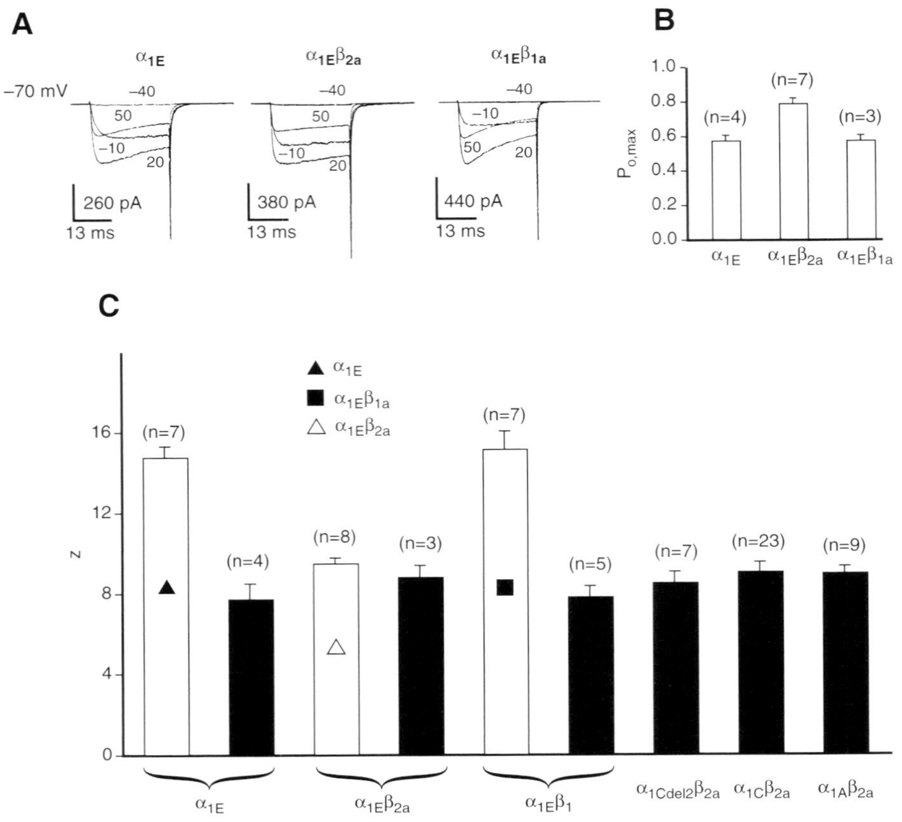

Fig. 5. Summary of results for various calcium channels with or without different β subunits. A) Representative records of calcium currents in cell-attached mode. B) Summary plots of $P_{o,max}$ for the neuronal α_{1E} calcium channel in the presence and absence of β subunits. $P_{o,max}$ = 0.56 ± 0.026 in α_{1E}, 0.57 ± 0.045 in $\alpha_{1E}\beta_{1a}$ and 0.78 ± 0.029 in $\alpha_{1E}\beta_{2a}$ (n = number of samples). C) Mean z (number of effective charges/channel) values ± SEM. Empty bars represent the results from the variance analysis, and filled bars are the results from the limiting slope experiments. Symbols in the variance analysis bars refer to fig. 2(G). Average value of z obtained with the limiting slope experiments = 8.58 ± 0.18 (Reproduced from The Journal of General Physiology by copyright permission of The Rockefeller University Press.[24])

$C \cdots C \longleftrightarrow O$ Scheme I

If a proportion of the channels do not open because of the existence of a parallel inactivated pathway with a kinetic model of the form:

$C \cdots C \longleftrightarrow O$

$I \cdots I \longleftrightarrow I$ Scheme II

N will be underestimated. If this fraction of silent channels carries charge movement, the Q_{max}:N ratio will be overestimated, which will lead to an exaggerated value for z. This might be the case for some calcium channels[37–40] or for C-inactivated potassium channels. The limiting slope method has an inherent experimental difficulty, in that the single exponential approximation is valid only at very low P_o.[19] This method detects all the charges that move in the activation pathway to a final single open state and can be applied to a strictly sequential model or to a parallel model in which the parallel branches carry the same charge. If sufficiently small values of P_o cannot be reached (because of low resolution of the system), the error introduced by this analysis will cause the number of effective charges per channel to be underestimated. A discrepancy between the results of this and the variance analysis will then be noted. In view of this, convergent results obtained with the two methods indicate the measurements and the predicted model to be reliable.

The different z values obtained with variance analysis of calcium channels can be explained by the model in scheme II. Under these conditions, α_{1E} and $\alpha_{1E}\beta_{1a}$ are found to have a higher e_0 (~15) than $\alpha_{1E}\beta_{2a}$ (9.50). On the other hand, the limiting slope analysis gives an average z value of 8.6 for all the tested calcium channel forms, including $\alpha_{1E}\beta_{2a}$. Thus, the z value for $\alpha_{1E}\beta_{2a}$ is similar with both methods. Consistent with scheme II, where an increase in the population of the open state (increase in $P_{o,max}$) would give a more accurate evaluation of z with the variance analysis method, coexpression with the β_{2a} subunit increased $P_{o,max}$ ($P_{o,max,\alpha 1E}$ = 0.56 and $P_{o,max,\alpha 1E\beta 1a}$ = 0.57 *vs* $P_{o,max,\alpha 1E\beta 2a}$ = 0.78). If scheme II is followed, the increase in $P_{o,max}$ induced by β_{2a} should be associated with a lower frequency of silent channels and an overall decrease in the null mode. Indeed, β_{2a} increases the coupling efficiency (g_{max}:Q_{max} ratio, where g_{max} is the limiting conductance) of α_{1E} calcium channels. Moreover, since these changes occur without modifications in the activation time constant of the calcium current, we can conclude that the current potentiation induced by β_{2a} is related to the presence of a smaller proportion of silent channels.

The efficiency of the movement of the voltage sensor on driving the rest of the molecule toward the open conformation will reflect on the biophysical properties of the channels such as the position of the g(V) curve relative to the Q(V) curve along the voltage axis. By comparing the properties of the neuronal α_{1E} with the cardiac α_{1C}, it has been shown that in the neuronal channel a proportionally much smaller charge movement is required to elicit ionic current than in the cardiac channel (see fig. 1). One may think that this difference could be related to a different number of charges per channel in the two clones, which have similar limiting maximal open probability. However, we have shown that there is clear evidence for a consistent number of charges per channel in the different calcium channels and that this is not related to the coexpression of any β subunit. Because of the equality of the number of charges per channel in the two clones, the reason for the difference in channel efficiency must lie in the way that the two voltage sensors are coupled to the channel opening. This is mainly reflected in the relative position of the g(V) curve along the voltage axis because the properties of the voltage sensors, as evaluated by the Q(V) curve, are similar.

Acknowledgements

This work was supported by National Institutes of Health (NIH) grants AR38970 to E.S. and AR43411 to L.B. N.Q. is the recipient of NIH National Research Service Award GM17120-02 and of the Amercan Heart Association AHA Scientist Development Grant

9630053N. This work was performed during the tenure of a Grant-in-Aid 113-GI1 award to R.O. from the American Heart Association Greater Los Angeles Affiliate.

References

1. Hodgkin AL, Huxley AF. A quantitative description of membrane current and its application to conduction and excitation in nerve. J Physiol 1952; 117: 500–44
2. Sigworth FJ. Voltage gating of ion channels. Q Rev Biophys 1994; 27: 1–40
3. Bezanilla F, Stefani E. Voltage dependent gating of ionic channels. Annu Rev Biophys Biochem Chem 1994; 23: 819–46
4. Sigg D, Stefani E, Bezanilla F. Gating current noise produced by elementary transitions in *Shaker* potassium channels. Science 1994; 264: 578–82
5. Yang N, George ALJ, Horn R. Molecular basis of charge movement in voltage-gated sodium channels. Neuron 1996; 16: 113–22
6. Larsson HP, Baker OS, Dhillon DS, et al. Transmembrane movement of the *Shaker* K^+ channel S4. Neuron 1996; 16: 387–97
7. Noda M, Shimizu S, Tanabe T, et al. Primary structure of *Electrophorus electricus* sodium channel deduced from cDNA sequence. Nature 1984; 312: 121–7
8. Greenblatt RE, Blatt Y, Montal M. The structure of the voltage-sensitive sodium channel. Inferences derived from computer-aided analysis in the *Electrophorus electricus* channel primary structure. FEBS Lett 1985; 193: 125–34
9. Guy HR, Seetharamulu P. Molecular model of the action potential sodium channel. Proc Natl Acad Sci U S A 1986; 83: 508–12
10. Catterall WA. Structure and function of voltage-sensitive ion channels. Science 1988; 242: 50–61
11. Stühmer W, Conti F, Suzuki H, et al. Structural parts involved in activation and inactivation of the sodium channel. Nature 1989; 339: 597–603
12. Papazian DM, Timpe LC, Jan YN, et al. Alteration of voltage-dependence of *Shaker* potassium channel by mutations in the S4 sequence. Nature 1991; 349: 305–10
13. Liman ER, Hess P, Weaver F, et al. Voltage-sensing residues in the S4 region of a mammalian K^+ channel. Nature 1991; 353: 752–6
14. Logothetis DE, Movahedi C, Satler C, et al. Incremental reductions of positive charge within the S4 region of a voltage-gated K^+ channel result in corresponding decreases in gating charge. Neuron 1992; 8: 531–40
15. Perozo E, Santacruz-Toloza L, Stefani E, et al. S4 mutations alter gating currents of *Shaker* K channels. Biophys J 1994; 66: 345–54
16. Seoh S-A, Sigg D, Papazian DM, et al. Voltage-sensing residues in the S2 and S4 segments of the *Shaker* K^+ channel. Neuron 1996; 16: 1159–67
17. Yang N, Horn R. Evidence for voltage-dependent S4 movement in sodium channels. Neuron 1995; 15: 213–18
18. Mannuzzu LM, Moronne MM, Isacoff EY. Direct physical measure of conformational rearrangement underlying potassium channel gating. Science 1996; 271: 213–16
19. Almers W. Gating currents and charge movements in excitatory membranes. Rev Physiol Biochem Pharmacol 1978; 82: 96–190
20. Almers W, Armstrong CM. Survival of K^+ permeability and gating currents in squid axons perfused with K^+-free media. J Gen Physiol 1980; 75: 61–78
21. Hirschberg B, Rovner A, Lieberman M, et al. Transfer of twelve charges is needed to open skeletal muscle Na^+ channels. J Gen Physiol 1995; 106: 1053–68
22. Schoppa NE, McCormack K, Tanouye MA, et al. The size of gating charge in wild-type and mutant *Shaker* potassium channels. Science 1992; 255: 1712–15
23. Zampighi GA, Kreman M, Boorer KJ, et al. A method for determining the unitary functional capacity of cloned channels and transporters expressed in *Xenopus laevis* oocytes. J Membr Biol 1995; 148: 65–78
24. Noceti F, Baldelli P, Wei X, et al. Effective gating charges per channel in voltage-dependent K^+ and Ca^{2+} channels. J Gen Physiol 1996; 108: 143–55
25. Olcese R, Neely A, Qin N, et al. Coupling between charge movement and pore opening in vertebrate neuronal α_{1E} calcium channels. J Physiol (Lond.) 497: 675–86
26. Starr TV, Prystay W, Snutch TP. Primary structure of a calcium channel that is highly expressed in the rat cerebellum. Proc Natl Acad Sci U S A 1991; 88: 5621–5
27. Schneider T, Wei X, Olcese R, et al. Molecular analysis and functional expression of the human type E neuronal Ca^{2+} channel alpha 1 subunit. Receptors Channels 1994; 2: 255–70
28. Wei X, Perez-Reyes E, Lacerda AE, et al. Heterologous regulation of the cardiac Ca^{2+} channel α_1 subunit by skeletal muscle β and γ subunits. Implications for the structure of cardiac L-type Ca^{2+} channels. J Biol Chem 1991; 266: 21943–7

29. Ruth P, Rohrkasten A, Biel M. Primary structure of the beta subunit of the DHP-sensitive calcium channel from skeletal muscle. Science 1989; 245: 1115–18
30. Castellano A, Wei X, Birnbaumer L, et al. Cloning and expression of a third calcium channel β subunit. J Biol Chem 1993; 268: 3450–5
31. Castellano A, Wei X, Birnbaumer L, et al. Cloning and expression of a neuronal calcium channel β subunit. J Biol Chem 1993; 268: 12359–66
32. Perez-Reyes E, Castellano A, Kim HS, et al. Cloning and expression of cardiac/brain β subunit of the L-type calcium channel. J Biol Chem 1992; 267: 1792–7
33. Stefani E, Toro L, Perozo E, et al. Gating of *Shaker* K^+ channels: I. Ionic and gating currents. Biophys J 1994; 66: 996–1010
34. Begenisich T, Stevens CF. How many conductance states do potassium channels have? Biophys J 1975; 15: 843–6
35. Sigworth FJ. The variance of sodium current fluctuations at the node of Ranvier. J Physiol 1980; 307: 97–129
36. Conti F, Hille B, Nonner W. Non-stationary fluctuations of the potassium conductance at the node of Ranvier of the frog. J Physiol 1984; 353: 199–230
37. Hess P, Lansman JB, Tsien RW. Different modes of Ca channel gating behaviour favoured by dihydropyridine Ca agonists and antagonists. Nature 1984; 311: 538–44
38. Yue DT, Herzig S, Marban E. β-Adrenergic stimulation of calcium channels occurs by potentiation of high-activity gating modes. Proc Natl Acad Sci U S A 1990; 87: 753–7
39. Cavalié A, Ochi R, Pelzer D, et al. Elementary currents through Ca^{2+} channels in guinea pig myocytes. Pflugers Arch 1983; 398: 284–97
40. Costantin JL, Qin N, Birnbaumer L, et al. β subunit coexpression induces long channel openings in the α_{1C} cardiac calcium channel [abstract]. Biophys J 1995; 68: A258

T-type calcium channels and G proteins in cardiac cells

G. Vassort,[1] J. Alvarez[2]

[1] INSERM U-390, Unité de Recherches de Physiopathologie Cardiovasculaire, CHU Arnaud de Villeneuve, Montpellier, France; [2] Instituto de Cardiología y Cirugía Cardiovascular, Habana, Cuba

Ca^{2+} entry through voltage-gated channels is essential for several cellular functions, including excitability, secretion, transmitter release and the regulation of calcium channel kinetics *per se*. In cardiac cells, two types of calcium channel have been identified on the basis of kinetics: a transient, low-voltage-activated current (T-type current) that can be differentiated from the long-lasting, high-voltage-activated (HVA) one (L-type current), which is sensitive to many pharmacological agents. Particularly, L-type current was shown to be modulated by isoproterenol in a reaction that involved phosphorylation by a cAMP-dependent protein kinase, protein kinase A. Several authors have reported modulations of T-type current by a variety of substances, although the mechanisms involved are far from clearly understood.[1]

In cells of the bullfrog atrium, though not of the ventricle, the two types of calcium channel, T and L, coexist. The T-type calcium channel activates and inactivates at relatively negative voltages. The amplitude and kinetics are unchanged when Ba^{2+} ions are substituted for Ca^{2+}. The T-type calcium channel is partially inhibited by 50 μM solutions of Cd^{2+} and blocked by 50 μM solutions of Ni^{2+}. In addition, T-type current is insensitive to tetrodotoxin and to changes in external Na^{+} concentration. Despite initial descriptions of a lack of sensitivity to agonist and antagonist dihydropyridines in cardiac and other tissues, there have recently been several reports of alterations in T-type current using concentrations that are similar to, or slightly greater than, those used to alter L-type current.[1] However, the presence of T-type channels in bullfrog atrium cardiac cells is contested.[2] T-type current has been described in atrial cells of most mammals, but has only been found in ventricular cells in guinea-pigs and hamsters. Besides inter-species variations, another source of variation might be related to the enzymatic dissociation procedure employed to identify the channels. For example, when pronase E was used, only 30% of bullfrog atrial cells were shown to contain T-type channels, compared to 91% when collagenase and trypsin are used.[3] The effects of proteases are well known and may be worse when the dissociation procedure is prolonged, perhaps over several hours, which might explain why the initial studies on human atrial cells failed to show the presence of T-type channels.

L- and T-type channel facilitation in the presence of isoprenaline

It has previously been established that β-adrenergic stimulation immediately induces an increase in T-type current amplitude that is independent of the cAMP pathway and is thus directly controlled by a G protein.[3] G proteins appear to apply close control over these voltage-dependent calcium channels and, although a direct interaction of G-protein subunits with the ion channel has yet to be demonstrated, there is evidence that receptor-activated G proteins can affect the activity of membrane-confined stimulatory (or inhibitory) mechanisms. It has been shown that various forms of the G_o subunit can activate calcium channels when applied to the cytoplasmic side,[4] an observation which led to the proposal that this was the mechanism accounting for β-adrenergic-induced increases in L-type current. Also, the photoactivation of intracellular guanosine (GTPγS) enhanced and then inhibited the T-type calcium current in a dose-dependent manner; the inhibitory response was sensitive to pertussis toxin (PTX).[5]

We also reported that the amplitude of T-type current elicited by depolarisation to –50 mV is dependent upon the short-term previous history of the membrane potential.[3] Following high depolarising prepulses T-type current is not completely inactivated, with the T-type current availability curve taking on a U-shape, similar to that of L-type current availability. Figure 1 shows the effects on T-type current of 10 consecutive 200 ms depolarising prepulses to +70 mV, evoked by a depolarisation

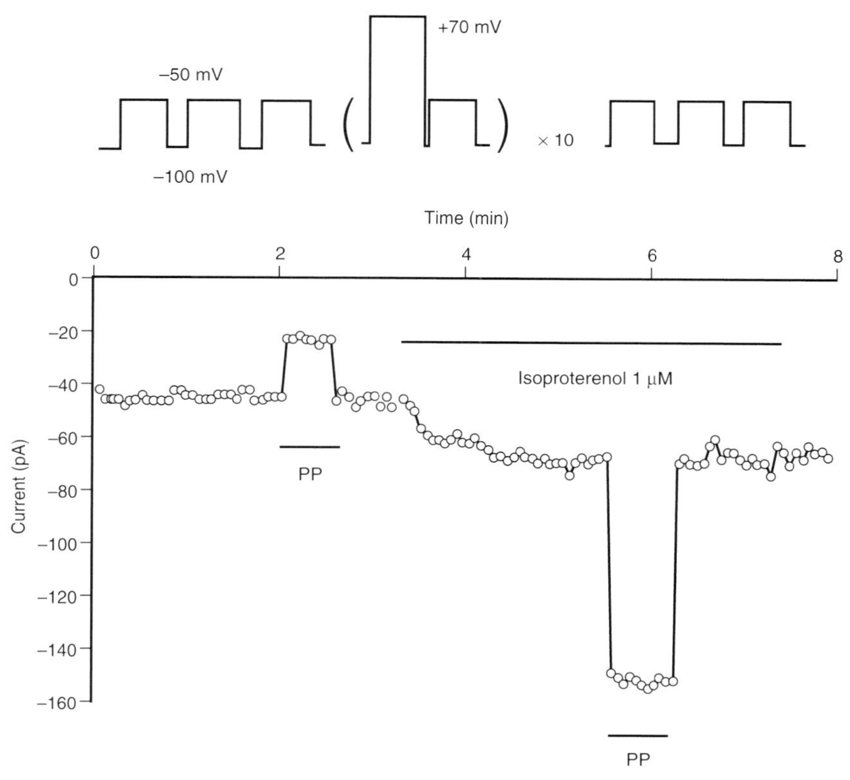

Fig. 1. Effects of depolarising prepulses up to +70 mV on T-type current elicited at –50 mV, under control conditions and in the presence of isoproterenol. Under control conditions, the prepulse to +70 mV partially inactivated T-type current elicited during the test pulse depolarisation to –50 mV (holding potential –100 mV). β-adrenergic stimulation induced a weak increase in T-type current and a large facilitation was then observed. Pulses were applied, as depicted in the top scheme, at a cycle length of 8 s. PP = the period during which the prepulses (+70 mV, 200 ms duration, 3 ms interpulse interval) were applied; circles indicate peak currents elicited by the test pulses.

to –50 mV applied after 3 ms. The test current relative to control current (relative current) is 0.59 ± 0.06 (n=27).

Under a variety of experimental conditions, the peak amplitude of the calcium current can be increased above the control value, a phenomenon called 'facilitation'. As previously reported, isoprenaline slightly increases T-type current, and this is accompanied by a large facilitation of T-type current after depolarising prepulses. The relative T-type current without prepulse is 1.20 ± 0.29, a value that differs significantly from that of 0.63 ± 0.09, observed in control conditions before applying the agonist. Under both control conditions and β-adrenergic stimulation, T-type current reaches a constant new amplitude on applying the first prepulse and recovers to its original amplitude on cessation of prepulse depolarisations. Similar observations have been obtained when the T-type current is carried by Sr^{2+} ions (when substituted for equimolar solutions containing Ca^{2+} ions). The same effect is obtained with Ca^{2+} in the presence of Cd^{2+} ions using 50 μM solutions. Partial relief of inhibition of T-type current under control conditions by a prepulse to +70 mV, and T-type current facilitation after isoprenaline, is short-lived; variation of the interval between pulses leads to T-type current inactivation with a 50 ms interval. Subsequently, it is reactivated with longer intervals.

Facilitation of T-type current is dependent on G proteins

The effects of dialysing the cells, using GPTγS or ATPγS, on T-type current have been studied. In GPTγS-dialysed cells, T-type current density is lower than in control cells. After T-type current reaches a steady-state value, superfusion of the cell with a 1 μM solution of isoprenaline induces a fast (30–40 s) increase in T-type current. However, this increase is short-lived and T-type current returns to control values when the isoprenaline is washed out. The isoprenaline-induced maximal increase in T-type current in GTPγS-dialysed cells approximates that of control cells (fig. 2).

In GPTγS-dialysed cells, high-prepulse depolarisation facilitates T-type current. The relative amplitude of T-type current evoked at –50 mV after a prepulse to +70 mV is significantly greater than that of control cells. T-type current facilitation is not sustained and it ceases when the conditioning pulses are stopped. In the presence of isoprenaline, conditioning prepulses also induce T-type current facilitation in GPTγS-dialysed cells.

In cells dialysed with ATPγS, there is a significantly greater density of T-type current than in the control cells. Similarly, isoprenaline induces a fast (30–40 s) increase in T-type current that is not sustained in most cells. The increase in T-type current induced by isoprenaline in these cells is greater in amplitude than that obtained in control cells (396.0 ± 11.0% *vs* 194.3 ± 16.0%). With regard to facilitation, similar results have been obtained with GTPγS- or ATPγS-dialysed cells, except that the relative amplitude of T-type current after a prepulse to +70 mV is greater in ATPγS- than in GTPγS-dialysed cells (see fig. 2). In each case, however, the facilitated currents

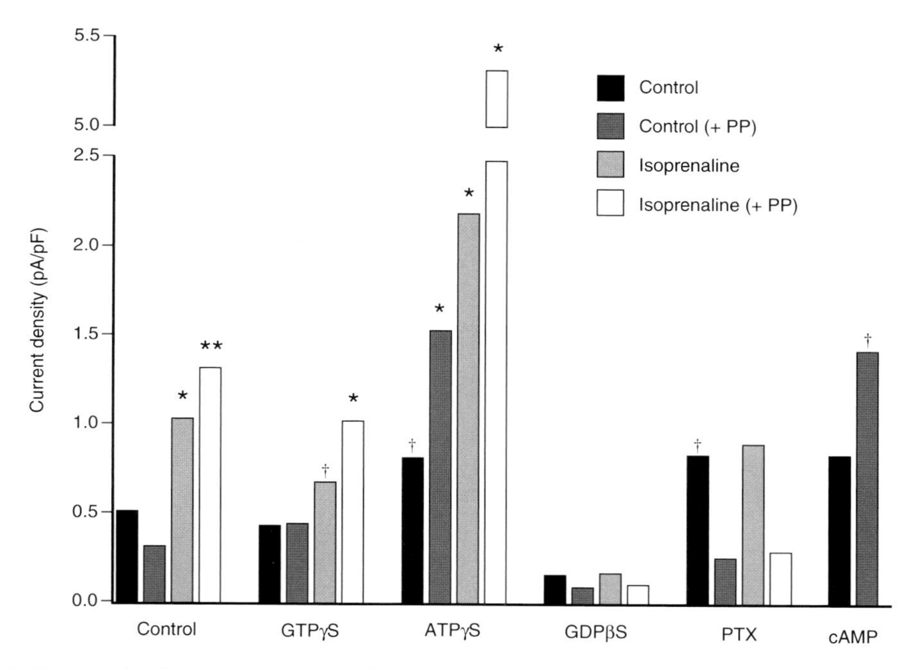

*Fig. 2. Changes in basal T-type current density and facilitation under conditions of altered G-protein activity. T-type current was elicited by a depolarising pulse to –50 mV in the absence of, or following, a +70 mV depolarising prepulse (PP) in control Ringer solution, in the presence of intracellularly applied GTPγS (400 μM), ATPγS (3 mM), GDPβS (1 mM) and cAMP (50 μM) before and after treatment with isoprenaline (1 μM). Some cells were pretreated for 12 hours with pertussis toxin (PTX 0.5 μg/ml). (n = 4–15 cells. † $p<0.01$ vs control; * $p<0.01$, ** $p<0.05$ vs its own control.*

were found to activate and inactivate faster than currents evoked without prepulses, an effect that could be attributed to a change in latency induced by prepulses.[6]

Experiments aimed at blocking G-protein activity have been performed on cells dialysed with a solution containing GDPγS and ADP in place of GTP and ATP. Basal T-type current density decreased and was subsequently unaffected by isoprenaline. There is no evidence of T-type current facilitation in these cells. The amplitude of T-type current was significantly increased after treatment with PTX, but there was no further increase when subsequently exposed to isoprenaline. In both control and β-adrenergic-stimulated conditions, T-type current appears relatively insensitive to depolarising prepulses of up to +70 mV (see fig. 2).

Is facilitation of T-type current phosphorylation-dependent?

The enhancement by isoprenaline of T-type current recovery after high depolarising prepulses, or T-type current facilitation, is thought to be related to activation of protein kinase A. To this end, experiments have been performed after adding cAMP 50 μM to the pipette dialysate solution. Under these conditions the amplitude of T-type current elicited at –50 mV is unaffected,[3] but the application of a +70 mV prepulse induces a large facilitation (see fig. 2). T-type current facilitation occurs with maximal amplitude on the first applied prepulse, and T-type current recovers its control pretest amplitude on cessation of prepulses. The large facilitation of T-type current recorded in the presence of cAMP was also observed when Sr^{2+} or Cd^{2+} (50 μM) were added to prevent contamination by L-type current.

L-type current has been shown to be regulated by the multifunctional Ca^{2+}- and calmodulin-dependent kinase II (CaMKII). Furthermore, Yuan and Bers provided evidence that phosphorylation can be voltage-dependent and thus proposed this mechanism to account for the rate-dependent, and voltage-dependent, facilitation of L-type current in cardiac cells.[7] However, this mechanism cannot explain the recovery from inactivation or the facilitation of T-type current. T-type current facilitation of similar amplitudes has been observed in control conditions during and following exposure to isoprenaline, Sr^{2+} ions and intracellular BAPTA 20 mM, and when CaMKII is inhibited following intracellular perfusion with the CaMKII-inhibitor peptide 290-309, which does not affect T-type current amplitude *per se* (Alvarez and Vassort, unpublished observations).

Discussion

T-type current density in bullfrog atrial cells has been shown to vary according to the G-protein activity dictated by the experimental conditions. T-type current density is slightly reduced by intracellular dialysis with GTPγS but increased by dialysis with ATPγS. Furthermore, pretreatment with PTX significantly increases basal T-type current. Doupnik and Pun showed an increase in HVA calcium current in PTX-treated chromaffin cells, further indicating that an inhibitory G protein controls L-type current.[8]

T-type current facilitation can be induced by a variety of experimental conditions, and a number of mechanisms have been suggested to account for this mechanism (reviewed by Dolphin[9]). These include:

- changes in calcium channel gating in which high-prepulse depolarisations drive the channel into a long-lived open state[10]
- recruitment of L-type calcium channels by a voltage-dependent phosphorylation process not involving G proteins, e.g. in chromaffin cells[11]
- voltage-dependent relief of G-protein-mediated tonic inhibition of N-type calcium current in neurons[12] and HVA calcium current in bovine chromaffin cells.[8]

To account for these findings, Swandulla et al. suggested that strong depolarisations may reorganise the negatively charged groups of G proteins, leading to a reversal of calcium channel inhibition.[13] A further mechanism, phosphorylation of the L-type calcium channel by the cAMP-dependent protein kinase as in skeletal muscle myoballs, has been proposed.[14] In cardiac cells, a double-pulse calcium current facilitation, similar to the one described on p. 325 (see also fig 1), has been reported by Pietrobon and Hess.[15] Strong depolarising prepulses drive the L-type calcium channel from its normal gating pattern into a gating mode characterised by long openings and high open probability. A role for calcium in mediating cardiac L-type current facilitation during repetitive stimulation has recently been analysed, and it was concluded that L-type current facilitation is related to activation of the Ca^{2+}/calmodulin- dependent protein kinase and phosphorylation of a site on, or near, the calcium channel.[7] Bates and Gurney also provided evidence that facilitation is mediated by Ca^{2+},[16] but this was independent of phosphorylation (although a nucleotide was involved).

In a number of cell types, a G-protein-dependent inhibition of calcium currents has been proposed to mediate the inhibitory effects of neuromediators. The mechanism of inhibition was attributed to a voltage-dependent inhibition between the G protein and the calcium channel. This suggestion followed the observation that a large depolarising prepulse applied immediately before the test pulse partially reverses the inhibition by agonist or direct G-protein activation.[17] A similar protocol applied to bullfrog atrial cells in the presence of GDPγS, or after pretreatment with PTX, leads to the suggestion that T-type current facilitation results from a voltage-dependent relief of a G-protein inhibitory tone, as proposed for other cell types.[8,13,18] In the course of the presently reported experiments, double-pulse T-type current facilitation was readily observed when the non-hydrolysable analogues GTPγS and ATPγS, as well as cAMP, were introduced intracellularly. Double-pulse T-type current facilitation was also observed following β-adrenergic stimulation. In all of these experimental conditions an increase in cAMP and the triggering of protein kinase A-dependent phosphorylation was expected. However, the T-type current facilitation induced by this pathway probably does not relate to phosphorylation of the T-type calcium channel itself, whereas it has been demonstrated that both the α and β subunits of the G_i protein could be phosphorylated by protein kinase A.[19] Protein kinase A-dependent phosphorylation of G_i protein has been reported in hepatocytes.[20] One can thus suggest that protein kinase A-dependent phosphorylation of a G_i protein alters the voltage effect on its interaction with the calcium channel protein and consequently increases the relief of inhibition.

Under normal circumstances in atrial and ventricular cells, T-type current is unlikely to play an important role in cardiac electrical activity. However, pharmacological dissection of guinea-pig ventricular myocytes using Ni^{2+} ions and nifedipine, under conditions of action potential clamping, reveals the presence of T-type current during the early phase of the action potential.

Furthermore, the steady-state voltage-dependence relationships for activation and inactivation are shifted by about 35 mV towards negative potential with respect to L-type current characteristics (fig. 3). This is only a few millivolts less than the Na^+ current potentials, making T-type current well suited to pacemaker activity.

T-type current might have an even more significant role in physiopathological conditions. It has been reported to be enhanced in Syrian hamsters with dilated cardiomyopathy[21] and to be produced in cat ventricular cells following pulmonary

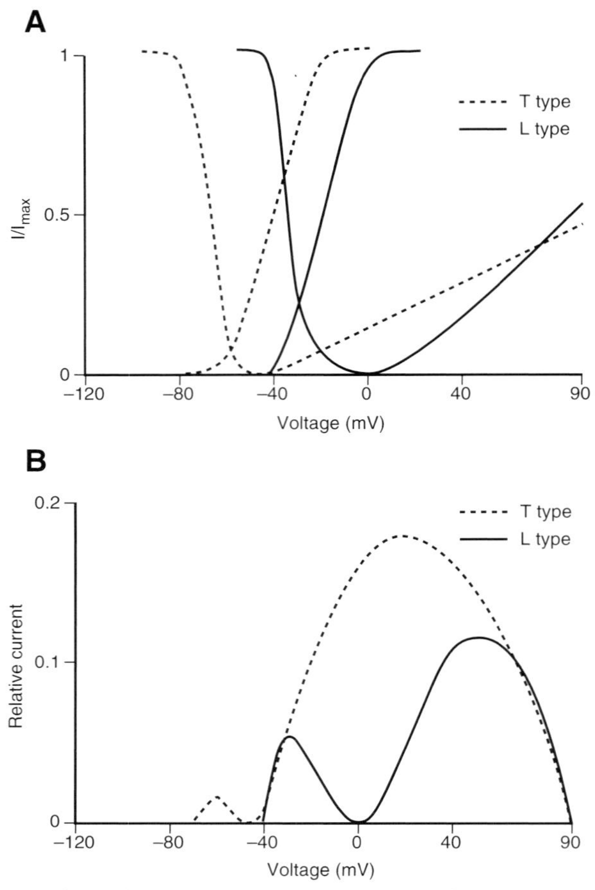

Fig. 3. T-type and L-type 'window' calcium currents. A) Voltage-dependence of activation and inactivation characteristics of both T-type (dotted lines) and L-type (solid lines) currents. B) Sustained T-type and L-type current, relative to maximal current at 0 mV (calculated assuming a calcium reversal potential at +90 mV and similar maximal conductances).

aortic banding.[22] Furthermore, extensive accumulation of Ca^{2+} in cells during ischaemia and hypoxia may be critical and may result in irreversible injury and cellular death as a consequence of a long-lasting weak depolarisation and maintained influx of Ca^{2+} through the 'window' T-type current. In fact, as a result of the bimodal voltage-dependency of T-type calcium channel availability, a current flowing through these channels might lead to Ca^{2+} loading and contribute to arrhythmias such as delayed after-depolarisations (DADs) and early after-depolarisations (EADs). A sustained inward T-type current will flow continuously at two ranges of potential; in other words, there are two 'window' currents (see fig. 3). In addition to the current occurring at the usual overlap between the activation and inactivation curves, some current may flow at membrane potentials above –30 mV, up to the calcium reversal potential. The same two 'window' currents exist for L-type current, but it should be recognised that the voltage-dependence of T-type current kinetics are more negative, by approximately 35 mV. Consequently, the two T-type current 'windows' sustain inward currents in two useful voltage ranges of the action potential. However, because of sensitivity to several pharmacological agents and neurotransmitters, as well as the lack of specific inhibitors, the precise role of T-type current is both difficult to establish and, conversely, to disprove.

T-type current has been reported in ventricular cells of neonatal rats.[23] This current showed biophysical and pharmacological properties, including T-type current facilitation, similar to those presently reported in bullfrog atrial cells (Alvarez and Vassort, unpublished observations). It is now possible to manipulate specific protein levels in these cells and thus possible to carry out experiments to evaluate the potential roles of T-type current in cardiac cells.

References

1. Alvarez JL, Vassort G. Cardiac T-type Ca current: pharmacology and roles in cardiac tissues. J Cardiovasc Electrophys 1994; 5: 376–93
2. Campbell DL, Gilles WR, Shibata EF. Ion transfer characteristics of the calcium current in bullfrog atrial myocytes. J Physiol (Lond) 1988; 403: 239–66
3. Alvarez JL, Vassort G. Properties of the low-threshold Ca current in frog atrial cardiomyocytes. A comparison with the high-threshold Ca current. J Gen Physiol 1992; 100: 519–45
4. Yatani A, Codina J, Imoto J, et al. A G-protein directly regulates mammalian cardiac calcium channels. Science 1987; 238: 1288–91
5. Scott RH, Wootton JF, Dolphin AC. Modulation of neuronal T-type calcium channel currents by photoactivation of intracellular guanosine 5′-O (3-thio) triphosphate. Neuroscience 1990; 38: 285–94
6. Droogmans G, Nilius B. Kinetic properties of the cardiac T-type calcium channel in the guinea-pig. J Physiol 1989; 419: 627–50
7. Yuan W, Bers DM. Ca^{2+}-dependent facilitation of cardiac Ca^{2+} current is due to Ca^{2+}-calmodulin-dependent protein kinase. Am J Phys 1994; 267: H982–93
8. Doupnik CA, Pun Ryk. G-protein activation mediates prepulse facilitation of Ca^{2+} channel currents in bovine chromaffin cells. J Membr Biol 1994; 140: 47–56
9. Dolphin AC. Facilitation of Ca^{2+} current in excitable cells. Trends Neurosci 1996; 19: 35–43
10. Hoshi T, Smith SJ. Large depolarizations induce long openings of voltage-dependent calcium channels in adrenal chromaffin cells. J Neurosci 1987; 7: 571–80
11. Artalejo CR, Rossie S, Perlman RL, et al. Voltage-dependent phosphorylation may recruit Ca current facilitation in chromaffin cells. Nature 1992; 358: 63–6
12. Ikeda S. Double-pulse calcium channel current facilitation in adult rat sympathetic neurons. J Physiol (Lond) 1991; 439: 181–214
13. Swandulla D, Carbone E, Lux HD. Do calcium channel classifications account for neuronal calcium channel diversity? Trends Neurosci 1991; 14: 46–51
14. Sculptoreanu A, Scheuer T, Catterall WA. Voltage-dependent potentiation of L-type Ca channels due to phosphorylation by cAMP-dependent protein kinase. Nature 1993; 364: 240–3
15. Pietrobon D , Hess P. A novel mechanism of voltage-dependent gating in L-type calcium channels. Nature 1990; 346: 651–5
16. Bates SE, Gurney AM. Ca-dependent block and potentiation of L-type calcium current in guinea-pig ventricular myocytes. J Physiol (Lond) 1993; 466: 345–65
17. Grassi F, Lux HD. Voltage-dependent GABA-induced modulation of calcium currents in chick sensory neurons. Neurosci Lett 1989; 105: 113–19
18. Gandia L, Garcia AG, Morad M. ATP modulation of calcium channels in chromaffin cells. J Physiol 1993; 470: 55–72
19. Watanabe Y, Imaizumi T, Misaki N, et al. Effects of phosphorylation of inhibitory GTP-binding G-protein by cyclic AMP-dependent protein kinase on its ADP-ribosylation by pertussis toxin, islet-activating G-protein. FEBS Lett 1988; 236: 372–4
20. Bushfield M, Lavan BE , Houslay MD. Okadaic acid identifies a phosphorylation-dephosphorylation cycle controlling the inhibitory guanine-nucleotide-binding regulatory protein G_{i2}. Biochem J 1991; 274: 317–21
21. Sen L, Smith TW. T-type Ca^{2+} channels are abnormal in genetically determined cardiomyopathic hamster hearts. Circ Res 1994; 75: 149–55
22. Nuss HB, Houser SR. T-type Ca^{2+} current is expressed in hypertrophied adult feline left ventricular myocytes. Circ Res 1993; 73: 777–82
23. Gomez JP, Portreau D, Branka JE, et al. Developmental changes in Ca^{2+} currents from newborn rat cardiomyocytes in primary culture. Pflugers Arch 1994; 428: 241–9

Regulation of human neuronal calcium channels by receptors and G proteins

Lee R. Shekter,[1] Louis H. Philipson,[2] Hyewhon Rhim,[1] Peter T. Toth,[2] Richard J. Miller[1]

[1] Department of Pharmacological and Physiological Sciences and
[2] Department of Medicine, University of Chicago, Chicago, Illinois, USA

Summary

Receptor/G-protein-mediated inhibition of neuronal calcium current is important for many reasons, including presynaptic regulation of neurotransmitter release. As discussed here, it is frequently observed that activation of receptors in neurons produces inhibition of neuronal N and P/Q currents while sparing L-type currents. We also show that cloned α_{1B} (N-type) calcium channels are regulated by G proteins much more strongly than α_{1E} (R-type) calcium channels. Regulation is mediated by G-protein $\beta\gamma$ subunits in each case and may involve competitive reactions between these subunits and the β subunit of the calcium channels.

Voltage-sensitive calcium channels are one of the major routes of Ca^{2+} entry into excitable cells. These channels control many important cellular functions, depending on cell type (e.g. the contraction of cardiac muscle and the secretion of neurotransmitters). In some types of cell, such as neurons, calcium channels may carry out different functions in the various parts of the cell.

Over the past few years great advances have been made in our understanding of the structures of the molecules responsible for these diverse functions. It is known that calcium channels comprise at least two families of related multisubunit complexes.[1,2] The pore-forming region of the calcium channel is the α_1 subunit, and the channel complexes also contain β and $\alpha_2\delta$ subunits, together with other modulatory proteins.[1,3] When cloned calcium channels are expressed in artificial systems, one subgroup exhibits sensitivity to dihydropyridine drugs, whereas the other does not (table I). It is clear that in many cases the properties of these cloned channels correspond closely to those of calcium currents in normal cells.[1,2] However, some mysteries remain. For example, the identity of the low-threshold T-type calcium currents and the precise functions of calcium channels formed from the α_{1E} clone are still unclear.

This laboratory has been particularly interested in the role of calcium channels in the control of neurotransmitter release. It is now clear that calcium channels often form clusters in nerve terminals to enable the delivery of a rapid pulse of Ca^{2+} at very high concentrations to vesicles filled with neurotransmitters waiting to be released.[3,4] Calcium channels found in these clusters are frequently of the N or Q type.[3,4] It is likely that these are formed by expression of the α_{1B} and α_{1A} clones, respectively.[5,6] A widely studied hallmark of these types of calcium channel is their inhibitory regulation by the action of neurotransmitters acting at 7 membrane-

Table I. Classification of calcium channels

Channel type	Subunits
L	α_{1C}, α_{1D}, α_{1S} (dihydropyridines)
Non-L	α_{1A} (P/Q: ω-Aga-IVA, ω-CTx-MVIIC) α_{1B} (N: ω-CTx-MVIIC) α_{1E} (R: Ni^{2+})

spanning G-protein-linked receptors.[7,8] This process is believed to be responsible for presynaptic inhibition of neurotransmitter release at many synapses.[7–10]

In this chapter, data relating to the mechanisms by which activation of receptors lead to the inhibition of neuronal calcium channels are presented. In particular, regulation of human α_{1B} and α_{1E} calcium channels will be compared in order to gain some insights into the possible functions of α_{1E}-based calcium channels.

Receptor regulation of calcium channels in neurons

Inhibitory receptor regulation of calcium channels in neurons has been very widely observed.[7,8] In the CNS these effects have been observed mainly in acutely isolated preparations of CNS neuronal cell bodies. However, it is thought likely that similar events occur at nerve terminals, where they would contribute to the regulation of neurotransmitter release.[10] Indeed, at central or peripheral synapses, results of studies with imaging techniques at the nerve-terminal level have reinforced observations in isolated neuronal preparations.[3,4,10]

This type of calcium channel regulation is shown by the action of opioid agonists in the nucleus of the solitary tract.[11] Such actions in this part of the brain are responsible for many of the well-known effects of opiates on the autonomic nervous system. As shown in figure 1, activation of μ-opioid receptors on acutely isolated cells from this nucleus results in inhibition of the high-threshold calcium current. However, not all components of this current are susceptible to inhibition. Inhibition by μ-opioids of components of the calcium current as a result of activation of N- (ω-CTx-GVIA-sensitive) or P-/Q-type (ω-Aga-IVA-sensitive) calcium channels was shown by selective blockade of different types of calcium channel. However, the component of the current that was blocked by nimodipine (L-type) was not inhibited by μ-opioids.

Similar results in the same nucleus have been observed upon activation of GABA-B or somatostatin receptors.[12] The properties of the inhibition observed in these instances are very similar to those observed in many studies in other parts of the brain. Thus, much of the inhibition is voltage-dependent and is blocked by pertussis toxin (PTX).[7,8] It is also quite common for receptors to produce inhibition of P/Q and N channels while ignoring L channels. Given the fact that it is the P/Q and N channels that seem to be responsible for triggering neurotransmitter secretion,[5,10,13,14] the premise that these same channels can be regulated by receptors seems quite

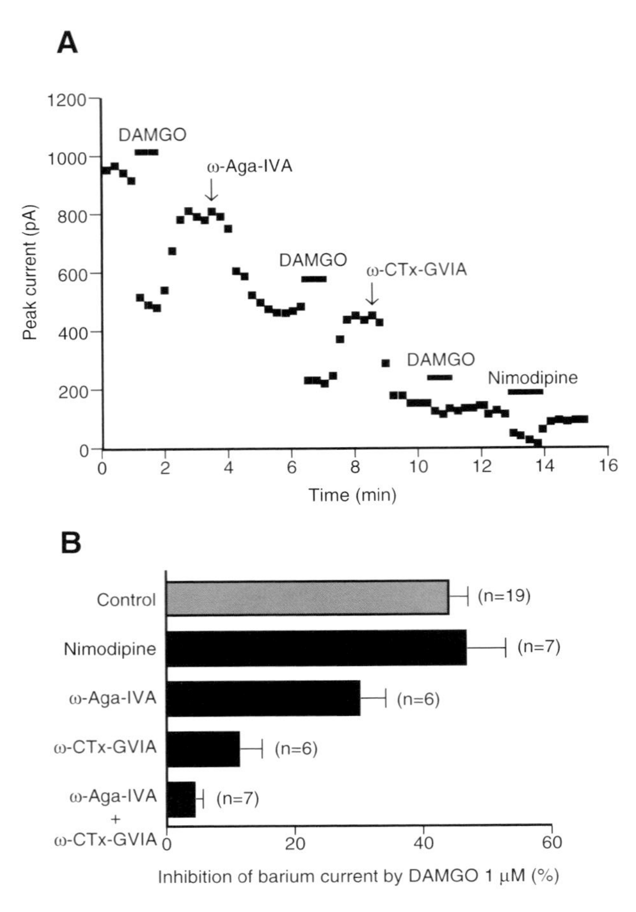

Fig. 1. Inhibition of ω-Aga-IVA- and ω-CTx-GVIA-sensitive calcium channels after activation of μ-opioid receptors in acutely isolated rat nucleus tractus solitarius (NTS) neurons. A) Time-course of barium current to show DAMGO effects before and after application of different calcium channel blockers. B) Pooled results from calcium channel blocker experiments to show the mean inhibition of barium current by DAMGO 1 μM. n = numbers of cells treated with each drug.[11]

reasonable. Although L-type channels are widely distributed in the nervous system, their functions in nerve cells are poorly understood.[15]

Regulation of cloned α_{1B} (N-type) calcium channels

Knowledge of the molecular basis of G-protein-mediated inhibition of calcium channels may indicate how these regulatory effects are produced. The most widely described mechanism is membrane-delimited (i.e. the presence of a diffusible second messenger appears not to be required) and frequently voltage-dependent.[7,16,17] Other types of inhibition include non-membrane-delimited effects and those that are membrane-delimited but not voltage-dependent.[7,18] It was originally thought that only PTX-sensitive G proteins participated in membrane-delimited inhibition. However, it is now apparent that other G proteins might couple receptors to calcium channels.[7,8]

As with G-protein-regulated inwardly rectifying potassium channels, it is clear that the $\beta\gamma$ subunits of the G protein, rather than the α subunits, are responsible for mediating the inhibition.[19] The apparent lack of involvement of a diffusible second messenger also indicates that the G-protein subunits might directly interact with part of the calcium channel complex. The availability of cloned calcium channels, expressed in tissue-culture cell lines, has made further investigation of this process possible.

Examination of the properties of human α_{1B} calcium channels, stably expressed in HEK293 cells with the ancillary subunits β_{1b} and $\alpha_{2B}\delta$ (G1A1 cells), showed that calcium currents could be evoked in these cells by step depolarisations (fig. 2).[20] These currents had properties that were very similar to those described for N-type calcium channels (e.g. they were completely blocked by ω-CTx-GVIA).

Activation of somatostatin receptors (reported to occur endogenously in these cells[21]) produced a rapid reversible inhibition of the calcium current (see fig. 2). Alternatively, the calcium currents in these cells were unaffected by agonists at κ-opioid or neuropeptide Y (NPY) receptors (these do not normally occur in these cells). The inhibition produced by somatostatin was partially voltage-dependent (see fig. 2 (B)) and was blocked by PTX (see fig. 2 (D)). Transfection of κ-opioid or Y1, Y2 or Y4 NPY receptors into the cells, however, resulted in κ-opioid- or NPY-mediated inhibition of the calcium current (unpublished observations; see also Toth et al.[20]). Here again the effects observed were sensitive to PTX and were relieved by a depolarising prepulse. Thus, the regulation of α_{1B} channels in these cells appears similar to the effects of many receptors on N-type calcium currents in neurons.

The regulation of α_{1B} calcium channels by G proteins was subsequently examined by perfusing cells with GTPγS, a procedure intended to activate 'irreversibly' all G proteins in these cells. In order to estimate whether calcium channels were inhibited under these circumstances, a double-pulse protocol was used in which the second pulse was preceded by a depolarising prepulse. If the perfusion with GTPγS resulted in an inhibited current, the size of the current was expected to be larger following the prepulse (providing that the inhibition was voltage-dependent). As can be seen in figure 3, this proved to be the case.

In order to identify the G-protein subunits responsible for the inhibition, a combination of β and γ subunits or mutant α subunits (constitutively activated α_o, α_s and α_{i2}) were overexpressed. As shown in figure 4, overexpression of a combination of β and γ G-protein subunits produced currents that exhibited a large degree of prepulse facilitation. However, overexpression of any of the mutant α subunits had no effect, as had overexpression of either the β or γ subunits alone. This strongly suggests that the $\beta\gamma$ subunits of the G protein are responsible for the inhibition, rather than the α subunit. These results are similar to those recently reported by Ikeda[22] and Herlitze et al.[23]

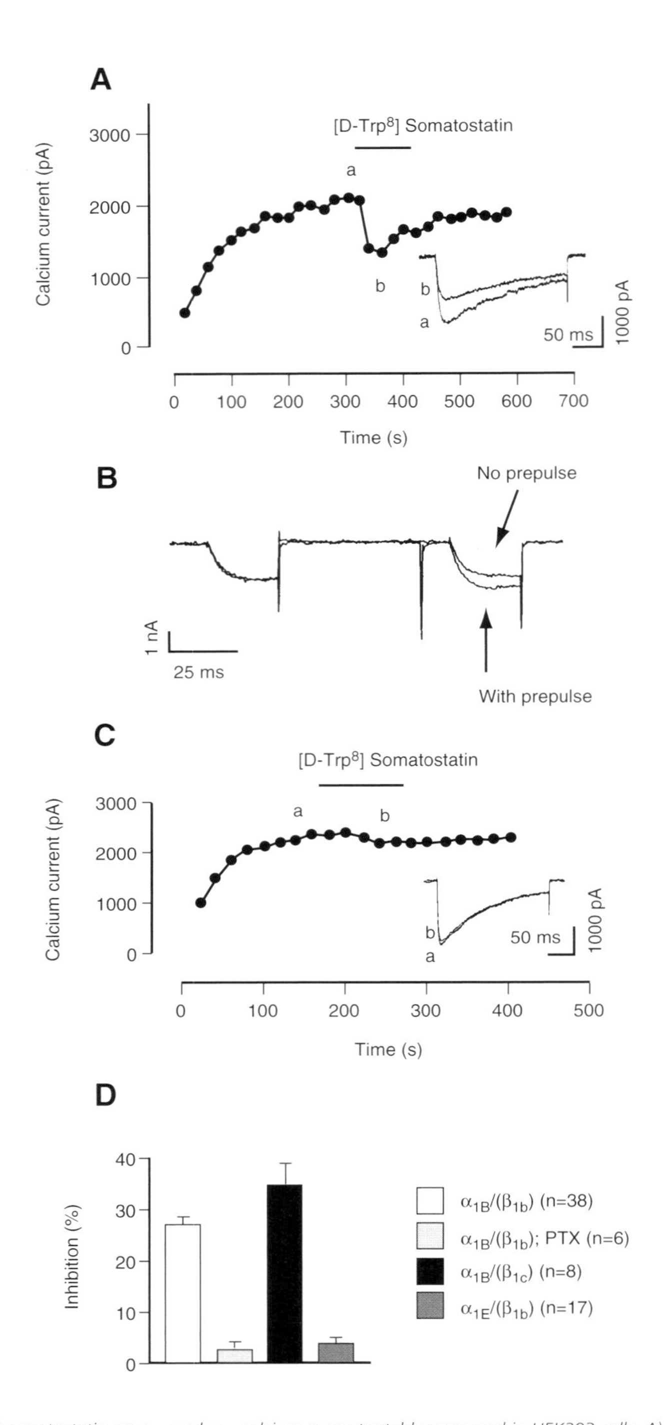

Fig. 2. Effect of somatostatin on α_{1B} and α_{1E} calcium currents stably expressed in HEK293 cells. A) α_{1B} calcium current versus time, showing a typical response to somatostatin 300 nM. Cell was depolarised from a holding potential of −90 mV to a test potential of +10 mV every 20 s. Inset: Calcium currents before and during somatostatin application. B) α_{1B} calcium currents evoked by a double-pulse protocol in the presence of somatostatin 300 nM. C) α_{1E} calcium current versus time. D) Mean (± SEM) responses to somatostatin 300 nM. n = numbers of experiments; PTX = pertussis toxin.[20]

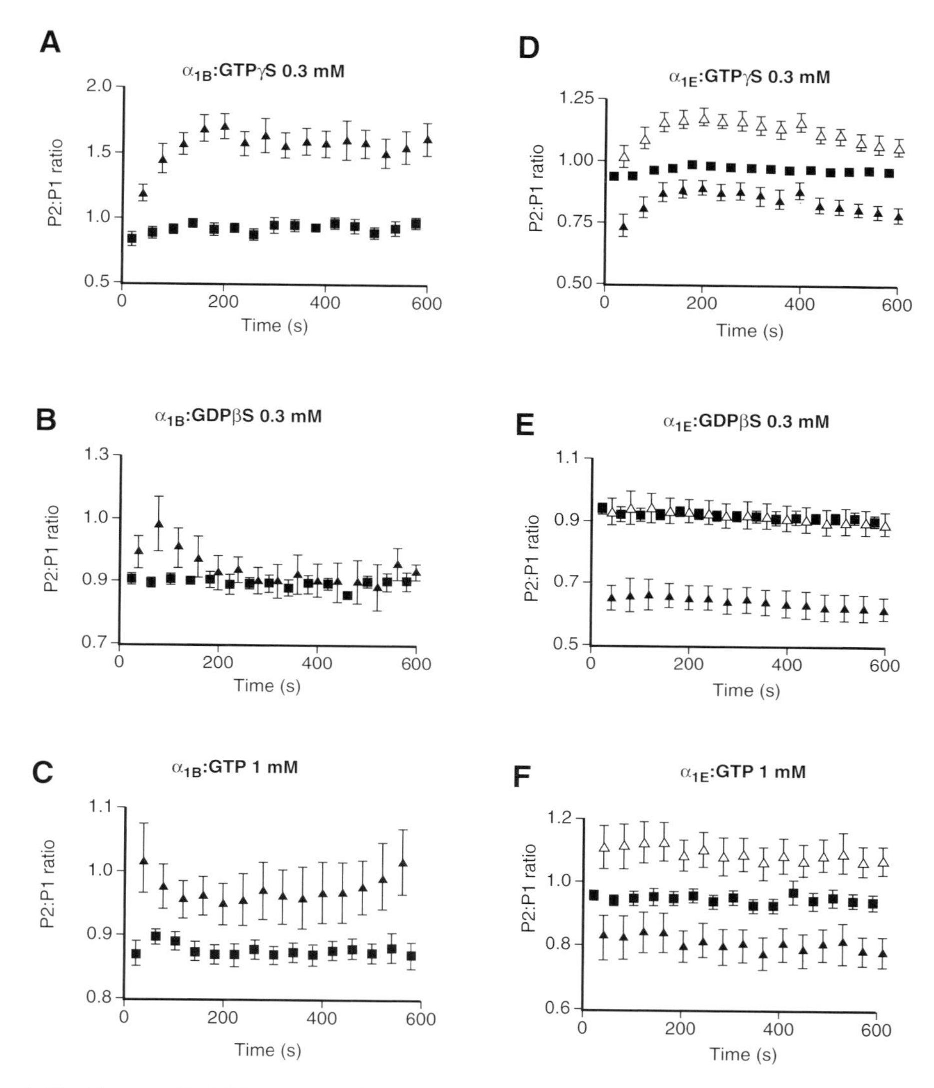

Fig. 3. Effect (mean ± SE) of different GTP analogues on α_{1B} (A–C) and α_{1E} (D–F) calcium currents stably expressed in HEK293 cells. A double-pulse protocol was used. ■ = P2:P1 ratio without prepulse. ▲ = P2:P1 ratio with prepulse. △ (D–F) = P2:P1 ratios with prepulse after 'subtraction' of voltage-dependent inactivation obtained from data with GDPβS in the patch pipette.[20]

Regulation of α_{1E} calcium currents

A similar series of experiments was conducted using an HEK293 cell line that stably expressed α_{1E} calcium currents together with the same ancillary subunits (E-52 cells).[23] The properties of the calcium currents observed in these cells can be seen in figures 2–5. It can be seen that α_{1E} currents tended to inactivate during the voltage step to a much greater extent than the currents obtained following expression of α_{1B}. Activation of somatostatin receptors in these HEK293 cells had almost no effect on the magnitude of the α_{1E} calcium current (see fig. 2). Furthermore, transfection of

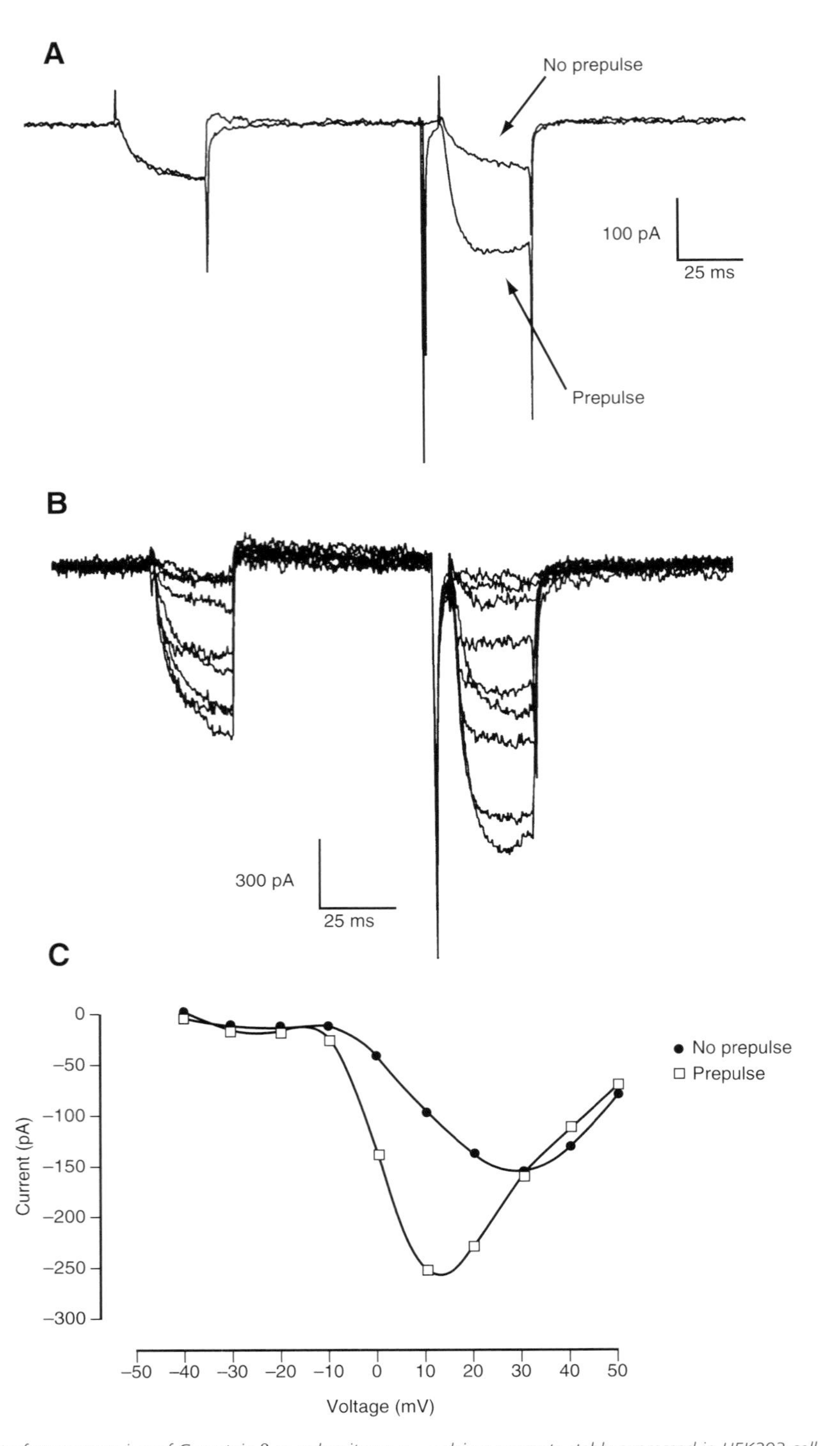

Fig. 4. Effect of overexpression of G-protein $\beta_2\gamma_2$ subunits on α_{1B} calcium currents stably expressed in HEK293 cells. A) A cell displaying characteristic peak current inhibition and slowing, which was then relieved following a prepulse. B) Current traces for the same cell as in panel A generated from the current–voltage protocol stepping from −60 mV to +50 mV. C) Current–voltage relationship of the traces shown in panel B.

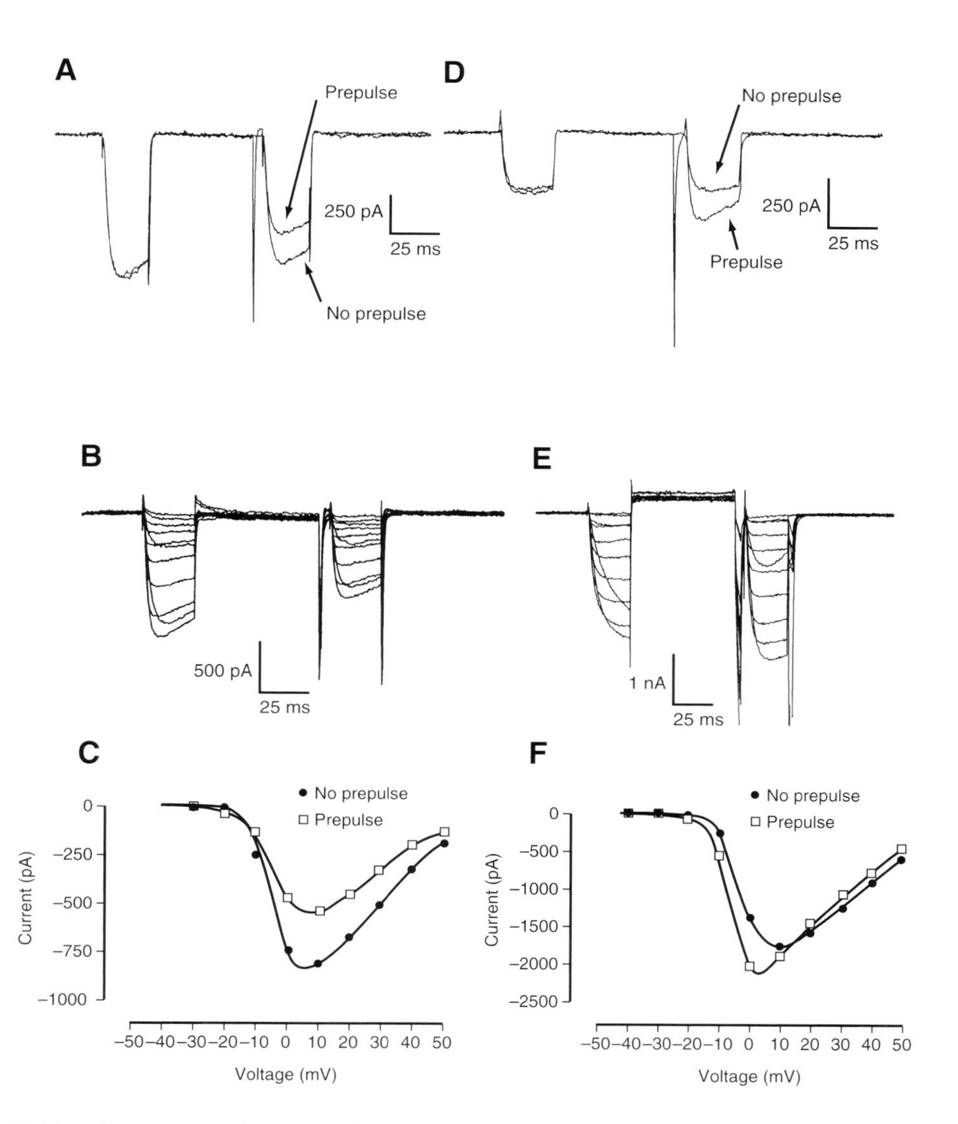

Fig. 5. Effect of $\beta_2\gamma_2$ overexpression on α_{1E} calcium currents stably expressed in HEK293 cells. A) Non-transfected cell. B) Current traces from the same cell as in panel A generated from a current–voltage protocol stepping from −60 mV to +50 mV, showing inhibition of current after a prepulse. C) Current–voltage relationship of traces shown in panel B to show the absence of shifts in peak current after a prepulse. D) $\beta_2\gamma_2$-transfected cell showing prepulse facilitation. E) Current traces showing facilitation after a prepulse; same voltage protocol as in panel D. F) Current–voltage relationship of traces displayed in panel E.

κ-opioid receptors into the cells also produced very little κ-agonist-induced inhibition of the calcium current (see Toth et al.[20]). Transfection of Y1, Y2 or Y4 NPY receptors did afford a significant voltage-dependent response to NPY (Sun and Miller, unpublished observations). However, the magnitude of these responses was much smaller than those observed in α_{1B}-expressing cell lines. These results indicate that receptors and G proteins may regulate α_{1E} calcium channels less efficiently than α_{1B} channels.

These conclusions were further strengthened by further experiments carried out with GTPγS. In the experiments summarised in figure 3, currents were evoked every 20 s in HEK293 cells expressing either α_{1B} or α_{1E} subunits by applying the double-pulse voltage protocol with GTPγS, GDPβS or GTP in the patch pipette. In the case of α_{1E}, the magnitude of the calcium current following a prepulse was always reduced owing to voltage-dependent inactivation.[24] Nevertheless, a small degree of prepulse facilitation was apparent in these cells. However, this was much smaller than that observed in the identical cell line expressing α_{1B}.

The effects of overexpression of different G-protein subunits on α_{1E} currents were assessed. Results were qualitatively similar to those with α_{1B}. Thus, following overexpression of βγ subunits, the magnitude of α_{1E} currents increased rather than decreased when a prepulse was used (see fig. 5). Nevertheless, the magnitude of this prepulse facilitation was smaller than for α_{1B} currents. Overexpression of the three mutant α subunits or of β or γ subunits alone produced no effect.

E-52 cells exhibited changed characteristics after extensive passaging, with the appearance of a population of cells that exhibited prepulse facilitation, even when not perfused with GTPγS or manipulated in any way that might provoke facilitation. Because some antagonistic relationship has been reported between G-protein regulation and the β subunit of calcium channels,[25,26] it was thought possible that expression of the β subunit had declined in these cells. Indeed, after overexpression of the calcium channel β subunit in these high-passage E-52 cells, the population of facilitating cells was no longer evident (data not shown). Transient expression paradigms were used in an attempt to reproduce this phenomenon. After expression of the $\alpha_{1E}\beta_{1b}\alpha_2\delta$ subunit combination, calcium currents with similar properties to those normally found in E-52 cells were observed. Alternatively, expression of α_{1E} and $\alpha_2\delta$ without the β subunit resulted in currents that exhibited prepulse facilitation (data not shown).

Discussion

The regulation of voltage-sensitive calcium channels by receptors, G proteins and second messengers is a particularly important physiological feature. Regulation of this type allows cells to 'fine-tune' the moment-to-moment influx of Ca^{2+} that is important for the control of many vital cellular functions.[8,25] It is widely believed that receptor regulation of calcium channels in the nervous system forms the basis of presynaptic inhibition in many cases.[7,8,25] For example, Toth et al. demonstrated that the inhibition of N-type calcium channels in the terminals of sympathetic neurons correlated with the ability of NPY to inhibit synaptic transmission at sympathetic neuroeffector junctions.[9]

An important question concerns the molecular mechanisms underlying the ability of receptors to produce inhibition of calcium channels. It has been shown that the secretion of neurotransmitters is most frequently under the control of non-dihydropyridine-sensitive calcium currents, particularly those of the N and Q types.[9,10,13,14] Recent studies have indicated that it may be the $\beta\gamma$ subunits of heterotrimeric G proteins that transduce inhibitory signals to these channels.[22,23] We have previously demonstrated a considerable difference in the ability of G-protein-linked receptors to inhibit α_{1B} and α_{1E} calcium channels expressed in HEK293 cells.[20] Similar data obtained with the frog oocyte expression system have been published by Bourinet et al.[26] These authors demonstrated that coexpression of μ-opioid receptors with α_{1A} or α_{1B} channels gave robust opioid inhibition of calcium currents, whereas inhibition of α_{1E} currents was minimal. These data are of particular interest when the homologous structures of α_{1B} and α_{1E} channels are considered.[6,24]

The experiments reported above represent attempts to investigate any underlying difference in the propensity of α_{1B} and α_{1E} calcium channels to be regulated by G proteins. The data indicate that both types of channel can be inhibited by G-protein $\beta\gamma$ subunits in a voltage-dependent fashion. However, effects on the α_{1E} channel were smaller. As we have also shown, these differences may be connected with the relative abilities of the two types of channel to interact with calcium channel β subunits and G-protein $\beta\gamma$ subunits. We observed that α_{1E} channels which expressed in the absence of their β subunits behaved in a manner resembling channels that were inhibited by G proteins. Thus, we conclude that the calcium channel α_1 subunit normally behaves in this way and presumably exists in the 'unwilling' conformation.[27] It is therefore possible that the role of the G protein is to stabilise the channel in this conformation, whereas the role of the calcium channel β subunit is to stabilise the channel in the 'willing' conformation. It is therefore possible that the ability of receptors and G proteins to regulate calcium channels may depend, to some extent, on the identity of the β subunit associated with the calcium channel complex.

Acknowledgements

We thank Dr M. Harpold of SIBIA Neuroscience for the gift of cells stably expressing human α_{1E} and α_{1B} calcium channels. This work was supported by Public Health Service grants DA02121, DA02575, MH40165, NS33502, DK42086 and DK44840.

References

1. Birnbaumer L, Campbell KP, Catterall WA, et al. The naming of voltage-gated calcium channels. Neuron 1994; 13: 505–6
2. Perez-Reyes E, Schneider T. Calcium channels, structure, function and classification. Drug Dev Res 1994; 33: 295–318
3. Sheng ZH, Rettig J, Cook T, et al. Calcium dependent interaction of N type calcium channels with the synaptic core complex. Nature 1996; 379: 451–4
4. Reuter H. Measurement of exocytosis from single presynaptic nerve terminals reveal heterogeneous inhibition by Ca channel blockers. Neuron 1995; 14: 773–9
5. Wheeler DB, Randall A, Sather WA, et al. Neuronal Ca channels encoded by the α_{1A} subunit and their contribution to excitatory synaptic transmission. Prog Brain Res 1995; 105: 65–78
6. Williams ME, Brust PF, Feldman DG, et al. Structure and functional expression of a ω-conotoxin sensitive human N type calcium channel. Science 1992; 257: 389–95

7. Hille B. Modulation of ion channels by G protein coupled receptors. Trends Neurosci 1994; 17: 531–5
8. Miller RJ. The receptor mediated regulation of calcium channels and neurotransmitter release. FASEB J 1990; 4: 3291–300
9. Toth PT, Bindokas VP, Bleakman D, et al. Mechanism of presynaptic inhibition by neuropeptide Y at sympathetic nerve terminals. Nature 1993; 364: 635–9
10. Wheeler DB, Randall A, Tsien RW. Roles of N-type and Q-type Ca^{2+} channels in supporting hippocampal synaptic transmission. Science 1994; 264: 107–11
11. Rhim HW, Miller RJ. Opioid receptors modulate diverse types of calcium channels in the nucleus tractus solitarius of the rat. J Neurosci 1994; 14: 7608–15
12. Rhim HW, Toth PT, Miller RJ. Mechanism of inhibition of calcium channels in rat nucleus tractus solitarius by neurotransmitters. Br J Pharmacol 1996; 118: 1341–50
13. Scholz KP, Miller RJ. Developmental changes in presynaptic calcium channels coupled to glutamate release in cultured rat hippocampal neurons. J Neurosci 1995; 15: 4612–17
14. Scholz KP, Miller RJ. Presynaptic inhibition at excitatory hippocampal synapses: development and role of presynaptic Ca^{2+} channels. J Neurophysiol 1996; 76: 39–46
15. Westenbroek RE, Ahlijanian MK, Catterall WA. Clustering of L-type Ca^{2+} channels at the base of major dendrites in hippocampal pyramidal neurons. Nature 1990; 347: 281–4
16. Lipscombe D, Kongsamut S, Tsien RW. Alpha-adrenergic inhibition of sympathetic neurotransmitter release mediated by modulation of N-type calcium-channel gating. Nature 1989; 340: 639–42
17. Hirning LD, Fox AP, Miller RJ. Inhibition of calcium currents in cultured myenteric neurons by neuropeptide Y: evidence for direct receptor/channel coupling. Brain Res 1990; 532: 120–30
18. Diverse-Pierluissi M, Goldsmith PK, Dunlap K. Transmitter mediated inhibition of N type calcium channels in sensory neurons involves multiple GTP binding proteins and subunits. Neuron 1995; 14: 191–200
19. Slesinger PA, Reveun E, Jan YN, et al. Identification of structural elements involved in the G protein gating of the GIRK-1 potassium channel. Neuron 1995; 15: 1145–56
20. Toth PT, Shekter LR, Ma GH, et al. Selective G protein regulation of neuronal calcium channels. J Neurosci 1996; 16: 4617–24
21. Law SF, Yasuda K, Bell GI, et al. Gia3 and Goa selectively associate with the cloned somatostatin receptor subtype SSTR2. J Biol Chem 1993; 268: 10721–7
22. Ikeda SR. Voltage dependent modulation of N type calcium channels by G protein β/γ subunits. Nature 1996; 380: 255–8
23. Herlitze S, Garcia DE, Mackie K, et al. Modulation of Ca^{2+} channels by G-protein β/γ subunits. Nature 1996; 380: 258–62
24. Williams ME, Marubio LM, Deal CR, et al. Structure and functional characterization of neuronal α_{1E} calcium channel subtypes. J Biol Chem 1994; 269: 22347–57
25. Dolphin AC. Voltage dependent calcium channels and their modulation by neurotransmitters and G proteins. Exp Physiol 1995; 80: 1–36
26. Bourinet E, Soong TW, Stea A, et al. Determinants of the G protein dependent opioid modulation of neuronal calcium channels. Proc Natl Acad Sci U S A 1996; 93: 1486–91
27. Bean BP. Neurotransmitter inhibition of neuronal calcium channels by changes in channel voltage dependence. Nature 1989; 340: 153–6

Regulation of the density of T-type calcium current by growth hormone and insulin-like growth factor 1 in atrial myocytes

Philip M. Best, Chien-Chang Chen, Xiaoping Xu

University of Illinois, Department of Molecular and Integrative Physiology and the College of Medicine, Urbana, Illinois, USA

Summary

In many instances, the expression of T-type calcium current in cardiac myocytes in postnatal mammals is linked to periods of rapid growth or hypertrophy. While the regulatory factors governing the expression of the cardiac T-type current are unknown, recent work suggests that in rat atrial myocytes growth hormone (GH) plays a critical role in determining the density of this current. When adult rats are hormonally induced to re-enter an active growth phase by implantation of GH-secreting tumours, atrial T-type current density increases 3-fold. Similarly, during normal postnatal development, the density of T-type current in atrial myocytes is positively correlated with growth rate. The increase in current density results from an increase in the number of channels per unit membrane area rather than a change in single-channel current or open probability. These results identify the GH–insulin-like growth factor 1 axis as a physiologically important regulator of T-type channel expression. The functional implications of varying T-type current density during altered physiological states remain to be determined.

Cardiac muscle undergoes dramatic alterations in phenotype during normal development and in response to altered physiological conditions.[1] In many cases, these functional changes have been shown to result from alterations in the expression of muscle-specific genes coding for proteins involved in the regulation of contraction. During hypertrophy, in particular, changes in the expression of genes coding for ion channels result in significant alterations in the electrical responses of cardiac cells (action potential duration is typically increased in these tissues). The underlying changes in ionic currents may involve inward calcium or outward potassium currents, or both, depending on the experimental model studied.[2–6] Conversely, during normal postnatal growth, the action potential shortens as a result of alterations in calcium and potassium currents.[7,8]

The physiological stimulus for hypertrophy is a chronic increase in haemodynamic load. In cultured cells, a number of agents, including adrenergic agonists, endothelin-1, insulin-like growth factor 1 (IGF-1), transforming growth factor β (TGF-β) and fibroblast growth factor (FGF), mimic the effect of pressure overload, in that similar muscle-specific proteins are affected. The signalling mechanisms activated by these stimuli are diverse and include cAMP, Ca^{2+} and various protein kinases, including protein kinase A and protein kinase C.[9]

The potential importance of intracellular Ca^{2+} as a mediator of the cardiac hypertrophic response is suggested by the fact that an early elevation of intracellular Ca^{2+} is a common effect of many agents that induce hypertrophy. Several recent studies support this idea. Elevated intracellular Ca^{2+}, with no alteration of protein kinase A or C levels, is sufficient to produce hypertrophy in cultured ventricular myocytes.[10] Specific over-expression of calmodulin in cardiac myocytes caused cardiac hypertrophy in several transgenic mouse cell lines. The effect is specific for those regions expressing the fusion gene and is not caused by an inactive form of calmodulin. This suggests that increased Ca^{2+} buffering does not contribute to this effect.[11]

In mammalian cardiac myocytes, two types of calcium currents, designated 'T' and 'L', can be distinguished on the basis of their pharmacological and biophysical properties.[12–14] L-type current is believed to play an important role in excitation–contraction coupling in heart muscle. Ca^{2+} influx through these channels is both a trigger for sarcoplasmic reticulum Ca^{2+} release and a source of Ca^{2+} for sarcoplasmic reticulum refilling. The physiological role of the cardiac T-type calcium current is not completely understood. In mammals, T-type current is seen in atrial myocytes isolated from many species, but it accounts for a small fraction only of the total calcium current activated during an action potential in atrial cells. In mature ventricular cells, T-type calcium current is rare, being perhaps most prevalent in guinea-pig but absent in rat and many other animals.[15,16] A possible involvement of T-type current in the generation of the pacemaker potential has been proposed on the basis of the negative voltage range of its activation. If this is so, such currents may be involved in the setting of the firing threshold in Purkinje fibres and nodal cells. Another possible role for T-type calcium current is indicated by the observation that this type of current is transiently expressed in many actively growing cells. This relationship has been reported in many tissues and has led several authors to postulate a link between T-type current and cell growth, proliferation and/or differentiation.[12,17]

Consistent with these observations, the expression of T-type current in cardiac myocytes seems to be linked in some instances to periods of rapid postnatal growth or hypertrophy. Embryonic ventricular cells display robust T-type currents that are apparently lost during maturation.[18] However, T-type currents are re-expressed in cat ventricular myocytes during hypertrophy.[19] Growth hormone (GH) and IGF-1 are known to play significant roles in regulating cardiac growth in postnatal mammals. Exogenous administration of these agents enhances hypertrophy and cardiac function.[20–22] It is therefore of some interest to determine whether GH and/or IGF-1 are also involved in the regulation of the expression of T-type calcium channels and whether the activity of these channels plays a significant role in the adaptation of the heart to altered physiological states.

Many of the growth-promoting effects of GH on differentiated cells are thought to be mediated indirectly via IGF-1.[23] GH stimulates the secretion of IGF-1 by the liver, and circulating IGF-1 forms complexes with specific binding proteins in the blood. GH also stimulates local IGF-1 production in non-hepatic tissues, including cardiac muscle cells. Elevated IGF-1 mRNA levels in cardiac muscle have been reported during GH-induced hypertrophy in some,[24,25] but not all,[26] studies. In general, circulating levels of IGF-1 correlate with periods of somatic growth, being low at birth, rising to a maximum at about the time of puberty and declining with advanced age.

The IGF-1 receptor is a ligand-activated tyrosine kinase.[27] In a skeletal muscle cell line, IGF-1 induced mRNA for the c-*fos* proto-oncogene.[28] The mechanisms coupling receptor occupancy with mRNA induction are not known. One possible mechanism that has received some experimental support is the correlation of Ca^{2+} influx with the growth-promoting action of IGF-1. Treatment of 3T3 cells with IGF-1 causes increases in Ca^{2+} influx and DNA synthesis with the same dose–response relationship.[29] Using single-channel patch-clamp techniques, Kojima and co-workers recorded inward currents through a voltage-independent, IGF-1-activated ion channel.[29] Co^{2+}, a non-specific calcium channel blocker, inhibited channel activity in cell-attached patches and the IGF-1-induced increase in intracellular Ca^{2+} and DNA synthesis. These results strongly support the notion that an increase in Ca^{2+} influx and subsequent increase in cell Ca^{2+} concentration plays a necessary role in the mitogenic action of IGF-1 in 3T3 cells.

Although the effect of elevated Ca^{2+} in these cells is unclear, a number of Ca^{2+}-dependent enzyme systems have been described,[30] and expression of the c-*fos* proto-oncogene is known to be regulated by Ca^{2+}.[31] The effect of IGF-1 on cellular Ca^{2+} influx is not surprising, as it is well known that mitogens and growth factors alter ion channel expression and transmembrane ion flux in many cell types.[32] In a neuronal cell line, IGF-1 has been shown to increase voltage-dependent calcium currents via a protein kinase C-dependent pathway.[33] Similar effects of IGF-1 on calcium currents are seen in clonal pituitary cells.[34] These studies suggest that, at least in some cells, IGF-1 modifies cellular Ca^{2+} levels by regulating the expression or activity of plasmalemmal calcium channels.

To test the hypothesis that an increase in T-type calcium current expression is correlated with periods of GH-dependent cardiac hypertrophy, we have looked for changes in T-type current density in fully differentiated cardiac myocytes stimulated to re-enter an active growth phase.[5] Cardiac myocytes from mature Wistar-Furth rats with implanted, GH-secreting tumours were chosen as an experimental model. The plasma GH concentration increases dramatically in tumour-bearing animals, and this increase is accompanied by rapid somatic and visceral growth. Macroscopic T-type calcium currents were recorded using the whole-cell configuration of the patch-clamp technique. Since atrial myocytes display a second calcium current (the L-type current) with a different voltage-dependency of inactivation, variation of the holding potentials was used to separate the two types of current. Pharmacological analysis confirmed the identity of the currents and the efficacy of the approaches used to study them.

Our analysis showed that T-type currents were significantly increased in atrial myocytes isolated from hearts undergoing GH-induced growth. Peak T-type current density was, on average, 3 times as high in atrial cells from the tumour-bearing rats (–1.24 pA/pF) as in those from age-matched controls (–0.41 pA/pF). Current densities were compared to account for the significant increase in myocyte size that began to occur several weeks after tumour implantation. Interestingly, T-type current density began to increase about 2 weeks before any measurable change in bodyweight, heart weight or myocyte size (fig. 1).[5] The increase in T-type current was therefore considered to result most likely from the influence of a circulating growth factor or factors (most likely GH) released by the tumour, rather than from the haemodynamic effects that accompany significant changes in bodyweight. The change in density was specific for the T-type current; the L-type calcium current was unaffected. A change in the transient outward potassium current was also observed, but this seemed to be correlated with the altered haemodynamic load that developed as a result of elevated GH levels.[6] Thus, the prediction that a specific increase in atrial T-type current would accompany a period of active growth and cardiac enlargement in mature animals seems to be correct.

We have also investigated the possibility of a similar correlation between atrial T-type current density and growth during normal postnatal development. We studied the changes in atrial T-type currents in rats as they aged from 3.5 to 14.5 weeks (which spans the period of maximal growth in these animals).[35] T-type current density was closely correlated with growth rate and was found to peak slightly before (males) or simultaneously with (females) the peak in growth rate that occurs at about postnatal week 5 in these animals (fig. 2).[35] T-type current then declined with growth rate. These results demonstrate that the association between atrial T-type calcium current density and heart growth rate occurs physiologically during periods of normal postnatal development. The results from normally developing rats are quite similar to those in rats with GH-secreting tumours in that the changes in atrial calcium currents are specific for the T-type current (L-type current is unaffected). We did not measure the GH levels in the normally growing rats. However, previously published reports

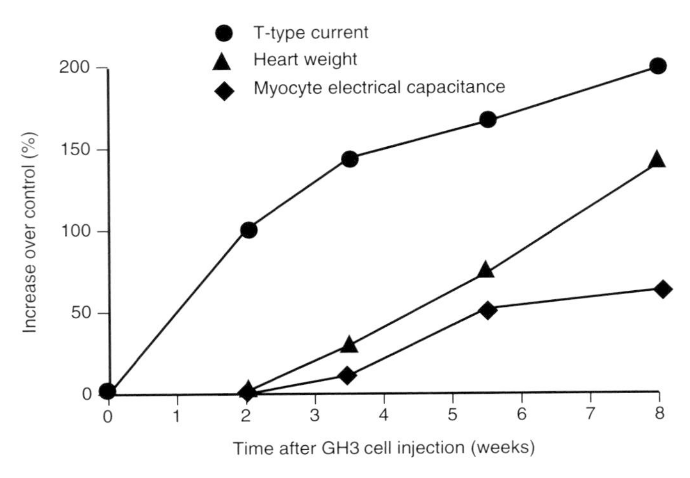

Fig. 1. Increase in atrial T-type current density in adult rats stimulated to re-enter a growth phase by the implantation of growth hormone-secreting tumours (reproduced with permission[5]).

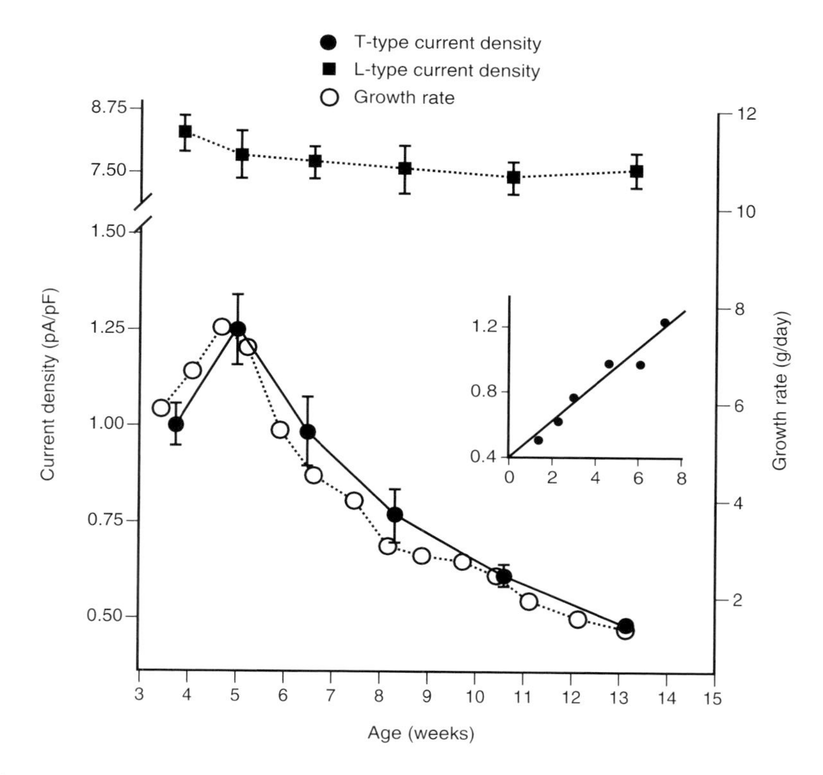

Fig. 2. Atrial myocyte T- and L-type current density and whole-animal growth rate as a function of postnatal age in female rats. Inset: correlation between T-type current density and growth rate. The correlation coefficient is 0.97 (reproduced with permission[35]).

suggest that plasma GH levels peak at about postnatal day 35 in rats,[36] which is similar to the time of maximal growth rate and T-type current density seen in this study.

The changes in macroscopic T-type current density described above could result from a number of different mechanisms. These include changes in channel density, single-channel conductance or channel open probability. To ascertain which of these mechanisms was involved, we measured single-channel conductance using fluctuation analysis.[35] The results showed that the single-channel current (about 0.12 pA in extracellular Ca^{2+} 5 mM) did not change (even with 5-fold variations in macroscopic current density) (fig. 3).[35] We also found that the voltage-dependency and kinetics of activation and inactivation of the macroscopic currents were unchanged in these cells. The simplest conclusion that may be drawn from these biophysical data is that the increase in macroscopic current density results from an increase in the number of T-type calcium channels per unit of membrane area. There is no direct evidence to suggest that either a new isoform of the channel with higher conductance is being expressed or that some modification of the channel has affected its conductance or gating. What is clear, however, is that the density of T-type calcium channel proteins in atrial myocytes is regulated hormonally, presumably by GH or IGF-1.

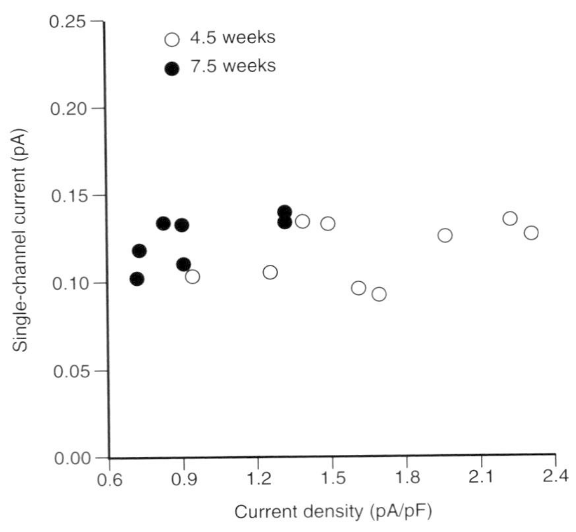

Fig. 3. T-type current density versus single-channel current in rat atrial myocytes using fluctuation analysis averaged about 0.12 pA (extracellular Ca^{2+} 5 mM) (reproduced with permission[35]).

To study the growth factor(s) and cellular mechanisms involved in the postnatal regulation of T-type current density, we have developed protocols for the short-term culture of acutely isolated atrial myocytes.[37] Single atrial myocytes are enzymatically isolated from 3-week-old rats. Our decision to use animals of this age was based on both empirical and theoretical considerations. Our goal is to study factors that influence T-type calcium channel expression postnatally, so we did not wish to use embryonic cells. We found, as is widely reported in the literature, that lower probabilities of obtaining successful primary cultures were associated with increased age. The major postnatal changes involving action potential shape, contractile protein isoform switching and related structural events are completed in atrial myocytes between postnatal weeks 2 and 3. Thus, cells isolated from 3-week-old rats are amenable to introduction into culture and can be considered as phenotypically 'adult' and therefore suitable for our experimental purposes. Once isolated, the cells are kept in a serum-containing medium (foetal bovine serum 10%) for 2 days. They are then placed in a serum-free medium for an additional day before electrophysiological recordings are made.

The expression of T-type calcium currents is stable in cells placed in serum-free conditions. We found that neither T-type calcium current density nor cell capacitance changed in cells cultured for 6 days after isolation (2 days in serum-containing media and 4 days in serum-free media). The average cell capacitance was 21.6 ± 0.4 pF (n=14) on culture day 4, compared with 20.2 ± 1.2 pF (n=6) on day 6. Peak T-type current density was –0.36 ± 0.03 pA/pF (n=9) and –0.56 ± 0.07 pA/pF (n=4) on days 4 and 6, respectively. These values are not significantly different either from one another or from values obtained from freshly isolated cells. This finding made possible the design of experiments to assess the role of individual growth factors in the regulation of the expression of T-type calcium currents.

We initially attempted to determine whether IGF-1 alters T-type current expression *in vitro*.[37] Similar to acutely isolated cells, cultured myocytes express both T- and L-type currents that can be separated by the use of different holding potentials. To assess the effects of IGF-1, we added 400 ng/ml to the culture medium at the end of day 4 (i.e. 48 hours after the cells had been washed and placed in serum-free conditions). Electrophysiological recording began on day 4, before the addition of IGF-1, and continued on days 5 and 6. Parallel cultures of cells, prepared by the same isolation procedure but not exposed to IGF-1, were used as paired controls. Our main findings were that peak T-type current density was significantly increased by day 5 in cells exposed to IGF-1 and that current density increased further by day 6. The increase in current density takes several hours to develop. This is unlike the more rapid effects seen with other agents and suggests that altered translational mechanisms might be involved. The effects of IGF-1 were specific for T-type current, and there was no consistent effect of added growth factor on the density, activation parameters or kinetics of the L-type current.

In summary, our findings indicate that in atrial myocytes acutely isolated from whole animals, there is a strong correlation between the density of T-type calcium current and periods of rapid cardiac growth induced by elevated serum GH levels. In primary cultures, a similar increase follows exposure of atrial cells to IGF-1. This indicates that this growth factor may be responsible for the increase seen physiologically. The physiological consequences of the increased T-type current density requires further clarification.

References

1. van Bilsen M, Chien KR. Growth and hypertrophy of the heart: towards an understanding of cardiac specific and inducible gene expression. Cardiovasc Res 1993; 27: 1140–9
2. Binal O, Rubinstein I, Gilat E. Effects of thyroid hormone on the action potential and membrane currents of guinea pig ventricular myocytes. Pflugers Arch 1987; 409: 214–16
3. Keung EC. Calcium current is increased in isolated adult myocytes from hypertrophied rat myocardium. Circ Res 1989; 64: 753–63
4. Kleiman RB, Houser SR. Outward currents in normal and hypertrophied feline ventricular myocytes. Am J Physiol 1989; 256: H1450–61
5. Xu X, Best PM. Increase in T-type calcium current in atrial myocytes from adult rats with growth hormone-secreting tumors. Proc Natl Acad Sci U S A 1990; 87: 4655–9
6. Xu X, Best PM. Decreased transient outward K current in ventricular myocytes from acromegalic rats. Am J Physiol 1991; 260: H935–42
7. Cohen NM, Lederer WJ. Changes in the calcium current of rat ventricular myocytes during development. J Physiol 1987; 406: 115–46
8. Kilborn MJ, Fedida D. A study of the developmental changes in outward currents of rat ventricular myocytes. J Physiol 1990; 430: 31–60
9. Morgan HE, Baker KM. Cardiac hypertrophy: mechanical, neural and endocrine dependence. Circulation 1991; 83: 13–25
10. McDonough PM, Glembotski CC. Induction of atrial natriuretic factor and myosin light chain-2 gene expression in cultured ventricular myocytes by electrical stimulation of contraction. J Biol Chem 1992; 267: 11665–8
11. Gruver CL, DeMayo F, Goldstein A, et al. Targeted development overexpression of calmodulin induces proliferative and hypertrophic growth of cardiomyocytes in transgenic mice. Endocrinology 1993; 133: 367–88
12. Bean BP. Two kinds of calcium channels in canine atrial cells. J Gen Physiol 1985; 86: 1–30
13. Vassort G, Alvarez J. Cardiac T-type calcium current: pharmacology and roles in cardiac tissue. J Cardiovasc Electrophysiol 1994; 5: 376–93

14. Hess P. Elementary properties of cardiac calcium channels: a brief review. Can J Physiol Pharmacol 1988; 66: 1218–23
15. Mitra P, Morad M. Two types of calcium channels in guinea pig ventricular myocytes. Proc Natl Acad Sci U S A 1986; 83: 5340–4
16. Nilius B, Hess P, Lansman JB, et al. A novel type of cardiac calcium channel in ventricular cells. Nature 1985; 316: 443–6
17. Kostyuk PG. Diversity of calcium ion channels in cellular membranes. Neuroscience 1989; 28: 253–61
18. Kawano S, DeHaan RL. Low threshold current is major calcium current in chick ventricular cells. Am J Physiol 1989; 256: H1505–8
19. Nuss HB, Houser J. T-type Ca current is expressed in hypertrophied adult feline left ventricular myocytes. Circ Res 1993; 73: 777–82
20. Stromer H, Cittadini A, Douglas PS, et al. Exogenously administered growth hormone and insulin like growth factor-1 alter intracellular Ca handling and enhance cardiac performance. Circ Res 1996; 79: 227–36
21. Yang R, Bunting S, Gillett N, et al. Growth Hormone improves cardiac performance in experimental heart failure. Circulation 1995; 92: 262–7
22. Duerr RL, Huang S, Miraliakbar HR, et al. Insulin-like growth factor-1 enhances ventricular hypertrophy and function during the onset of experimental cardiac failure. J Clin Invest 1995; 95: 619–27
23. Sara VR, Hall K. Insulin-like growth factors and their binding proteins. Physiol Rev 1990; 70: 591–614
24. D'Ercole AJ, Stiles AD, Underwood LE. Tissue concentrations of somatomedin C: further evidence for multiple sites of synthesis and paracrine and autocrine mechanisms of action. Proc Natl Acad Sci U S A 1984; 81: 935–9
25. Turner J, Rotwein P, Novakofski J, et al. Induction of mRNA for IGF-I and -II during growth hormone stimulated muscle hypertrophy. Am J Physiol 1988; 255: E513–17
26. Kupfer JS, Rubin JB. Differential regulation of insulin-like growth factor by growth hormone and thyroid hormone in the heart of juvenile hypophysectomized rats. J Mol Cell Cardiol 1992; 24: 631–9
27. Rubin JB, Shia MA, Pilch PF. Stimulation of tyrosine-specific phosphorylation *in vitro* by insulin-like growth factor 1. Nature 1983; 305: 438–40
28. Ong J, Yamashita S, Melmed S. Insulin like growth factor I induces c-fos messenger RNA in L6 rat skeletal muscle cells. Endocrinology 1987; 120: 353–7
29. Kojima I, Matsunaga K, Kurokawa K, et al. Calcium influx: an intracellular message of the mitogenic action of IGF-1. J Biol Chem 1988; 263: 16561–7
30. Cohen P. The role of protein phosphorylation in the hormonal control of enzyme activity. Eur J Biochem 1985; 151: 439–48
31. Tsuda T, Hamamori Y, Yamashita T, et al. Involvement of three intracellular messenger systems in the regulation of c-fos gene expression in Swiss 3T3 cells. FEBS Lett 1986; 208: 39–42
32. Soltoff SP, Cantley LC. Mitogens and ion fluxes. Annu Rev Physiol 1988; 50: 207–23
33. Kleppisch T, Klinz FJ, Hescheler J. Insulin like growth factor 1 modulates voltage dependent calcium channels in neuronal cells. Brain Res 1992; 591: 283–8
34. Selinfreund R, Blair AC. Insulin like growth factor 1 induces a rapid increase in calcium current and spontaneous membrane activity in clonal pituitary cells. Mol Pharmacol 1994; 45: 1215–20
35. Xu X, Best PM. Postnatal changes in T-type calcium current density in rat atrial myocytes. J Physiol 1992; 454: 657–72
36. Ojeda SR, Jameson HE. Developmental patterns of plasma and pituitary growth hormone (GH) in the female rat. Endocrinology 1987; 100: 881–9
37. Chen CC, Best PM. Effects of IGF-1 on T-type calcium currents in cultured atrial myocytes. FASEB J 1996; 10: A310

Molecular basis of drug interactions with calcium channels: a constructive approach

J. Mitterdorfer, S. Hering, S. Aczel, S. Berjukow, V. Degtiar, F. Döring, M. Grabner, R. Kraus, M.J. Sinnegger, J. Striessnig, Z. Wang, H. Glossmann

Institut für Biochemische Pharmakologie, Universität Innsbruck, Innsbruck, Austria

Summary

Pharmacological modulation of voltage-dependent L-type calcium channels is a major therapeutic principle in the treatment of cardiovascular disorders. The binding domains of the three commonly used classes of compounds (i.e. 1,4-dihydropyridines, phenylalkylamines and benzothiazepines) are located on the α_1 subunit of the hetero-oligomeric channel complex. We used gain-of-function chimeras, coexpressed with the auxiliary $\alpha_2\delta$ and β_{1a} subunits in Xenopus *oocytes, to identify defined regions within the L-type α_1 subunits that transfer 1,4-dihydropyridine, phenylalkylamine and benzothiazepine sensitivity to a drug-insensitive non-L-type calcium channel. The molecular determinants of these drug-binding domains were further delineated by using gain-of-function α_{1A} subunit mutants. Our findings indicate that the binding sites for 1,4-dihydropyridines, phenylalkylamines and benzothiazepines are located in close proximity to each other on the α_1 subunit. Moreover, they provide important information for the development of non-L-type calcium channel drugs that are potentially useful in the treatment of mental disorders, stroke and pain.*

Introduction

The function of voltage-dependent L-type calcium channels can be pharmacologically modulated by 1,4-dihydropyridines, phenylalkylamines and benzothiazepines (for a review, see Glossmann and Striessnig[1]). This feature is used therapeutically to treat cardiovascular disorders such as arrhythmia, hypertension and ischaemic heart disease.[2] It also represents a means of classification of calcium channels that can be used to distinguish L-type from T-, N-, P-, Q- and R-type channels.[3]

The sensitivity of L-type calcium channels to drugs or toxins is determined by the α_1 subunit, which is the principal, pore-forming constituent of a hetero-oligomeric complex consisting of at least an α_1, β and $\alpha_2\delta$ subunit (for a review, see Catterall[4]). Six different α_1 subunit genes have been isolated so far (for a review, see Hofmann et al.[5]). Class C, D and S α_1 subunits form drug-sensitive L-type calcium channels, whereas classes A, B and E (corresponding to P-/Q-, N- and R-type calcium channels, respectively) are considered to be insensitive to classical L-type calcium channel drugs, commonly referred to as 'calcium antagonists'.

The mechanism of action of dihydropyridine channel blockers (e.g. isradipine, nifedipine and nimodipine) is explained by a stabilisation of the inactivated state of the channel,[6] whereas dihydropyridine calcium agonists (e.g. BayK8644) promote the open state.[7] The efficacy of phenylalkylamines (e.g. devapamil, gallopamil) and benzothiazepines (e.g. diltiazem) as antiarrhythmic and antihypertensive drugs is related to their voltage- and use-dependent block of L-type calcium channels.[8] The binding domains of these drugs on the α_1 subunit are allosterically coupled to each other and a Ca^{2+} binding site[1] that has been identified as the calcium channel selectivity filter.[9,10] To fully understand how calcium channels are modulated by these drugs, the identification of amino acid residues that interact with each compound is required.

Biochemical studies addressed this task by combining photoaffinity labelling with antibody mapping and identifying defined regions within repeats III and IV of the L-type α_1 subunit that participate in the formation of the drug binding domains.[11–14] In subsequent work, recombinant DNA technology in conjunction with heterologous expression was used to construct chimeric or mutant calcium channels, which were monitored for loss of or reduction in drug sensitivity.[15–17]

In contrast to this 'screening for loss of function', we favoured a 'constructive' approach. This comprises a stepwise reduction of L-type sequence introduced into the background of a drug-insensitive α_{1A} subunit[18] until the minimum L-type sequence content necessary to sustain drug sensitivity is obtained. Using this method we were able to identify the minimum sequence requirements for dihydropyridine, phenylalkylamine and benzothiazepine sensitivity.[19–21]

Results and discussion

1,4-Dihydropyridine receptor

Minimum chimera AL12

From peptide mapping experiments[12,13] and a chimeric approach (in which the dihydropyridine sensitivity of the α_{1C} subunit was reduced by specific insertions of corresponding parts of a dihydropyridine-insensitive α_{1A} subunit[15]), the molecular determinants of dihydropyridine interaction with L-type calcium channel α_1 subunits have been shown to be located within transmembrane segments IIIS6, IVS6 and the S5–S6 linkers of repeats III and IV. Summarising these findings, we transposed the corresponding regions from the L-type α_{1S} subunit[22] into the dihydropyridine-insensitive α_{1A} subunit.[18] The resulting chimera AL1 (fig. 1 (A)) was insensitive to dihydropyridine agonist and antagonist modulation after coexpression with β_{1a}[24] and $\alpha_2\delta$[25] subunits in *Xenopus* oocytes.[19] This finding indicated that additional L-type sequence is required to elicit dihydropyridine modulation. Following these observations, we constructed a set of chimeras by expanding the L-type sequence content of AL1, followed by a stepwise reduction to obtain a dihydropyridine agonist- and antagonist-sensitive α_1 chimeric construct containing only a minimal quantity of L-type sequence. This yielded the 'minimum chimeras' (see fig. 1 (A)), referred to as 'AL12s' (L-type sequence from carp α_{1S}) and 'AL12h' (L-type sequence from α_{1C}).[26] The L-type sequence content of the AL12 constructs differed from AL1 only with respect to segment IIIS5 (see fig. 1 (A)), being derived from class A

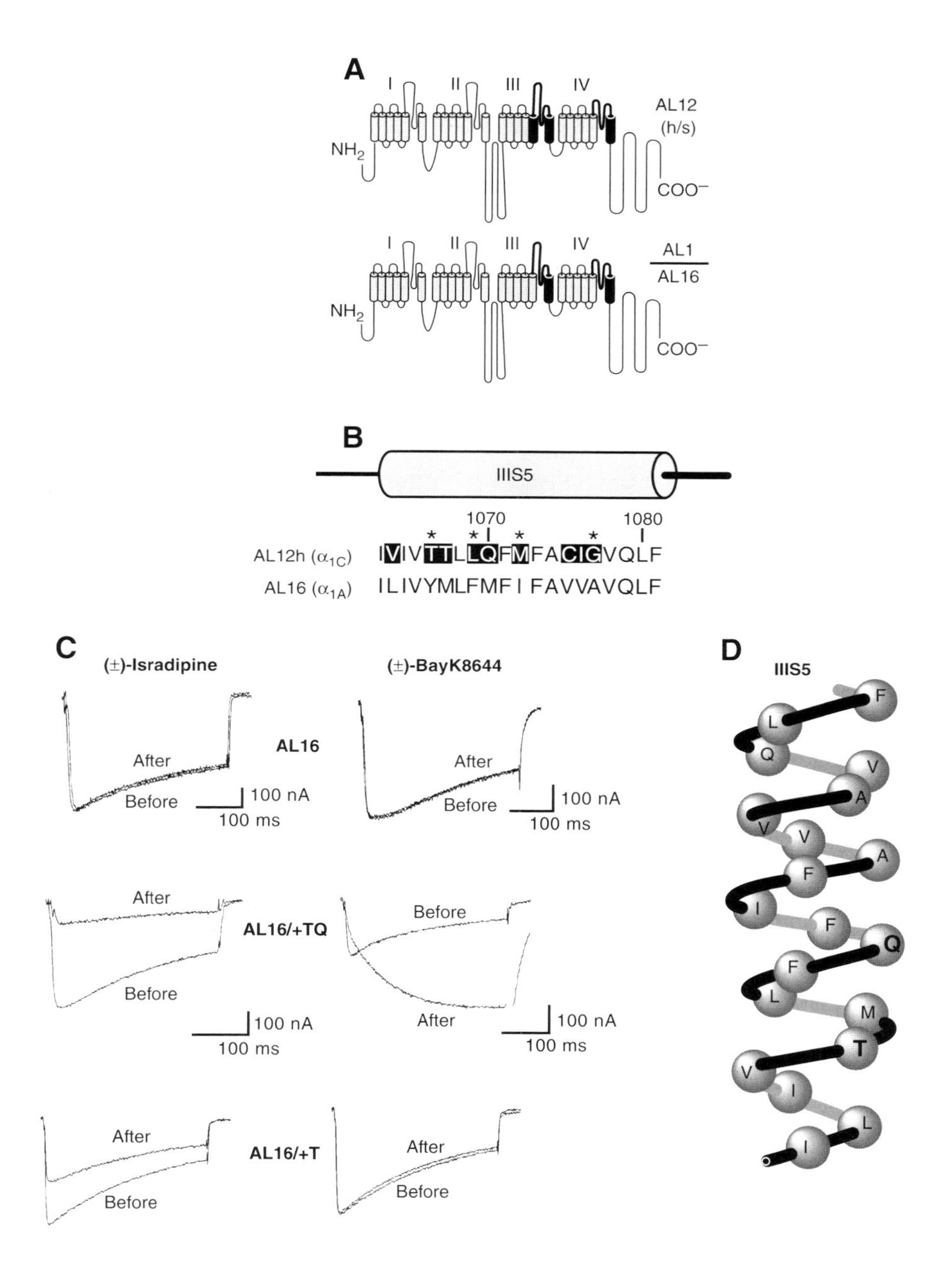

Fig. 1. Contributions of two amino acid residues in IIIS5 to dihydropyridine sensitivity. A) Schematic representation of α_1 subunit chimeras AL12h, AL12s, AL1 and AL16. Light grey segments and thin lines represent sequence from dihydropyridine-insensitive α_{1A}. L-type sequence stretches from dihydropyridine-sensitive α_{1C-a} are indicated by black segments and bold lines. B) Amino acid sequence alignment of IIIS5 segments from α_{1C-a} and α_{1A}. Non-conserved amino acid residues of α_{1C-a} are boxed. Asterisks indicate residues identical for all L- and non-L-type calcium channels cloned to date, but different between L- and non-L-type calcium channels. C) Barium current of AL16, AL16/+TQ and AL16/+T before and after exposure to 10 μM solutions of the dihydropyridine antagonists (±)-isradipine and (±)-BayK8644. Barium current was elicited by depolarisation to a test potential of 0 mV (antagonist) or –20 mV (agonist) from a holding potential of –80 mV. Representative current traces from at least 3 experiments are shown. D) α-helical model of segment IIIS5 of chimera AL16/+TQ. Amino acid residues (T and Q) interacting with dihydropyridine agonists and antagonists are indicated by bold letters. (Reproduced with permission.[23])

sequence in AL1 and L-type sequence in AL12. By applying our constructive approach we were therefore able to confirm the findings from peptide mapping experiments and to demonstrate for the first time the critical role played by IIIS5 in the determination of dihydropyridine sensitivity.[19]

The AL12 constructs, which comprise more than 90% class A sequence, were similar to α_{1A} subunits with respect to their current kinetics (fig. 2) and sensitivity to the peptide neurotoxin ω-Aga-IVA.[19] This suggested that introduction of L-type sequence into α_{1A} did not impair electrophysiological or pharmacological properties of class A channels. In contrast, dihydropyridine sensitivity of the minimum chimeras closely resembled L-type calcium channels as exemplified by AL12s (see fig. 2). Current increase by (±)-BayK8644 (see fig. 2 (A)) was associated with the typical shifts in the maxima of the current–voltage curves towards more negative potentials and changes in current kinetics found in wild-type α_1 subunits.[19] Current inhibition by isradipine was concentration-dependent, stereoselective (see fig. 2 (E & F)) and of similar apparent magnitude to current block mediated by α_{1C} (see fig. 2 (D)). Sensitivity of AL12s toward other calcium channel modulators was found for the enantiomers of the benzoxadiazol-dihydropyridine of 202-791 (see fig. 2 (C & D)) and for the benzoylpyrrole L-type calcium channel agonist FPL 64176 (see fig. 2 (G)). It has been suggested that FPL 64176 interacts with a site distinct from the dihydropyridine binding domain,[28,29] and sensitivity to this drug is absent in α_{1A}.[30] The introduction of FPL 64176 sensitivity into chimera AL12s (see fig. 2 (G)) suggests that critical determinants of the FPL 64176 and dihydropyridine binding domains are located in close proximity within the α_1 subunit.

In summary, these results demonstrate that an L-type α_1 sequence content of 9.4%, covering transmembrane segments IIIS5 and IIIS6 (including their connecting linker (pore loop), together with a second motif that consists of the IVS5–IVS6 linker plus transmembrane segment IVS6), is sufficient to induce sensitivity to dihydropyridine agonists and antagonists in α_{1A}.

Molecular determinants for dihydropyridine agonist and antagonist activity in transmembrane segment IIIS5

As demonstrated by the different dihydropyridine sensitivities of chimeras AL1 and AL12, transmembrane segment IIIS5 is crucial for the transfer of the dihydropyridine

Fig. 2. Electrophysiological and pharmacological properties of chimera AL12s. Typical recordings from at least 3 experiments are shown in each case. A & B) Families of currents recorded in Ba^{2+} 40 mM at test potentials from –30 to +10 mV from a holding potential of –80 mV are shown before (left) and after (centre) application of 10 µM of (±)-BayK8644 (A) or (±)-isradipine (B). The corresponding current–voltage curves (peak barium current) before and during drug application are also shown (right). C) Stereoselective inhibition of barium current through chimera AL12s 3–4 min after perfusion with solutions containing 1 µM of (+)- or (–)-isradipine. D) Concentration–response curves of (+)-isradipine and (–)-isradipine for inhibition of peak barium current carried by chimera AL12s, compared with the effects of (±)-isradipine on L-type chimera Lh. Data are means of 3 recordings (SEM <20%). IC_{50} values were calculated by fitting the experimental data to the general dose–response equation (slope factor = 1).[27] Lh (±)-isradipine: IC_{50} = 1.6 µM; AL12s (+)-isradipine: IC_{50} = 910 nM; AL12s (-)-isradipine: IC_{50} = 45 µM. E–G) Sensitivity of chimera AL12s to 10 µM solutions of the dihydropyridine agonist (+)-S202-791 (E), dihydropyridine antagonist (–)-S202-791 (F) and the non-dihydropyridine agonist FPL 64176 (G). Representative current traces recorded during depolarisation to a test potential of +10 mV from a holding potential of –80 mV (© 1995 Cell Press, reproduced with permission[19]).

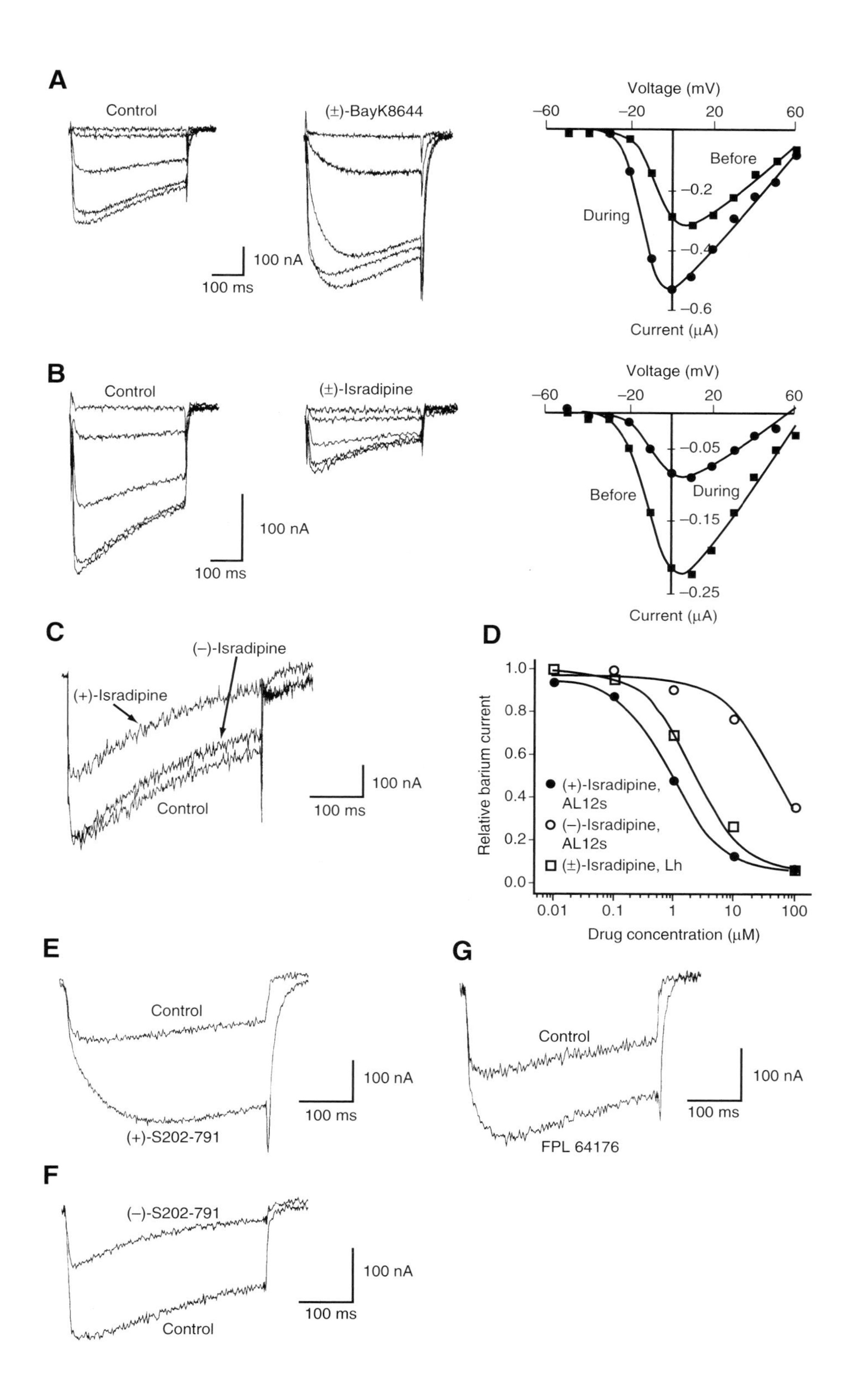
A
Control
(±)-BayK8644
100 nA
100 ms
Voltage (mV)
−60
−20
20
60
Before
During
−0.2
−0.4
−0.6
Current (μA)
B
Control
(±)-Isradipine
100 nA
100 ms
Voltage (mV)
−60
−20
20
60
−0.05
Before
During
−0.15
−0.25
Current (μA)
C
(−)-Isradipine
(+)-Isradipine
Control
100 nA
100 ms
D
Relative barium current
1.0
0.8
0.6
0.4
0.2
0.0
(+)-Isradipine, AL12s
(−)-Isradipine, AL12s
(±)-Isradipine, Lh
0.01
0.1
1
10
100
Drug concentration (μM)
E
Control
100 nA
100 ms
(+)-S202-791
G
Control
100 nA
100 ms
FPL 64176
F
(−)-S202-791
100 nA
100 ms
Control

sensitivity from L-type to class A calcium channels.[19] We employed site-directed mutagenesis to determine which L-type amino acid residues are responsible for dihydropyridine interaction within this segment.[23] AL16 was constructed as a dihydropyridine-insensitive parent chimera (see fig. 1 (A & B)) by replacing the L-type IIIS5 segment of AL12h (L-type sequence derived from α_{1C-a}) with the corresponding α_{1A} sequence. Like AL1 (L-type sequence derived from carp α_{1S}), AL16 was insensitive to dihydropyridine agonists and antagonists. To introduce dihydropyridine sensitivity into this chimera, 5 residues in the α_{1A}-derived IIIS5 segment of AL16 (Tyr-1393, Phe-1396, Met-1397, Ile-1399 and Ala-1404) were simultaneously replaced with their α_{1C} counterparts (Thr-1066, Leu-1069, Gln-1070, Met-1072 and Gly-1077). These residues were selected because each set is highly conserved within L-type and non-L-type IIIS5 segments, respectively. The resulting mutant AL17 did indeed display sensitivity to dihydropyridine agonists and antagonists that was comparable to that of the minimum chimera AL12h. A series of single-point mutations, where L-type amino acids reverted to α_{1A} residues, revealed that two amino acids in the IIIS5 segment of L-type calcium channels are essential for dihydropyridine sensitivity and possess different properties. While mutation T1066Y resulted in a complete loss of dihydropyridine agonist and antagonist modulation, Gln-1070 is required for an agonist effect and an increase in antagonist sensitivity. This was confirmed directly by introducing Thr-1066 only or Thr-1066 plus Gln-1070 (see fig. 1 (D)) into the class A IIIS5 segment of AL16, to give the mutants AL16/+T (Y1393T) and AL16/+TQ (Y1393T plus M1397Q).

As in wild-type α_{1C} subunits or our 'minimum chimera' AL12h, barium inward currents of AL16/+TQ were stimulated by the dihydropyridine agonist (±)-BayK8644 (10 μM), and the peak barium current was blocked by the dihydropyridine antagonist (±)-isradipine (10 μM) (see fig. 1 (C)). AL16/+TQ displayed the features of agonist modulation previously described for AL12s or native L-type currents.[31,32] BayK8644 increased barium inward current, slowed current activation, shifted the peak as well as the midpoint voltage of the current activation curve to more negative potentials[23] and slowed channel deactivation (see fig. 1 (C)). AL16/+T was unique with respect to its modulation by dihydropyridines. While (±)-isradipine 10 μM blocked the barium inward current, the agonist (±)-BayK8644 (10 μM) was clearly ineffective in stimulating it (see fig. 1 (C)). However, as a consequence of a decrease in dihydropyridine antagonist affinity, the extent of block by (±)-isradipine 10 μM was reduced compared with chimeras AL12h[23] or AL16/+TQ (see fig. 1 (C)). Nevertheless, both AL16/+TQ and AL16/+T were clearly stereoselective for the enantiomers of isradipine.[23]

The effects elicited by the (+) (agonist) and (–) (antagonist) enantiomers of the benzoxdiazol-dihydropyridine 202-791 were indistinguishable from those of (±)-BayK8644 and (±)-isradipine, respectively.[23] Like BayK8644, (+)-202-791 required Gln-1070 of AL16/+TQ to display the typical agonist effect.[23] The same was demonstrated for the benzoylpyrrole L-type calcium channel agonist FPL 64176, which is structurally unrelated to dihydropyridines. FPL 64176 (10 μM) activated the current through AL16/+ but not AL16/+T.[23] Since radioligand binding studies have shown a non-competitive interaction between FPL 64176 and dihydropyridines,[28,29] these drugs may interact with different residues in other regions of the dihydropyridine binding pocket. However, Gln-1070 seems to function as a common molecular determinant for the action of these channel activators.

In summary, threonine and glutamine residues in IIIS5 both participate in the formation of a fully functional dihydropyridine binding pocket. When simultaneously introduced into non-L-type IIIS5, these residues (Thr-1066 and Gln-1070) conferred dihydropyridine agonist and antagonist actions indistinguishable from dihydropyridine-sensitive wild-type α_1 subunits or AL12h.[23] Moreover, these residues contribute to dihydropyridine sensitivity in different ways: whereas threonine is an absolute requirement for dihydropyridine action, glutamine supported no dihydropyridine sensitivity in the absence of threonine but is required for an agonist effect and an increase in antagonist sensitivity.

These results suggest that Thr-1066 and Gln-1070, which are located in close vicinity on the same side of a putative α helix (see fig. 1 (D)), together form a crucial dihydropyridine interaction site within transmembrane segment IIIS5.

Phenylalkylamine and benzothiazepine receptor

Transfer of high sensitivity for phenylalkylamines and benzothiazepines from L-type to class A (BI) calcium channels

Phenylalkylamines such as verapamil or gallopamil and the benzothiazepine diltiazem (antiarrhythmic and antihypertensive drugs) modulate L-type calcium channels in a voltage- and use-dependent manner.[8] Yet the structural basis of the channel state-dependent interaction of phenylalkylamines and benzothiazepines with calcium channels remains unknown. Studies on cloned α_1 subunits of different calcium channel classes (C, B, A and E) have resulted in a more precise characterisation of their pharmacological features[33] and have revealed a weak phenylalkylamine sensitivity of class A calcium channels relative to L-type calcium channels.[20] The differing phenylalkylamine sensitivities of α_{1A} and α_{1C} or α_{1S} prompted us to transfer sequence stretches from α_{1S} to α_{1A} in an attempt to transfer phenylalkylamine sensitivity. Indeed, implantation of segment IVS6 from α_{1S} into α_{1A} produced an enhancement of phenylalkylamine sensitivity of the resulting α_{1A}/α_{1S} chimera.[20]

To identify the molecular determinants of the high-affinity benzothiazepine interaction domain of L-type calcium channels, we again applied the 'constructive' approach and introduced sequence stretches or single amino acids of the L-type IVS6 segment into α_{1A}. As with phenylalkylamine sensitivity, the diltiazem sensitivity of the resulting α_1 chimeras was measured as use-dependent barium current block after coexpression with β_{1a}[24] and $\alpha_2\delta$[25] in *Xenopus* oocytes. Barium current with our L-type chimera Lh[19] was more efficiently blocked by D-*cis*-diltiazem than by the L-*cis* diastereomer. Class A calcium channels were only weakly sensitive, and blockade by diltiazem was not enantiomer-selective.[21]

The first L-type/class A chimera examined for benzothiazepine sensitivity was AL12h, which was sensitive to dihydropyridine agonists and antagonists (see figs 1 (A) and 2 (A)). AL12h was also sensitive to D-*cis*-diltiazem. Barium current block was use-dependent and comparable to Lh. Removal of L-type sequence from transmembrane segment IIIS5 (chimera AL1) and IIIS6 plus the IIIS5–IIIS6 linker (chimera AL22) did not affect sensitivity to D-*cis*-diltiazem.[21]

Three amino acids transfer phenylalkylamine and benzothiazepine sensitivity to the α_{1A} subunit

Three amino acids of the L-type IVS6 were previously identified as high-affinity determinants for phenylalkylamine action (Y1463, A1467 and I1470 of α_{1C-c}).[16] As shown in figures 3 and 4, transfer of these L-type residues into α_{1A} (to give the triple mutant AL25) was sufficient to induce high sensitivity for both D-*cis*-diltiazem and the phenylalkylamine (–)-gallopamil into the class A channel.

The impact of each of these amino acid substitutions (I1804Y, S1808A and M1811I) on channel block by D-*cis*-diltiazem and (–)-gallopamil was studied in the respective double mutants. Mutants AL25/-Y, AL25/-A and AL25/-I (see fig. 3 (A)) all displayed significantly ($p<0.01$) less current inhibition by D-*cis*-diltiazem 100 μM or (–)-gallopamil 100 μM relative to AL25, which suggests a contribution by each of these amino acids to calcium channel block by benzothiazepines and phenylalkylamines (see fig. 3 (B)).

To study possible differences between benzothiazepine and phenylalkylamine interactions with pore-forming IVS6 residues, we investigated the effect of an additional substitution (F1805M) in AL25-yielding chimera AL25/M (see fig. 3 (A)). This mutation induced a more pronounced use-dependent barium current inhibition by (–)-gallopamil 100 μM compared with chimera AL25. In contrast, block by D-*cis*-diltiazem 100 μM remained at the level of chimera AL25 (see fig. 3 (B)). This suggested a contribution of Met-1387 (numbering refers to carp α_{1S}) for phenylalkylamine but not for benzothiazepine interaction. We subsequently studied chimera AL25/-Y,M, where the L-type (α_{1S}) Tyr-1386 was mutated to the class A Ile-1804 (see fig. 3 (A)). Indeed, chimera AL25/-Y,M was more efficiently blocked by (–)-gallopamil 10 μM than by D-*cis*-diltiazem 10 μM (fig. 5 (A–D)), which indicates that in addition to Tyr-1386, Ala-1390 and Ile-1393, Met-1387 forms part of the phenylalkylamine interaction site but has no detectable impact on use-dependent calcium channel blockade by D-*cis*-diltiazem.

Our results demonstrate that the characteristics of stereospecific use-dependent L-type calcium channel block by diltiazem and of L-type sensitivity for phenylalkylamines can be transferred to α_{1A} by three putatively pore-orientated L-type amino acids of IVS6 (I1804Y, S1808A and M1811I) identical to previously identified high-affinity determinants of L-type calcium channel block by phenylalkylamines.[16] Met-1387 of the L-type IVS6 appeared to be more important for use-dependent channel block by gallopamil than for diltiazem, which suggests

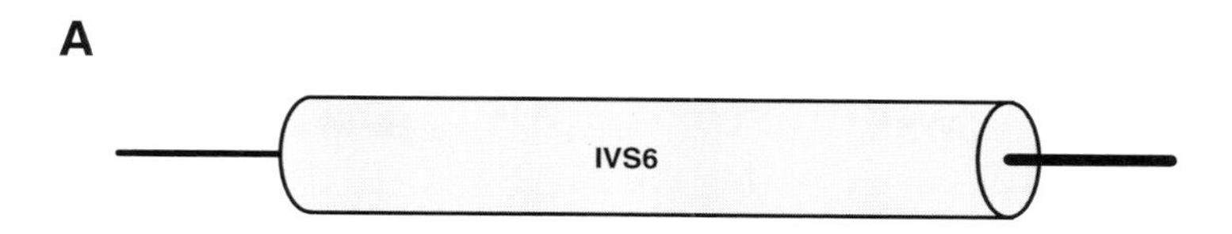

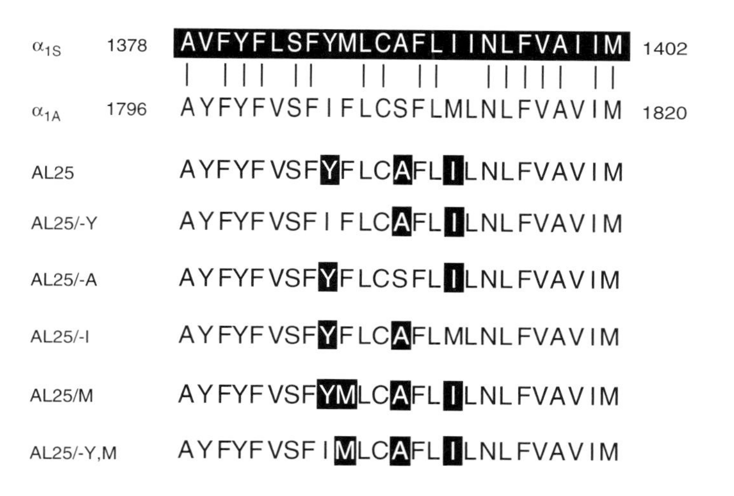

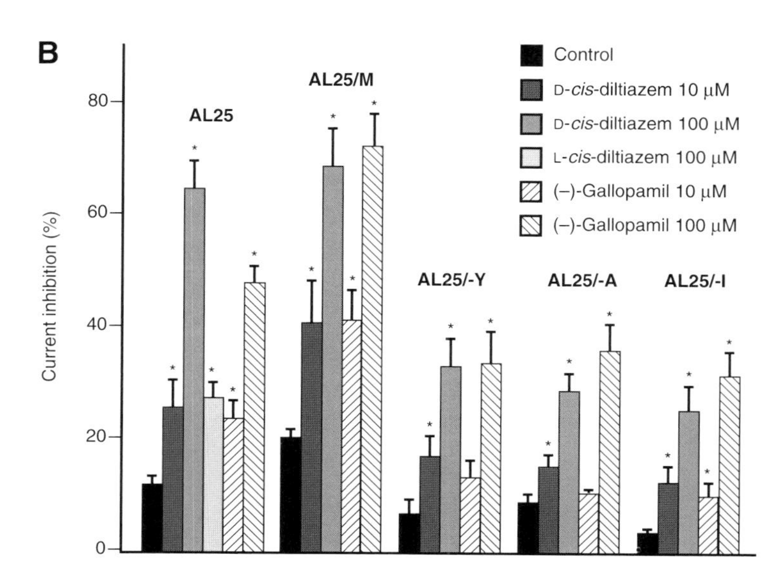

Fig. 3. Contribution of individual L-type amino acids in transmembrane segment IVS6 for benzothiazepine and phenylalkylamine sensitivity. A) Sequence alignment of transmembrane segments IVS6 of the carp skeletal muscle α_{1S}, the class A α_{1A} subunit and α_{1A}/α_{1S} chimeras AL25, AL25/-Y, AL25/-A, AL25/-I, AL25/M and AL25/-Y,M. L-type amino acids inserted into α_{1A} are highlighted. B) Use-dependent barium current inhibition by D*-cis-diltiazem 10 and 100 μM or* L*-cis-diltiazem (100 μM) during 15 test pulses (mean ± SEM, n=4–13), compared with peak current decay in control. Hatched columns represent use-dependent barium current inhibition of the chimeras by (–)-gallopamil 10 and 100 μM. * p<0.01 for barium current block versus control. Tonic barium current inhibition by 100 μM was less than 10% (not shown). (Reproduced with permission.[21])*

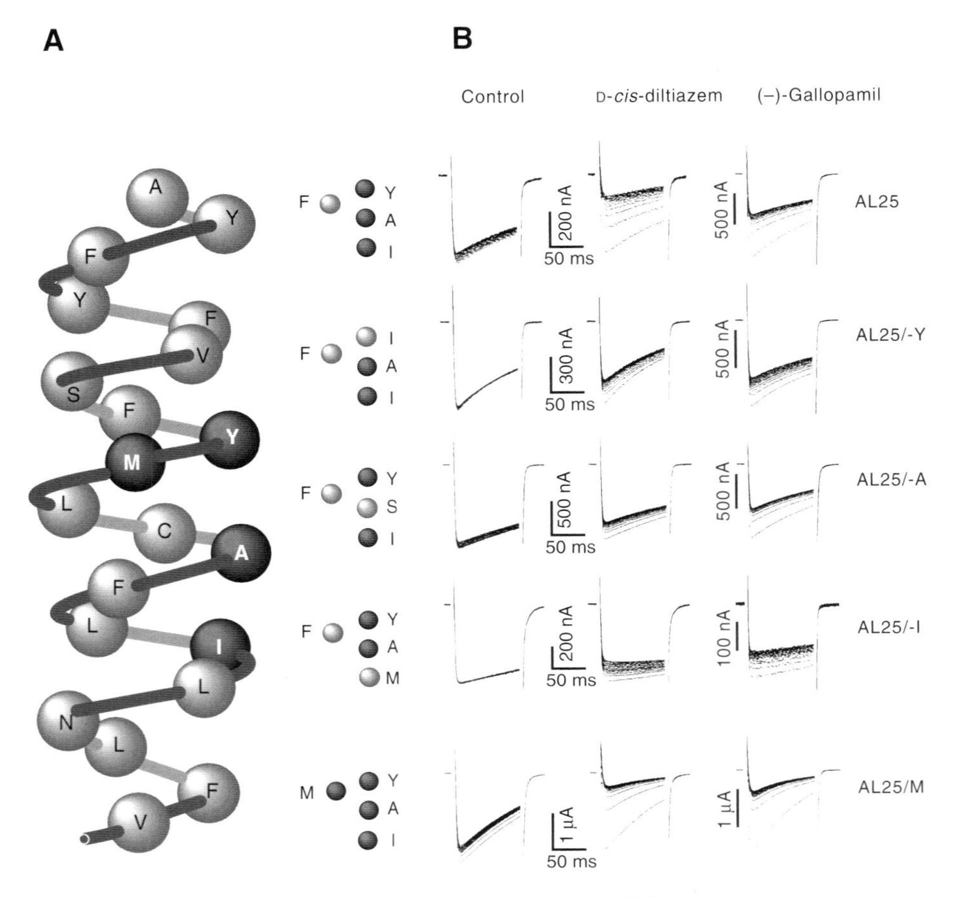

Fig. 4. Contribution of individual L-type amino acids in transmembrane segment IVS6 for benzothiazepine and phenylalkylamine sensitivity. A) Positions of the amino acid residues required for transfer of diltiazem and gallopamil sensitivity from L-type α_1 to α_{1A} subunit in an α-helical model of transmembrane segment IVS6 of AL25 mutants. Amino acids are indicated in single-letter code and the crucial residues (Y, A, I, M) are highlighted. B) Typical barium current recordings of AL25 and AL25-deduced chimeras (see panel A and schemes on the left). Currents during the control pulse train (left), corresponding currents during a train of pulses in D-cis-diltiazem 100 µM (centre) and typical use-dependent block of barium current in the presence of (–)-gallopamil 100 µM (right). All recordings were made at a holding potential of –80 mV and test pulses applied to 20 mV. Note the different time-course of current inactivation in the control traces of AL25 and related chimeras. (Reproduced with permission.[21])

that the L-type calcium channel receptor domains for phenylalkylamines and benzothiazepines have common but not identical molecular determinants in repeat IVS6. The partial overlap of high-affinity determinants for benzothiazepine, phenylalkylamine and dihydropyridine[17,34] action in IVS6 (see fig. 5 (E)) provides the molecular basis for previously described non-competitive interactions between these drug receptors.[1]

Amino acids critical for calcium channel block by diltiazem and gallopamil affect current inactivation of class A channels

Interestingly, the transfer of segment IVS6 from the slowly inactivating L-type chimera L_S to α_{1A} did not result in a transfer of the slower L-type inactivation kinetics

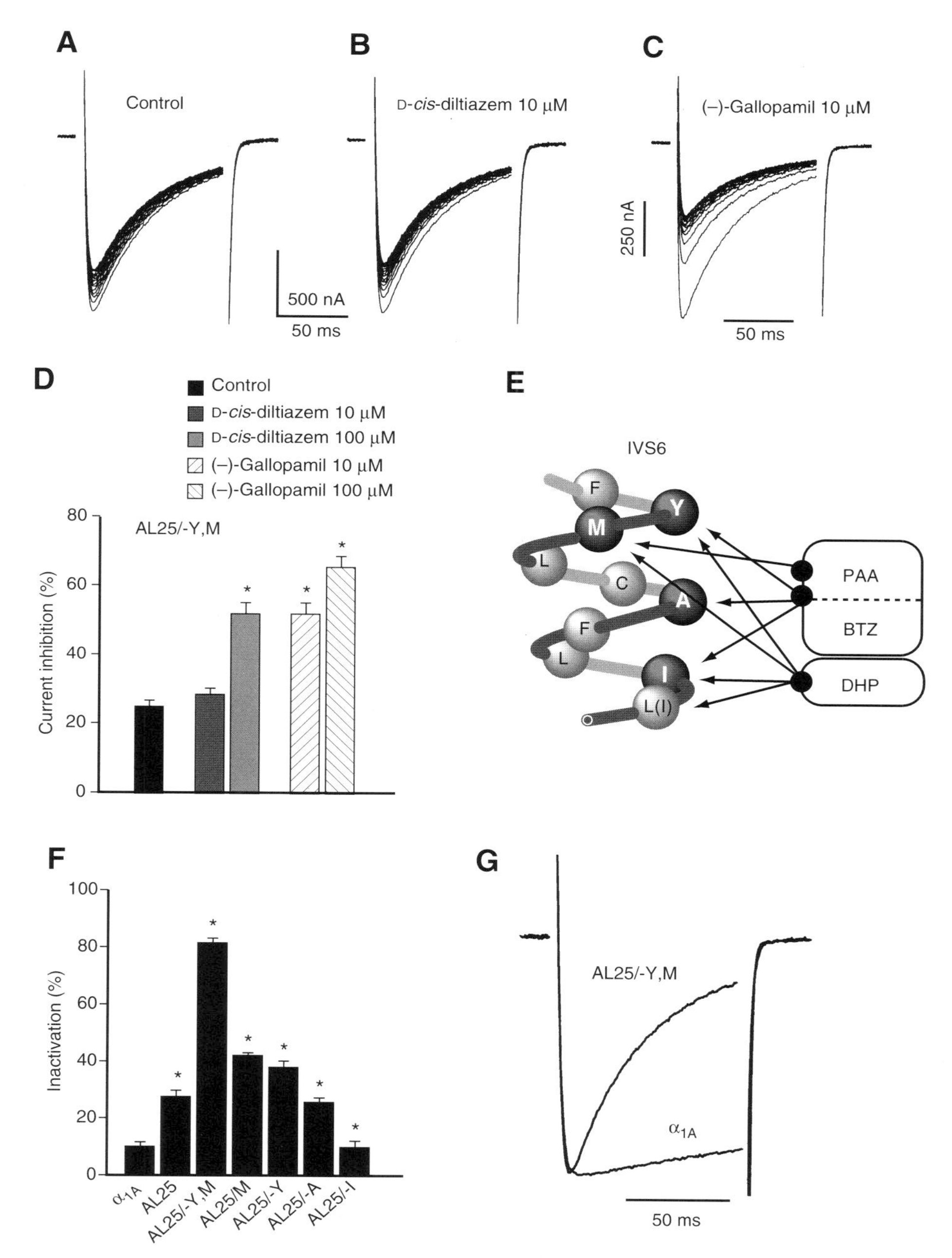

Fig. 5. Single-point mutations in transmembrane segment IVS6 of class A calcium channels affect inactivation kinetics and calcium channel block by (–)-gallopamil. Barium current of mutant AL25/-Y,M. A) During a train of 100 ms pulses applied at 0.1 Hz from –80 mV to 20 mV in the absence of drug. B) Currents of AL25/-Y,M in the presence of D-cis-*diltiazem 10 µM. C) (–)-Gallopamil 10 µM induced significantly more barium current block of AL25/-Y,M than* D-cis-*diltiazem 10 µM. D) Use-dependent peak barium current inhibition of AL25/-Y,M (mean ± SEM, n=7–13) by* D-cis-*diltiazem 10 and 100 µM or (–)-gallopamil 10 and 100 µM compared with peak current decay in the absence of drug (control); * $p<0.01$ for barium current block versus control. E) Schematic α-helical representation of amino acid sequence Phe-1803 to Leu-1812 of the IVS6 segment of α_{1A} (light grey) with substituted putative pore-orientated L-type amino acids (dark grey) participating in high-affinity interaction with benzothiazepine (BTZ) and/or*

(continued overleaf)

to the faster-inactivating α_{1A}; rather, it accelerated the inactivation kinetics relative to those of α_{1A}.[20] This finding illustrated a scenario where kinetic properties of calcium channels are not simply transposed by swapping corresponding sequences between different α_1 subunits, as was previously shown for structural elements of repeat I.[35] On the one hand, the replacement of IVS6 by an L-type sequence accelerated dramatically the time-course of inactivation whereas, on the other hand, removal of the L-type IVS6 and the IVS5-S6 linker from chimera AL12h dramatically slowed the inactivation rate in chimera AL20. Removal of L-type IIIS6 and the IIIS5–S6 linker from chimera AL1 also substantially accelerated inactivation in the resulting chimera AL22.[20,21]

By making use of our diltiazem- and gallopamil-sensitive calcium channel chimeras (see figs 3 and 4), we analysed the impact of individual amino acid changes in IVS6 on the time-course of current inactivation in more detail. As shown in panels F and G of figure 5, mutation of only three putatively pore-lining amino acids (AL25/-Y,M) (see fig. 5 (G)) resulted in an acceleration of current inactivation comparable to chimera AL23[20] and chimera DB18[35], in which nine α_{1E} amino acids implanted into α_{1A} accelerated inactivation properties to a similar extent. Taken together, our data indicate that individual putatively pore-lining residues in IVS6 of α_{1A} are involved in inactivation gating of class A calcium channels. Interestingly, mutations in S6 regions of repeats I or III also affect inactivation kinetics of calcium channels (see Tang et al.[15] and Zhang et al.[35]), which suggests that non-covalent interactions between the putative pore-lining S6 segments (and possibly pore-forming regions in the S5–S6 linkers) participate in voltage-dependent inactivation of calcium channels.

Conclusion

By using recombinant DNA technology combined with functional expression in *Xenopus* oocytes, we were able to identify the minimum structural requirements for sensitivity of calcium channels to the three major classes of calcium channel modulators. The special feature of our approach was the transfer of the molecular determinants that are critical for drug interaction to a drug-insensitive calcium channel α_1 subunit. We chose drug-sensitive L-type α_1 subunits (α_{1S} and α_{1C}) as donor molecules, and the α_{1A} subunit, which displays weak or no sensitivity at all to the different chemical classes of drugs studied, as the acceptor subunit. The construction of chimeras between these pharmacologically distinct α_1 subunits enabled us to reduce in a stepwise fashion the transplanted L-type sequence content

(fig. 5 continued)
*phenylalkylamine (PAA). Amino acids contributing to phenylalkylamine and dihydropyridine (DHP) action were identified by Hockerman et al.[16] and Peterson et al.[17] F) Comparison of barium current inactivation of mutant AL25/-Y,M with wild-type class A, AL25, AL25/M, AL25/-Y, AL25/-A and AL25/-I, measured as barium current decay during a 100 ms test pulse from –80 mV to 20 mV; * p<0.01 for acceleration of current inactivation versus class A channel barium current (n=4–9). Holding potential –80 mV (A–D), pulses applied to 20 mV. G) Representative normalised barium current traces of the mutant AL25/-Y,M and wild-type class A calcium channels illustrate the effect of 3-point mutations in segment IVS6 on the time-course of current inactivation. Holding potential –80 mV and test pulse potential 20 mV for all experiments shown. (Reproduced with permission.[21])*

in the α_{1A} environment until a minimum motif for drug interaction with voltage-dependent calcium channels was obtained. In the case of phenylalkylamine and benzothiazepine interaction, the transfer of as few as three amino acids (Tyr-1463, Ala-1467 and Ile-1470), located in transmembrane segment IVS6, was sufficient to generate a drug-sensitive α_{1A} subunit. From recent work carried out by several groups,[17,23,34] at least nine L-type amino acid residues contained within transmembrane segments IIIS5, IIIS6 and IVS6 are expected to be required for dihydropyridine sensitivity.

Our findings do not, however, preclude interaction of the drug molecule with additional amino acids that are homologous with α_{1A} and L-type α_1 subunits. One striking example for this is Tyr-1463 in transmembrane segment IIIS6, which was identified by alanine mutagenesis and essentially contributes to dihydropyridine sensitivity,[17] even though this amino acid is entirely conserved between L-type and non-L-type α_1 subunits. For several reasons the identification of such residues is difficult. Alanine-scanning mutagenesis[36] can be successfully carried out but requires a large number of point mutations. Another possible approach consists of the construction of chimeras analogous to AL12, but with a different dihydropyridine-insensitive α_1 subunit (e.g. α_{1B}) as a host sequence. The high level of sequence homology among non-L-type α_1 subunits is the main impediment to this approach.

In accordance with biochemical drug–channel interaction data, the S6 segments of repeats III and IV represent privileged regions for pharmacological modulation of voltage-dependent L-type calcium channels. Similarly, in sodium channels, the IVS6 segment of the α subunit carries the receptor domain for local anaesthetics[36] and, in close proximity, elements of a putative hydrophobic receptor site for an inactivation gate.[37] We found a comparable situation for segment IVS6 of voltage-dependent calcium channel mutants, where putatively pore-orientated amino acid residues not only form drug binding sites for benzothiazepines, phenylalkylamines and dihydropyridines but also affect inactivation (see fig. 5 (F & G)). It is therefore tempting to speculate that amino acids which participate in stabilisation of the calcium channel molecule in a closed, inactivated conformation are structurally suited to the support of channel blockade by calcium antagonists.

In summary, we were able to identify the minimum sequence requirements for dihydropyridine, phenylalkylamine and benzothiazepine interaction with calcium channel α_1 subunits. This demonstrates the validity and value of a constructive approach to complement and extend findings obtained by methods that rely on removing drug sensitivity by the construction of drug-insensitive chimeras or alanine-scanning mutagenesis. This information on the structural basis of drug interaction, combined with the identification of structural determinants underlying the molecular mechanism of voltage-dependent channel gating, will eventually generate a refined picture of calcium channel function.

Acknowledgements

We thank Drs Y. Mori and K. Imoto for the gift of the α_{1A} cDNA, Dr A. Schwartz for providing the α_{1C-a} and $\alpha_2\delta$ cDNA, and B. Kurka and D. Kandler for expert technical assistance. This work was supported by grants P-12689-MOB (H.G.), S 6601 (H.G.), S 6602 (J.S.) and S 6603 (S.H.) of the Fonds zur Förderung der Wissenschaftlichen Forschung (FWF). We thank Dr Traut (Knoll AG, Ludwigshafen, Germany) for providing the phenylalkylamine (–)-gallopamil. D-*cis*- and L-*cis*-enantiomers of diltiazem were kindly provided by Dr Satzinger (Goedecke AG, Germany).

References

1. Glossmann H, Striessnig J. Molecular properties of calcium channels. Rev Physiol Biochem Pharmacol 1990; 114: 1–105
2. Triggle DJ. Calcium-channel antagonists: mechanisms of action, vascular selectivities, and clinical relevance. Cleve Clin J Med 1992; 59: 617–27
3. Birnbaumer L, Campbell KP, Catterall WA, et al. The naming of voltage gated calcium channels. Neuron 1994; 13: 505–6
4. Catterall WA. Structure and function of voltage-gated ion channels. Annu Rev Biochem 1995; 64: 493–531
5. Hofmann F, Biel M, Flockerzi V. Molecular basis for Ca^{2+} channel diversity. Annu Rev Neurosci 1994; 17: 399–418
6. Bean BP. Nitrendipine block of cardiac calcium channels: high-affinity binding to the inactivated state. Proc Natl Acad Sci U S A 1984; 81: 6388–92
7. Hess P. Calcium channels in vertebrate cells. Annu Rev Neurosci 1990; 13: 337–56
8. Lee KS, Tsien RW. Mechanism of calcium channel blockade by verapamil, D600, diltiazem and nitrendipine in single dialysed heart cells. Nature 1983; 302: 790–4
9. Mitterdorfer J, Sinnegger MJ, Grabner M, et al. Coordination of Ca^{2+} by the pore region glutamates is essential for high-affinity dihydropyridine binding to the cardiac Ca^{2+} channel α_1 subunit. Biochemistry 1995; 34: 9350–5
10. Peterson BZ, Catterall WA. Calcium binding in the pore of L-type calcium channels modulates high affinity dihydropyridine binding. J Biol Chem 1995; 270: 18201–4
11. Striessnig J, Glossmann H, Catterall WA. Identification of a phenylalkylamine binding region within the α1 subunit of skeletal muscle Ca^{2+} channels. Proc Natl Acad Sci U S A 1990; 87, 9108–12
12. Nakayama H, Taki M, Striessnig J, et al. Identification of 1,4 dihydropyridine binding regions within the α1 subunit of skeletal muscle calcium channels by photoaffinity labeling. Proc Natl Acad Sci U S A 1991; 88: 9203–7
13. Striessnig J, Murphy BJ, Catterall WA. Dihydropyridine receptor of L-type Ca^{2+}-channels: identification of binding domains for [^{3}H](+)-PN200-110 and [^{3}H]azidopine within the α1 subunit. Proc Natl Acad Sci U S A 1991; 88: 10769–73
14. Kraus R, Reichl B, Kimball SD, et al. Identification of benz(othi)azepine-binding regions within L-type calcium channel α1 subunits. J Biol Chem 1996; 271: 20113–18
15. Tang S, Yatani A, Bahinski A, et al. Molecular localization of regions in the L-type calcium channel critical for dihydropyridine action. Neuron 1993; 11: 1013–21
16. Hockerman GH, Johnson BD, Scheuer T, et al. Molecular determinants of high affinity phenylalkylamine block of L-type calcium channels. J Biol Chem 1994; 270: 22119–22
17. Peterson BZ, Tanada TN, Catterall WA. Molecular determinants of high affinity dihydropyridine binding in L-type calcium channels. J Biol Chem 1996; 271: 5293–6
18. Mori Y, Friedrich T, Kim MS, et al. Primary structure and functional expression from complementary DNA of a brain calcium channel. Nature 1991; 350: 398–402
19. Grabner M, Wang Z, Hering S, et al. Transfer of 1,4-dihydropyridine sensitivity from L-type to class A (BI) calcium channels. Neuron 1996; 16: 207–18
20. Döring F, Degtiar VE, Grabner M, et al. Transfer of L-type calcium channel IVS6 segment increases phenylalkylamine sensitivity of α1A. J Biol Chem 1996; 271: 11745–9
21. Hering S, Aczel S, Grabner M, et al. Transfer of high sensitivity for benzothiazepines from L-type to class A (BI) calcium channels. J Biol Chem 1996; 271: 24471–5
22. Grabner M, Friedrich K, Knaus HG, et al. Calcium channels from *Cyprinus carpio* skeletal muscle. Proc Natl Acad Sci U S A 1991; 88: 727–31
23. Mitterdorfer J, Wang Z, Sinnegger MJ, et al. Two amino acid residues in the IIIS5 segment of L-type calcium channels differentially contribute to 1,4-dihydropyridine sensitivity. J Biol Chem 1996; 271: 30330–5

24. Ruth P, Roehrkasten A, Biel M, et al. Primary structure of the beta subunit of the DHP-sensitive calcium channel from skeletal muscle. Science 1989; 245: 1115–18
25. Ellis SB, Williams ME, Ways NR, et al. Sequence and expression of mRNAs encoding the α_1 and α_2 subunits of a DHP-sensitive calcium channel. Science 1988; 241: 1661–4
26. Mikami A, Imoto K, Tanabe T, et al. Primary structure and functional expression of the cardiac dihydropyridine-sensitive calcium channel. Nature 1989; 340: 230–3
27. DeLean A, Munson PJ, Rodbard D. Simultaneous analysis of families of sigmoid curves: application to bioassays, radioligand assay and physiological dose–response curves. Am J Physiol 1978; 4: E97–102
28. Kunze DL, Rampe D. Characterization of the effects of a new Ca^{2+} channel activator, FPL 64176, in GH3 cells. Mol Pharmacol 1992; 42: 666–70
29. Ginap T, Dooley DJ, Feuerstein TJ. The non-dihydropyridine L-type voltage-sensitive calcium channel activator FPL 64176 enhances K(+)-evoked efflux of [^{3}H]norepinephrine from rat neocortical slices. Neurosci Lett 1993; 156: 35–8
30. Sather WA, Tanabe T, Zhang JF, et al. Distinctive biophysical and pharmacological properties of class A (BI) calcium channel α1 subunits. Neuron 1993; 11: 291–303
31. Kass RS. Voltage-dependent modulation of cardiac calcium channel current by optical isomers of Bay K 8644: implications for channel gating. Circ Res 1987; 61: 1–5
32. Hering S, Hughes AD, Timin EN, et al. Modulation of calcium channels in arterial smooth muscle cells by dihypropyridine enantiomers. J Gen Physiol 1993; 101: 393–410
33. Bezprozvanny I, Tsien RW. Voltage-dependent blockade of diverse types of voltage-gated Ca^{2+} channels expressed in *Xenopus* oocytes by the Ca^{2+} channel antagonist mibefradil (Ro 40-5967). Mol Pharmacol 1995; 48: 540–9
34. Schuster A, Lacinova L, Klugbauer N, et al. The IVS6 segment of the L-type calcium channel is critical for the action of dihydropyridines and phenylalkylamines. EMBO J 1996; 15: 2365–70
35. Zhang JF, Ellinor PT, Aldrich RW, et al. Molecular determinants of voltage-dependent inactivation in calcium channels. Nature 1994; 372: 97–100
36. Ragsdale DS, McPhee JC, Scheuer T, et al. Molecular determinants of state-dependent block of Na^+ channels by local anesthetics. Science 1994; 265: 1724–8
37. McPhee JC, Ragsdale DS, Scheuer T, et al. A mutation in segment IVS6 disrupts fast inactivation of sodium channels. Proc Natl Acad Sci U S A 1994; 91: 12346–50

Addendum

The construction of a functional 1,4-dihydropyridine interaction domain by mutational conversion of only a few amino acid residues has been accomplished for α_{1E} (Ho et al. Mol Pharmacol 1997; 52: 735–40) and for α_{1A} (Sinnegger et al. J Biol Chem 1997; 272: 27686–93). In addition, the link between inactivation and use-dependent calcium channel block by phenylalkylamines has been established (Hering et al. Proc Natl Acad Sci U S A 1997; 94: 13323–8).

Block of L- and T-type calcium channels in vascular muscle cells by mibefradil

Kent Hermsmeyer

Oregon Regional Primate Research Center and Departments of Medicine and Cell and Developmental Biology, Oregon Health Sciences University, Beaverton, Oregon, USA

Summary

The search for functions of the enigmatic transient T-type calcium channel has taken an important first step. Characterisation of the new calcium antagonist mibefradil shows that it is a selective T-type calcium channel blocker with inhibitory actions on blood vessel wall thickening. The advantages of T-type calcium channel blockade putatively include vascular selectivity, freedom from negative cardiac inotropism, consistent and predictable reduction in heart rate, reduction of subendothelial proliferation, and vasodilator effectiveness independent of depolarisation state. Mibefradil as the selective prototype increases coronary blood flow without increasing myocardial oxygen consumption, and by decreasing heart rate (and thus time spent in diastole) improves subendocardial and small artery perfusion. Improved perfusion of the myocardial wall and lowered heart rate may normalise underlying pathophysiological factors and provide long-term protection. Therefore, mibefradil at least, and possibly other T-type calcium channel blockers to follow, is markedly different from the fast-onset, short-duration L-type calcium antagonists recently criticised and may offer an excellent solution to the several flaws that beset currently available calcium antagonists. If these interpretations should prove correct, T-type calcium channel blockade would securely address these criticisms and extend the possibility for negative modulation of vascular muscle calcium signals by offering the promise of significant cardiovascular protective benefits in long-term treatment of hypertension and angina pectoris.

Introduction

Cardiovascular disorders are the most common cause of death in Western civilisation, but calcium antagonists have allowed major improvements in the management of cardiovascular disease.[1] Our first expectation of calcium antagonists is that they are effective vasodilators, lowering blood pressure and relieving vasoconstriction without compromising heart function or interfering with the nervous or endocrine systems. Calcium antagonists have proved quite effective for this purpose, and they enjoy considerable popularity as antihypertensive and antianginal drugs.[2]

However, in addition to assessing calcium antagonists as vasodilators, it is important to consider effects of therapy over many years. In the ideal case, calcium antagonists should decrease cardiovascular risks significantly, reducing both the incidence of the diseases and the proportion of deaths from cardiovascular diseases. The vascular limitations of the presently available calcium antagonists include vasodilation as the only significant action, and weak inhibition of proliferation, and thus lack of long-term protective function. Cardiac limitations include depression of contractility, reflex activation of the sympathetic drive that accelerates heart rate and results in increased O_2 demand by the myocardium, and an increased risk of arrhythmias.

Calcium antagonists have not been as successful as angiotensin-converting enzyme (ACE) inhibitors in reducing wall thickness, implying that mechanisms in addition to inhibition of Ca^{2+} entry might be important for the intended reduction of the wall:lumen ratio.[3] Since the major complications of hypertension with adverse prognostic significance in both humans and animals are blood vessel and left ventricular wall thickening, the wall:lumen ratio is an issue of major importance in the long-term protection of the cardiovascular system against catastrophic events.[4] It is important to ask what the mechanism of protection is, and why calcium antagonists have been less effective than ACE inhibitors as judged by the important criterion of effect on wall thickness.

Published reports on the existing calcium antagonists raise the question: 'Why should calcium antagonists (which lower blood pressure as effectively as ACE inhibitors) be less cardioprotective, as defined by a decreased incidence of myocardial infarction and sudden heart deaths?'[5] The most apparent answers to that question are found in the weaknesses listed above. All of the existing calcium antagonists when used at therapeutic concentrations act solely or primarily on L-type calcium channels.[5–8] Thus, the result of the almost immediate fall in blood pressure associated with taking these drugs is a reflex activation of the sympathetic nervous system with an increase in heart rate.[9,10] Practical limits of the currently available vasodilators are, in fact, the consequence of increased activation of the powerful sympathetic accelerator drive to the heart. Certainly, tachycardia is an unwanted effect when cardioprotection is considered.[10] Furthermore, reduction of the thickness of the blood vessel wall, by prevention of the vascular remodelling which is associated with hypertension, is a most desirable action that appears to be lacking in L-type calcium channel blockade.[11,12]

One hypothesis is that the remodelling signal is the key to predicting cardiovascular risk.[3] The corollary is that prevention of remodelling should have a major cardioprotective effect against hypertension and its sequelae.[13,14] Remodelling (as the form of hypertrophy that occurs in genetic hypertension) is the increase in wall thickness by rearrangement of the same number of cells into more layers, resulting in increased wall:lumen ratio,[15] and thus increased risk of cardiovascular disease and death.[10] The cellular mechanisms for control of thickening are not known but probably involve Ca^{2+} and protein kinase C.[16,17] T-type calcium channels have recently been discovered to be associated with growth or remodelling.[18,19] In embryonic and neonatal animals, there is a high density of T-type calcium channels in cardiac and vascular muscle cells.[20,21] In adults, T-type calcium channels are only found in the ventricle when there is hypertrophy.[19,21] In subcultures of cell lines, there is also an association of T-type calcium channels with proliferation. For example, subculture of American Type Culture Collection (ATCC) CCL 226 cells, which are notable for a high proliferation rate, contain one of the highest known densities of T-type calcium channels.[22] These cells, derived from mouse embryo mesangial tissue appear appropriate as a useful model in which to investigate features of embryonic-stage blood vessels and heart cells. If T-type calcium channels were shown to promote vascular remodelling, perhaps blockade of these channels would prove a therapeutic mechanism for preventing increased wall:lumen ratios in hypertension, and thus offer cardioprotection.

Calcium channels in the cardiovascular system

Of the several identified types (L, N, P, Q, R and T) of calcium channels, only the T- and L-types are found in cardiac and vascular muscle cells.[6–8] Several features distinguish these two major calcium channel types in the cardiovascular system. Representative example traces of low-voltage-activated (LVA) T- and high-voltage-activated L-types of calcium currents are shown in fig. 1. T-type calcium channel currents activated by small depolarisations are found in the upper three traces in panel A, and pure L-type calcium channel currents activated by larger depolarisations are found in panel B. These two types of cardiovascular system calcium channels are readily differentiated by voltage dependencies (threshold and peak current voltages), kinetics, single-channel conductance, permeability to Ba^{2+} ions and pharmacology, as summarised in table I.[6–8] The LVA T-type calcium channel current at the –20 mV depolarisation in panel A is notably smaller than the L-type calcium channel current in panel B at +20 mV (there is no T-type calcium channel contribution in this trace because the –30 mV holding potential completely inactivates T-type calcium channels).

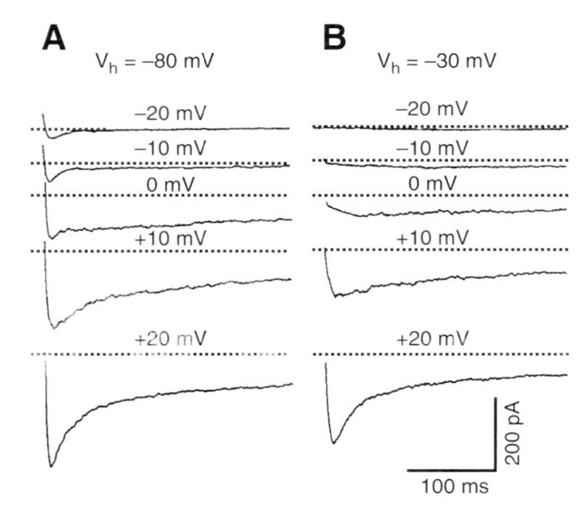

Fig. 1. Individual barium current traces from a rat vascular muscle cell illustrate the two types of calcium channel currents (T and L type). Small, transient responses (low-voltage-activated currents) are shown in the top two traces of panel A, representing depolarisations to –20 and –10 mV from the holding potential (V_h) at –80 mV. The lower three traces in panel A are depolarisations to 0, +10 and +20 mV (from the same –80 mV holding potential), which activate the combination of T- and L-type barium current. The less negative –30 mV holding potential in panel B isolates L-type calcium channels by inactivating the T-type channel, and depolarisations to –20, –10, 0, +10 and +20 mV trigger pure L-type barium current. The dotted line represents 0 current in each trace, and downward indicates inward current. (Reproduced with permission.[23])

Table I. Properties of calcium channels in rat vascular muscle cells

Property	T type	L type
Voltage domain for activation	–60 to +10 mV	–30 to +60 mV
Voltage for >95% inactivation	–30 mV	+20 mV
Width at half maximum	35 ms	>500 ms
Deactivation time constant	5 ms	0.2 ms
Single-channel conductance	7 pS	22 pS
Ba^{2+}:Ca^{2+} permeability	1.0	3.5
DHP concentration for 50% block	>100 μM	1 μM
Other names	Transient, tiny	Long-lasting, large

Abbreviation: DHP = dihydropyridine.

L-type calcium channels have been studied far more extensively than T-type calcium channels and virtually all generalisations about calcium channels have been made on the basis of these studies. L-type calcium channels are closely correlated with signalling and modulating the strength of contractions. It is because existing calcium channel blockers act on L-type calcium channels that there is the extensive base of knowledge about this important membrane signal mechanism, as exemplified in many recent reviews.[1,2,5–8,16,24–26] Abundant L-type calcium channels are found in virtually all excitable cells, including skeletal, cardiac, smooth muscle, nerve, pituitary, adrenal and other endocrine cells, as well as connective tissue cells (fibroblasts), and they are extensively described in the cited reviews.

The appearance of T-type calcium channels is associated with development or growth of both vascular and cardiac muscle cells, and they are found in spontaneously active blood vessels and the pacemaker cells of the sinoatrial and atrioventricular nodes.[6,7,19] Based on the association of T-type calcium channels with pacemaker and remodelling functions, hypotheses have been developed based on each correlation. The powerful voltage-clamp approach and the rapid time-course of pacemaker potentials allow definitive establishment of T-type calcium channel currents as an important pacemaker mechanism.[6,26] However, at present there is only weak evidence that T-type calcium channels are the signal for cardiac or vascular growth, proliferation, development and remodelling. On the other hand, the membrane signals for proliferation in general, and remodelling specifically, remain unknown. In fact, T-type calcium channels provide the most likely known candidate for the remodelling signal.[18] However, the interplay of membrane signals may be important, as there is also evidence that vascular muscle cell growth can be inhibited by blockade of only L-type calcium channels.[27] The density of T-type calcium channel currents is significantly increased in extremely hypertensive, stroke-prone rats.[20] It has been suggested that a combination of T- and L-type calcium channels may be important as the signal for remodelling in vascular muscle cells.[27] If this hypothesis is correct, a dynamic balance of T- and L-type calcium channels may be important for long-term blood vessel regulation. T-type calcium channels are limited in their distribution and only appear under certain conditions (such as remodelling), whereas the distribution of L-type calcium channels is very wide.[6,8] The distribution of cell types with T-type calcium channels, and the functional states in which they are found, will probably prove important in the solution to the puzzle of the function of T-type calcium channels.

Further differentiation of L- and T-type calcium channel functions are of interest, especially where such functions have a direct clinical relevance. For example, selectivity for blood vessels in preference to heart tissue allows vasodilator efficacy without the complication of cardiac depression. Specificity for coronary arteries would be particularly useful. Thus, it is important to ask: 'What might be the basis for selectivity of action on vascular muscle versus cardiac muscle?' It is instructive to consider the possible basis for selective actions on blood vessels. For example, there might be:

i) different functional roles of calcium channels (especially T-type calcium channels) in excitation–contraction coupling
ii) different combinations of T-type versus L-type calcium channels, and/or
iii) differences in resting membrane potential between vascular muscle cells and cardiac muscle cells.

Additional explanations might include:

iv) a smaller range (–60 to 0 mV) of voltage excursions in vascular muscle cells than cardiac muscle cells
v) vascular muscle cell binding sites with higher affinity than cardiac muscle, and/or
vi) intracellular Ca^{2+} release and other mechanisms that may be more important for excitation–contraction coupling in vascular muscle cells than in cardiac muscle cells.

Various calcium antagonists have been partially selective for vascular muscle cells, with depressant actions on cardiac contraction limited to less than 50% of that on vascular muscle, when measured as percentage force reduction.[2,6,24] Drugs such as amlodipine and felodipine are considered to show high vascular selectivity.[5,24] However, none of the popular calcium antagonists are entirely free of negative inotropic effects at concentrations that dilate coronary arteries maximally.[2,28] Thus, there is a continuing need for development of calcium antagonists that approach the ideal of achieving maximum coronary vasodilation without significant cardiodepression. This seemingly elusive goal may now become possible. The major criterion will be selective inhibition of vascular muscle cell contraction without inhibition of cardiac muscle contraction. T-type calcium channel blockade can be hypothesised as one basis for vascular selectivity. When T-type calcium channel blockade is combined with excitation–contraction coupling and voltage-dependency differences between vascular and cardiac muscle, a feasible model for targeted action on vascular muscle emerges.

Selectivity for vascular muscle cells on the basis of inhibition of T-type calcium channels was a prediction made at the time of discovery of the two membrane ion channel types.[29] Although the functions of T-type calcium channels can only be hypothesised until a specific T-type calcium antagonist is discovered, several important signals (such as vascular remodelling) remain potential candidates for modulation by this channel. T-type calcium channels found in spontaneously depolarising cardiac and vascular cells have the correct voltage domains and kinetic properties to explain pacemaker depolarisations, and thus have been associated with pacemaker function.[6,8,19,26] There are therefore indications that block of T-type calcium channels might be useful therapeutically where decreased spontaneous frequency is desirable. Furthermore, there are suggestions that blockade of T-type calcium channels may block vascular remodelling (see the introduction to this chapter). With the arrival of the novel calcium antagonist mibefradil (Ro 40-5967), such predictions about the selectivity of a specific T-type calcium channel blocker have become possible to test.[23]

Mechanism of action of mibefradil (Ro 40-5967)

Mibefradil is an effective vasodilator with remarkable freedom from cardiac negative inotropism.[28,30] To determine the effects of mibefradil on individual calcium channel currents (e.g. barium currents) in vascular muscle cells, membrane potential was first stepped from –80 mV to –20 mV (the identifying protocol for LVA calcium channels), and pure T-type barium current resulted (fig. 2 (A)).[23] Mibefradil reduced this current to practically zero (see fig. 2 (A)). This action is unique to mibefradil, at least at calcium antagonist concentrations that are therapeutically useful.

Furthermore, when holding potential was –30 mV, the step to +20 mV (the protocol for activation of L-type calcium channels) revealed partial blockade of the barium current by mibefradil (see fig. 2(B)). Barium current measured in the presence of

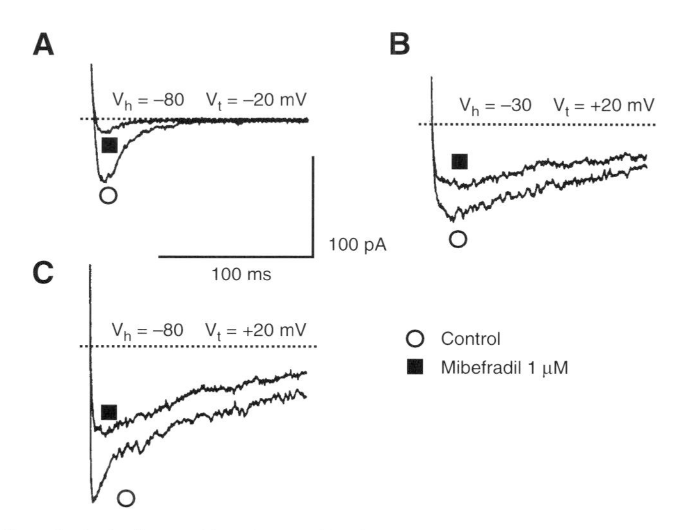

Fig. 2. A & B) Effect of mibefradil on T- (A) and L-type (B) calcium channel barium current. C) Composite of both T- and L-type currents. While the T-type calcium currents were inhibited by 80% after 5 min of exposure to mibefradil 1 μM, L-type calcium currents were inhibited by only about 25% even 3 min later. All tracings are from the same vascular muscle cell. V_h = holding potential; V_t = test potential. (Reproduced with permission.[23])

mibefradil was significantly smaller than the control current, but the trace was similar in shape. Mibefradil-blocked currents fell rapidly from the peak, parallel to the control L-type currents in both early peak and subsequent sustained phases. The fractional inhibition of late-phase current amplitude indicates the extent to which mibefradil blocked L-type calcium channels. Thus mibefradil (1 μM) blocked L-type channels by about 25–30% but blocked >95% of T-type calcium channel currents and inhibited contraction. Therefore, there was a lesser degree of L-type than T-type calcium channel blockade, and mibefradil was shown to exhibit T-type calcium channel selectivity.

Selective T-type calcium channel block was furthermore supported by a sequential blocker experiment, in which L-type current was first blocked by a dihydropyridine to leave pure T-type calcium channel barium current (fig. 3). A voltage-clamp step from –80 mV to –20 mV evoked only T-type calcium current which, predictably, was unaffected by nisoldipine (an L-type calcium antagonist). Under conditions of L-type calcium channel block, only T-type calcium channel current remained, and mibefradil 1 μM completely blocked the remaining T-type transient current.[23] This was a key experiment because it showed that mibefradil, in combination with a conventional L-type calcium channel antagonist, could be used to achieve total calcium channel blockade. The ability to block residual T-type currents in this type of protocol has not been demonstrated previously using any other calcium antagonist. Until now, it has only been possible to use interventions that would primarily block L-type calcium channels. With the advent of mibefradil, it is possible for the first time to block T-type calcium currents at low concentrations, allowing for selective blockade. The significance is that mibefradil offers a new pharmacological tool which will allow identification of

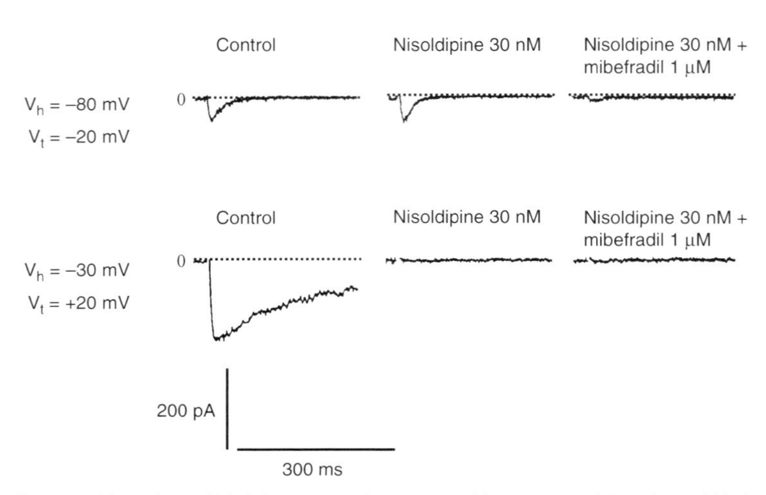

Fig. 3. Test of T-type calcium channel block by sequential treatment with an L-type calcium channel blocker followed by mibefradil in a vascular muscle cell. The T-type calcium channel barium current (top) was not inhibited by the 1,4-dihydropyridine L-type calcium channel blocker nisoldipine but was almost completely blocked by mibefradil. The L-type calcium channel barium current (middle) was blocked effectively by nisoldipine but was not interfered with by mibefradil. Block of the two currents thus appeared to be independent. The lowest effective concentrations for complete L- and T-type calcium channel block were 30 nM for nisoldipine and 1 μM for mibefradil, respectively. V_h = holding potential; V_t = test potential. (Reproduced with permission.[23])

the functions of T-type calcium channels in vascular muscle cells and other excitable cells. Although evidence from studies of calcium channel currents expressed in *Xenopus* oocytes has demonstrated that mibefradil can block virtually all of the tested types (L-, N-, P-, Q- and R-type, and molecular variants),[31] the concentrations necessary in cardiac cells were always 10–100 times higher than those effective in vascular muscle cells.

The plasma mibefradil concentration of patients treated for hypertension is 0.5–1 μM,[9] the 1 μM concentration being optimal for realising the benefit of selectivity for T- over L-type calcium channels, as shown in the dose–response plots for calcium channel blockade (fig. 4). Based on block of barium current in single vascular muscle cells, mibefradil was 30–100 times as potent on T-type calcium channels as on L-type calcium channels. The concentration for 50% reduction of peak barium current was 0.1 μM for T-type calcium channels and 10 μM for L-type calcium channels: a ratio of 1:100. At therapeutic concentrations of 0.5–1 μM, mibefradil would be predicted to block >80% of T-type calcium channels and only 25% of L-type calcium channels. There is no other compound capable of such selectivity. We have tested amlodipine, felodipine, nitrendipine, nisoldipine, nimodipine, isradipine, diltiazem and verapamil, all of which are selective blockers of L-type calcium channels with only minor, if any, effects on T-type calcium channels at therapeutically relevant concentrations.

These observations are in contrast to the assertion that all calcium antagonists can block T-type calcium channels.[32] However, there are serious flaws in the claims that T-type calcium channels can be blocked using dihydropyridines, benzothiazepines and phenylalkylamines.[23] In those experiments, the investigators used hydrofluoric acid 5 mM to isolate T-type calcium channels. However, the procedure would

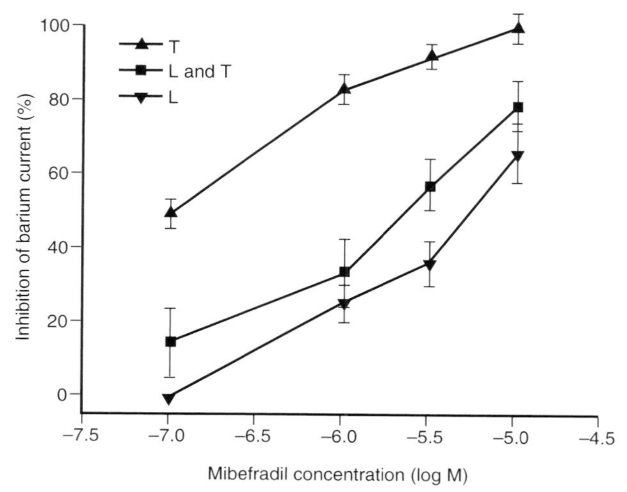

Fig. 4. Selectivity of mibefradil for T- and L-type calcium channel barium current and the overview of total barium current. From the points for 50% inhibition of T- and L-type calcium channels, there is between 30 and 100 times greater selectivity of mibefradil for T- versus L-type channels, although T-type calcium channel barium current is smaller than L-type calcium channel barium current. Values are means ± SEM for 6–16 vascular muscle cells at each point. (Reproduced with permission.[23])

phosphorylate L-type calcium channels and the leftwards shift of barium current along the voltage axis would allow the L-type barium current to appear to be T-type calcium channel currents. What these authors interpreted as T-type calcium channels were probably left-shifted (on the voltage axis) L-type calcium currents.[23] This incorrect interpretation (caused by using voltage domain alone) is one reason why the more definitive 'sequential blocker' experiment, explained above and shown in figure 3, was devised. Only mibefradil blocks T-type calcium channels after inhibition of L-type channels; no other calcium antagonist has yet been shown to achieve the 'sequential blocker' effect.

Another important effect of mibefradil on vascular muscle cells is inhibition of protein kinase C which, we hypothesise, is important for Ca^{2+} release, particularly that occurring several minutes after stimulation.[17] The reduction in protein kinase C translocation, and presumably activation, would amplify the relaxant action of mibefradil even in strong agonist-induced constrictions. Reduced protein kinase C activity at the cell membrane might also limit the function of calcium channels[33] and, therefore, the signal for contraction. Perhaps related to the protein kinase C effect, mibefradil also selectively inhibited release of trigger Ca^{2+} from subsarcolemmal stores that would physiologically be amplified into Ca^{2+} release from larger central stores to provide the Ca^{2+} that activates contraction.[34]

Myocardial actions of mibefradil appear to be limited to suppression of the pacemaker currents in the sinoatrial and atrioventricular nodes,[35] as predicted by T-type calcium channel block. There was no depression of myocardial contraction at the maximally effective concentration for coronary vasodilation (1 μM),[35] and no depression of conduction through the atrioventricular node.[36] Lack of inhibition of cardiac contraction has been demonstrated in both animal experiments and clinical trials.[9,37,38] In fact, the vasodilation, combined with lowered heart rate, allows sufficiently enhanced coronary blood flow to improve contractility in certain conditions, e.g. heart failure.[9,38,39] Reduction of heart rate at all times is another unique consequence of selective T-type calcium channel inhibition. Even though certain currently available calcium antagonists (e.g. verapamil) decrease heart rate during long-term treatment, there is often an early transient phase of increased heart rate caused by reflex sympathetic activation caused by the fall in blood pressure. This increased sympathetic drive to the heart with vasodilation would be dangerous in instances when tachyarrhythmia develops, a risk that limits the usefulness of most available vasodilators.[10] However, the selective T-type calcium channel blocker mibefradil does not increase heart rate, even in the initial stages of vasodilation and decreased blood pressure.[9,35] Therefore, the cardiac actions of mibefradil are unique and apparently establish a more optimal profile. Unlike vascular actions of mibefradil, which are relatively voltage-insensitive,[40] cardiac actions of mibefradil are voltage-sensitive.[41] This tends to prevent actions on cardiac muscle cells that have relatively electronegative resting potentials. Vascular muscle calcium channel currents were inhibited maximally from the first depolarisation, another factor which allows for vascular selectivity.[40]

Based on the mechanism of action and several other factors, mibefradil appears to be a new type of calcium antagonist. It is chemically novel (the tetraline family) and exists as a single form; there are no asymmetric carbon atoms in the structure.[28] Unlike other calcium antagonists, mibefradil is stable, water soluble and insensitive to light.[28]

Long-term protection

There are clearly unique properties that accompany selective T-type calcium channel block, the most important of which may be the long-term effects. Although T-type calcium channel currents are smaller and less prevalent, and thus often overlooked, the implications of the signal may be as important as vascular remodelling and reduced heart rate. If so, T-type calcium channel block may be the optimal rationale for antihypertensive treatment. Calcium antagonists are usually prescribed for many years to slow, or prevent, the consequences of high blood pressure, but the benefits to the patient of a reduced wall:lumen ratio found with ACE inhibitors have not been achieved by the presently available (L-type channel) calcium channel antagonists. The possible role of T-type calcium channels in these wall-thickening processes remains intriguing. If remodelling were signalled by T-type calcium channels, the key step in preventing the adverse consequences of hypertensive pathophysiology might be identified. Support for the hypothesis that T-type calcium channels are involved in vascular remodelling is provided by the observations that mibefradil effectively reduced subendothelial thickening in the carotid arteries of hypertensive rats,[42] and decreased the wall:lumen ratio and prevented strokes in stroke-prone spontaneously hypertensive rats.[43]

If these observations continue to be borne out by clinical studies, T-type calcium channel block as exemplified by mibefradil may be the first calcium antagonist mechanism to achieve the goal of long-term protection of the cardiovascular system during treatment of hypertension and angina pectoris.

Acknowledgements

This research was supported by National Institutes of Health grant HL 51723 and by F. Hoffmann La Roche, Basle, Switzerland.

References

1. Bühler FR. Calcium antagonists. In: Laragh JH, Brenner BM, editors. Hypertension: pathophysiology, diagnosis, and management. 2nd edn. New York: Raven Press, 1995: 2801–14
2. Triggle DJ. Calcium channel drugs: structure-function relations and selectivity of action. J Cardiovasc Pharmacol 1991; 18 Suppl. 10: S1–6
3. Mulvany MJ. Structural changes in the resistance vessels in human hypertension. In: Laragh JH, Brenner BM, editors. Hypertension: pathophysiology, diagnosis, and management. 2nd edn. New York: Raven Press, 1995: 503–14
4. Folkow B. The structural factor in hypertension with special emphasis on the altered geometric design of the systemic resistance arteries. In: Laragh JH, Brenner BM, editors. Hypertension: pathophysiology, diagnosis, and management. 2nd edn. New York: Raven Press, 1995: 481–502

5. Triggle DJ. 'Calcium, calcium channels, and calcium antagonists.' Drugs in development, Ca^{2+} antagonists in CNS. Brandord, Conn.: Neva Press, 1993: 3–13
6. Bean BP. Pharmacology of calcium channels in cardiac muscle, vascular muscle, and neurons. Am J Hypertens 1991; 4: 406–11S
7. Hermsmeyer K. Ion channels as targets for drugs. In: Sperelakis N, editor. Cell physiology source book. San Diego: Academic Press, 1995: 404–13
8. Tsien RW, Ellinor PT, Horne WA. Molecular diversity of voltage-dependent Ca^{2+} channels. Trends Pharmacol Sci 1991; 12: 349–54
9. Rousseau MF, Hayashida W, van Eyll C, et al. Hemodynamic and cardiac effects of the selective T-type and L-type calcium channel blocking agent mibefradil in patients with varying degrees of left ventricular systolic dysfunction. J Am Coll Cardiol 1996; 28: 972–9
10. Ruzicka M, Leenen FHH. Relevance of intermittent increases in sympathetic activity for adverse outcome on short-acting calcium antagonists. In: Laragh JH, Brenner BM, editors. Hypertension: pathophysiology, diagnosis, and management. 2nd edn. New York: Raven Press, 1995: 2815–25
11. Thybo NK, Stephens N, Cooper A, et al. Effect of antihypertensive treatment on small arteries of patients with previously untreated essential hypertension. Hypertension 1995; 25: 174–81
12. Ting CT, Chen JW, Chang MS, et al. Arterial hemodynamics in human hypertension: effects of calcium channel antagonist nifedipine. Hypertension 1995; 25: 1326–32
13. Mulvany MJ. Resistance vessel structure in hypertension: growth or remodeling? J Cardiovasc Pharmacol 1993; 22 Suppl. 5: S44–7
14. Thybo NK, Korsgaard N, Mulvany MJ. Morphology and function of mesenteric resistance arteries in transgenic rats with low-renin hypertension. J Hypertens 1992; 10: 1191–6
15. Mulvany MJ, Baumbach GL, Aalkjaer C, et al. Vascular remodeling. Hypertension 1996; 28: 505–6
16. Hermsmeyer K, Erne P. Vascular muscle ion channels and cellular calcium regulation in hypertension. In: Laragh JH, Brenner BM, editors. Hypertension: pathophysiology, diagnosis, and management. 2nd edn. New York: Raven Press, 1995: 673–83
17. Hermsmeyer K, Miyagawa K. Protein kinase C mechanism enhances vascular muscle relaxation by the Ca^{2+} antagonist Ro 40-5967. J Vasc Res 1996; 33: 71–7
18. de Gasparo M, Bottari S, Levens NR. Characteristics of angiotensin II receptors and their role in cell and organ physiology. In: Laragh JH, Brenner BM, editors. Hypertension: pathophysiology, diagnosis, and management. 2nd edn. New York: Raven Press, 1995: 1695–720
19. Vassort G, Alvarez J. Cardiac T-type calcium current: pharmacology and roles in cardiac tissues. J Cardiovasc Electrophysiol 1994; 5: 376–93
20. Self DA, Bian K, Mishra SK, et al. Stroke-prone SHR vascular muscle Ca^{2+} current amplitudes correlate with lethal increases in blood pressure. J Vasc Res 1994; 31: 359–66
21. Nuss HB, Houser SR. T-type Ca^{2+} current is expressed in hypertrophied adult feline left ventricular myocytes. Circ Res 1993; 73: 777–82
22. Wang Z, Estacion M, Mordan LJ. Ca^{2+} influx via T-type channels modulates PDGF-induced replication of mouse fibroblasts. Am J Physiol 1993; 265: C1239–46
23. Mishra SK, Hermsmeyer K. Selective inhibition of T-type Ca^{2+} channels by Ro 40-5967. Circ Res 1994; 75: 144–8
24. Godfraind T, Miller R, Wibo M. Calcium antagonism and calcium entry blockade. Pharmacol Rev 1986; 38: 321–416
25. Hermsmeyer, K. Differences of calcium channels in vascular muscle in hypertension. Am J Hypertens 1991; 4: 412–15S
26. Rusch NJ, Hermsmeyer RK. Vascular muscle calcium channels in hypertension. In: Coca A, Garay RP, editor: Ionic transport in hypertension: new perspectives. Boca Raton, Fla.: CRC Press, 1994: 197–227
27. Jackson CL, Schwartz SM. Pharmacology of smooth muscle cell replication. Hypertension 1992; 20: 713–36
28. Clozel JP, Osterrieder W, Kleinbloesem CH, et al. Ro 40-5967: a new non-dihydropyridine calcium antagonist. Cardiovasc Drug Rev 1991; 19: 4–17
29. Sturek M, Hermsmeyer K. Calcium and sodium channels in spontaneously contracting vascular muscle cells. Science 1986; 233: 475–8
30. Osterrieder W, Holck M. *In vitro* pharmacologic profile of Ro 40-5967, a novel Ca^{2+} channel blocker with potent vasodilator but weak inotropic action. J Cardiovasc Pharmacol 1989; 13: 754–9
31. Bezprozvanny I, Tsien RW. Voltage-dependent blockade of diverse types of voltage-gated Ca^{2+} channels expressed in *Xenopus* oocytes by the Ca^{2+} channel antagonist mibefradil (Ro 40-5967). Mol Pharmacol 1995; 48: 540–9
32. Kuga T, Sadoshima J, Tomoike H, et al. Actions of Ca^{2+} antagonists on two types of Ca^{2+} channels in rat aorta smooth muscle cells in primary culture. Circ Res 1990; 67: 469–80
33. Stea A, Soong TW, Snutch TP. Determinants of PKC-dependent modulation of a family of neuronal calcium channels. Neuron 1995; 15: 929–40
34. Mishra SK, Hermsmeyer K. Inhibition of trigger Ca^{2+} in dog coronary arterial muscle cells by Ro 40-5967. J Cardiovasc Pharmacol 1994; 24: 1–7
35. Bernink PJLM, Prager G, Schelling A, et al. Antihypertensive properties of the novel calcium antagonist mibefradil (Ro 40-5967): a new generation of calcium antagonists? Hypertension 1996; 27: 426–32

36. Billman GE, Hamlin RL. The effects of mibefradil, a novel calcium channel antagonist on ventricular arrhythmias induced by myocardial ischemia and programmed electrical stimulation. J Pharmacol Exp Ther 1996; 277: 1517–26
37. Braun S, van der Wall EE, Emanuelsson H, et al. Effects of a new calcium antagonist, mibefradil (Ro 40-5967), on silent ischemia in patients with stable chronic angina pectoris: a multicenter placebo-controlled study. J Am Coll Cardiol 1996; 27: 317–22
38. Muntinga HJ, van der Vring JAFM, Niemeyer MG, et al. Effect of mibefradil on left ventricular diastolic function in patients with congestive heart failure. J Cardiovasc Pharmacol 1996; 27: 652–6
39. Roux S, Bühler M, Clozel J-P. Mechanism of the anti-ischemic effect of mibefradil, a selective T calcium channel blocker in dogs: comparison with amlodipine. J Cardiovasc Pharmacol 1996; 27: 132–9
40. Mishra SK, Hermsmeyer K. Resting state block and use independence of rat vascular muscle Ca^{2+} channels by Ro 40-5967. J Pharmacol Exp Ther 1994; 269: 178–83
41. Benardeau A, Ertel EA. Selective block of myocardial T-type calcium channels by mibefradil: a comparison with the 1,4-dihydropyridine amlodipine. J Pharmacol Exp Ther. In press
42. Gray GA, Clozel M, Clozel J, et al. Effects of calcium channel blockade on the aortic intima in spontaneously hypertensive rats. Hypertension 1993; 22: 569–76
43. Vacher E, Richer C, Fornes, et al. Mibefradil, a selective calcium T-channel blocker, in stroke-prone spontaneously hypertensive rats. J Cardiovasc Pharmacol 1996; 27: 686–94

Interaction of mibefradil with T- and L-type calcium channels

Norbert Klugbauer, Xiangang Zong, Franz Hofmann

Institut für Pharmakologie und Toxikologie der Technischen Universität München, Munich, Germany

Summary

Mibefradil is a new addition to the group of drugs that affect voltage-dependent calcium channels. We have studied the pharmacological properties of mibefradil using the T-type calcium channel present in human medullary thyroid carcinoma (hMTC) cells and expressed L-type calcium channels. These studies show that mibefradil blocks the T-type calcium channel of hMTC cells at 10-fold lower concentrations than it blocks the current through the expressed L-type α_{1C} calcium channel. Site-directed studies indicate that mibefradil interacts with the α_{1C} calcium channel at a different site from those that bind the dihydropyridine isradipine and the phenylalkylamine devapamil. These studies support the notion that mibefradil is a new type of calcium channel with a preference towards T-type calcium channels.

Introduction

Mibefradil is a novel calcium channel blocker with a potential widespread use as an antihypertensive and antianginal agent.[1] The interaction of mibefradil with the voltage-dependent calcium channel has been studied at various levels, including intact animals,[2] isolated hearts,[3] strips of vascular and intestinal smooth muscle,[3] myocytes isolated from cardiac atria and ventricles, the coronary artery and saphenous vein,[4–6] isolated cultivated cells[7] and cloned and expressed voltage-dependent calcium channels.[8–11] Mibefradil decreased blood pressure 3–5 times more effectively than verapamil in hypertensive rats and had a weaker negative inotropic effect on cardiac contractility than verapamil.[2] The affinity of mibefradil for different L-type calcium channels was in the order: coronary artery > saphenous vein > heart.[4,5] The molecular mechanism of the interaction of mibefradil with the L-type calcium channel protein has not been studied in great detail, although it was suggested initially that mibefradil interacted in a voltage-dependent manner with the L-type calcium channel.[4] Later investigators showed that mibefradil interacted specifically with T-type calcium channels in vascular smooth muscle,[12] human medullary thyroid carcinoma (hMTC) cells[7] and atrial myocardial cells.[6]

We have used the stably expressed α_{1C} subunit of the L-type calcium channel and the low-voltage-activated (LVA) T-type calcium channel of hMTC cells to investigate the molecular mechanism underlying the modulatory effects of mibefradil on the calcium current. The α_{1C} subunit of the cardiac calcium channel is responsible for the voltage-gated ion conductance activated at high membrane potentials and contains the binding sites for the three classes of organic calcium channel blockers, i.e. the dihydropyridines, the phenylalkylamines and the benzothiazepines.[13] In the present paper, Chinese hamster ovary (CHO) cells expressing the stable α_{1C-a} and α_{1C-b} subunits (which may represent the α_{1C} subunits of the cardiac and smooth muscle L-type calcium channel)[14] have been expressed alone or in combination with other calcium channel subunits and have been used to analyse the interaction of mibefradil with the calcium channel.

Methods

Cells and transfection of cells

The hMTC cells were grown in RPMI-1640 medium supplemented with foetal calf serum 16%, penicillin (30 U/ml) and streptomycin (30 mg/ml) in the presence of CO_2 5% as previously described.[15]

CHO cells were transfected with the protein coding sequence of the cardiac and smooth muscle calcium channel α_{1C-a} and α_{1C-b} subunits alone and in combination with (i) α_{1C-b} and β_1 subunits, (ii) α_{1C-b} and β_3 subunits, or (iii) α_{1C-a} and β_3 subunits, as previously described.[8–10] The site-directed mutagenesis and the transient expression of the α_{1C} constructs in HEK293 cells were carried out as previously described.[16]

Electrophysiological recordings

Barium currents were recorded at room temperature (19–22 °C) using the whole-cell configuration of the patch-clamp technique.[17] To measure only the currents passing through calcium channels, potassium currents were blocked with TEA and Cs^+. Under the experimental conditions, no voltage-dependent sodium currents were identified in hMTC, HEK293 or CHO cells. The standard extracellular solution contained NaCl 82 mM, $BaCl_2$ 30 mM, CsCl 5.4 mM, $MgCl_2$ 1 mM, TEA 20 mM, HEPES 5 mM and glucose 10 mM. The pH was adjusted to 7.4. The patch pipettes were filled with a solution containing CsCl 112 mM, $MgCl_2$ 3 mM, EGTA 10 mM, Na_2-ATP 3 mM and HEPES 5 mM, also at pH 7.4.

An EPC-9 patch-clamp amplifier (HEKA elektronik, Lambrecht, Germany) connected to a Macintosh computer or an EPC-7 (HEKA electronik, Lambrecht, Germany) connected to an IBM-compatible computer equipped with the pCLAMP 6.0 system (Axon Instruments, Foster City, California, USA) was used for data acquisition. All currents were filtered at 2 kHz and were corrected for leakage and capacitive currents. All values are presented as the average ± SEM. The significance of differences was calculated by the two-tailed t-test, and theoretical functions were fitted to data using commercial, least-squares, software.

The barium currents through calcium channels were measured according to the following protocol. The cells were clamped to a holding potential (usually –100 mV for hMTC cells or –80 mV for CHO cells), and test pulses were applied at 0.1 Hz to a membrane potential of –10 mV in the hMTC cells and +20 mV in the CHO cell. The maximum current was normalised by the cell capacitance.

Stock solutions of mibefradil (10 mM) and devapamil (10 mM) were made up in water, while isradipine (2 mM) was made up in ethanol. Prior to the tests, control experiments were performed to show that ethanol did not influence barium currents even at the highest intended test concentrations.

Results

Characteristics of the T-type current in hMTC cells

The hMTC cells have a current that shows the main characteristics of a T-type calcium channel; barium current decayed rapidly and almost completely. The current was at maximal amplitude at a potential of –14 ± 3.2 mV (n=40). In comparison, the barium current of the CHO cells transfected with the $\alpha_{1C\text{-}b}$ subunit inactivated slowly and was maximally activated at 24 ± 1.1 mV (n=40). The inactivation rate constants at maximal barium current were 416 ± 26 ms (n=31) in the CHO cells and 33.4 ± 4.1 ms (n=15) in the hMTC cells. The current–voltage relationship revealed threshold potentials of about –50 mV and –10 mV for the T-type current of the hMTC cells and the L-type current of the CHO cells, respectively. Half-maximum steady-state inactivation occurred at –15 ± 5 mV (n=5) and –45 ± 4 mV (n=6) for the L- and T-type calcium channels, respectively. Replacement of Ba^{2+} by Ca^{2+} as the charge carrier affected the current of the hMTC cells much less than that of the CHO cells (fig. 1). Ni^{2+} blocked barium current in the hMTC cells with an IC_{50} value close to 10 µM. Cd^{2+}, which effectively blocks high-voltage-activated (HVA) calcium channels, showed either no effect or, at most, a small stimulatory effect at 10 µM, while blocking barium current by 40% at a concentration of 100 µM.

Characteristics of the mibefradil block in hMTC and CHO cells

The two cell lines characterised above were used to investigate interactions with mibefradil. As expected, the L-type calcium channel of a CHO cell was readily blocked by mibefradil 10 µM (table I). The IC_{50} values determined at the two holding potentials of –80 and –40 mV were 18.6 and 3.1 µM, respectively. At a holding potential of –100 mV, the T-type current of the hMTC cells was inhibited by 70% rapidly and reversibly, with no effect on the current–voltage relationship, in the presence of mibefradil 10 µM. Blockade of T-type barium current by mibefradil was concentration-dependent. The experimental points were fitted very well by a curve assuming a 1:1 binding stoichiometry with an apparent IC_{50} of 2.7 µM (see table I). Replacement of Ba^{2+} by Ca^{2+} shifted the inhibition curve to lower concentrations of mibefradil with an apparent IC_{50} value of 0.2 µM. In hMTC cells, the inhibition of the barium current amplitude by mibefradil was not affected significantly by the holding potential, because a shift in the holding potential from –100 to –60 mV decreased the IC_{50} value from 2.7 to 1.9 µM.

These data suggested that mibefradil blocked the T-type current in the resting state, whereas the L-type current of the $\alpha_{1C\text{-}b}$ subunit was blocked in a membrane potential-dependent manner. Figure 2 shows an experiment in which the membrane potential of an hMTC cell was held for 3 min without depolarisation at –100 mV in

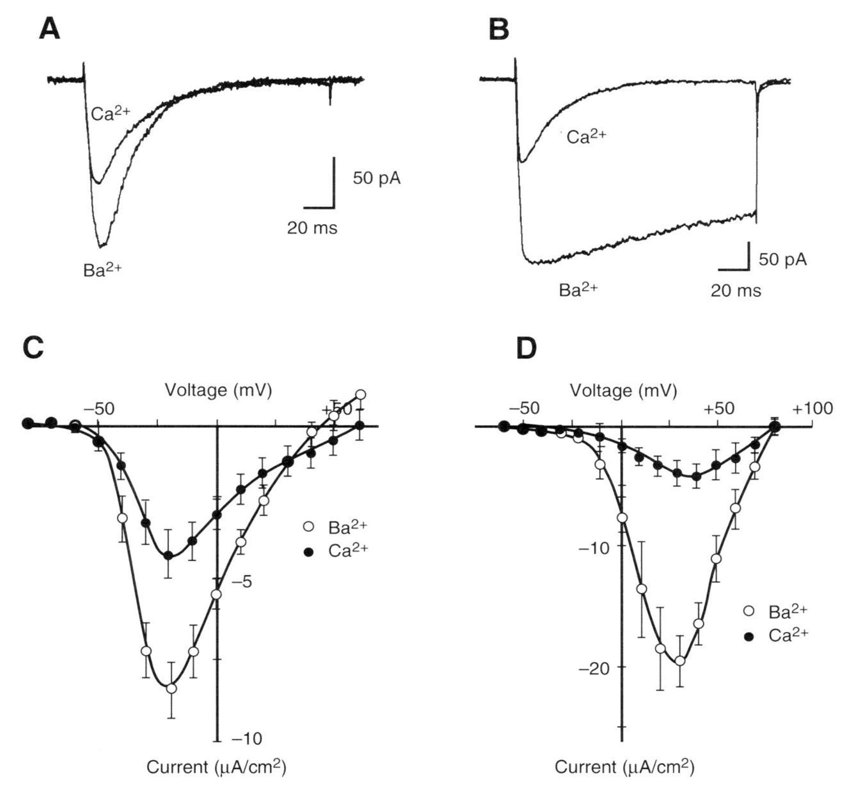

Fig. 1. Whole-cell barium and calcium currents in T-type calcium channels (A & C) in human medullary thyroid (hMTC) cells and L-type calcium channels (B & D) in Chinese hamster ovary (CHO) cells transfected with the α_{1C-b} subunit. The concentration of Ba^{2+} and Ca^{2+} was 30 mM. Calcium current was measured 1 min after changing the bath solution. A) T-type current traces elicited by a voltage step from –80 mV to +30 mV. C & D) Current–voltage relationship of T- (n=3) and L-type (n=4) channels. Holding potentials for hMTC and CHO cells were –100 mV and –80 mV, respectively. The inactivation kinetic of the T-type current was affected only minimally and its peak amplitude was lowered by only 40% if the current charge carrier was changed from Ba^{2+} to Ca^{2+}. The voltage-dependence of T-type channels was almost unaffected by changing the current charge carrier. In contrast, the inactivation kinetic and the amplitude of the L-type current were highly sensitive to Ca^{2+}. The current–voltage curve of the L-type channel was shifted by Ca^{2+} by about 10 mV to the right.

the presence of mibefradil 10 μM. Thereafter, the first test pulse to –10 mV did not elicit a significant barium current, confirming that mibefradil blocked the T-type channel in the resting state. In contrast, the same experiment carried out with the L-type channel showed that mibefradil interacted with the α_{1C} subunit in a voltage-dependent manner (see fig. 2 (D)). Further experiments in which the depolarisation frequency was varied between 0.1 and 1 Hz confirmed that mibefradil blocked L-type calcium channels in a voltage- and use-dependent manner, whereas it inhibited T-type calcium channels in a manner that was independent of both voltage and use.

Site for mibefradil at the α_{1C} channel

The α_{1C} gene was spliced to two different mRNAs which yield the α_{1C-a} and α_{1C-b} channels in cardiac and smooth muscle and in association with different β subunits. The potential effect of the splice variation and of the coexpression of different subunits

Table I. IC_{50} values for the block by mibefradil of T-type channel and the cloned and expressed L-type channel

Channel type	HP (mV)	β subunit	IC_{50} (μM)	Study
T-type	–100	–	2.7	Mehrke et al.[7]
hMTC cells	–60	–	1.9	
L-type	–80	–	18.6	
α_{1C-b}	–40	–	3.1	
L-type	–80	β_1	16.7	Welling et al.[8]
α_{1C-b}	–80	β_3	19.4	
	–40	β_1	0.8	
	–40	β_3	0.4	
L-type	–80	–	4.9	Lacinova et al.[10]
α_{1C-a}	–80	β_3	4.3	
	–80	–	1.4	
	–80	β_3	0.9	

Abbreviation: hMTC = human medullary thyroid carcinoma.

has been studied.[9,10,14] As is evident from the data (see table I), coexpression of the two α_{1C} subunits with either the β_1 or the β_3 subunits had no significant influence on the IC_{50} value for mibefradil. However, the voltage-dependence of the mibefradil block was minimal when the α_{1C-b} channel was exchanged with the cardiac α_{1C-a} channel. This suggested that the voltage-dependence of the block is caused by the splice type of the α_{1C} channel and is not a general property of the L-type calcium channel.

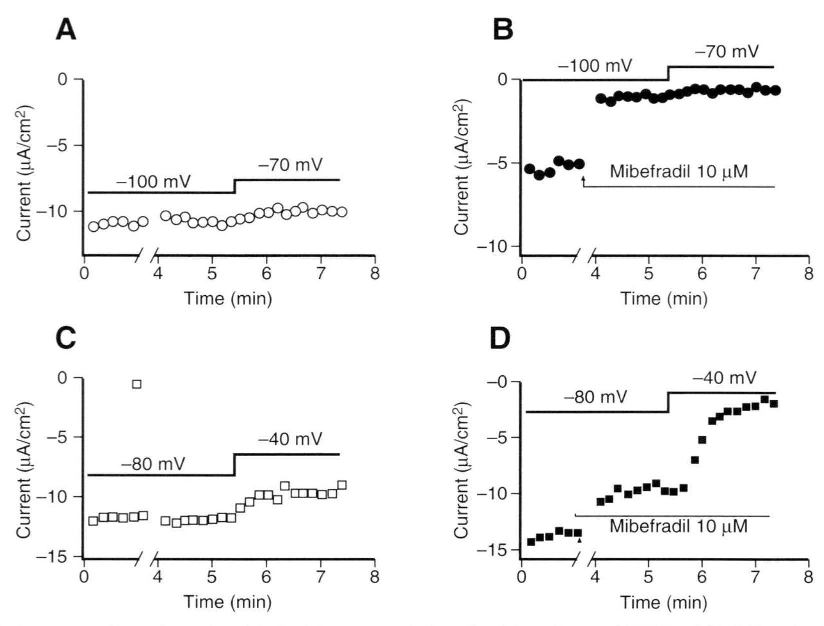

Fig. 2. Tonic versus voltage-dependent block. A human medullary thyroid carcinoma (hMTC) cell (A & B) and a Chinese hamster ovary (CHO) cell expressing the α_{1C-b} subunit (C & D) were superfused for 3 min with (B & D) and without (A & C) mibefradil 10 μM at the indicated membrane potentials at 0 Hz. Thereafter, the cells were depolarised at 0.1 Hz and the holding potential was shifted to the indicated potentials. The shift in the membrane potential had only a negligible effect in the absence of the drug.

In a previous publication it was reported that mibefradil inhibited the binding of devapamil to the cardiac calcium channel,[18] which suggests that mibefradil might interact with the phenylalkylamine site of the α_{1C} subunit. This potential interaction of mibefradil has also been analysed by mutation of the IVS6 segment of the α_{1C} cDNA.[16] The mutation of Y1481I, M1482F and I1493L (in chimera Ch30) decreased the block by the dihydropyridine isradipine 100-fold. The mutation of Y1481I, A1485S and I1492M (Ch31) decreased the block by the phenylalkylamine devapamil 30-fold. However, the affinity for mibefradil (IC_{50} between 2 and 4 μM) was not significantly different from that of the wild type in either chimera (table II (experiment A)). Further mutations demonstrated that mibefradil does not interact with the high-affinity site for the dihydropyridines.[19] The mutation of Thr-1061 to Tyr in IIIS5 decreased the affinity for isradipine, a neutral dihydropyridine, by over 1000-fold without affecting the IC_{50} value for mibefradil (see table II (experiment B)). These results clearly show that mibefradil interacts with the cloned L-type calcium channel at a site that is distinct from that for dihydropyridines and phenylalkylamines.

Channel identity

Several strategies were tested to identify the transcript for the hMTC T-type calcium channel. Voltage-activated calcium and sodium channels are derived from common-ancestor molecules,[20] and one might expect that LVA channels belong to the same supergene family. Additionally, some common basic electrophysiological characteristics make it likely that there are also common structural features. Screening of cDNA libraries from hMTC cells with specific probes derived from the conserved segments of calcium and sodium channels led to the identification of the now well-known calcium channels. However, through this approach a novel cDNA, related to this supergene family, was also found. The transient expression of the cDNA demonstrated that the novel channel is selective for Na^+ but not for Ca^{2+}.[21] So far, all attempts using homology screening of cDNA libraries and polymerase chain reaction strategies with degenerate primers have failed to contribute to the identity of any novel channel proteins encoding for T-type channels.

Table II. Block of L-type calcium channel mutants by mibefradil, isradipine and desmethoxyverapamil (devapamil)

Chimera[a]		Mibefradil IC_{50} (μM)	Isradipine IC_{50} (μM)	Devapamil IC_{50} (μM)
Experiment A	**(Segment IVS6)**			
α_{1C}	YMLCAFLII	2.5	0.016	0.5
Ch30	**IF**LCAFLI**L**	4.2	1.7	3.2
Ch31	**I**MLC**S**FL**M**I	3.3	0.04	15.5
Experiment B	**(Segment IIIS5)**			
α_{1C}	V**T**TLQF	1.2	0.012	3.1
EC5	V**Y**TLQF	1.1	NI	3.1

[a] The IVS6 (experiment A) and IIIS5 (experiment B) segments were mutated in the α_{1C-b} cDNA between Tyr-1485 and Ile-1493 and between Va-11060 and Phe-1066, respectively.

Abbreviation: NI = no inhibition of barium current with isradipine 3 μM. For details of expression and current recording, see Schuster et al.[19]

Discussion

A major finding of our studies is that mibefradil, a non-dihydropyridine calcium channel blocker, acts on L-type as well as T-type calcium channels, but in a different manner. At similar concentrations, mibefradil blocked both the T-type calcium channel and the expressed L-type channel of the hMTC cells. However, the T-type channel block occurred at hyperpolarised membrane potentials and showed no significant voltage- or use-dependence. The IC_{50} values for mibefradil were affected slightly at different holding potentials. A mild but unmistakable voltage-dependence was observed by Randall and Tsien.[22] The affinity of mibefradil for the T-type calcium channel increased when Ba^{2+} was replaced with Ca^{2+}. A similar observation was made by Lee and Tsien,[23] who found that the nitrendipine block of L-type calcium channels was much stronger with Ca^{2+} than Ba^{2+}.

Mibefradil was found to block L-type calcium channels in a voltage-dependent manner, confirming previous reports.[4,6] It was most effective at depolarised membrane potentials, suggesting that it binds tightly to the inactivated state of the calcium channel. Mibefradil is less potent at negative potentials. A small block of the α_{1C-a} and the α_{1C-b} calcium channels was observed at a membrane potential of –80 mV, indicating that the α_{1C} subunit may bind mibefradil at the resting state when the compound is present at relatively high concentrations. This potential-dependent block was less apparent when the α_{1C-a} subunit was used.[9,10] The affinity for the block was not affected when either the β_1 or β_3 subunit was coexpressed with the α_{1C} subunit. Site-directed mutagenesis of the α_{1C} cDNA showed that mibefradil does not interact with the dihydropyridine or phenylalkylamine binding site. A similar conclusion may be drawn from experiments showing that mibefradil blocked each cloned HVA channel in *Xenopus* oocytes.[11]

In conclusion, the new non-dihydropyridine calcium channel blocker mibefradil is not a prominent L-type calcium channel blocker. At negative (resting) membrane potentials, T-type calcium channels are completely blocked, whereas L-type calcium channels are barely affected; this confirms similar recently published observations.[6] It is possible, but so far not proved, that this property may contribute to an antiarrhythmic activity for mibefradil.

References

1. Clozel J-P, Osterrieder W, Kleinbloesem CH, et al. Ro 40-5967: a new nondihydropyridine calcium antagonist. Cardiovasc Drug Rev 1991; 9: 4–17
2. Hefti F, Clozel J-P, Osterrieder W. Antihypertensive properties of the novel calcium antagonist (1S,2S)-2-[2-[[3-(2-benzimidazolyl) propyl]methylamino] ethyl]-6-fluoro-1,2,3,4-tetrahydro-1-isopropyl-2-naphthyl methoxyacetate dihydrochloride in rat models of hypertension. Comparison with verapamil. Arzneimittelforschung 1990; 40: 417–21
3. Osterrieder W, Holck M. *In vitro* pharmacologic profile of Ro 40-5967, a novel Ca^{2+} channel blocker with potent vasodilator but weak inotropic action. J Cardiovasc Pharmacol 1989; 13: 754–9
4. Fang LM, Osterrieder W. Potential-dependent inhibition of cardiac Ca^{2+} inward currents by Ro 40-5967 and verapamil: relation to negative inotropy. Eur J Pharmacol 1991; 196: 205–7
5. Bian K, Hermsmeyer K. Ca^{2+} channel actions of the non-dihydropyridine Ca^{2+} channel antagonist Ro 40-5967 in vascular muscle cells cultured from dog coronary and saphenous arteries. Naunyn Schmiedebergs Arch Pharmacol 1993; 348: 191–6

6. Ertel EA. Mibefradil (Ro 40-5967) is a selective blocker of myocardial T-type *vs.* L-type Ca channels. Biophys J 1996; 70: A315
7. Mehrke G, Zong XG, Flockerzi V, et al. The Ca^{2+}-channel blocker Ro 40-5967 blocks differently T-type and L-type Ca^{2+} channels. J Pharmacol Exp Ther 1994; 271: 1483–8
8. Welling A, Lacinova L, Donatin K, et al. Expression of the L-type calcium channel with two different β subunits and its modulation by Ro 40-5967. Pflugers Arch 1995; 429: 400–11
9. Lacinova L, Welling A, Bosse E, et al. Interaction of Ro 40-5967 and verapamil with the stably expressed α_1-subunit of the cardiac L-type calcium channel. J Pharmacol Exp Ther 1995; 274: 54–63
10. Lacinova L, Ludwig, A, Bosse E, et al. The block of the expressed L-type calcium channel is modulated by the β3 subunit. FEBS Lett 1995; 373: 103–7
11. Bezprozvanny I, Tsien, RW. Voltage-dependent blockade of diverse types of voltage-gated Ca^{2+} channels expressed in *Xenopus* oocytes by the Ca^{2+} channel antagonist mibefradil (Ro 40-5967). Mol Pharm 1995; 48: 540–9
12. Mishra SK, Hermsmeyer K. Selective inhibition of T-type Ca^{2+} channels by Ro 40-5967. Circ Res 1994; 75: 144–8
13. Hofmann F, Biel M, Flockerzi V. Molecular basis of Ca^{2+} channel diversity. Ann Rev Neurosci 1994; 17: 399–418
14. Welling A, Kwan YW, Bosse E, et al. Subunit-dependent modulation of recombinant L-type calcium channels. Molecular basis for dihydropyridine tissue selectivity. Circ Res 1993; 73: 974–80
15. Scherübl H, Schultz G, Hescheler JA. Slowly inactivating calcium current works as a calcium sensor in calcitonin-secreting cells. FEBS Lett 1990; 273: 51–4
16. Schuster A, Lacinova L, Klugbauer N, et al. The IVS6 segment of the L-type calcium channel is critical for the action of dihydropyridines and phenylalkylamines. EMBO J 1996; 15: 2365–70
17. Hamill OP, Marty A, Neher E, et al. Improved patch-clamp techniques for high resolution current recording from cells and cell free membrane patches. Pflugers Arch 1981; 391: 85–100
18. Rutledge A, Triggle DJ. The binding interactions of Ro 40-5967 at the L-type Ca^{2+} channel in cardiac tissue. Eur J Pharmacol 1995; 280: 155–8
19. Ito H, Klugbauer N, Hofmann F. Transfer of the high-affinity dihydropyridine sensitivity from L-type to non T-type calcium channel. Mol Pharmacol 1997; 52: 735–40
20. Strong M, Chandy KG, Gutmann GA. Molecular evolution of voltage-sensitive ion channel genes: on the origin of electrical excitability. Mol Biol Evol 1993; 10: 221–42
21. Klugbauer N, Lacinova L, Flockerzi V, et al. Structure and functional expression of a new member of the tetrodotoxin-sensitive voltage activated sodium channel family from human neuroendocrine cells. EMBO J 1995; 14: 1084–90
22. Randall RA, Tsien RW. Contrasting biophysical and pharmacological properties of T-type and R-type calcium channels. Neuropharmacology 1997; 36: 879–93
23. Lee KS, Tsien RW. Mechanism of calcium channel blockade by verapamil, D600, diltiazem and nitrendipine in single dialysed heart cells. Nature 1983; 302: 790–4

Selective block of myocardial T-type calcium channels by mibefradil: a comparison with the 1,4-dihydropyridine amlodipine

Agnes Benardeau, Eric A. Ertel

Pharma Division, Preclinical Research Department, F. Hoffmann-La Roche Ltd, Basle, Switzerland

Summary

The calcium antagonist mibefradil (Ro 40-5967) preferentially blocks T-type over L-type calcium channels in vascular smooth muscle. We report here that mibefradil also blocks primarily T-type calcium channels in guinea-pig atrial myocytes ($IC_{50} \approx 1.6$ µM vs 28 µM for L-type channels, from a holding voltage of –90 mV). Under the same conditions, amlodipine, a 1,4-dihydropyridine, preferentially blocks L-type calcium channels (0.48 µM vs 5.6 µM for T-type channels). Like amlodipine, mibefradil blocks in a voltage-dependent manner, so that depolarisation enhances the block of both channel types by approximately 20-fold. Furthermore, block by mibefradil is highly use-dependent. Thus, mibefradil binds preferentially to open or inactivated calcium channels. In conclusion, mibefradil selectively blocks T-type calcium channels in heart myocytes, in a highly voltage- and use-dependent manner.

Introduction

Two distinct populations of voltage-gated calcium channels are found in non-neuronal cells: T type (or low voltage activated; LVA) and L type (or high voltage activated; HVA).[1] The classical calcium antagonists such as verapamil, diltiazem and the 1,4-dihydropyridines (e.g. nifedipine, felodipine, amlodipine) produce their antihypertensive action through the block of L-type calcium channels in vascular muscle. However, concomitant block of cardiac L-type calcium channels is probably responsible for a reduction in heart contractility (negative inotropy), a common side effect of calcium antagonists.[2–4] Mibefradil (Ro 40-5967) is from a new chemical class of calcium antagonists (tetralol derivatives) and has an antihypertensive activity similar to that of the dihydropyridines, but it is devoid of the major side effects of these drugs.[5,6] An important pharmacological feature of this newly developed drug is that mibefradil slows heart rate slightly without decreasing cardiac contractility.[5,6]

Mibefradil has been shown to preferentially block T-type calcium channels in vascular myocytes.[7] This raises the possibility that mibefradil reduces heart rate through the block of cardiac T-type calcium channels, which are thought to be involved in the early depolarising phase of the action potential.[8] Conversely, weaker block of L-type calcium channels would explain the absence of negative inotropy. The present study was designed to characterise the effects of mibefradil on cardiac calcium channels and to compare them with those of amlodipine. Guinea-pig atrial myocytes were used because the components of the calcium channel current can be readily quantified and the pharmacological properties of these currents are well documented. A preliminary report of part of this work has been published.[9]

Materials and methods

Whole-cell voltage-clamp measurements

Freshly dissociated single guinea-pig atrial myocytes were prepared from male Füllingsdorf Albino guinea-pigs as described previously.[10,11] Cells were voltage-clamped at room temperature (20–25 °C) using the whole-cell configuration of the patch-clamp technique and an EPC-9 amplifier (HEKA elektronik, Lambrecht, Germany) and associated software (Pulse v. 7–8 on Macintosh). Membrane current was low-pass filtered using the internal four-pole Bessel filter of the EPC-9 with a cut-off frequency (f_c; –3 d) of 5 kHz and was digitised at 50 kHz. Linear leak and capacity currents were subtracted by the standard p/4 method. Zero calcium current was defined as the current at the holding voltage. Tail currents were fitted by the sum of two exponential functions plus a constant, using the Levenberg–Marquardt non-linear curve-fitting procedure[12] and the computer software Igor Pro (v. 2–3, Wavemetrics, Lake Oswego, Oregon, USA). Changes in membrane voltage were complete ≤350 μs after a change in command voltage and data collected during this interval were excluded from analysis and display. The reported tail current amplitudes represent the magnitude of the exponential functions at the end of this period. Where specified, data were fitted by a two-state Boltzmann distribution:

$$I/I_{max} = \{1 + \exp[(V - V_{½})/k]\}^{-1}$$

where I_{max} is the maximum amplitude, $V_{½}$ is the half-action potential, and k is the slope factor.

Solutions and drugs

The external (bath) and internal (pipette) solutions were designed to minimise currents through sodium and potassium channels. The internal solution contained caesium glutamate 107 mM, CsCl 20 mM, tetrabutylammonium-chloride 1 mM, BAPTA 11 mM, $CaCl_2$ 0.9 mM, $MgCl_2$ 1 mM, HEPES 20 mM, Mg^{2+}-ATP 5 mM and Li_2-GTP 0.1 mM, adjusted to pH 7.2 with CsOH. The bath solution contained TEAC 157 mM, $CaCl_2$ 5 mM, $MgCl_2$ 0.5 mM and HEPES 10 mM, adjusted to pH 7.5 with TEA-OH. Solutions were bubbled with O_2 100%. Mibefradil (1S,2S)-2-[2[[3-(2-benzimidazolyl]propyl] methylamino]ethyl]-6-fluoro-1,2,3,4-tetrahydro-1-isopropyl-2-naphthylmethoxyacetate dihydrochloride) and amlodipine (2-[(2-aminoethoxy)methyl]-4-(2-chlorophenyl)-3-ethoxycarbonyl-5-methoxycarbonyl-6-methyl-1,4-dihydropyridine) were synthesised at F. Hoffmann-La Roche. Mibefradil was prepared as a 10 mM stock solution in water and amlodipine as a 10 mM stock solution in DMSO.

Results

Currents through cardiac T- and L-type calcium channels were differentially blocked by mibefradil and amlodipine (fig. 1). These currents were quantified by measuring

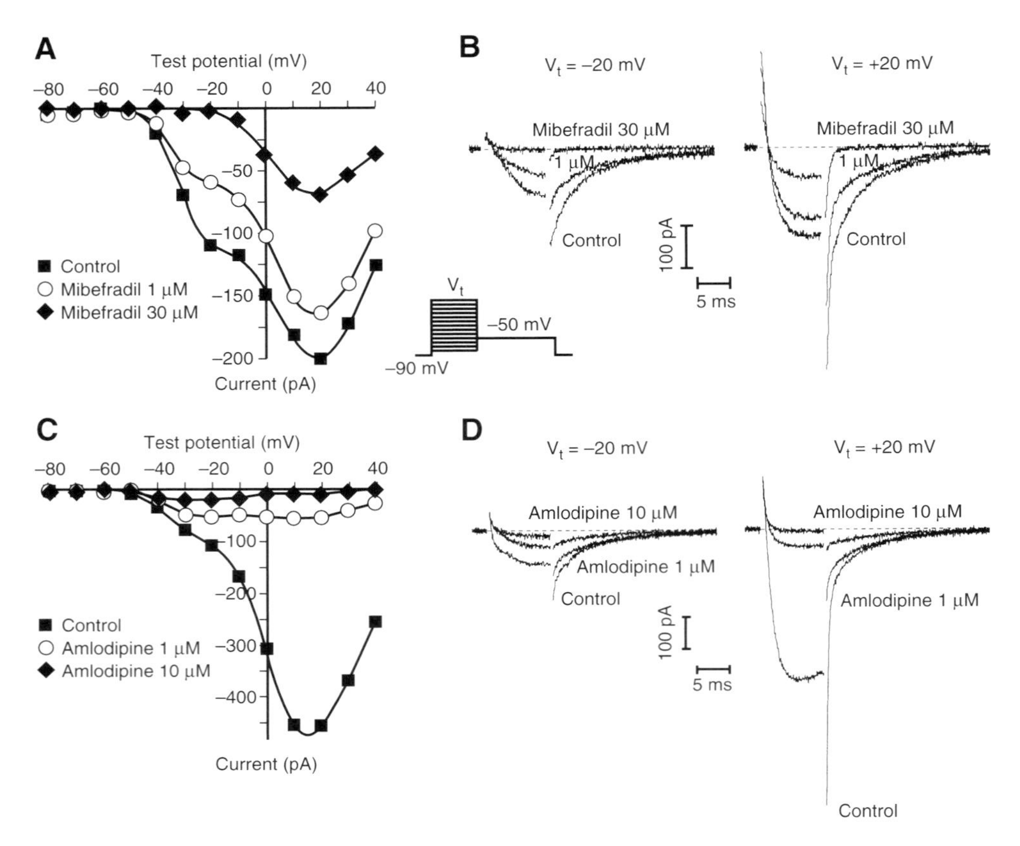

Fig. 1. Block of cardiac T- and L-type calcium channels by mibefradil (A & B) and amlodipine (C & D). A) Peak inward calcium current during 10-ms pulses to various test potentials (V_t) from a holding potential of –90 mV. B) Superimposed current records for test potentials of –20 mV and +20 mV. C) Peak inward calcium current during 10-ms pulses to various test potentials from a holding potential of –90 mV. D) Superimposed current records for test potentials of –20 mV and +20 mV.

the peak inward current during a test pulse applied from a hyperpolarised holding potential (–90 mV).[13] Plotting this current against the test-pulse voltage produces a characteristic bimodal current–voltage curve with the T-type calcium channels opening at lower voltages than the L-type calcium channels.[13] Mibefradil (1 μM) partially but selectively blocked the LVA component (T type), while both T- and L-type calcium channels were blocked at higher concentrations (see fig. 1 (A & B)). Conversely, amlodipine primarily blocked the HVA current at 1 μM but blocked both components at 10 μM (see fig. 1 (C & D)). However, as is apparent in figure 1, it is difficult to clearly separate the currents through T- and L-type calcium channels using the magnitude of the test-pulse voltage. Thus, in panel C of figure 1, the LVA component is small and heavily dominated by the HVA one. Consequently, there is no voltage at which T-type calcium currents are reasonably large but L-type calcium channels contribute no current.

To quantify more precisely the block of T- and L-type calcium channels by mibefradil and amlodipine, tail current analysis was performed.[14] Tail currents are measured when the membrane is repolarised after a depolarising pulse that activates channels and their time-course follows the rate of channel closing (deactivation). Because L-type calcium channels deactivate 10- to 40-fold more rapidly than T-type calcium channels,[11,14,15] the time-course of tail currents in atrial cells was markedly biexponential (see fig. 1 (B & D)). The respective contribution of T- and L-type calcium channels can be readily measured by fitting a biexponential function to the tail current data. Mibefradil (1 μM) had no effect on the rapidly decaying component of tail current, confirming that this agent does not block L-type calcium channels (see figs 1 (B) and 2 (A)). In contrast, the slowly decaying component of the tail current was reduced by approximately 40%, indicating a substantial block of T-type calcium channels. Contrary to the effects of mibefradil, amlodipine (1 μM) reduced the rapidly decaying component of tail current by about 90% but blocked the slowly decaying component of tail current by only 20%. At 10 μM, amlodipine significantly reduced both components of the tail current.

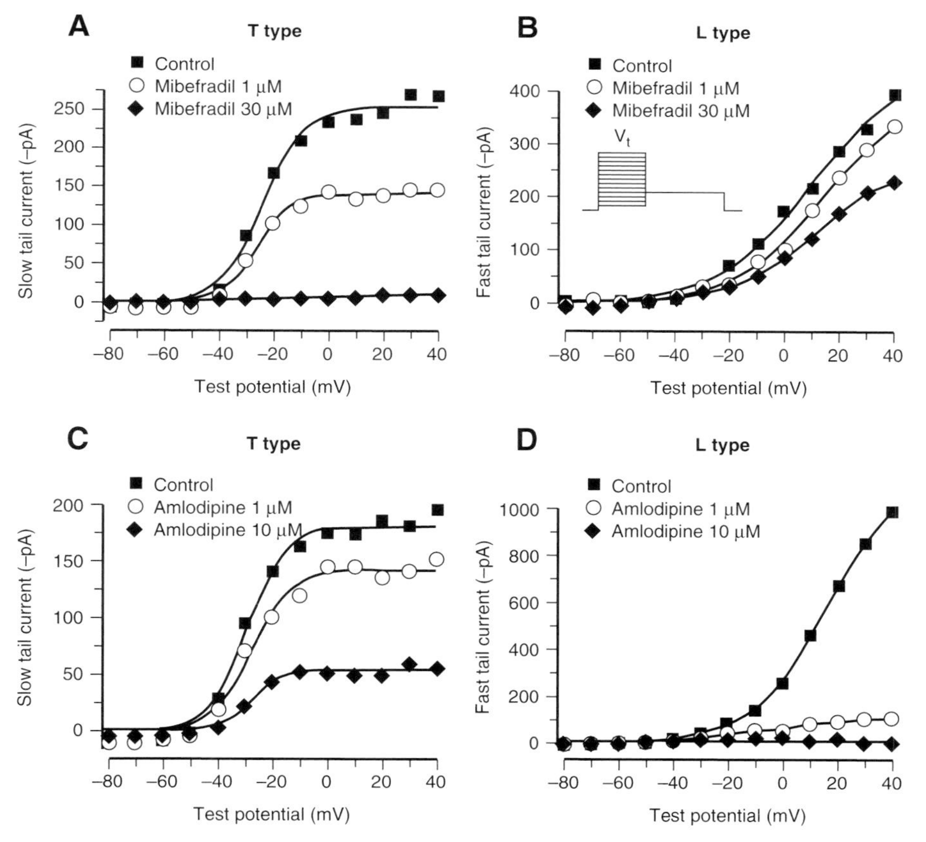

Fig. 2. Block of the slowly and the rapidly decaying calcium channel tail currents by mibefradil (A & B) and amlodipine (C & D). A) The half-action potentials ($V_{½}$) and slopes (k), respectively, are −24.3 and 7.3 mV for the control and −26.4 and 5.7 mV for mibefradil 1 μM, and the curve is flat for mibefradil 30 μM. B) $V_{½}$ = +12.2 mV, k = 16.3 mV for the control; $V_{½}$ = +15.1 mV, k = 14.5 mV for mibefradil 1 μM; $V_{½}$ = +11.7 mV, k = 14.8 mV for mibefradil 30 μM. C) $V_{½}$ = −29.4 mV, k = 7.0 mV for the control; $V_{½}$ = −27.7 mV, k = 7.5 mV for amlodipine 1 μM; $V_{½}$ = −28.5 mV, k = 5.2 mV for amlodipine 10 μM. D) $V_{½}$ = +15.8 mV, k = 13.1 mV for the control; $V_{½}$ = −2.2 mV, k = 16.2 mV for amlodipine 1 μM; the curve is flat for amlodipine 10 μM.

The dose–response curves for the block of atrial T- and L-type calcium channels by mibefradil and amlodipine are shown in figure 3. T-type calcium channels were quantified using the slowly decaying tail currents, and L-type calcium channels using the rapidly decaying currents. Mibefradil blocks T-type calcium channels with about 17-fold selectivity over L-type channels ($IC_{50} \approx 1.6$ *vs* 28 μM). Conversely, amlodipine blocks L-type calcium channels with about 12-fold selectivity over T-type channels ($IC_{50} \approx 0.48$ *vs* 5.6 μM). As expected, from a holding voltage of –90 mV, amlodipine was not very potent at blocking L-type calcium channels because, like most dihydropyridine antagonists, its blocking activity is highly voltage-dependent.[11,16–18]

The voltage-dependence of L-type calcium channel block by dihydropyridines is a major pharmacological feature of this class of drugs. In particular, it is likely this feature contributes to their selectivity for vascular over cardiac muscle as well as for diseased over healthy tissue.[16,19] For this reason, we compared the voltage-dependence of calcium channel block by mibefradil and amlodipine (fig. 4). In these experiments, drug binding equilibrated during 30 s 'prepulses' to various potentials before channel block was measured. This allowed the steady-state population of channels available to open from a given prepulse potential to be determined. Amlodipine blocks atrial L-type calcium channels with high voltage-dependence, as demonstrated by a 28-mV leftward shift of the midpoint of the availability curve (see fig. 4 (D)). Using the modulated receptor theory and the slope of the availability curves in control,[17,18,20–22] the ratio of the dissociation constants of amlodipine from the rested (K_R) and inactivated states (K_I) of the L-type calcium channels was calculated to be 21 ± 7 (n=11). Thus, amlodipine is about 20-fold more potent on inactivated than rested L-type channels. Similarly, amlodipine blocks T-type calcium channels with high voltage dependence, converting to a 20-fold increase in potency (20 ± 5; n=11) (see fig. 4 (C)). Voltage-dependent block of both T- and L-type calcium

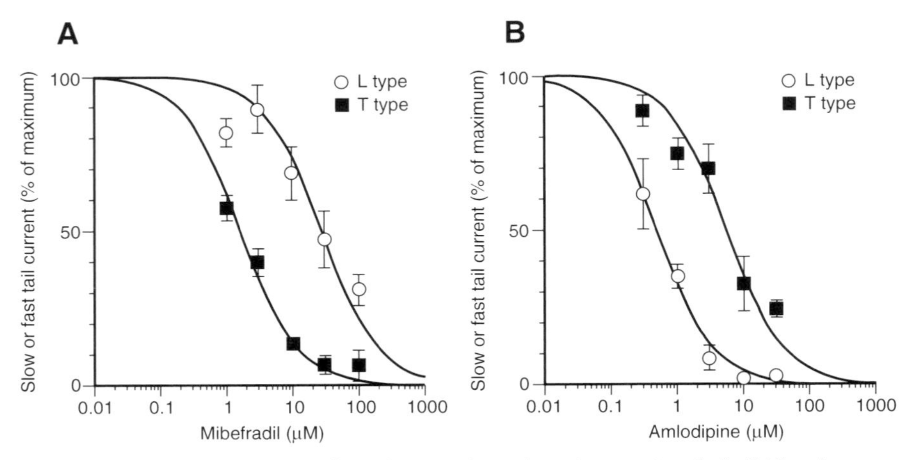

Fig. 3. Dose–response curves for the block of T- and L-type calcium channel currents by mibefradil (A) and amlodipine (B). Current through T-type calcium channels is measured as the amplitude of the slowly decaying tail current (T) and current through L-type calcium channels as the rapidly decaying tail current (L). The data are fitted with 1:1 binding curves, with IC_{50} values of: (A) T type, 1.6 μM; L type, 28 μM; (B) T type, 5.6 μM; L type, 0.48 μM. Data are means ± SEM of 23 cells for mibefradil and 18 cells for amlodipine.

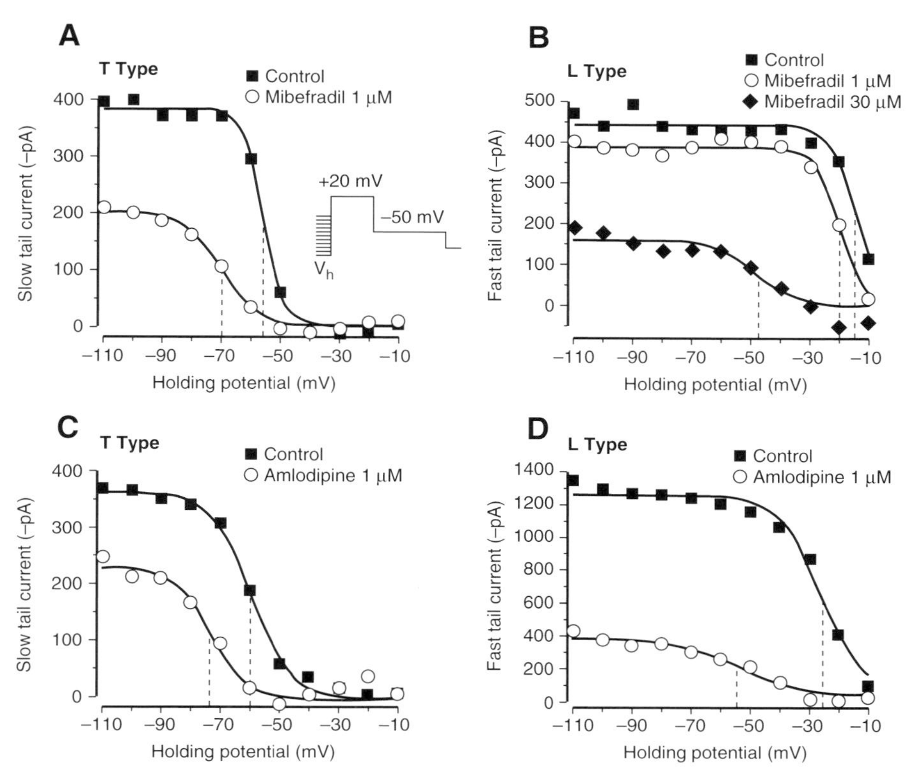

Fig. 4. Voltage-dependent block of the slowly and the rapidly decaying calcium channel tail currents by mibefradil (A & B) and amlodipine (C & D). A) The half-action potentials ($V_{1/2}$) and slopes (k), respectively, are −55.9 and −3.4 mV for the control and −70.2 and −6.5 mV for mibefradil 1 μM. B) $V_{1/2}$ = −14.5 mV, k = −4.6 mV for the control; $V_{1/2}$ = −20.2 mV, k = −4.3 mV for mibefradil 1 μM; $V_{1/2}$ = −47.8 mV, k = −7.3 mV for mibefradil 30 μM. C) $V_{1/2}$ = −59.4 mV, k = −6.8 mV for the control; $V_{1/2}$ = −73.0 mV, k = −6.2 mV for amlodipine 1 μM. D) $V_{1/2}$ = −26.1 mV, k = −7.3 mV for the control; $V_{1/2}$ = −53.8 mV, k = −11.4 mV for amlodipine 1 μM.

channels has previously been reported for other dihydropyridines (felodipine, isradipine, nimodipine, nifedipine).[11]

Block of calcium channels by mibefradil is also voltage-dependent (see fig. 4 (A & B)). With drug concentrations that block T-type (1 μM) or L-type (30 μM) calcium channels, the availability curves are shifted to the left. In this study, using the modulated-receptor theory, we obtained K_R:K_I ratios of 24 ± 11 and 19 ± 11 for T- and L-type calcium channels, respectively (n=11). Thus, mibefradil blocks atrial voltage-gated calcium channels with a voltage-dependence similar to that of amlodipine and other dihydropyridines, suggesting that it also preferentially binds to active channels (open or inactivated).

A common feature of compounds that bind preferentially to open or inactivated voltage-gated ion channels is to exhibit use-dependent block. As expected, mibefradil exhibits use-dependent block of T-type calcium channels (fig. 5 (A)). Calcium channel currents were measured before and after trains of 20 depolarisations of constant duration (10 ms). Under control conditions and at fast pulsing rates (>1 Hz), T-type

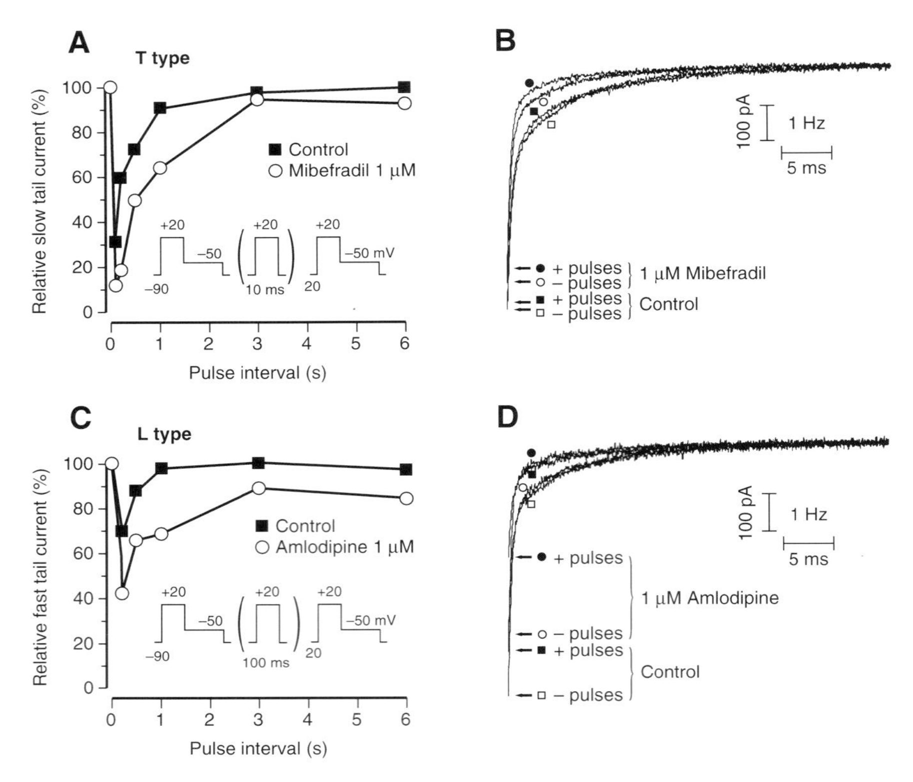

Fig. 5. Use-dependent block of the slowly and the rapidly decaying calcium channel tail currents by mibefradil and amlodipine. A) Mibefradil enhances the accumulation of inactivation of the slowly decaying tail current (T type) induced by trains of twenty 10-ms depolarisations at different frequencies. B) Tail currents for the 1-s data points. C) Amlodipine enhances the accumulation of inactivation of the rapidly decaying tail current (L type) induced by trains of twenty 100-ms depolarisations at different frequencies. D) Tail currents for the 1-s data points.

calcium channels became inactivated, producing a smaller, slowly decaying tail current after the train of depolarisations. In the presence of mibefradil 1 µM and at pulse rates up to 3 Hz, inactivation of T-type calcium channels occurred even more readily. Panel B of figure 5 shows the tail currents for the 1-Hz pulsing rate and demonstrates the presence of use-dependent (phasic) block on top of resting state (tonic) block. Amlodipine has a similar effect on these channels (not shown).

Using 10-ms depolarisations, there was little or no inactivation of L-type calcium channels and use-dependent block was not seen with either mibefradil or amlodipine (not shown). However, if trains of 100-ms depolarisations were used, use-dependent block of L-type calcium channels was observed with mibefradil (not shown) and amlodipine (see fig. 5 (C & D)).

Discussion

Mibefradil is an antihypertensive calcium antagonist with substantial clinical advantages over other available drugs. In particular, at therapeutic doses, it is devoid of the typical side effects associated with classical calcium channel blockers.[23] Indeed, it slows heart rate slightly without negative inotropy. Since mibefradil, like the other calcium antagonists, was originally shown to block L-type calcium channels,[24] these unique properties were unexplained. However, two reports demonstrating that mibefradil is somewhat selective for T- versus L-type calcium channels raised the possibility that this drug acts partly by blocking T-type calcium channels.[7,25] In addition, the cardiac properties of mibefradil potentially arise from the selective block of cardiac T-type calcium channels. These channels are thought to play a role in the pacemaker activity of node cells by participating in the slow depolarisation that initiates the action potentials.[8] Thus, blocking these channels may slow heart rate. Conversely, L-type calcium channels are the major pathway for the massive Ca^{2+} influx needed for contraction, and their block reduces heart contractility.

The results of the present study agree with this concept. Thus, mibefradil blocks cardiac T-type calcium channels with approximately 17-fold selectivity over L-type channels. This ratio is almost the opposite of that for amlodipine, which exhibits about a 12-fold selectivity for L-type over T-type calcium channels. Under the experimental conditions described for figures 1–3, block of L-type calcium channels by amlodipine was weak since the cells were well polarised (≈ −90 mV). As with most dihydropyridine antagonists, the potency of amlodipine increases markedly when the cells were depolarised, indicating that this drug binds preferentially to open or inactivated L-type calcium channels.[11,16–18] The binding constant for amlodipine at inactivated channels is approximately 20 times lower than that at rested channels and is well into the nanomolar range. Results with mibefradil are very similar, with an increase in binding potency of around 20-fold under depolarised conditions for both T- and L-type calcium channels. In addition, consequent to the preferential binding of the two compounds to open or inactivated channels, they exhibit use-dependent block, so that repetitive depolarisations enhance block.

This similarity in the molecular mechanisms of action of mibefradil and amlodipine is somewhat surprising considering two previous observations. First, the binding sites of these compounds on the L-type calcium channel appear to be sufficiently distinct to preclude competition in binding experiments.[26] Second, mutations of the L-type calcium channel α subunit that eliminate dihydropyridine binding have little or no effect on mibefradil binding.[27] However, most calcium antagonists interact with neighbouring elements of the S6 segments of domains III and IV of the L-type calcium channel α subunit.[28,29] Thus, a better understanding of the structure and location of the binding site of mibefradil on the L-type calcium channel will probably reveal similarities and/or interactions with other drug sites. Advances in sequencing and cloning T-type calcium channels would also further our understanding of the mechanism of action of this new calcium antagonist.

Acknowledgements

We thank M. Weber for excellent technical assistance.

References

1. Bean BP. Classes of calcium channels in vertebrate cells. Annu Rev Physiol 1989; 51: 367–84
2. Aroney CN, Semigran MJ, Dec GW, et al. Inotropic effect of nicardipine in patients with heart failure: assessment by left ventricular end-systolic pressure-volume analysis. J Am Coll Cardiol 1989; 14: 1331–8
3. Pouleur H. Calcium entry blockers in congestive heart failure and in asymptomatic left ventricular dysfunction. In: Barnett D, Pouleur H, Francis G, editors. Heart failure. New-York: Marcel Dekker, 1993: 287–301
4. Packer M, Lee WH, Medina N, et al. Prognostic importance of the immediate hemodynamic response to nifedipine in patients with severe left ventricular dysfunction. J Am Coll Cardiol 1987; 10: 1303–11
5. Ertel SI, Clozel J-P. Mibefradil (Ro 40-5967): the first selective T-type Ca^{2+} channel blocker. Exp Opin Invest Drugs 1997; 6: 569–82
6. Clozel J-P, Osterrieder W, Kleinbloesem CH, et al. Ro 40-5967: a new nondihydropyridine calcium antagonist. Cardiovasc Drug Rev 1991; 9: 4–17
7. Mishra SK, Hermsmeyer K. Selective inhibition of T-type Ca^{2+} channels by Ro 40-5967. Circ Res 1994; 75: 144–8
8. Vassort G, Alvarez J. Cardiac T-type calcium current: pharmacology and roles in cardiac tissues. J Cardiovasc Electrophysiol 1994; 5: 376–93
9. Ertel EA. Mibefradil (Ro 40-5967) is a selective blocker of myocardial T-type vs. L-type Ca channels. Biophys J 1996; 70: A315
10. Mitra R, Morad M. A uniform enzymatic method for dissociation of myocytes from hearts and stomachs of vertebrates. Am J Physiol 1985; 249: H1056–60
11. Cohen CJ, Spires S, Van Skiver D. Block of T-type Ca channels in guinea pig atrial cells by antiarrhythmic agents and calcium channel antagonists. J Gen Physiol 1992; 100: 703–28
12. Press WH, Flannery BP, Teukolsky SA, et al. Numerical recipes. Cambridge, UK: Cambridge University Press, 1986
13. Bean BP. Two kinds of calcium channels in canine atrial cells. J Gen Physiol 1985; 85: 1–30
14. Matteson DR, Armstrong CM. Properties of two types of calcium channels in clonal pituitary cells. J Gen Physiol 1986; 87: 161–82
15. Ertel EA, Smith MM, Leibowitz MD, et al. Isolation of myocardial L-type calcium channel gating currents with the spider toxin ω-Aga-IIIA. J Gen Physiol 1994; 103: 731–53
16. Kuriyama H, Kitamura K, Nabata H. Pharmacological and physiological significance of ion channels and factors that modulate them in vascular tissues. Pharmacol Rev 1995; 47: 387–573
17. Sanguinetti MC, Kass RS. Voltage-dependent block of calcium channel current in the calf cardiac Purkinje fiber by dihydropyridine calcium channel antagonists. Circ Res 1984; 55: 336–48
18. Bean BP. Nitrendipine block of cardiac calcium channels: high affinity binding to the inactivated state. Proc Natl Acad Sci U S A 1984; 81: 6388–92
19. Ertel EA, Cohen CJ. Voltage-dependent interactions: the influence and significance of membrane potential on drug-receptor interactions. Drug Dev Res 1994; 33: 203–13
20. Bean BP, Cohen CJ, Tsien RW. Lidocaine block of cardiac sodium channels. J Gen Physiol 1983; 81: 613–42
21. Hondeghem LM, Katzung BG. Antiarrhythmic agents: the modulated receptor mechanism of action of sodium and calcium channel-blocking drugs. Annu Rev Pharmacol Toxicol 1984; 24: 387–423
22. Bezprozvanny I, Tsien RW. Voltage-dependent blockade of diverse types of voltage-gated Ca^{2+} channels expressed in *Xenopus* oocytes by the Ca^{2+} channel antagonist mibefradil (Ro 40-5967). Mol Pharmacol 1995; 48: 540–9
23. Portegies MC, Schmitt R, Kraaij CJ, et al. Lack of negative inotropic effects of the new calcium antagonist Ro 40-5967 in patients with stable angina pectoris. J Cardiovasc Pharmacol 1991; 18: 746–51
24. Fang LM, Osterrieder W. Potential-dependent inhibition of cardiac Ca^{2+} inward currents by Ro 40-5967 and verapamil: relation to negative inotropy. Eur J Pharmacol 1991; 196: 205–7
25. Mehrke G, Zong XG, Flockerzi V, et al. The Ca^{++}-channel blocker Ro 40-5967 blocks differently T-type and L-type Ca^{++} channels. J Pharmacol Exp Ther 1994; 271: 1483–8
26. Rutledge A, Triggle DJ. The binding interactions of Ro 40-5967 at the L-type Ca^{2+} channel in cardiac tissue. Eur J Pharmacol 1995; 280: 155–8
27. Schuster A, Lacinova L, Klugbauer N, et al. The IVS6 segment of the L-type calcium channel is critical for the action of dihydropyridines and phenylalkylamines. EMBO J 1996; 15: 2365–70
28. Catterall WA, Striessnig J. Receptor sites for Ca^{2+} channel antagonists. Trends Pharmacol Sci 1992; 13: 256–62
29. Hockerman GH, Johnson BD, Scheuer T, et al. Molecular determinants of high affinity phenylalkylamine block of L-type calcium channels. J Biol Chem 1995; 270: 22119–22